PAUL AUSTER – COLLECTED NOVELS

Volume 4

*Also by Paul Auster*

*Novels:*
THE NEW YORK TRILOGY
IN THE COUNTRY OF LAST THINGS
MOON PALACE
THE MUSIC OF CHANCE
LEVIATHAN
MR VERTIGO
TIMBUKTU
THE BOOK OF ILLUSIONS
ORACLE NIGHT
THE BROOKLYN FOLLIES
TRAVELS IN THE SCRIPTORIUM
MAN IN THE DARK
INVISIBLE SUNSET PARK
COLLECTED NOVELS: VOLUME I
COLLECTED NOVELS: VOLUME II
COLLECTED NOVELS: VOLUME III

*Non-Fiction:*
THE INVENTION OF SOLITUDE
THE ART OF HUNGER
THE RED NOTEBOOK
HAND TO MOUTH
COLLECTED PROSE
WINTER JOURNAL HERE AND NOW (with J. M. Coetzee)
REPORT FROM THE INTERIOR

*Screenplays:*
SMOKE & BLUE IN THE FACE
LULU ON THE BRIDGE
THE INNER LIFE OF MARTIN FROST
COLLECTED SCREENPLAYS

*Poetry:*
SELECTED POEMS
COLLECTED POEMS

*Editor:*
TRUE TALES OF AMERICAN LIFE

*Translation:*
CHRONICLE OF THE GUAYAKI INDIANS
by Pierre Clastres

# PAUL AUSTER

# Collected Novels

VOLUME 4

*Travels in the Scriptorium*

*Man in the Dark*

*Invisible*

*Sunset Park*

ff

FABER & FABER

First published in the UK in 2016
by Faber & Faber Ltd,
Bloomsbury House,
74–77 Great Russell Street,
London WC1B 3DA

Printed and bound in the UK by CPI Group (UK), Croydon CR0 4YY



A CIP record for this book is available from the British Library

ISBN 978–0–571–32215–2

FSC
www.fsc.org
MIX
Paper from responsible sources
FSC® C101712

2 4 6 8 10 9 7 5 3 1

# Contents

# TRAVELS IN THE SCRIPTORIUM

for Lloyd Hustvedt
(in memory)

The old man sits on the edge of the narrow bed, palms spread out on his knees, head down, staring at the floor. He has no idea that a camera is planted in the ceiling directly above him. The shutter clicks silently once every second, producing eighty-six thousand four hundred still photos with each revolution of the earth. Even if he knew he was being watched, it wouldn't make any difference. His mind is elsewhere, stranded among the figments in his head as he searches for an answer to the question that haunts him.

Who is he? What is he doing here? When did he arrive and how long will he remain? With any luck, time will tell us all. For the moment, our only task is to study the pictures as attentively as we can and refrain from drawing any premature conclusions.

There are a number of objects in the room, and on each one a strip of white tape has been affixed to the surface, bearing a single word written out in block letters. On the bedside table, for example, the word is TABLE. On the lamp, the word is LAMP. Even on the wall, which is not strictly speaking an object, there is a strip of tape that reads WALL. The old man looks up for a moment, sees the wall, sees the strip of tape attached to the wall, and pronounces the word *wall* in a soft voice. What cannot be known at this point is whether he is reading the word on the strip of tape or simply referring to the wall itself. It could be that he has forgotten how to read but still recognizes things for what they are and can call them by their names, or, conversely, that he has lost the ability to recognize things for what they are but still knows how to read.

He is dressed in blue-and-yellow striped cotton pajamas, and his feet are encased in a pair of black leather slippers. It is unclear to him exactly where he is. In the room, yes, but in what building is the room located? In a house? In a hospital? In a prison? He can't remember how long he has been here or the nature of the circumstances that precipitated his removal to this place. Perhaps he has always been here; perhaps this is where he has lived since the day he was born. What he knows is that his heart is filled with an implacable sense of guilt. At the same time, he can't escape the feeling that he is the victim of a terrible injustice.

There is one window in the room, but the shade is drawn, and as far as he can remember he has not yet looked out of it. Likewise with the door and its white porcelain knob. Is he locked in, or is he free to come and go as he wishes? He has yet to investigate this matter – for, as stated in the first paragraph above, his mind is elsewhere, adrift in the past as he wanders among the phantom beings that clutter his head, struggling to answer the question that haunts him.

The pictures do not lie, but neither do they tell the whole story. They are merely a record of time passing, the outward evidence. The old man's age, for example, is difficult to determine from the slightly out-of-focus black-and-white images. The only fact that can be set down with any certainty is that he is not young, but the word *old* is a flexible term and can be used to describe a person anywhere between sixty and a hundred. We will therefore drop the epithet *old man* and henceforth refer to the person in the room as Mr. Blank. For the time being, no first name will be necessary.

Mr. Blank stands up from the bed at last, pauses briefly to steady his balance, and then shuffles over to the desk at the other end of the room. He feels tired, as if he has just woken from a fitful, too-short night of sleep, and as the soles of his slippers scrape along the bare wood floor, he is reminded of the sound of sandpaper. Far off in the distance, beyond the room, beyond the building in which the room is located, he hears the faint cry of a bird – perhaps a crow, perhaps a seagull, he can't tell which.

Mr. Blank lowers his body into the chair at the desk. It is an exceedingly comfortable chair, he decides, made of soft brown leather and equipped with broad armrests to accommodate his elbows and forearms, not to speak of an invisible spring mechanism that allows him to rock back and forth at will, which is precisely what he begins to do the moment he sits down. Rocking back and forth has a soothing effect on him, and as Mr. Blank continues to indulge in these pleasurable oscillations, he remembers the rocking horse that sat in his bedroom when he was a small boy, and then he begins to relive some of the imaginary journeys he used to take on that horse, whose name was Whitey and who, in the young Mr. Blank's mind, was not a wooden object adorned with white paint but a living being, a true horse.

After this brief excursion into his early boyhood, anguish rises up into Mr. Blank's throat again. He says out loud in a weary voice: I mustn't allow this to happen. Then he leans forward to examine the piles of papers and photographs stacked neatly on the surface of the mahogany desk. He takes hold of the pictures first, three dozen eight-by-ten black-

and-white portraits of men and women of various ages and races. The photo on top shows a young woman in her early twenties. Her dark hair is cropped short, and there is an intense, troubled look in her eyes as she gazes into the lens. She is standing outdoors in some city, perhaps an Italian or French city, because she happens to be positioned in front of a medieval church, and because the woman is wearing a scarf and a woolen coat, it is safe to assume the picture was taken in winter. Mr. Blank stares into the eyes of the young woman and strains to remember who she is. After twenty seconds or so, he hears himself whisper a single word: Anna. A feeling of overpowering love washes through him. He wonders if Anna isn't someone he was once married to, or if, perhaps, he isn't looking at a picture of his daughter. An instant after thinking these thoughts, he is attacked by a fresh wave of guilt, and he knows that Anna is dead. Even worse, he suspects that he is responsible for her death. It might even be, he tells himself, that he was the person who killed her.

Mr. Blank groans in pain. Looking at the pictures is too much for him, so he pushes them aside and turns his attention to the papers. There are four piles in all, each about six inches high. For no particular reason that he is aware of, he reaches for the top page on the pile farthest to the left. The handwritten words, printed out in block letters similar to the ones on the strips of white tape, read as follows:

Viewed from the outermost reaches of space, the earth is no larger than a speck of dust. Remember that the next time you write the word *humanity*.

From the look of disgust that comes over his face as he scans these sentences, we can be fairly confident that Mr. Blank has not lost the ability to read. But who the author of these sentences might be is still open to question.

Mr. Blank reaches out for the next page on the pile and discovers that it is a typed manuscript of some sort. The first paragraph reads:

The moment I started to tell my story, they knocked me down and kicked me in the head. When I climbed to my feet and started to talk again, one of them hit me across the mouth, and then another one punched me in the stomach. I fell down. I managed to get up again, but just as I was about to begin the story for the third time, the Colonel threw me against the wall and I passed out.

There are two more paragraphs on the page, but before Mr. Blank can begin reading the second one, the telephone rings. It is a black rotary model from the late forties or early fifties of the past century, and since it

is located on the bedside table, Mr. Blank is forced to stand up from the soft leather chair and shuffle over to the other side of the room. He picks up the receiver on the fourth ring.

Hello, says Mr. Blank.

Mr. Blank? asks the voice on the other end.

If you say so.

Are you sure? I can't take any chances.

I'm not sure of anything. If you want to call me Mr. Blank, I'm happy to answer to that name. Who am I talking to?

James.

I don't know any James.

James P. Flood.

Refresh my memory.

I came to visit you yesterday. We spent two hours together.

Ah. The policeman.

Ex-policeman.

Right. The ex-policeman. What can I do for you?

I want to see you again.

Wasn't one conversation enough?

Not really. I know I'm just a minor character in this business, but they said I was allowed to see you twice.

You're telling me I have no choice.

I'm afraid so. But we don't have to talk in the room if you don't want to. We can go out and sit in the park if you'd prefer that.

I don't have anything to wear. I'm standing here dressed in pajamas and slippers.

Look in the closet. You have all the clothes you need.

Ah. The closet. Thank you.

Have you had your breakfast, Mr. Blank?

I don't think so. Am I allowed to eat?

Three meals a day. It's still a bit early, but Anna should be coming around pretty soon.

Anna? Did you say Anna?

She's the person who takes care of you.

I thought she was dead.

Hardly.

Maybe it's a different Anna.

I doubt it. Of all the people involved in this story, she's the only one who's completely on your side.

And the others?

Let's just say there's a lot of resentment, and we'll leave it at that.

It should be noted that in addition to the camera a microphone is embedded in one of the walls, and every sound Mr. Blank makes is being reproduced and preserved by a highly sensitive digital tape recorder. The least groan or sniffle, the least cough or fleeting flatulence that emerges from his body is therefore an integral part of our account as well. It goes without saying that this aural data also includes the words that are variously mumbled, uttered, or shouted by Mr. Blank, as with, for example, the telephone call from James P. Flood recorded above. The conversation ends with Mr. Blank reluctantly giving in to the ex-policeman's demand to pay him a visit some time that morning. After Mr. Blank hangs up the phone, he sits down on the edge of the narrow bed, assuming a position identical to the one described in the first sentence of this report: palms spread out on his knees, head down, staring at the floor. He ponders whether he should stand up and begin looking for the closet Flood referred to, and if that closet exists, whether he should change out of his pajamas and put on some clothes, assuming there are clothes in the closet – if indeed that closet exists. But Mr. Blank is in no rush to engage in such mundane chores. He wants to go back to the typescript he started reading before he was interrupted by the telephone. He therefore stands up from the bed and takes a first tentative step toward the other side of the room, feeling a sudden rush of dizziness as he does so. He realizes that he will fall down if he remains standing any longer, but rather than return to the bed and sit there until the crisis passes, he puts his right hand against the wall, leans the full brunt of his weight against it, and gradually lowers himself to the floor. Now on his knees, Mr. Blank pitches himself forward and plants his palms on the floor as well. Dizzy or not, such is his determination to reach the desk that he crawls there on all fours.

Once he manages to climb into the leather chair, he rocks back and forth for several moments to steady his nerves. In spite of his physical efforts, he understands that he is afraid to go on reading the typescript. Why this fear should have taken hold of him is something he cannot account for. It's only words, he tells himself, and since when have words had the power to frighten a man half to death? It won't do, he mutters in a low, barely audible voice. Then, to reassure himself, he repeats the same sentence, shouting at the top of his lungs: IT WON'T DO!

Inexplicably, this sudden burst of sound gives him the courage to continue. He takes a deep breath, fixes his eyes on the words in front of him, and reads the following two paragraphs:

They have kept me in this room ever since. From all I can gather, it is not a typical cell, and it does not seem to be part of the military stockade or the territorial house of detention. It is a small, bare enclosure, measuring roughly twelve feet by fifteen feet, and because of the simplicity of its design (dirt floor, thick stone walls), I suspect that it once served as a storehouse for food supplies, perhaps for sacks of flour and grain. There is a single barred window at the top of the western wall, but it is too far off the ground for me to get my hands on it. I sleep on a straw mat in one corner, and two meals are given to me every day: cold porridge in the morning, tepid soup and hard bread in the evening. According to my calculations, I have been here for forty-seven nights. This tally could be wrong, however. My first days in the cell were interrupted by numerous beatings, and because I can't remember how many times I lost consciousness – nor how long the oblivions lasted when I did – it is possible that I lost count somewhere and failed to notice when a particular sun might have risen or another might have set.

The desert begins just outside my window. Each time the wind blows from the west, I can smell the sage and juniper bushes, the minima of those dry distances. I lived out there on my own for close to four months, wandering freely from one place to another, sleeping outdoors in all kinds of weather, and to return from the openness of that country to the narrow confines of this room has not been easy for me. I can bear up to the enforced solitude, to the absence of conversation and human contact, but I long to be in the air and the light again, and I spend my days hungering for something to look at besides these jagged stone walls. Every now and then, soldiers walk below my window. I can hear their boots crunching on the ground, the irregular bursts of their voices, the clatter of carts and horses in the heat of the unattainable day. This is the garrison at Ultima: the westernmost tip of the Confederation, the place that stands at the edge of the known world. We are more than two thousand miles from the capital here, overlooking the unmapped expanses of the Alien Territories. The law says that no one is allowed to go out there. I went because I was ordered to go, and now I have returned to give my report. They will listen to me or they won't listen to me, and then I will be taken outside and shot. I am fairly certain of that now. The important thing is not to delude myself, to resist the temptation of hope. When

they finally put me up against the wall and aim their rifles at my body, the only thing I will ask of them is to remove the blindfold. It's not that I have any interest in seeing the men who kill me, but I want to be able to look at the sky again. That is the extent of what I want now. To stand out in the open and look up at the immense blue sky above me, to gaze at the howling infinite one last time.

Mr. Blank stops reading. His fear has been replaced by confusion, and while he has grasped every word of the text so far, he has no idea what to make of it. Is it an actual report, he wonders, and what is this place called the Confederation, with its garrison at Ultima and its mysterious Alien Territories, and why does the prose sound like something written in the nineteenth century? Mr. Blank is well aware of the fact that his mind is not all it should be, that he is entirely in the dark about where he is and why he is there, but he is reasonably certain that the present moment can be situated sometime in the early twenty-first century and that he lives in a country called the United States of America. This last thought reminds him of the window, or, to be more precise, of the window shade, on which a strip of white tape has been attached bearing the word SHADE. With the soles of his feet pressing against the floor and his arms pressing against the armrests of the leather chair, he swivels right by ninety to a hundred degrees in order to have a look at said window shade – for not only is this chair endowed with the ability to rock back and forth, it can turn in circles as well. This last discovery is so pleasing to Mr. Blank that he momentarily forgets why he wanted to look at the window shade, exulting instead in this hitherto unknown property of the chair. He spins around once, then twice, then three times, and as he does so he remembers sitting in the chair at the barbershop as a young boy and being spun around in a similar fashion by Rocco the barber both before and after his hair was cut. Fortunately, when Mr. Blank comes to rest again, the chair is more or less in the same position as when he started going around in circles, which means that he is once again looking at the window shade, and again, after this enjoyable interlude, Mr. Blank wonders if he shouldn't walk over to the window, pull up the shade, and have a look outside to see where he is. Perhaps he's no longer in America, he says to himself, but in some other country, abducted in the dead of night by secret agents working for a foreign power.

His triple revolution in the chair has left him somewhat dizzy, however, and he hesitates to budge from his spot, fearing a recurrence of the episode that forced him to travel across the room on all fours some

minutes ago. What Mr. Blank is still unaware of at this point is that, in addition to being able to rock back and forth and turn around in circles, the leather chair is further equipped with a set of four small wheels, which would make it possible for him to journey over to the window shade without having to stand up. Not knowing that other means of propulsion are available to him besides his legs, Mr. Blank therefore stays where he is, sitting in the chair with his back to the desk, looking at the once white but now yellowing window shade, trying to remember his conversation the previous afternoon with the ex-policeman James P. Flood. He casts about in his mind for an image, some hint as to what the man looks like, but rather than conjure forth any clear pictures, his mind is once again overwhelmed by a paralyzing sensation of guilt. Before this fresh bout of torments and terrors can build into a full-blown panic, however, Mr. Blank hears someone rapping on the door, and then the sound of a key entering the lock. Does this mean that Mr. Blank is imprisoned in the room, unable to leave except through the grace and good will of others? Not necessarily. It could be that Mr. Blank has locked the door from within and that the person now trying to enter the room must undo that lock in order to cross the threshold, thus sparing Mr. Blank the trouble of having to stand up and open the door himself.

One way or the other, the door now opens, and in walks a small woman of indeterminate age – anywhere between forty-five and sixty, Mr. Blank thinks, but it is difficult to be certain. Her gray hair is cut short, she is dressed in a pair of dark blue slacks and a light blue cotton blouse, and the first thing she does after entering the room is smile at Mr. Blank. This smile, which seems to combine both tenderness and affection, banishes his fears and puts him in a state of calm equilibrium. He has no idea who she is, but he is nevertheless happy to see her.

Did you sleep well? the woman asks.

I'm not sure, Mr. Blank replies. To be perfectly honest, I can't remember if I slept or not.

That's good. It means the treatment is working.

Rather than comment on this enigmatic pronouncement, Mr. Blank studies the woman for several moments in silence, then asks: Forgive me for being such a fool, but your name wouldn't be Anna, would it?

Once again, the woman gives him a tender and affectionate smile. I'm glad you remembered it, she says. Yesterday, it kept slipping out of your mind.

Suddenly perplexed and agitated, Mr. Blank swivels around in the

leather chair until he is facing the desk, then removes the portrait of the young woman from the pile of black-and-white photographs. Before he can turn around again to look at the woman, whose name appears to be Anna, she is standing beside him with her hand poised gently on his right shoulder, looking down at the picture as well.

If your name is Anna, Mr. Blank says, his voice quivering with emotion, then who is this? Her name is Anna, too, isn't it?

Yes, the woman says, studying the portrait closely, as if remembering something with equal but opposite feelings of revulsion and nostalgia. This is Anna. And I'm Anna, too. This is a picture of me.

But, Mr. Blank stammers, but . . . the girl in the picture is young. And you . . . you have gray hair.

Time, Mr. Blank, Anna says. You understand the meaning of time, don't you? This is me thirty-five years ago.

Before Mr. Blank has a chance to respond, Anna puts the portrait of her younger self back on the pile of photographs.

Your breakfast is getting cold, she says, and without another word she leaves the room, only to return a moment later, wheeling in a stainless steel cart with a platter of food on it, which she positions alongside the bed.

The meal consists of a glass of orange juice, a slice of buttered toast, two poached eggs in a small white bowl, and a pot of Earl Grey tea. In due course, Anna will help Mr. Blank out of the chair and lead him over to the bed, but first she hands him a glass of water and three pills – one green, one white, and one purple.

What's wrong with me? Mr. Blank asks. Am I sick?

No, not at all, Anna says. The pills are part of the treatment.

I don't feel sick. A little tired and dizzy, maybe, but otherwise nothing too terrible. Considering my age, not too terrible at all.

Swallow the pills, Mr. Blank. Then you can eat your breakfast. I'm sure you're very hungry.

But I don't want the pills, Mr. Blank replies, stubbornly holding his ground. If I'm not sick, I'm not going to swallow these wretched pills.

Rather than snap back at Mr. Blank after his rude and aggressive statement, Anna bends over and kisses him on the forehead. Dear Mr. Blank, she says. I know how you feel, but you promised to take the pills every day. That was the bargain. If you don't take the pills, the treatment won't work.

I promised? says Mr. Blank. How do I know you're telling the truth?

Because it's me, Anna, and I would never lie to you. I love you too much for that.

The mention of the word *love* softens Mr. Blank's resolve, and he impulsively decides to back down. All right, he says, I'll take the pills. But only if you kiss me again. Agreed? But it has to be a real kiss this time. On the lips.

Anna smiles, then bends over once more and kisses Mr. Blank squarely on the lips. In that it lasts for a good three seconds, the kiss qualifies as more than just a peck, and even though no tongues are involved, this intimate contact sends a tingle of arousal coursing through Mr. Blank's body. By the time Anna straightens up, he has already begun to swallow the pills.

Now they are sitting beside each other on the edge of the bed. The food cart is in front of them, and as Mr. Blank drinks down his orange juice and takes a bite of his toast and a first sip of the tea, Anna softly rubs his back with her left hand, humming a tune that he is unable to identify but which he knows is familiar to him, or was once familiar to him. Then he begins to attack the poached eggs, piercing one of the yolks with the tip of the spoon and gathering up a modest combination of yellow and white in the hollow of the utensil, but when he tries to lift the spoon toward his mouth, he is bewildered to discover that his hand is shaking. Not just some mild tremor, but a pronounced and convulsive twitching that he is powerless to control. By the time the spoon has traveled six inches from the bowl, the spasm is so extreme that the better part of the yellow-and-white mixture has splattered onto the tray.

Would you like me to feed you? Anna asks.

What's wrong with me?

It's nothing to worry about, she answers, patting his back in an attempt to reassure him. A natural reaction to the pills. It will pass in a few minutes.

That's some treatment you've cooked up for me, Mr. Blank mutters in a self-pitying, sullen tone of voice.

It's all for the best, Anna says. And it's not going to last forever. Believe me.

So Mr. Blank allows Anna to feed him, and as she calmly goes about the business of scooping out portions of the poached eggs, holding the teacup to his lips, and wiping his mouth with a paper napkin, Mr. Blank begins to think that Anna is not a woman so much as an angel, or, if you will, an angel in the form of a woman.

Why are you so kind to me? he asks.

Because I love you, Anna says. It's that simple.

Now that the meal is finished, the time has come for excretions, ablutions, and the putting on of clothes. Anna pushes the cart away from the bed and then extends her hand to Mr. Blank to help him to his feet. To his immense astonishment, he finds himself standing in front of a door, a door that until now has escaped his notice, and attached to the surface of this door is yet another strip of white tape, marked with the word BATHROOM. Mr. Blank wonders how he could have missed it, since it is no more than a few steps from the bed, but, as the reader has already learned, his thoughts have largely been elsewhere, lost in a fogland of ghost-like beings and broken memories as he searches for an answer to the question that haunts him.

Do you have to go? Anna asks.

Go? he replies. Go where?

To the bathroom. Do you need to use the toilet?

Ah. The toilet. Yes. Now that you mention it, I think that would be a good idea.

Do you want me to help you, or can you manage on your own?

I'm not sure. Let me give it a try, and we'll see what happens.

Anna turns the white porcelain knob for him, and the door opens. As Mr. Blank shuffles into the white, windowless room with the black-and-white tile floor, Anna shuts the door behind him, and for several moments Mr. Blank just stands there, looking at the white toilet against the far wall, suddenly feeling bereft, aching to be with Anna again. Finally, he whispers to himself: Get a grip, old man. You're acting like a child. Nevertheless, even as he shuffles over to the toilet and begins lowering his pajama bottoms, he feels an overpowering urge to cry.

The pajama bottoms fall to his ankles; he sits down on the toilet seat; his bladder and bowels prepare to evacuate their pent-up liquids and solids. Urine flows from his penis, first one stool and then a second stool slide from his anus, and so good does it feel to be relieving himself in this manner that he forgets the sorrow that took hold of him just moments before. Of course he can manage on his own, he tells himself. He's been doing it ever since he was a little boy, and when it comes to pissing and shitting, he's as capable as any person in the world. Not only that, but he's an expert at wiping his ass as well.

Let Mr. Blank have his little moment of hubris, for successful as he is in completing the first part of the operation, the second part does not go

nearly as well. He has no trouble lifting himself off the seat and flushing the toilet, but once he does so he realizes that his pajama bottoms are still gathered around his ankles and that in order to pull them up he must either bend over or crouch down and grab hold of the waist with his hands. Neither bending nor crouching is an activity he feels particularly comfortable with today, but of the two he is somewhat more fearful of bending, since he understands the potential for losing his balance once he lowers his head, and he is apprehensive that if he should indeed lose his balance, he might fall to the floor and crack his skull against the black-and-white tiles. He therefore concludes that crouching is the lesser of the two evils, although he is far from confident that his knees can bear the strain that will be put upon them. We will never know if they can or can't. Alerted by the sound of the flushing toilet, Anna, no doubt assuming that Mr. Blank has finished the job he set out to do, opens the door and enters the bathroom.

One might think that Mr. Blank would be embarrassed to find himself in such a compromising position (standing there with his pants down, his limp penis dangling between his naked, scrawny legs), but such is not the case. Mr. Blank feels no false modesty in front of Anna. If anything, he is more than glad to let her see whatever there is to see, and instead of hastily crouching down to pull up his pajama bottoms, he begins undoing the buttons of his pajama top in order to remove the shirt as well.

I'd like to have my bath now, he says.

A real bath in the tub, she asks, or just a sponge bath?

It doesn't matter. You decide.

Anna looks at her watch and says: Maybe just a sponge bath. It's getting a bit late now, and I still have to dress you and make the bed.

By now, Mr. Blank has removed both the top and the bottoms of his pajamas as well as his slippers. Unperturbed by the sight of the old man's naked body, Anna walks over to the toilet and lowers the seat cover, which she pats a couple of times with the palm of her hand as an invitation for Mr. Blank to sit down. Mr. Blank sits, and Anna then perches herself beside him on the edge of the bathtub, turns on the hot water, and begins soaking a white washcloth under the spigot.

The moment Anna begins touching Mr. Blank's body with the warm, soapy cloth, he falls into a trance of languid submission, luxuriating in the feel of her gentle hands upon him. She starts at the top and works her way slowly downward, washing his ears and behind his ears, the front

and back of his neck, has him turn on the toilet seat in order to move the cloth up and down his back, then turn again in order to do the same to his chest, pausing every fifteen seconds or so to douse the cloth under the spigot, alternately adding more soap to it and rinsing the soap out of it, depending on whether she is about to wash a particular part of Mr. Blank's body or remove the soap from an area that has just been cleaned. Mr. Blank shuts his eyes, his head suddenly emptied of the shadow-beings and terrors that have haunted him since the first paragraph of this report. By the time the washcloth has descended to his belly, his penis has begun to alter its shape, growing longer and thicker and becoming partially erect, and Mr. Blank marvels that even at his advanced age his penis continues to act as it always did, never once modifying its behavior since his earliest adolescence. So much has changed for him since then, but not that, not that one thing, and now that Anna has brought the washcloth into direct contact with that part of his body, he can feel it stiffening to full extension, and as she goes on rubbing and stroking it with the warm sudsy water, it is all he can do not to cry out and beg her to finish the job.

We're feeling frisky today, Mr. Blank, Anna says.

I'm afraid so, Mr. Blank whispers, his eyes still shut. I can't help it.

If I were you, I'd feel proud of myself. Not every man your age is still . . . still capable of this.

It has nothing to do with me. The thing has a life of its own.

Suddenly, the cloth moves over to his right leg. Before Mr. Blank can register his disappointment, he feels Anna's bare hand sliding up and down the well-lubricated erection. Her right hand is continuing to wash him with the cloth, but her left hand is now engaged in this other task for him, and even as he succumbs to the practiced ministrations of that left hand, he wonders what he has done to deserve such generous treatment.

He gasps when the semen comes spurting out of him, and it is only then, after the deed has been done, that he opens his eyes and turns to Anna. She is no longer sitting on the edge of the tub but kneeling on the floor in front of him, wiping up the ejaculation with the washcloth. Her head is down, and therefore he cannot see her eyes, but nevertheless he leans forward and touches her left cheek with his right hand. Anna looks up then, and as their eyes meet she gives him another one of her tender and affectionate smiles.

You're so good to me, he says.

I want you to be happy, she answers. This is a hard time for you, and if you can find some moments of pleasure in all this, I'm glad to help.

I've done something terrible to you. I don't know what it is, but something terrible . . . unspeakable . . . beyond forgiveness. And here you are, taking care of me like a saint.

It wasn't your fault. You did what you had to do, and I don't hold it against you.

But you suffered. I made you suffer, didn't I?

Yes, very badly. I almost didn't make it.

What did I do?

You sent me off to a dangerous place, a desperate place, a place of destruction and death.

What was it? Some kind of mission?

I guess you could call it that.

You were young then, weren't you? The girl in the photo.

Yes.

You were very pretty, Anna. You're older now, but I still find you pretty. Just about perfect, if you know what I mean.

You don't have to exaggerate, Mr. Blank.

I'm not. If someone told me that I had to look at you twenty-four hours a day for the rest of my life, I wouldn't have any objections.

Once again, Anna smiles, and once again Mr. Blank touches her left cheek with his right hand.

How long were you in that place? he asks.

A few years. Much longer than I was expecting to be.

But you managed to get out?

Eventually, yes.

I feel so ashamed.

You mustn't. The fact is, Mr. Blank, without you I wouldn't be anyone.

Still . . .

No *still*. You're not like other men. You've sacrificed your life to something bigger than yourself, and whatever you've done or haven't done, it's never been for selfish reasons.

Have you ever been in love, Anna?

Several times.

Are you married?

I was.

Was?

My husband died three years ago.

What was his name?

David. David Zimmer.

What happened?

He had a bad heart.

I'm responsible for that, too, aren't I?

Not really . . . Only indirectly.

I'm so sorry.

Don't be. Without you, I never would have met David in the first place. Believe me, Mr. Blank, it isn't your fault. You do what you have to do, and then things happen. Good things and bad things both. That's the way it is. We might be the ones who suffer, but there's a reason for it, a good reason, and anyone who complains about it doesn't understand what it means to be alive.

It should be noted that a second camera and a second tape recorder have been planted in the bathroom ceiling, making it possible for all activities in that space to be recorded as well, and because the word *all* is an absolute term, the transcription of the dialogue between Anna and Mr. Blank can be verified in every one of its details.

The sponge bath goes on for several more minutes, and when Anna has finished washing and rinsing the remaining areas of Mr. Blank's body (legs, front and back; ankles, feet, and toes; arms, hands, and fingers; scrotum, buttocks, and anus), she fetches a black terry-cloth robe from a hook on the door and helps Mr. Blank put it on. Then she picks up the blue-and-yellow striped pajamas and walks into the other room, making sure to leave the door open. While Mr. Blank stands in front of the small mirror above the sink, shaving with a battery-operated electric razor (for obvious reasons, traditional razor blades are forbidden), Anna folds the pajamas, makes the bed, and opens the closet to select Mr. Blank's clothes for the day. She moves quickly and efficiently, as if trying to make up for lost time. So rapid is her completion of these tasks that when Mr. Blank finishes shaving with the electric razor and walks into the other room, he is startled to see that his clothes have already been laid out on the bed. Remembering his conversation with James P. Flood and the mention of the word *closet*, he was hoping to catch Anna in the act of opening the closet door, if indeed the closet exists, in order to determine where it is located. Now, as his eyes scan the room, he sees no sign of it, and another mystery remains unsolved.

He could, of course, ask Anna where it is, but once he sees Anna

herself, sitting on the bed and smiling up at him, he is so moved to be in her presence again that the question escapes his mind.

I'm beginning to remember you now, he says. Not everything, but little flashes, bits and pieces here and there. I was very young the first time I saw you, wasn't I?

About twenty-one, I think, Anna says.

But I kept losing you. You'd be there for a few days, and then you'd vanish. A year would go by, two years, four years, and then you'd suddenly pop up again.

You didn't know what to do with me, that's why. It took you a long time to figure it out.

And then I sent you on your . . . your mission. I remember being frightened for you. But you were a real battler back in those days, weren't you?

A tough and feisty girl, Mr. Blank.

Exactly. And that's what gave me hope. If you hadn't been a resourceful person, you never would have made it.

Let me help you with your clothes, Anna says, glancing down at her watch. Time is marching on.

The word *marching* induces Mr. Blank to think about his dizzy spells and earlier difficulties with walking, but now, as he travels the short distance from the threshold of the bathroom to the bed, he is encouraged to note that his brain is clear and that he feels in no danger of falling. With nothing to support the hypothesis, he attributes this improvement to the beneficent Anna, to the mere fact that she has been there with him for the past twenty or thirty minutes, radiating the affection he so desperately longs for.

The clothes turn out to be all white: white cotton trousers, white button-down shirt, white boxer shorts, white nylon socks, and a pair of white tennis shoes.

An odd choice, Mr. Blank says. I'm going to look like the Good Humor man.

It was a special request, Anna replies. From Peter Stillman. Not the father, the son. Peter Stillman, Junior.

Who's he?

You don't remember?

I'm afraid not.

He's another one of your charges. When you sent him out on his mission, he had to dress all in white.

How many people have I sent out?

Hundreds, Mr. Blank. More people than I can count.

All right. Let's get on with it. I don't suppose it makes any difference.

Without further ado, he unties the belt of the robe and lets the robe fall to the floor. Once again, he is standing naked in front of Anna, feeling not the slightest hint of embarrassment or modesty. Glancing down and pointing to his penis, he says: Look how small it is. Mr. Bigshot isn't so big now, is he?

Anna smiles and then pats the bed with the palm of her hand, beckoning him to sit down next to her. As he does so, Mr. Blank is once more thrust back into his early childhood, back to the days of Whitey the rocking horse and their long journeys together through the deserts and mountains of the Far West. He thinks about his mother and how she used to dress him like this in his upstairs bedroom with the morning sun slanting through the venetian blinds, and all at once, realizing that his mother is dead, probably long dead, he wonders if Anna hasn't somehow become a new mother for him, even at his advanced age, for why else would he feel so comfortable with her, he who is generally so shy and self-conscious about his body in front of others?

Anna climbs off the bed and crouches down in front of Mr. Blank. She begins with the socks, slipping one over his left foot and then the other one over his right foot, moves on to the undershorts, which she slides up his legs and, as Mr. Blank stands to accommodate her, farther up to his waist, thus concealing the former Mr. Bigshot, who no doubt will rise again to assert his dominance over Mr. Blank before too many hours have passed.

Mr. Blank sits down on the bed a second time, and the process is repeated with the trousers. When Mr. Blank sits down for the third time, Anna puts the sneakers on his feet, first the left one, then the right one, and immediately begins to tie the laces, first on the left shoe, then on the right shoe. After that, she emerges from her crouch and sits down on the bed beside Mr. Blank to help him with the shirt, first guiding his left arm through the left sleeve, then his right arm through the right sleeve, and finally buttoning the buttons from the bottom up, and during all this slow and laborious procedure, Mr. Blank's thoughts are elsewhere, back in his boyhood room with Whitey and his mother, remembering how she used to do these same things for him with the same loving patience, so many years ago now, in the long-ago beginning of his life.

*

Now Anna is gone. The stainless steel cart has vanished, the door has been

shut, and once again Mr. Blank is alone in the room. The questions he was meaning to ask her – about the closet, about the typescript concerning the so-called Confederation, about whether the door is locked from the outside or not – have all gone unasked, and therefore Mr. Blank is as much in the dark about what he is doing in this place as he was before Anna's arrival. For the time being, he is sitting on the edge of the narrow bed, palms spread out on his knees, head down, staring at the floor, but soon, as soon as he feels the strength of will to do so, he will stand up from the bed and once more make his way over to the desk to look through the pile of photographs (if he can summon the courage to face those images again) and continue his reading of the typescript about the man trapped in the room in Ultima. For the time being, however, he does nothing more than sit on the bed and pine for Anna, wishing she were still there with him, wishing he could take her in his arms and hold her.

Now he is on his feet again. He tries to shuffle toward the desk, but he forgets that he is no longer wearing his slippers, and the rubber sole of his left tennis shoe sticks on the wood floor – in such an abrupt and unforeseen way that Mr. Blank loses his balance and nearly falls. Damn, he says, damn these stupid little white fucks. He longs to change out of the tennis shoes and put on the slippers again, but the slippers are black, and if he put them on he would no longer be dressed all in white, which was something Anna explicitly asked of him – as per the demand of one Peter Stillman, Junior, whoever on earth he might be.

Mr. Blank therefore abandons the shuffling strides he used with the slippers and travels toward the desk with something that resembles an ordinary walk. Not quite the brisk heel-to-toe step one sees in the young and the vigorous, but a slow and heavy gait whereby Mr. Blank lifts one foot an inch or two off the ground, propels the leg attached to that foot approximately six inches forward, and then plants the entire sole of the shoe on the floor, heel and toe together. A slight pause follows, and then he repeats the process with the other foot. It might not be beautiful to watch, but it is sufficient to his purpose, and before long he finds himself standing in front of the desk.

The chair has been pushed in, which means that in order to sit down, Mr. Blank is obliged to pull it out. In so doing, he finally discovers that the chair is equipped with wheels, for instead of scraping along the floor as he is expecting it will, the chair rolls out smoothly, with scarcely any effort on his part. Mr. Blank sits down, astonished that he could have overlooked this feature of the chair during his earlier visits to the desk.

He presses his feet against the floor, gives a little shove, and back he goes, covering a distance of some three or four feet. He considers this an important discovery, for pleasant as rocking back and forth and turning around in circles might be, the fact that the chair can move about the room is potentially of great therapeutic value – as, for example, when his legs are feeling especially tired, or when he is attacked by another one of his dizzy spells. Instead of having to stand up and walk at those times, he will be able to use the chair to travel from place to place in a sitting position, thus conserving his strength for more urgent matters. He feels comforted by this thought, and yet, as he inches the chair back toward the desk, the crushing sense of guilt that largely disappeared during Anna's visit suddenly returns, and by the time he makes it to the desk he understands that the desk itself is responsible for these oppressive thoughts – not the desk as desk, perhaps, but the photographs and papers piled on its surface, which no doubt contain the answer to the question that haunts him. They are the source of his anguish, and even though it would be simple enough to return to the bed and ignore them, he feels compelled to go on with his investigations, tortuous and painful as they might be.

He glances down and notices a pad of paper and a ballpoint pen – objects he does not remember having been there during his last visit to the desk. No matter, he says to himself, and without another thought he picks up the pen with his right hand and opens the pad to the first page with his left. In order not to forget what has happened so far today – for Mr. Blank is nothing if not forgetful – he writes down the following list of names:

James P. Flood
Anna
David Zimmer
Peter Stillman, Jr.
Peter Stillman, Sr.

This small task accomplished, he closes the pad, puts down the pen, and pushes them aside. Then, reaching for the top pages on the pile farthest to the left, he discovers that they have been stapled together, perhaps twenty to twenty-five pages in all, and when he puts down the sheaf in front of him, he further discovers that it is the typescript he was reading before Anna's arrival. He assumes that she was the one

who stapled the pages together – to make things easier for him – and then, realizing that the typescript is not terribly long, he wonders if he will have time to finish it before James P. Flood comes knocking at the door.

He turns to the fourth paragraph on the second page and begins reading:

For the past forty days, there have been no beatings, and neither the Colonel nor any members of his staff have shown their faces to me. The only person I have seen is the sergeant who delivers my food and changes the slop bucket. I have tried to act in a civil manner with him, always making some small remark when he comes in, but he is apparently under orders to remain silent, and not once have I extracted a single word from this giant in the brown uniform. Then, less than an hour ago, an extraordinary event took place. The sergeant unlocked the door, and in walked two young privates carrying a small wooden table and a straight-backed chair. They set them down in the middle of the room, and then the sergeant came in and put a tall stack of blank paper on the table along with a bottle of ink and a pen.

–You're allowed to write, he said.

–Is that your way of making conversation, I asked, or are you trying to give me an order?

–The Colonel says you're allowed to write. You can take that in any way you choose.

–What if I choose not to write?

–You're free to do what you want, but the Colonel says it's unlikely that a man in your position would pass up the opportunity to defend himself in writing.

–I assume he's planning to read what I write.

–It would be logical to assume that, yes.

–Will he be sending it to the capital afterward?

–He didn't speak of his intentions. He simply said that you were allowed to write.

–How much time do I have?

–The subject wasn't discussed.

–And what if I run out of paper?

–You'll be given as much ink and paper as you need. The Colonel wanted me to tell you that.

–Thank the Colonel for me, and tell him I understand what he's doing. He's giving me a chance to lie about what happened in order to save my

neck. That's very sporting of him. Please tell him that I appreciate the gesture.

–I will convey your message to the Colonel.

–Good. Now leave me in peace. If he wants me to write, I'll write, but in order to do that, I have to be alone.

I was only guessing, of course. The truth is that I have no idea why the Colonel did what he did. I would like to think he's begun to pity me, but I doubt it can be as simple as that. Colonel De Vega is hardly a compassionate man, and if he suddenly wants to make my life less uncomfortable, giving me a pen is surely an odd way to go about it. A manuscript of lies would serve him well, but he can't possibly think that I'd be willing to change my story at this late date. He has already tried to make me recant, and if I didn't do it when I was nearly beaten to death, why would I do it now? What it comes down to is a matter of caution, I think, a way of preparing himself for whatever might happen next. Too many people know that I'm here for him to execute me without a trial. On the other hand, a trial is something that must be avoided at all costs – for once the case is taken to court, my story will become public knowledge. By allowing me to put the story in writing, he is gathering evidence, irrefutable evidence that will justify any action he decides to take against me. Assume, for example, that he goes ahead and has me shot without a trial. Once the military command in the capital gets wind of my death, they will be obliged by law to open an official inquiry, but at that point he will only have to give them the pages I've written, and he will be exonerated. No doubt they will reward him with a medal for resolving the dilemma so neatly. It could be that he has already written to them about me, in fact, and that I am holding this pen in my hand now because they instructed him to put it there. Under normal circumstances, it takes about three weeks for a letter to reach the capital from Ultima. If I have been here for a month and a half, then perhaps he received his answer today. Let the traitor put his story in writing, they probably said, and then we'll be free to dispose of him in any way we like.

That is one possibility. It could be that I'm exaggerating my importance, however, and that the Colonel is merely playing with me. Who knows if he hasn't decided to amuse himself with the spectacle of my suffering? Distractions are scarce in a town like Ultima, and unless you're resourceful enough to invent your own, you could easily lose your mind from the boredom. I can imagine the Colonel reading my words out loud to his mistress, the two of them sitting up in bed at night and laughing

at my pathetic little phrases. That would be amusing, wouldn't it? Such a welcome diversion, such unholy mirth. If I keep him sufficiently entertained, perhaps he'll let me go on writing forever, and bit by bit I'll be turned into his personal clown, his own jester-scribe scribbling forth my pratfalls in endless streams of ink. And even if he should tire of my stories and have me killed, the manuscript will remain, won't it? That will be his trophy – one more skull to add to his collection.

Still, it is difficult for me to suppress the joy I am feeling at this moment. Whatever Colonel De Vega's motives might have been, whatever traps and humiliations he might have in store for me, I can honestly say that I am happier now than at any time since my arrest. I am sitting at the table, listening to the pen as it scratches along the surface of the paper. I stop. I dip the pen into the inkwell, then watch the black shapes form as I move my hand slowly from left to right. I come to the edge and then return to the other side, and as the shapes thin out, I stop once more and dip the pen into the inkwell. So it goes as I work my way down the page, and each cluster of marks is a word, and each word is a sound in my head, and each time I write another word, I hear the sound of my own voice, even though my lips are silent.

Immediately after the sergeant locked the door, I picked up the table and carried it to the western wall, placing it directly below the window. Then I went back for the chair, put the chair on top of the table, and hoisted myself up – first onto the table, then onto the chair. I wanted to see if I could get my fingers around the bars of the window, hoping I might be able to pull myself up and hang there long enough to catch a glimpse of the outside. No matter how hard I strained, however, the tips of my fingers fell short of the goal. Not wanting to abandon the effort, I removed my shirt and tried flinging it up toward the bars, thinking I might be able to thread it through, then grab hold of the dangling sleeves, and in that way manage to haul myself up. But the shirt wasn't quite long enough, and without a tool of some sort to guide the cloth around the metal bars (a stick, a broom handle, even a twig), I could do no more than wave the shirt back and forth, like a white flag of surrender.

In the end, it is probably just as well to put those dreams behind me. If I can't spend my days looking out the window, then I will be forced to concentrate on the task at hand. The essential thing is to stop worrying about the Colonel, to push all thoughts of him out of my mind and set down the facts as I know them. What he chooses to do with this report is strictly his business, and there is nothing I can do to influence

his decision. The only thing I can do is tell the story. Given the story I have to tell, that will be difficult enough.

Mr. Blank pauses for a moment to rest his eyes, to run his fingers through his hair, to ponder the meaning of the words he has just read. When he thinks about the narrator's failed attempt to climb up and look out the window, he suddenly remembers his own window, or, more precisely, the window shade that covers the window, and now that he has a means of traveling over there without having to stand up, he decides that this is the moment to lift the shade and have a peek outdoors. If he can take stock of his surroundings, perhaps some memory will come back to him to help explain what he is doing in this room; perhaps the mere glimpse of a tree or the cornice of a building or a random patch of sky will furnish him with an insight into his predicament. He therefore temporarily abandons his reading of the typescript to journey toward the wall in which the window is located. When he reaches his destination, he thrusts out his right hand, takes hold of the bottom of the shade, and gives it a quick tug, hoping to engage the spring that will send the shade flying upward. It is an old shade, however, and much of its bounce has been lost, and rather than ascend to reveal the window behind it, it sags down several inches below the sill. Frustrated by this botched attempt, Mr. Blank tugs harder and longer the second time, and just like that, the shade decides to act like a proper shade and goes rolling up to the top of the window.

Imagine Mr. Blank's disappointment when he peers through the window and sees that the shutters have been closed, blocking any possibility of looking out to discover where he is. Nor are these the classic wooden shutters with movable slats that allow a bit of light to filter through; they are industrial-strength metal panels with no apertures of any kind, painted a dull shade of gray, with areas of rust showing through that have begun to corrode the surface. Once Mr. Blank rebounds from his shock, he understands that the situation is not as dire as he supposed. The shutters lock from within, and in order to get his fingers on the lock, all he has to do is raise the window sash to its maximum height. Then, once the latch has been unhooked, he will be able to push the shutters open and look out at the world around him. He knows that he will have to stand up from the chair to gain the leverage necessary for such an operation, but that is a small price to pay, and so he lifts his body out of the seat, checks to make sure the window is unlocked (it is), places the heels of his two hands firmly under the top bar of the sash, pauses for a

moment to prepare for the exertions ahead, and then pushes for all he is worth.

Unexpectedly, the window does not budge. Mr. Blank stops to catch his breath, then tries again – with the same negative result. He suspects that the window has jammed somehow – either because of excess moisture in the air or an excess of paint that has inadvertently glued the upper and lower halves of the window together – but then, as he examines the top bar of the sash more closely, he discovers something that previously eluded his notice. Two large construction nails, almost invisible because the heads of the nails are painted over, have been hammered into the bar. One large nail to the left, one large nail to the right, and because Mr. Blank knows it will be impossible for him to extract those nails from the wood, the window cannot be opened – not now, he realizes, not later, not ever under any circumstances at all.

Proof has been given at last. Someone, perhaps several someones, has or have locked Mr. Blank in this room and is or are holding him prisoner against his will. At least that is what he concludes from the evidence of the two nails hammered into the window sash, but damning as that evidence might be, there is still the question of the door, and until Mr. Blank determines whether the door is locked from the outside, if indeed it is locked at all, the conclusion he has drawn could well be false. If he were thinking clearly, his next step would be to walk or wheel himself over to the door and investigate the matter at once. But Mr. Blank does not move from his spot by the window, for the simple reason that he is afraid, so afraid of what he might learn from the door that he cannot bring himself to risk a confrontation with the truth. Instead, he sits back down in the chair and decides to break the window. For whether he is locked in or not, he is above all desperate to find out where he is. He thinks about the man in the typescript he has been reading, and then wonders if he, too, won't eventually be taken outside and shot. Or, even more sinister to his imagination, if he won't be murdered right here in the room, strangled to death by the powerful hands of some thug.

There are no blunt objects in the vicinity. No hammers, for example, no broom handles or shovels, no pickaxes or battering rams, and thus even before he begins, Mr. Blank knows his effort is doomed to defeat. Nevertheless, he gives it a try, for not only is he afraid, he is angry, and in his anger he slips off his right tennis shoe, grips the toe firmly in his right hand, and starts pounding the heel against the glass. A normal window might give way under such an assault, but this is a double-paned

thermal window of the strongest quality, and it scarcely trembles as the old man strikes it with his feeble weapon of rubber and canvas. After twenty-one consecutive blows, Mr. Blank gives up and lets the shoe drop to the floor. Now, both angry and frustrated, he pounds his fist against the glass several times, not wanting to let the window have the last word, but flesh and bone are no more effective in cracking the pane than the shoe was. He wonders if smashing his head against the window might not do the trick, but even though his mind is not all it should be, Mr. Blank is still lucid enough to understand the folly of inflicting grave physical harm upon himself in what is no doubt a hopeless cause. With a heavy heart, therefore, he slumps back in the chair and closes his eyes – not only afraid, not only angry, but exhausted as well.

The moment he shuts his eyes, he sees the shadow-beings marching through his head. It is a long, dimly-lit procession composed of scores if not hundreds of figures, and among them are included both men and women, both children and old people, and while some are short, others are tall, and while some are round, others are lean, and as Mr. Blank strains to listen in on them, he hears not only the sound of their footsteps but something he would liken to a groan, a barely audible collective groan rising from their midst. Where they are and where they are going he cannot say, but they seem to be tramping through a forgotten pasture somewhere, a no man's land of scrawny weeds and barren earth, and because it is so dark, and because each figure is moving forward with his or her head down, Mr. Blank cannot distinguish anyone's face. All he knows is that the mere sight of these figments fills him with dread, and once again he is overwhelmed by an implacable sense of guilt. He speculates that these people are the ones he sent off on various missions over the years, and, as was the case with Anna, perhaps some of them, or many of them, or all of them did not fare so terribly well, even to the point of being subjected to unbearable suffering and/or death.

Mr. Blank can't be sure of anything, but it strikes him as possible that there is a connection between these shadow-beings and the photographs on the desk. What if the pictures represent the same people whose faces he is unable to identify in the scene that is playing itself out in his head? If that is so, then the phantoms he is observing are not figments so much as memories, memories of actual people – for when was the last time anyone took a photograph of a person who did not exist? Mr. Blank knows there is nothing to support his theory, that it is only the wildest of wild conjectures, but there has to be some reason, he tells himself, some

cause, some principle to explain what is happening to him, to account for the fact that he is in this room with these photographs and these four piles of manuscripts, and why not investigate a little further to see if there is any truth to this blind stab in the dark?

Forgetting about the two nails hammered into the window, forgetting about the door and whether it is locked from the outside or not, Mr. Blank wheels himself over to the desk, picks up the photographs, and then puts them down directly in front of him. Anna is on top, of course, and he spends a few moments looking at her again, studying her unhappy but beautiful young face, gazing deep into the gaze of her dark, burning eyes. No, he says to himself, we were never married. Her husband was a man named David Zimmer, and now Zimmer is dead.

He puts the photograph of Anna aside and looks at the next one. It is another woman, perhaps in her mid-twenties, with light brown hair and steady, watchful eyes. The bottom half of her body is obscured, since she is standing in the doorway of what looks like a New York apartment with the door only partially open, as if in fact she has just opened it to welcome a visitor, and in spite of the cautious look in her eyes, a small smile is creasing the corners of her mouth. Mr. Blank feels a momentary twinge of recognition, but as he struggles to recall her name, nothing comes to him – not after twenty seconds, not after forty seconds, not after a minute. Given that he found Anna's name so quickly, he assumed he would be able to do it with the others as well. But such, apparently, is not the case.

He looks at another ten pictures with the same disappointing results. An old man in a wheelchair, as thin and delicate as a sparrow, wearing the dark glasses of the blind. A grinning woman with a drink in one hand and a cigarette in the other, wearing a 1920s flapper dress and a cloche hat. A frighteningly obese man with an immense hairless head and a cigar jutting from his mouth. Another young woman, this one Chinese, dressed in a dancer's leotard. A dark-haired man with a waxed mustache, decked out in tails and a top hat. A young man sleeping on the grass in what looks like a public park. An older man, perhaps in his mid-fifties, lying on a sofa with his legs propped up on a pile of pillows. A bearded, scraggly-looking homeless person sitting on a sidewalk with his arms around a large mutt. A chubby black man in his sixties holding up a Warsaw telephone book from 1937–38. A slender young man sitting at a table with five cards in his hand and a stack of poker chips in front of him.

With each successive failure, Mr. Blank grows that much more discouraged, that much more doubtful about his chances with the next one – until, muttering something under his breath in such a low voice that the tape recorder cannot pick up the words, he abandons the effort and pushes the photographs aside.

He rocks back and forth in the chair for close to a minute, doing what he can to regain his mental equilibrium and put the defeat behind him. Then, without giving the matter another thought, he picks up the typescript and begins reading again:

My name is Sigmund Graf. I was born forty-one years ago in the town of Luz, a textile center in the northwestern part of Faux-Lieu Province, and until my arrest by Colonel De Vega, I worked in the demographics division of the Bureau of Internal Affairs. As a young man I earned a bachelor's degree in classical literature from All Souls University and then served as an army intelligence officer in the Southeast Border Wars, taking part in the battle that led to the unification of the Petit-Lieu and Merveil principalities. I was honorably discharged with the rank of captain and received a distinguished service medal for my work in intercepting and decoding enemy messages. On returning to the capital after my demobilization, I entered the Bureau as a field coordinator and researcher. At the time of my departure for the Alien Territories, I had been a member of the staff for twelve years. My last official title was that of Deputy Assistant Director.

Like every citizen of the Confederation, I have known my share of suffering, have lived through prolonged moments of violence and upheaval, and have borne the marks of loss upon my soul. I was not yet fourteen when the riots at the Sanctus Academy in Beauchamp led to the outbreak of the Faux-Lieu Language Wars, and two months after the invasion I saw my mother and younger brother burn to death during the Sacking of Luz. My father and I were among the seven thousand who took part in the exodus to the neighboring province of Neue Welt. The journey covered some six hundred miles and took more than two months to complete, and by the time we reached our destination, our number had been reduced by a third. For the last hundred miles, my father was so weak from illness that I had to carry him on my back, staggering half-blind through the mud and winter rains until we came to the outskirts of Nachtburg. For six months we begged in the streets of that gray city to keep ourselves alive, and when we were finally rescued by a loan from relatives in the north, we were on the point of starvation. Life improved

for us after that, but no matter how prosperous my father became in the years that followed, he never fully recovered from those months of hardship. When he died ten summers ago at the age of fifty-six, the toll of his experiences had aged him so much that he looked like a man of seventy.

There have been other pains as well. A year and a half ago, the Bureau sent me on an expedition to the Independent Communities of Tierra Blanca Province. Less than a month after my departure, the cholera epidemic swept through the capital. Many now refer to this plague as the Blight of History, and considering that it struck just as the long and elaborately planned Unification ceremonies were about to begin, one can understand how it could be interpreted as an evil sign, a judgment on the very nature and purpose of the Confederation itself. I am not personally of that opinion, but my own life was nevertheless permanently altered by the epidemic. Cut off from all news of the city, I went about my work for the next four and a half months, traveling back and forth among the remote, mountainous communities to the south, pursuing my investigations into the various religious sects that had taken root in the area. When I returned in August, the crisis was already over – but not before my wife and fifteen-year-old daughter had disappeared. The majority of our neighbors in the Closterham District had either fled the city or succumbed to the illness themselves, but among those who had remained, not a single person could remember having seen them. The house was untouched, and nowhere in it could I find any evidence to suggest that the disease had infiltrated its walls. I made a thorough search of every room, but no secret was unveiled to me as to how or when they might have abandoned the premises. No missing clothes or jewels, no hastily discarded objects lying about the floor. The house was just as I had left it five months earlier, except that my wife and daughter were no longer in it.

I spent several weeks combing the city for clues of their whereabouts, growing increasingly desperate with each failed attempt to uncover information that would put me on their trail. I began by talking to friends and colleagues, and once I had exhausted the circle of familiars (in which I include my wife's female acquaintances, the parents of my daughter's classmates, as well as the shopkeepers and merchants of our district), I started reaching out to strangers. Armed with portraits of my wife and daughter, I questioned countless doctors, nurses, and volunteers who had worked in the makeshift hospitals and schoolrooms where the sick and dying had been cared for, but among all the hundreds of people who

looked at those miniatures, not one could recognize the faces I held in my hand. In the end, there was only one conclusion to be drawn. My darlings had been carried off by the scourge. Along with thousands of other victims, they were lying in one of the mass graves on Viaticum Bluff, the burial ground of the anonymous dead.

I do not mention these things in order to put myself in a sympathetic light. No one has to feel sorry for me, and no one has to make excuses for the errors I committed in the aftermath of these events. I am a man, not an angel, and if the grief that overtook me occasionally blurred my vision and led to certain lapses of conduct, that in no way should cast doubt on the truth of my story. Before anyone tries to discredit me by pointing to those stains on my record, I come forward of my own free will and openly pronounce my guilt to the world. These are treacherous times, and I know how easily perceptions can be twisted by a single word spoken into the wrong ear. Impugn a man's character, and everything that man does is made to seem underhanded, suspect, fraught with double motives. In my own case, the flaws in question stemmed from pain, not malice; confusion, not cunning. I lost my way, and for several months I sought comfort in the obliterating powers of alcohol. Most nights I drank alone, sitting in the darkness of my empty house, but some nights were worse than others. Whenever I encountered one of those bad turns, my thoughts would begin to sabotage me, and before long I would be choking on my own breath. My head would fill with images of my wife and daughter, and again and again I would see their mud-splattered bodies being lowered into the ground, again and again I would see their naked limbs entwined among the limbs of other corpses in the hole, and suddenly the darkness of the house would become too much to bear. I would venture out into public places, hoping to break the spell of those images in the noise and tumult of crowds. I frequented taverns and alehouses, and it was in one of those establishments that I did the most damage to myself and my reputation. The incident occurred on a Friday night in November when a man named Giles McNaughton picked a quarrel with me in the Auberge des Vents. McNaughton claimed that I attacked him first, but eleven witnesses testified otherwise in court, and I was acquitted of all charges. It was no more than a small victory, however, for the fact remained that I had broken the man's arm and shattered his nose, and I never would have responded with such vehemence if I hadn't been going to hell by way of drink. The jury found me innocent, judging that I had acted in legitimate self-defense, but that did not remove the stigma

of the trial itself – nor the scandal that broke out when it was discovered that a ranking member of the Bureau of Internal Affairs had been engaged in a bloody barroom brawl. Within hours of the verdict, rumors began circulating that officials from the Bureau had bribed certain members of the jury to vote in my favor. I have no knowledge of any corrupt dealings on my behalf, but I would tend to dismiss those accusations as mere gossip. What I do know for certain is that I had never seen McNaughton before that night. He, on the other hand, knew enough about me to address me by name, and when he approached my table and began to talk about my wife, suggesting that he was privy to information that would help solve the mystery of her disappearance, I told him to go away. The man was after money, and one look at his mottled, unhealthy face convinced me that he was a fraud, an opportunist who had got wind of my tragedy and meant to turn a profit from it. McNaughton apparently didn't like being dismissed in such a perfunctory manner. Instead of excusing himself, he sat down in the chair next to mine and angrily grabbed hold of my vest. Then, pulling me forward until our faces were almost touching, he leaned into me and said, What's the matter, citizen? Are you afraid of the truth? His eyes were full of rage and contempt, and because we were so close to each other, those eyes were the only objects in my field of vision. I could feel the hostility flowing through his body, and an instant later I felt it pass directly into mine. That was when I went after him. Yes, he had touched me first, but the moment I started to fight back, I wanted to hurt him, to hurt him as badly as I could.

That was my crime. Take it for what it was, but don't let it interfere with the reading of this report. Trouble comes to all men, and each man makes his peace with the world in his own way. If the force I used against McNaughton that night was unwarranted, the greater wrong was the pleasure I took in using that force. I do not pardon my actions, but considering my state of mind during that period, it is remarkable that the incident in the Auberge des Vents was the only one in which I did harm to another person. All the other harm was inflicted upon myself, and until I learned to curb my desire for drink (which was in fact a desire for death), I ran the risk of utter annihilation. In the course of time, I managed to take hold of myself again, but I confess that I am no longer the man I used to be. If I have gone on living, it is largely because my work at the Bureau has given me a reason to live. Such is the irony of my predicament. I am accused of being an enemy of the Confederation, and yet for the past nineteen years there has been no servant more loyal to

the Confederation than myself. My record shows that, and I am proud to have lived in an age that allowed me to participate in such a vast human endeavor. My work in the field has taught me to love the truth above all else, and therefore I have cleared the air pertaining to my sins and transgressions, but that does not mean I can accept guilt for a crime I did not commit. I believe in what the Confederation stands for, and I have passionately defended it with my words, my deeds, and my blood. If the Confederation has turned against me, it can only mean that the Confederation has turned against itself. I cannot hope for life anymore, but if these pages should fall into the hands of someone with sufficient strength of heart to read them in the spirit with which they were written, then perhaps my murder will not have been an entirely useless act.

Far off in the distance, beyond the room, beyond the building in which the room is located, Mr. Blank again hears the faint cry of a bird. Distracted by the sound, he looks up from the page in front of him, temporarily abandoning the dolorous confessions of Sigmund Graf. A sudden feeling of pressure invades his stomach, and before Mr. Blank can decide whether to call that feeling one of pain or simple discomfort, his intestinal tract bugles forth an ample, resonant fart. Ho ho, he says out loud, grunting with pleasure. Hopalong Cassidy rides again! Then he tips back in the chair, closes his eyes, and begins to rock, soon lapsing into one of those dull, trance-like states in which the mind is emptied of all thoughts, all emotions, all connection to the self. Thus trapped in his reptilian stupor, Mr. Blank is, as it were, absent, or at least momentarily cut off from his surroundings, which means that he does not hear the hand that has begun knocking on the door. Worse than that, he does not hear the door open, and therefore, even though someone has entered the room, he is still in the dark as to whether the door is locked from the outside or not. Or soon will be still in the dark, once he emerges from his trance.

Someone taps him on the shoulder, but before Mr. Blank can open his eyes and swivel around in the chair to see who it is, that person has already begun to speak. From the timbre and intonation of the voice, Mr. Blank instantly recognizes that it belongs to a man, but he is perplexed by the fact that it is talking to him in what sounds like a cockney accent.

I'm sorry, Mr. Blank, the man says to him. I knocked and knocked, and when you didn't open the door, I thought I should come in and see if anything was wrong.

Mr. Blank now swivels around in the chair and takes a close look at

his visitor. The man appears to be in his early fifties, with neatly combed hair and a small brown mustache with flecks of gray in it. Neither short nor tall, Mr. Blank says to himself, but more on the short side than the tall, and from his erect, almost ramrod posture as he stands there in his tweed suit, he looks like a military man of some kind, or perhaps a lower-level civil servant.

And you are? Mr. Blank asks.

Flood, sir. First name James. Middle name Patrick. James P. Flood. Don't you remember me?

Dimly, only dimly.

The ex-policeman.

Ah. Flood, the ex-policeman. You were going to pay me a visit, weren't you?

Yes, sir. Exactly, sir. That's why I'm here. I'm paying you the visit now.

Mr. Blank casts his eyes about the room, looking for a chair so he can offer Flood a place to sit, but apparently the only chair in the room is the one he now occupies himself.

Something wrong? Flood asks.

No, no, Mr. Blank replies. I'm just looking for another chair, that's all.

I can always sit on the bed, Flood answers, gesturing to the bed. Or, if you're feeling up to it, we could go to the park across the way. No shortage of benches there.

Mr. Blank points down at his right foot and says: I'm missing a shoe. I can't go outside with only one shoe.

Flood turns around and immediately spots the white tennis shoe on the floor below the window. There's the other one, sir. We could get it back on you in two shakes of a cat.

A cat? What are you talking about?

Just an expression, Mr. Blank. No harm intended. Flood pauses for a moment, looks back at the shoe on the floor, and then says: Well, what about it? Should we put it on or not?

Mr. Blank lets out a long, weary sigh. No, he says, with a tinge of sarcasm in his voice, I don't want to put it on. I'm sick of these goddamned shoes. If anything, I'd rather take the other one off, too.

The moment these words escape his mouth, Mr. Blank is heartened to realize that such an act falls within the realm of possibility, that in this one trifling instance he can take matters into his own hands. Without a moment's hesitation, he therefore bends down and removes the sneaker from his left foot.

Ah, that's better, he says, lifting his legs and wiggling his toes in the air. Much better. And I'm still dressed all in white, aren't I?

Of course you are, Flood says. What's so important about that?

Never mind, says Mr. Blank, waving off Flood's question as of no account. Just sit down on the bed and tell me what you want, Mr. Flood.

The former inspector from Scotland Yard lowers himself onto the foot of the mattress, positioning his body in the left-hand quadrant in order to align his face with the face of the old man, who is sitting in the chair with his back to the desk, roughly six feet away. Flood clears his throat, as if searching for the appropriate words to start with, and then, in a low voice trembling with anxiety, he says: It's about the dream, sir.

The dream? Mr. Blank asks, confounded by Flood's statement. What dream?

My dream, Mr. Blank. The one you mentioned in your report on Fanshawe.

Who's Fanshawe?

You don't remember?

No, Mr. Blank declares in a loud, irritable voice. No, I don't remember Fanshawe. I can hardly remember anything. They're pumping me full of pills, and nearly everything is gone now. Most of the time, I don't even know who I am. And if I can't remember myself, how do you expect me to remember this . . . this . . .

Fanshawe.

Fanshawe . . . And who, pray tell, is he?

One of your operatives, sir.

You mean someone I sent out on a mission?

An extremely perilous mission.

Did he survive?

No one is sure. But the prevailing opinion is that he's no longer with us.

Groaning softly to himself, Mr. Blank covers his face with his hands and whispers: Another one of the damned.

Excuse me, Flood interjects, I didn't catch what you said.

Nothing, Mr. Blank replies in a louder voice. I said nothing.

At that point, the conversation stops for several moments. Silence reigns, and in that silence Mr. Blank imagines that he hears the sound of wind, a powerful wind blowing through a stand of trees somewhere near, quite near, but whether that wind is real or not he cannot say. All the while, Flood's eyes remain fixed on the old man's face. When the silence

has become unbearable, he at last makes a timid venture to resume the dialogue. Well? he says.

Well what? Mr. Blank replies.

The dream. Can we talk about the dream now?

How can I talk about another man's dream if I don't know what it is?

That's just the problem, Mr. Blank. I have no memory of it myself.

Then I can't do anything for you, can I? If neither one of us knows what happened in your dream, there's nothing to talk about.

It's more complicated than that.

Hardly, Mr. Flood. It's very simple.

That's only because you don't remember writing the report. If you concentrate now, I mean really focus your mind on it, maybe it will come back to you.

I doubt it.

Listen. In the report you wrote on Fanshawe, you mention that he was the author of several unpublished books. One of them was entitled *Neverland*. Unfortunately, except for concluding that certain events in the book were inspired by similar events in Fanshawe's life, you say nothing about the subject, nothing about the plot, nothing about the book at all. Only one brief aside – written in parentheses, I might add – which reads as follows. I quote from memory: *(Montag's house in chapter seven; Flood's dream in chapter thirty)*. The point being, Mr. Blank, that you must have read *Neverland* yourself, and in that you're one of the only people in the world to have done so, I would deeply appreciate it, appreciate it from the very bottom of my miserable heart, if you would make an effort to recall the content of that dream.

From the way you talk about it, *Neverland* must be a novel.

Yes, sir. A work of fiction.

And Fanshawe used you as a character?

Apparently so. There's nothing strange about that. From what I understand, writers do it all the time.

Maybe they do, but I don't see why you should get so worked up about it. The dream never really happened. It's nothing but words on a page – pure invention. Forget about it, Mr. Flood. It's not important.

It's important to me, Mr. Blank. My whole life depends on it. Without that dream, I'm nothing, literally nothing.

The passion with which the normally reserved ex-policeman delivers this last remark – a passion provoked by the sting of a genuine, soul-rending despair – strikes Mr. Blank as nothing short of hilarious,

and for the first time since the opening words of this account, he bursts out laughing. As one might expect, Flood takes offense, for no one enjoys having his feelings trampled upon in such a heartless manner, least of all someone as fragile as Flood is at this moment.

I resent that, Mr. Blank, he says. You have no right to laugh at me.

Maybe not, Mr. Blank says, once the spasm in his chest has subsided, but I couldn't help it. You take yourself so damned seriously, Flood. It makes you look ridiculous.

I might be ridiculous, Flood says, with anger rising in his voice, but you, Mr. Blank . . . you're cruel . . . cruel and indifferent to the pain of others. You play with people's lives and take no responsibility for what you've done. I'm not going to sit here and bore you with my troubles, but I blame you for what's happened to me. I most sincerely blame you, and I despise you for it.

Troubles? Mr. Blank says, suddenly softening his tone, doing his best to show some sympathy. What kind of troubles?

The headaches for one thing. Being forced into early retirement for another. Bankruptcy for yet another. And then there's the business with my wife, or rather my ex-wife, not to speak of my children, who no longer want anything to do with me. My life is in ruins, Mr. Blank. I walk around the world like a ghost, and sometimes I question whether I even exist. Whether I've ever existed at all.

And you think learning about that dream is going to solve all this? It's highly doubtful, you know.

The dream is my only chance. It's like a missing part of me, and until I find it, I'll never really be myself again.

I don't remember Fanshawe. I don't remember reading his novel. I don't remember writing the report. I wish I could help you, Flood, but the treatment they're giving me has turned my brain into a lump of rusty iron.

Try to remember. That's all I ask of you. Try.

As Mr. Blank looks into the eyes of the shattered ex-policeman, he notices that tears have begun to roll down his cheeks. Poor devil, Mr. Blank says to himself. For a moment or two he considers whether to ask Flood to help him locate the closet, for he remembers now that Flood was the one who mentioned it on the phone earlier that morning, but in the end, after weighing the pros and cons of making such a request, he decides against it. Instead he says: Please forgive me, Mr. Flood. I'm sorry I laughed at you.

*

Now Flood is gone, and once again Mr. Blank is alone in the room. In the aftermath of their disturbing encounter, the old man feels grumpy and out of sorts, wounded by the unjust and belligerent accusations he was subjected to. Still, not wanting to squander any opportunity to increase his knowledge of his present circumstances, he swivels around in the chair until he is facing the desk, then reaches out for the pad and the ballpoint pen. He understands enough at this point to know that unless he writes it down at once, the name will soon fly out of his head, and he doesn't want to run the risk of forgetting it. He therefore opens the pad to the first page, picks up the pen, and adds another entry to his list:

James P. Flood
Anna
David Zimmer
Peter Stillman, Jr.
Peter Stillman, Sr.
Fanshawe

In writing Fanshawe's name, it occurs to him that a second name was mentioned during Flood's visit as well, a name he heard in association with the reference to Flood's dream in chapter thirty of the book, but grapple as he does to recall what it was, he cannot come up with the answer. Something to do with chapter seven, he says to himself, something to do with a house, but the rest is a blank in Mr. Blank's mind. Galled by his own inadequacy, he nevertheless decides to put down something, hoping the name will come back to him at some future moment. The list now reads as follows:

James P. Flood
Anna
David Zimmer
Peter Stillman, Jr.
Peter Stillman, Sr.
Fanshawe
Man with house

As Mr. Blank puts down the pen, a word begins resounding in his head, and for several moments after that, as the word continues to echo within him, he senses that he is on the brink of a serious breakthrough,

a crucial turning point that will help clarify something about what the future has in store for him. The word is *park*. He remembers now that shortly after entering the room, Flood suggested they hold their conversation in *the park across the way*. If nothing else, that would seem to contradict Mr. Blank's previous assertion that he is being held captive, confined to the space in which these four walls surround him, blocked forever from sallying forth into the world. He is somewhat encouraged by this thought, but he also knows that even if he is allowed to visit the park, that does not necessarily prove he is free. Perhaps such visits are possible only under strict supervision, and once Mr. Blank has savored a welcome dose of sunlight and fresh air, he is promptly led back to the room, whereupon he is again held prisoner against his will. He finds it a pity that he did not have the presence of mind to question Flood about the park – in order to determine whether it is a public park, for example, or merely some wooded or grassy area that belongs to the building or institution or asylum in which he is now living. More important, he realizes for what must be the umpteenth time in the past several hours that it all comes down to the nature of the door, and whether it is locked from the outside or not. He closes his eyes and strains to recall the sounds he heard after Flood left the room. Was it the sound of a bolt sliding shut, the sound of a key turning in a cylinder plug, or simply the click of a latch? Mr. Blank cannot remember. By the time the conversation with Flood came to an end, he was so agitated by that disagreeable little man and his whining recriminations that he was too distracted to be paying attention to such petty concerns as locks and bolts and doors.

Mr. Blank wonders if the moment hasn't finally come to investigate the matter for himself. Afraid though he might be, would it not be better to learn the truth once and for all instead of living in a state of perpetual uncertainty? Perhaps, he says to himself. And then again, perhaps not. Before Mr. Blank can decide whether he has the courage to travel over to the door at last, a new and more urgent problem suddenly asserts itself – what might most accurately be called an *urgent urge*. Pressure has once again begun to build in Mr. Blank's body. Unlike the earlier episode, which was situated in the general area of his stomach, this one appears in a spot several inches lower, in the southernmost region of Mr. Blank's belly. From long experience with such matters, the old man understands that he has to pee. He considers traveling over to the bathroom in the chair, but knowing that the chair will not fit through the bathroom doorway, and further knowing that he cannot execute the pee while sitting in

the chair, that a moment will inevitably come when he will have to stand up (if only to sit down again on the toilet seat if he is attacked by another rush of dizziness), he decides to make the journey on foot. He therefore rises from the chair, pleased to note as he does so that his equilibrium is steady, with no signs of the vertigo that plagued him earlier. What Mr. Blank has forgotten, however, is that he is no longer wearing the white tennis shoes, not to speak of no longer wearing the black slippers, and that there is nothing on his feet anymore but the white nylon socks. In that the material of those socks is exceedingly thin, and in that the wooden floor is exceedingly smooth, Mr. Blank discovers after the first step that it is possible to slide his way forward – not with the rasping shuffle of the slippers, but as if he were moving along on ice skates.

A new form of pleasure has become available to him, and after two or three experimental glides between the desk and the bed, he concludes that it is no less enjoyable than rocking back and forth and spinning around in the chair – perhaps even more so. The pressure in his bladder is mounting, but Mr. Blank delays his trip to the bathroom in order to prolong his turn on the imaginary ice by a few moments, and as he skates around the room, now lifting one foot into the air, now the other, or else floating along with both feet on the floor, he again returns to the distant past, not as far back as the era of Whitey the rocking horse or the mornings when he would sit in his mother's lap as she dressed him on the bed, but a long while ago just the same: Mr. Blank in his high middle boyhood, roughly ten years old, perhaps eleven, but on no account as advanced as twelve. It's a cold Saturday afternoon in January or February. The pond in the little town where he grew up has frozen over, and there is the young Mr. Blank, who was then referred to as Master Blank, skating hand in hand with his first love, a girl with green eyes and reddish brown hair, long reddish brown hair tousled by the wind, her cheeks red from the cold, her name now forgotten, but beginning with the letter *S* Mr. Blank says to himself, he is certain of that – perhaps Susie, he thinks, or Samantha or Sally or Serena, but no, none of those, and yet no matter, for in that it was the first time he ever held a girl's hand, what he remembers most keenly now is the sensation of having entered a new world, a world in which holding a girl's hand was a good to be desired above all others, and such was his ardor for this young creature whose name began with the letter *S* that once they stopped skating and sat down on a tree stump at the edge of the pond, Master Blank was bold enough to lean forward and kiss her on the lips. For reasons that both

baffled and wounded him at the time, Miss S. burst out laughing, turned away her head, and rebuked him with a sentence that has stayed with him ever since – even now, in his present abject circumstances, when all is not right in his head and so many other things have vanished: Don't be silly. For the object of his affections understood nothing of such matters, being but ten or eleven years old and not yet ripened to the point where amorous advances from a member of the opposite sex would have any meaning for her. And so, rather than respond to Master Blank's kiss with a kiss of her own, she laughed.

The rebuff lingered for days afterward, causing such pain in his soul that one morning, noticing her son's grim demeanor, his mother asked him what was wrong. Mr. Blank was still young enough to feel no compunctions about confiding in his mother, and therefore he told her the full story. To which she replied: Don't worry, there are other pebbles on the shore. It was the first time Mr. Blank had heard the expression, and he found it curious that girls should be compared to pebbles, which they in no way resembled, he felt, at least not in his experience. Nevertheless, he grasped the metaphor, but in spite of understanding what his mother was trying to tell him, he disagreed with her, since passion is and always will be blind to all but one thing, and as far as Mr. Blank was concerned, there was only one pebble on the shore that counted, and if he couldn't have that one, he wasn't interested in any of the others. Time changed all that, of course, and as the years went on he came to see the wisdom of his mother's remark. Now, as he continues to glide around the room in his white nylon socks, he wonders how many pebbles there have been since then. Mr. Blank can't be sure, for his memory is nothing if not defective, but he knows there are dozens, perhaps even scores of them – more pebbles in his past than he can possibly count, right up to and including Anna, the long-lost girl of so many years ago, rediscovered this very day on the infinite shore of love.

These musings fly through Mr. Blank's head in a matter of seconds, perhaps twelve, perhaps twenty, and all the while, as the past wells up within him, he struggles to maintain his concentration so as not to lose his balance as he skates around the room. Short as those seconds may be, however, a moment comes when the bygone days overtake the present, and instead of thinking and moving at the same time, Mr. Blank forgets that he is moving and focuses exclusively on his thoughts, and not long after that, perhaps less than a second, two seconds at most, his feet slip out from under him and he falls to the floor.

Luckily, he does not land on his head, but in all other respects the tumble qualifies as a nasty spill. Pitching backward into the void as his stockinged feet struggle to gain a purchase on the slippery wooden planks, he thrusts his hands out behind him in the vain hope of softening the impact, but he nevertheless hits the floor smack on his tailbone, which sends forth a cascade of volcanic fire through his legs and torso, and given that he has also fallen on his hands, his wrists and elbows are suddenly ablaze as well. Mr. Blank writhes around on the floor, too stunned even to feel sorry for himself, and as he wrestles to absorb the pain that has engulfed him, he forgets to contract the muscles in and around his penis, which he has been doing for the last little while as he skated into his past. For Mr. Blank's bladder is full to bursting, and without making a conscious effort to hold it in, as it were, he is on the verge of producing a shameful and embarrassing accident. But the pain is too much for him. It has pushed all other thoughts out of his mind, and once he begins to relax the aforementioned muscles, he feels his urethra give way to the inevitable, and a moment later he is pissing in his pants. No better than an infant, he says to himself as the warm urine flows out of him and runs down his leg. Then he adds: Mewling and puking in his nurse's arms. And then, once the deluge has ceased, he shouts at the top of his lungs: Idiot! Idiot old man! What the hell is wrong with you?

Now Mr. Blank is in the bathroom, stripping off his pants, underwear, and socks, all of which have been drenched and yellowed by his involuntary loss of control. Still rattled by the blunder, his bones still aching from the crash to the floor, he flings each article of clothing angrily into the tub, then takes the white washcloth Anna used for the sponge bath earlier and wipes down his legs and crotch with warm water. As he does so, his penis begins to swell from its present flaccid state, rising from the perpendicular to a forty-five-degree angle. In spite of the multiple indignities Mr. Blank has been subjected to in the past minutes, he can't help feeling consoled by this development, as if it somehow proved that his honor was still intact. After a few more tugs, his old companion is sticking out from his body at a full ninety-degree thrust, and in this way, preceded by his second erection of the morning, Mr. Blank exits the bathroom, walks over to the bed, and climbs into the pajama bottoms that Anna stowed under the pillow. Mr. Bigshot has already begun to shrink by the time the old man pushes his feet into his leather slippers, but what else can be expected in the absence of further friction

or mental stimulation of some kind? Mr. Blank feels more comfortable in the pajama bottoms and slippers than he did in the white trousers and tennis shoes, but at the same time he can't help feeling guilty about these sartorial changes, for the fact is that he is no longer dressed all in white, which means that he has broken his promise to Anna – as per the demand of Peter Stillman, Junior – and this pains him deeply, even more deeply than the physical pain that is still reverberating through his body. As he shuffles over to the desk to resume his reading of the typescript, he resolves to make a clean breast of it the next time he sees her, hoping she will find it in her heart to forgive him.

Several moments later, he is once again sitting in the chair, his tailbone throbbing as he wriggles his backside around until he settles into a more or less acceptable position. Then he begins to read:

I first heard about the trouble in the Alien Territories six months ago. It was a late afternoon in midsummer, and I was sitting alone in my office, working on the last pages of my semi-annual report. We were well into the season of white cotton suits by then, but the air that day had been especially hot, bearing down with such stifling heaviness that even the thinnest clothing felt excessive. At ten o'clock, I had instructed the men in my department to remove their coats and ties, but as that seemed to have little effect, I dismissed them at noon. Since the staff had done nothing all morning but fan their faces and wipe sweat from their foreheads, it seemed pointless to hold them hostage any longer.

I remember dining at the Bruder Hof, a small restaurant around the corner from the Foreign Ministry building. Afterward, I took a stroll down Santa Victoria Boulevard, going as far as the river to see if I couldn't coax a breeze to blow against my face. I saw the children launching their toy boats into the water, the women walking by in groups of three and four with their yellow parasols and bashful smiles, the young men loafing on the grass. I have always loved the capital in summer. There is a stillness that envelops us at that time of year, a trance-like quality that seems to blur the difference between animate and inanimate things, and with the crowds along the avenues so much thinner and quieter, the frenzy of the other seasons becomes almost unimaginable. Perhaps it is because the Protector and his family are gone from the city then, and with the palace standing empty and blue shutters covering the familiar windows, the reality of the Confederation begins to feel less substantial. One is aware of the great distances, of the endless territories and people, of the chaos and clamor

of lives being lived – but they are all at a remove, somehow, as if the Confederation had become something internal, a dream that each person carried within himself.

After I returned to the office, I worked steadily until four o'clock. I had just put down my pen to mull over the concluding paragraphs when I was interrupted by the arrival of the Minister's secretary – a young man named Jensen or Johnson, I can't recall which. He handed me a note and then looked off discreetly in the other direction while I read it, waiting for an answer to carry back to the Minister. The message was very brief. *Would it be possible for you to stop by my house this evening? Excuse the last-minute invitation, but there is a matter of great importance I need to discuss with you. Joubert.*

I wrote out a reply on department stationery, thanking the Minister for his invitation and telling him that he could expect me at eight. The red-headed secretary went off with the letter, and for the next few minutes I remained at my desk, puzzling over what had just happened. Joubert had been installed as Minister three months earlier, and in that time I had seen him only once – at a formal banquet held by the Bureau to celebrate his appointment. Under ordinary circumstances, a man in my position would have little direct contact with the Minister, and I found it odd to have been invited to his house, especially at such short notice. From all I had heard about him so far, he was neither an impulsive nor a flamboyant administrator, and he did not flaunt his power in an arbitrary or unreasonable way. I doubted that I had been summoned to this private meeting because he was planning to criticize my work, but at the same time, judging from the urgency of his message, it was clear that this was to be more than just a social visit.

For a person who had attained such an exalted rank, Joubert did not cut an impressive figure. Just short of his sixtieth birthday, he was a squat and diminutive man with bad eyesight and a bulbous nose who continually adjusted and readjusted his pince-nez throughout our conversation. A servant led me down the central corridor to a small library on the ground floor of the Minister's residence, and when Joubert rose to welcome me, dressed in an out-of-fashion brown frock coat and a ruffled white cravat, I had the feeling that I was shaking hands with an assistant law clerk rather than one of the most important men in the Confederation. Once we began to speak, however, that illusion was quickly dispelled. He had a clear and attentive mind, and each one of his remarks was delivered with authority and conviction. After he had apologized for calling me to his house at

such an inopportune moment, he gestured to the gilded leather chair on the opposite side of his desk, and I sat down.

–I take it you've heard of Ernesto Land, he said, wasting no more time on empty formalities.

–He was one of my closest friends, I replied. We fought together in the Southeast Border Wars and then worked as colleagues in the same intelligence division. After the Consolidation Treaty of the Fourth of March, he introduced me to the woman I eventually married – my late wife, Beatrice. A man of exceptional courage and ability. His death during the cholera epidemic was a great loss to me.

–That's the official story. A death certificate is on file at the Municipal Hall of Records, but Land's name has cropped up again recently on several occasions. If these reports are true, it would appear he's still alive.

–That's excellent news, sir. It makes me very glad.

–For the past several months, rumors have been drifting back to us from the garrison at Ultima. Nothing has been confirmed, but according to these stories, Land crossed over the border into the Alien Territories some time after the cholera epidemic ended. It's a three-week journey from the capital to Ultima. That would mean Land departed just after the outbreak of the scourge. Not dead, then – simply missing.

–The Alien Territories are off limits. Everyone knows that. The No-Entrance Decrees have been in force for ten years now.

–Nevertheless, Land is there. If the intelligence reports are correct, he was traveling with an army of more than a hundred men.

–I don't understand.

–We think he's stirring up discontent among the Primitives, preparing to lead them in an insurrection against the western provinces.

–That's impossible.

–Nothing is impossible, Graf. You of all people should know that.

–No one believes in the principles of the Confederation more fervently than he does. Ernesto Land is a patriot.

–Men sometimes change their views.

–You must be mistaken. An uprising is impossible. Military action would require unity among the Primitives, and that has never happened and never will. They are as various and divided as we are. Their social customs, their languages, and their religious beliefs have kept them at odds for centuries. The Tackamen in the east bury their dead, just as we do. The Gangi in the west put their dead on elevated platforms and leave the corpses to rot in the sun. The Crow People in the south burn

their dead. The Vahntoo in the north cook the bodies and eat them. We call it an offense against God, but to them it's a sacred ritual. Each nation is divided into tribes, which are further subdivided into small clans, and not only have all the nations fought against one another at various times in the past, but tribes within those nations have waged war against one another as well. I simply can't see them banding together, sir. If they were capable of unified action, they never would have been defeated in the first place.

–I understand that you know the Territories quite well.

–I spent more than a year among the Primitives during my early days with the Bureau. That was before the No-Entrance Decrees, of course. I moved from one clan to another, studying the workings of each society, investigating everything from dietary laws to mating rituals. It was a memorable experience. My work since then has always engaged me, but I consider that to have been the most challenging assignment of my career.

–Everything used to be theirs. Then the ships arrived, bringing settlers from Iberia and Gaul, from Albion, Germania, and the Tartar kingdoms, and little by little the Primitives were pushed off their lands. We slaughtered them and enslaved them and then we herded them together in the parched and barren territories beyond the western provinces. You must have encountered much bitterness and resentment during your travels.

–Less than you would think. After four hundred years of conflict, most of the nations were glad to be at peace.

–That was more than ten years ago. Perhaps they've rethought their position by now. If I were in their place, I'd be sorely tempted to reconquer the western provinces. The ground is fertile there. The forests are full of game. It would give them a better, easier life.

–You're forgetting that all the Primitive nations endorsed the No-Entrance Decrees. Now that the fighting has stopped, they would prefer to live in their own separate world, with no interference from the Confederation.

–I hope you're right, Graf, but it's my duty to protect the welfare of the Confederation. Whether they prove groundless or not, the reports about Land must be investigated. You know him, you've spent time in the Territories, and of all the members of the Bureau, I can think of no one better qualified to handle the job. I'm not ordering you to go, but I would be deeply grateful if you accepted. The future of the Confederation could depend on it.

–I feel honored by your confidence in me, sir. But what if I'm not allowed to cross the border?

–You'll be carrying a personal letter from me to Colonel De Vega, the officer in charge of the garrison. He won't be pleased about it, but he'll have no choice. An order from the central government must be obeyed.

–But if what you say is true, and Land is in the Alien Territories with a hundred men, it raises a perplexing question, doesn't it?

–A question?

–How did he manage to get there? From what I'm told, there are troops stationed along the entire frontier. I can imagine one man slipping past them, but not a hundred men. If Land got through, then he must have done it with Colonel De Vega's knowledge.

–Possibly. Possibly not. That's one of the mysteries you'll be entrusted to solve.

–When do you want me to leave?

–As soon as you can. A carriage from the Ministry will be at your disposal. We'll furnish you with supplies and make all the necessary arrangements. The only things you'll need to carry with you are the letter and the clothes on your back.

–Tomorrow morning, then. I've just finished writing my semi-annual report, and my desk is clear.

–Come to the Ministry at nine o'clock for the letter. I'll be waiting for you in my office.

–Very good, sir. Tomorrow morning at nine.

The moment Mr. Blank comes to the end of the conversation between Graf and Joubert, the telephone starts to ring, and once again he is forced to interrupt his reading of the typescript. Cursing under his breath as he extricates himself from the chair, he hobbles slowly across the room toward the bedside table, moving with difficulty because of his recent injuries, and so plodding is his progress that he doesn't pick up the receiver until the seventh ring, whereas he was nimble enough to answer the previous call from Flood on the fourth.

What do you want? Mr. Blank says harshly, as he sits down on the bed, suddenly feeling a flutter of the old dizziness whirling around inside him.

I want to know if you've finished the story, a man's voice calmly answers.

Story? What story is that?

The one you've been reading. The story about the Confederation.

I didn't know it was a story. It sounds more like a report, like something that really happened.

It's make-believe, Mr. Blank. A work of fiction.

Ah. That explains why I've never heard of that place. I know my mind isn't working too well today, but I thought Graf's manuscript must have been found by someone years after he wrote it and then copied out by a typist.

An honest mistake.

A stupid mistake.

Don't worry about it. The only thing I need to know is whether you've finished it or not.

Almost. Just a few more pages to go. If you hadn't interrupted me with this goddamned call, I'd probably be at the end by now.

Good. I'll come round in fifteen or twenty minutes, and we can begin the consultation.

Consultation? What are you talking about?

I'm your doctor, Mr. Blank. I come to see you every day.

I don't remember having a doctor.

Of course not. That's because the treatment is beginning to take effect.

Does my doctor have a name?

Farr. Samuel Farr.

Farr . . . Hmm . . . Yes, Samuel Farr . . . You wouldn't happen to know a woman named Anna, would you?

We'll talk about that later. For now, the only thing you have to do is finish the story.

All right, I'll finish the story. But when you come to my room, how will I know it's you? What if it's someone else pretending to be you?

There's a picture of me on your desk. The twelfth one in from the top of the pile. Take a good look at it, and when I show up, you won't have any trouble recognizing me.

Now Mr. Blank is sitting in the chair again, hunched over the desk. Rather than look for Samuel Farr's picture in the pile of photographs, as he was instructed to do, he reaches for the pad and ballpoint pen and adds another name to his list:

James P. Flood
Anna

David Zimmer
Peter Stillman, Jr.
Peter Stillman, Sr.
Fanshawe
Man with house
Samuel Farr

Pushing aside the pad and pen, he immediately picks up the typescript of the story, forgetting all about his intention to look for Samuel Farr's photograph, in the same way that he has long since forgotten about looking for the closet that is supposedly in the room. The last pages of the text read as follows:

The long journey to Ultima gave me ample time to reflect upon the nature of my mission. A series of coachmen took over the reins at two-hundred-mile intervals, and with nothing for me to do but sit in the carriage and stare out at the landscape, I felt a growing sense of dread as I neared my destination. Ernesto Land had been my comrade and intimate friend, and I had the greatest trouble accepting Joubert's verdict that he had turned traitor to a cause he had defended all his life. He had remained in the military after the Consolidations of Year 31, continuing his work as an intelligence officer under the aegis of the Ministry of War, and whenever he had dined with us at our house or I had met with him for an afternoon meal at one of the taverns near the Ministry Esplanade, he had talked with enthusiasm about the inevitable victory of the Confederation, confident that all we had dreamed of and fought for since our earliest youth would finally come to pass. Now, according to Joubert's agents in Ultima, not only had Land escaped death during the cholera epidemic, he had in fact falsified his death in order to disappear into the wilderness with a small army of anti-Confederationists to foment rebellion among the Primitives. Judging from all I knew about him, this seemed an absurd and preposterous accusation.

Land had grown up in the northwestern farming region of Tierra Vieja Province, the same part of the world where my wife, Beatrice, was born. They had been playmates as small children, and for many years it was taken for granted by their two families that they would eventually marry. Beatrice once confessed to me that Ernesto had been her first love, and when he later turned his back on her and was betrothed to Hortense Chatterton, the daughter of a wealthy shipping family from Mont Sublime, she felt as if her life had ended. But Beatrice was a strong girl,

too proud to share her suffering with anyone, and in a demonstration of remarkable courage and dignity, she accompanied her parents and two brothers to the lavish wedding festival at the Chatterton estate. That was where we were introduced. I lost my heart to her that first evening, but it was only after a prolonged courtship of eighteen months that she finally accepted my proposal of marriage. I knew that in her eyes I was no match for Land. I was neither as handsome nor as brilliant as he was, and it took some time before she understood that my steadiness of character and fierce devotion to her were no less important qualities on which to build a lifelong union. Much as I admired Land, I was also aware of his flaws. There had always been something wild and obstreperous about him, a headstrong assurance in his superiority to others, and despite his charm and persuasiveness, that inborn power to draw attention to himself wherever he happened to be, one also sensed an incurable vanity lurking just below the surface. His marriage to Hortense Chatterton proved to be an unhappy one. He was unfaithful to her almost from the start, and when she died in childbirth four years later, he recovered quickly from his loss. He went through all the rituals of mourning and public sorrow, but at bottom I felt he was more relieved than brokenhearted. We saw quite a bit of him after that, much more than had been the case in the early years of our marriage. To his credit, Land became deeply attached to our little daughter, Marta, always bringing presents when he visited the house and showering her with such affection that she came to regard him as a heroic figure, the greatest man who walked the earth. He behaved with utmost decorum whenever he was among us, and yet who could fault me if I sometimes questioned whether the fires that had once burned in my wife's soul for him had been fully extinguished? Nothing untoward ever happened – no words or glances between them that could have aroused my jealousy – but in the aftermath of the cholera epidemic that had supposedly killed them both, what was I to make of the fact that Land was now reported to be alive and that in spite of my assiduous efforts to learn something about Beatrice's fate, I hadn't uncovered a single witness who had seen her in the capital during the scourge? If not for my disastrous run-in with Giles McNaughton, which had been set off by ugly innuendos concerning my wife, it seemed doubtful that I would have tormented myself with such dark suspicions on my way to Ultima. But what if Beatrice and Marta had run off with Land while I was traveling through the Independent Communities of Tierra Blanca Province? It seemed impossible, but as Joubert had said to me the night

before my departure, nothing was impossible, and of all the people in the world, I was the one who should know that best.

The wheels of the carriage turned, and by the time I'd reached the outskirts of Wallingham, the midway point of the journey, I understood that I was approaching a twofold horror. If Land had betrayed the Confederation, my instructions from the Minister were to put him under arrest and transport him back to the capital in chains. That thought was gruesome enough, but if my friend had betrayed me by stealing my wife and daughter, then I was planning to kill him. That much was certain, no matter what the consequences were. May God damn me for thinking it, but for Ernesto's sake and my own, I prayed that Beatrice was already dead.

Mr. Blank tosses the typescript onto the desk, snorting with dissatisfaction and contempt, furious that he has been compelled to read a story that has no ending, an unfinished work that has barely even begun, a mere bloody fragment. What garbage, he says out loud, and then, swiveling the chair around by a hundred and eighty degrees, he wheels himself over to the bathroom door. He is thirsty. With no beverages on hand, the only solution is to pour himself a glass of water from the bathroom sink. He stands up from the chair, opens the door, and shuffles forward to do just that, all the while regretting having wasted so much time on that misbegotten excuse of a story. He drinks one glass of water, then another, leaning his left hand on the sink to steady his balance as he gazes forlornly at the soiled clothes in the tub. Now that he happens to be in the bathroom, Mr. Blank wonders if he shouldn't take another shot at peeing, just to play it safe. Worried that he might fall again if he stays on his feet too long, he lets his pajama bottoms drop to his ankles and sits down on the toilet. Just like a woman, he says to himself, suddenly amused by the thought of how different his life would have been if he hadn't been born a man. After his recent accident, his bladder has little to say for itself, but eventually he manages to dribble forth a few measly squirts. He pulls up the pajama bottoms as he climbs to his feet, flushes, rinses his hands at the sink, dries those same hands with a towel, then turns around and opens the door – whereupon he sees a man standing in the room. Another lost opportunity, Mr. Blank says to himself, realizing that the noise of the flushing toilet must have drowned out the sound of the stranger's entrance, thus leaving unanswered the question of whether the door is locked from the outside or not.

Mr. Blank sits down in the chair and does an abrupt half-turn in order to take a look at the new arrival, a tall man in his mid-thirties dressed in blue jeans and a red button-down shirt open at the collar. Dark hair, dark eyes, and a gaunt face that looks as if it hasn't cracked a smile in years. No sooner does Mr. Blank make this observation, however, than the man smiles at him and says: Hello, Mr. Blank. How are you feeling today?

Do I know you? Mr. Blank asks.

Didn't you look at the picture? the man replies.

What picture?

The photograph on your desk. The twelfth one in from the top of the pile. Remember?

Oh, that. Yes. I think so. I was supposed to look at it, wasn't I?

And?

I forgot. I was too busy reading that dumb story.

No problem, the man says, turning around and walking toward the desk, where he picks up the photographs and searches through the pile until he comes to the picture in question. Then, putting the other photographs back on the desk, he walks over to Mr. Blank and hands him the portrait. You see, Mr. Blank? the man says. There I am.

You must be the doctor, then, Mr. Blank says. Samuel . . . Samuel something.

Farr.

That's right. Samuel Farr. I remember now. You have something to do with Anna, don't you?

I did. But that was a long time ago.

Holding the picture firmly in his two hands, Mr. Blank lifts it up until it is directly in front of his face, then studies it for a good twenty seconds. Farr, looking very much as he does now, is sitting in a garden somewhere dressed in a white doctor's coat with a cigarette burning between the second and third fingers of his left hand.

I don't get it, Mr. Blank says, suddenly besieged by a new attack of anguish that burns like a hot coal in his chest and tightens his stomach into the shape of a fist.

What's wrong? Farr asks. It's a good likeness, don't you think?

A perfect likeness. You might be a year or two older now, but the man in the picture is definitely you.

Is that a problem?

It's just that you're so young, Mr. Blank says in a tremulous voice, doing all he can to fight back the tears that are forming in his eyes. Anna

is young in her picture, too. But she told me it was taken more than thirty years ago. She's not a girl anymore. Her hair is gray, her husband is dead, and time is turning her into an old woman. But not you, Farr. You were with her. You were in that terrible country I sent her to, but that was more than thirty years ago, and you haven't changed.

Farr hesitates, clearly uncertain about how to answer Mr. Blank. He sits down on the edge of the bed, spreads his palms out on his knees, and looks down at the floor, inadvertently settling into the same position the old man was discovered in at the beginning of this report. A long moment of silence follows. At last he says, speaking in a low voice: I'm not allowed to talk about it.

Mr. Blank looks at him in horror. You're telling me you're dead, he cries out. That's it, isn't it? You didn't make it. Anna lived, but you didn't.

Farr lifts his head and smiles. Do I look dead, Mr. Blank? he asks. We all go through our rough moments, of course, but I'm just as alive as you are, believe me.

Well, who's to say if I'm alive or not? Mr. Blank says, staring grimly at Farr. Maybe I'm dead, too. The way things have been going for me this morning, I wouldn't be a bit surprised. Talk about *the treatment*. It's probably just another word for death.

You don't remember now, Farr says, standing up from the bed and taking the photograph out of Mr. Blank's hands, but the whole thing was your idea. We're just doing what you asked us to do.

Bullshit. I want to see a lawyer. He'll get me out of here. I have my rights, you know.

That can be arranged, Farr answers, carrying the photograph back to the desk, where he reinserts it into the pile. If you like, I'll have someone stop by to see you this afternoon.

Good, Mr. Blank mumbles, somewhat thrown by Farr's solicitous and accommodating manner. That's more like it.

Glancing at his watch, Farr returns from the desk and once again sits down on the bed facing Mr. Blank, who is still in his chair beside the bathroom door. It's getting late, the young man says. We have to begin our talk.

Talk? What kind of talk?

The consultation.

I understand the word, but I have no idea what you mean by it.

We're supposed to discuss the story.

What's the point? It's only the beginning of a story, and where I come from, stories are supposed to have a beginning, a middle, and an end.

I couldn't agree with you more.

Who wrote that piece of drivel, by the way? The bastard should be taken outside and shot.

A man named John Trause. Ever hear of him?

Trause . . . Hmmm . . . Perhaps. He wrote novels, didn't he? It's all a bit fuzzy now, but I think I might have read some of them.

You have. Rest assured that you have.

So why not give me one of those to read – instead of some half-assed, unfinished story without a title?

Trause did finish it. The manuscript comes to a hundred and ten pages, and he wrote it in the early fifties, when he was just starting out as a novelist. You might not think much of it, but it's not bad work for a kid of twenty-three or twenty-four.

I don't understand. Why not let me see the rest of it?

Because it's part of the treatment, Mr. Blank. We didn't put all those papers on the desk just to amuse you. They're here for a purpose.

Such as?

To test your reflexes, for one thing.

My reflexes? What do they have to do with it?

Mental reflexes. Emotional reflexes.

And?

What I want you to do is tell me the rest of the story. Starting at the point where you stopped reading, tell me what you think should happen now, right up to the last paragraph, the last word. You have the beginning. Now I want you to give me the middle and the end.

What is this, some kind of parlor game?

If you like. I prefer to think of it as an exercise in imaginative reasoning.

A pretty phrase, doctor. *Imaginative reasoning*. Since when does the imagination have anything to do with reason?

Since now, Mr. Blank. From the moment you begin to tell me the rest of the story.

All right. It's not as if I have anything better to do, is it?

That's the spirit.

Mr. Blank closes his eyes in order to concentrate on the task at hand, but blocking out the room and his immediate surroundings has the disturbing effect of summoning forth the procession of figment beings who marched through his head at earlier points in the narrative.

Mr. Blank shudders at the ghastly vision, and an instant later he opens his eyes again to make it disappear.

What's wrong? Farr asks, with a look of concern on his face.

The damned specters, Mr. Blank says. They're back again.

Specters?

My victims. All the people I've made suffer over the years. They're coming after me now to take their revenge.

Just keep your eyes open, Mr. Blank, and they won't be there anymore. We have to get on with the story.

All right, all right, Mr. Blank says, letting out a long, self-pitying sigh. Give me a minute.

Why don't you tell me some of your thoughts about the Confederation? That might help get you started.

The Confederation . . . The Con-fed-e-ra-tion . . . It's all very simple, isn't it? Just another name for America. Not the United States as we know it, but a country that has evolved in another way, that has another history. But all the trees, all the mountains, and all the prairies of that country stand exactly where they do in ours. The rivers and oceans are identical. Men walk on two legs, see with two eyes, and touch with two hands. They think double thoughts and speak out of both sides of their mouths at once.

Good. Now what happens to Graf when he gets to Ultima?

He goes to see the Colonel with Joubert's letter, but De Vega acts as if he's just been handed a note from a child, since he's in on the plot with Land. Graf reminds him that an order from an official of the central government must be obeyed, but the Colonel says that he works for the Ministry of War, and they've put him under strict orders to abide by the No-Entrance Decrees. Graf mentions the rumors about Land and the hundred soldiers who have entered the Alien Territories, but De Vega pretends to know nothing about it. Graf then says he has no alternative but to write to the Ministry of War and ask for an exemption to bypass the No-Entrance Decrees. Fine, De Vega says, but it takes six weeks for a letter to travel back and forth from the capital, and what are you going to do in the meantime? Take in the sights of Ultima, Graf says, and wait for the response to come – knowing full well that the Colonel will never allow his letter to get through, that it will be intercepted the moment he tries to send it.

Why is De Vega in on the plot? From all I can gather, he appears to be a loyal officer.

He is loyal. And so is Ernesto Land with his hundred troops in the Alien Territories.

I don't follow.

The Confederation is a fragile, newly formed state composed of previously independent colonies and principalities, and in order to hold this tenuous union together, what better way to unite the people than to invent a common enemy and start a war? In this case, they've chosen the Primitives. Land is a double agent who's been sent into the Territories to stir up rebellion among the tribes there. Not so different from what we did to the Indians after the Civil War. Get the natives riled up and then slaughter them.

But how does Graf know that De Vega is in on it, too?

Because he didn't ask enough questions. He should have at least pretended to be curious. And then there's the fact that he and Land both work for the Ministry of War. Joubert and his crowd at the Bureau of Internal Affairs know nothing about the plot, of course, but that's perfectly normal. Government agencies keep secrets from one another all the time.

And then?

Joubert has given Graf the names of three men, spies who work for the Bureau in Ultima. None of them is aware of the others' existence, but collectively they've been the source of Joubert's information about Land. After his conversation with the Colonel, Graf goes out to look for them. But one by one he discovers that all three, as the saying goes, have been dispatched to other parts. Let's find some names for them. It's always more interesting when a character has a name. Captain . . . hmmm . . . Lieutenant-Major Jacques Dupin was transferred to a post in the high central mountains two months earlier. Dr. Carlos . . . Woburn . . . left town in June to volunteer his services after an outbreak of smallpox in the north. And Declan Bray, Ultima's most prosperous barber, died from food poisoning in early August. Whether by accident or design it's impossible to know, but there's poor Graf, completely cut off from the Bureau now, without a single ally or confidant, all alone in that bleak, godforsaken corner of the earth.

Very nice. The names are a good touch, Mr. Blank.

My brain is turning at a hundred miles an hour. Haven't felt so full of beans all day.

Old habits die hard, I suppose.

What's that supposed to mean?

Nothing. Just that you're in good form, beginning to hit your stride. What happens next?

Graf hangs around Ultima for more than a month, trying to figure out a way to cross the border into the Territories. He can't go on foot, after all. He needs a horse, a rifle, provisions, probably a donkey as well. In the meantime, with nothing else to occupy his days, he finds himself getting drawn into Ultima society – such as it is, considering that it's nothing more than a pukey little garrison town in the middle of nowhere. Of all people, it's the hypocrite De Vega who makes a great show of befriending him. He invites Graf to dinner parties – long, tedious affairs attended by military officers, town officials, members of the merchant class, along with their wives, their lady friends, and so on – takes him to the best brothels, and even goes out hunting with him a couple of times. And then there's the Colonel's mistress . . . Carlotta . . . Carlotta Hauptmann . . . a debauched sensualist, the proverbial horny widow, whose principal entertainments in life are fucking and playing cards. The Colonel is married, of course, married with two small children, and since he can visit Carlotta only once or twice a week, she's available for romps with other men. It isn't long before Graf enters into a liaison with her. One night, as they're lying in bed together, he questions her about Land, and Carlotta confirms the rumors. Yes, she says, Land and his men crossed into the Territories a little more than a year ago. Why does she tell him this? Her motives aren't quite clear. Perhaps she's smitten with Graf and wants to be helpful, or perhaps the Colonel has put her up to it for hidden reasons of his own. This part has to be handled delicately. The reader can never be certain if Carlotta is luring Graf into a trap or if she simply talks too much for her own good. Don't forget that this is Ultima, the dreariest outpost of the Confederation, and sex, gambling, and gossip are about the only fun to be had.

How does Graf make it across the border?

I'm not sure. Probably a bribe of some sort. It doesn't really matter. The important thing is that he gets across one night, and the second part of the story begins. We're in the desert now. Emptiness all around, a ferocious blue sky overhead, pounding light, and then, when the sun goes down, a chill to freeze the marrow in your bones. Graf rides west for several days, mounted on a chestnut horse who goes by the name of Whitey, so called because of a splash of white between the animal's eyes, and since Graf knows the terrain well from his visit twelve years before, he heads in the direction of the Gangi, the tribe with whom he got along

best during his earlier travels and whom he found to be the most peaceful of all the Primitive nations. Late one morning, he finally approaches a Gangi encampment, a small village of fifteen or twenty hogans, which would suggest a population of somewhere between seventy and a hundred people. When he's approximately thirty yards from the edge of the settlement, he calls out a greeting in the local Gangi dialect to signal his arrival to the inhabitants – but no one responds. Growing alarmed now, Graf quickens the horse's pace and trots into the heart of the village, where not a single sign of human life can be seen. He dismounts, walks over to one of the hogans, and pushes aside the buffalo skin that serves as the door to the little house. The moment he enters, he's greeted by the overpowering stench of death, the sickening smell of decomposing bodies, and there, in the dim light of the hogan, he sees a dozen slaughtered Gangi – men, women, and children – all of them shot down in cold blood. He staggers out into the air, covering his nose with a handkerchief, and then one by one inspects the other hogans in the village. They're all dead, every last soul is dead, and among them Graf recognizes a number of people he befriended twelve years before. The girls who have since grown into young women, the boys who have since grown into young men, the parents who have since become grandparents, and not a single one is breathing anymore, not a single one will grow a day older for the rest of time.

Who was responsible? Was it Land and his men?

Patience, doctor. A thing like this can't be rushed. We're talking about brutality and death, the murder of the innocent, and Graf is still reeling from the shock of his discovery. He's in no shape to absorb what's happened, but even if he were, why would he think Land had anything to do with it? He's working on the assumption that his old friend is trying to start a rebellion, to form an army of Primitives that will invade the western provinces of the Confederation. An army of dead men can't fight very well, can it? The last thing Graf would conclude is that Land has killed his own future soldiers.

I'm sorry. I won't interrupt anymore.

Interrupt all you like. We're involved in a complicated story here, and not everything is quite what it seems to be. Take Land's troops, for example. They have no idea what their real mission is, no idea that Land is a double agent working for the Ministry of War. They're a bunch of well-educated dreamers, political radicals opposed to the Confederation, and when Land enlisted them to follow him into the Alien Territories,

they took him at his word and assumed they were going to help the Primitives annex the western provinces.

Does Graf ever find Land?

He has to. Otherwise, there wouldn't be any story to tell. But that doesn't happen until later, until several weeks or months down the road. About two days after Graf leaves the massacred Gangi village, he comes across one of Land's men, a delirious soldier staggering through the desert with no food, no water, no horse. Graf tries to help him, but it's already too late, and the kid hangs on for just a few more hours. Before he gives up the ghost, he raves on to Graf in a stream of incoherent babble about how everyone is dead, how they never had a chance, how the whole thing was a fraud from the start. Graf has trouble following him. Who does he mean by *everyone*? Land and his troops? The Gangi? Other tribes among the Primitives? The boy doesn't answer, and before the sun goes down that evening, he's dead. Graf buries the body and moves on, and a day or two after that, he comes to another Gangi settlement filled with corpses. He no longer knows what to think. What if Land is responsible after all? What if the rumor of an insurrection is no more than a blind to cover up a far more sinister undertaking: a quiet slaughter of the Primitives that would enable the government to open their territory to white settlement, to expand the reach of the Confederation all the way to the shores of the western ocean? And yet, how can such a thing be accomplished with such a paucity of troops? One hundred men to wipe out tens of thousands? It doesn't seem possible, and yet if Land has nothing to do with it, then the only other explanation is that the Gangi were killed by another tribe, that the Primitives are at war among themselves.

Mr. Blank is about to continue, but before he can get another word out of his mouth, he and the doctor are interrupted by a knocking at the door. Engrossed as he is in elaborating the story, content as he is to be spinning out his version of far-flung, imaginary events, Mr. Blank instantly understands that this is the moment he's been waiting for: the mystery of the door is about to be solved at last. Once the knock is heard, Farr turns his head in the direction of the sound. Come in, he says, and just like that the door opens, and in walks a woman pushing a stainless steel cart, perhaps the same one Anna used earlier, perhaps one that is identical to it. For once, Mr. Blank has been paying attention, and to the best of his knowledge he heard no sound of a lock being opened – nothing that resembled the sound of a bolt or a latch or a key – which would suggest

that the door was unlocked to begin with, unlocked all along. Or so Mr. Blank surmises, beginning to rejoice at the thought of his liberty to come and go as he wants, but a moment later he understands that things are possibly not quite as simple as that. It could be that Dr. Farr forgot to lock the door when he entered. Or, even more likely, that he didn't bother to lock it, knowing he would have no trouble overpowering Mr. Blank if his prisoner tried to escape. Yes, the old man says to himself, that's probably the answer. And he, who is nothing if not pessimistic about his prospects for the future, once again resigns himself to living in a state of constant uncertainty.

Hello, Sam, the woman says. Sorry to barge in on you like this, but it's time for Mr. Blank's lunch.

Hi, Sophie, Farr says, simultaneously looking down at his watch and standing up from the bed. I hadn't realized it was so late.

What's happening? Mr. Blank asks, pounding the arm of his chair and speaking in a petulant tone of voice. I want to go on telling the story.

We've run out of time, Farr says. The consultation is over for today.

But I haven't finished! the old man shouts. I haven't come to the end!

I know, Farr replies, but we're working on a tight schedule around here, and it can't be helped. We'll go on with the story tomorrow.

Tomorrow? Mr. Blank roars, both incredulous and confused. What are you talking about? Tomorrow I won't remember a word I said today. You know that. Even I know that, and I don't know a blasted thing.

Farr walks over to Mr. Blank and pats him on the shoulder, a classic gesture of appeasement for one skilled in the subtle art of bedside manner. All right, he says, I'll see what I can do. I have to get permission first, but if you want me to come back this evening, I can probably work it out. Okay?

Okay, Mr. Blank mumbles, feeling somewhat mollified by the gentleness and concern in Farr's voice.

Well, I'm off then, the doctor announces. See you later.

Without another word, he waves good-bye to Mr. Blank and the woman called Sophie, walks to the door, opens it, steps across the threshold, and shuts the door behind him. Mr. Blank hears the click of the latch, but nothing more. No clatter of a bolt, no turning of a key, and he wonders now if the door isn't simply one of those contraptions that locks automatically the instant you close it.

All the while, the woman called Sophie has been busy wheeling the stainless steel cart alongside the bed and transferring the various dishes

of Mr. Blank's lunch from the bottom shelf of the cart to the upper surface. Mr. Blank notes that there are four dishes in all and that each plate is hidden by a round metal cover with a hole in the center. Seeing those covers, he is suddenly reminded of room-service meals in hotels, which in turn provokes him to speculate on how many nights he has spent in hotels over the course of his life. Too many to count, he hears a voice within him say, a voice that is not his own, at least not a voice he recognizes as his own, and yet because it speaks with such authority and conviction, he acknowledges that it must be telling the truth. If that is the case, he thinks, then he has done a good deal of traveling in his time, moving around from place to place in cars, trains, and airplanes, and yes, he further says to himself, airplanes have taken him all over the world, to many countries on several continents, and no doubt those trips had something to do with the missions he sent all those people on, the poor people who suffered so much because of him, and that is surely why he is confined to this room now, no longer permitted to travel anywhere, stuck inside these four walls because he is being punished for the grave harm he has inflicted on others.

This fleeting reverie is cut off in mid-flow by the sound of the woman's voice. Are you ready for your lunch? she asks, and as he lifts his head to take a look at her, Mr. Blank realizes that he can no longer remember her name. She is somewhere in her late forties or early fifties, and although he finds her face both delicate and attractive, her body is too full and chunky to allow her to be classified as an ideal woman. For the record, it should be noted that her clothes are identical to the ones worn by Anna earlier in the day.

Where's my Anna? Mr. Blank asks. I thought she was the one who takes care of me.

She does, the woman says. But she had some last-minute errands to do, and she asked me to fill in for her.

That's terrible, Mr. Blank says, in a mournful tone of voice. Nothing against you, of course, whoever you might be, but I've been waiting for hours to see her again. That woman is everything to me. I can't live without her.

I know that, the woman says. We all know that. But – and here she gives him a friendly little smile – what can I do about it? I'm afraid you're stuck with me.

Alas, Mr. Blank sighs. I'm sure you mean well, but I'm not going to pretend I'm not disappointed.

You don't have to pretend. You have the right to feel what you feel, Mr. Blank. It's not your fault.

As long as we're stuck with each other, as you put it, I suppose you should tell me who you are.

Sophie.

Ah. That's right. Sophie . . . A very pretty name. And it begins with the letter *S*, doesn't it?

It would seem so.

Think back, Sophie. Are you the little girl I kissed at the pond when I was ten years old? We had just finished ice skating, and then we sat down on a tree stump, and I kissed you. Unfortunately, you didn't kiss me back. You laughed.

It couldn't have been me. When you were ten, I hadn't even been born.

Am I that old?

Not old, exactly. But a lot older than I am.

All right. If you're not that Sophie, which Sophie are you?

Instead of answering him, the Sophie who was not the girl Mr. Blank kissed when he was ten walks over to the desk, retrieves one of the photographs from the pile, and holds it up in the air. That's me, she says. Me as I was about twenty-five years ago.

Come closer, Mr. Blank says. You're too far away.

Several seconds later, Mr. Blank is holding the picture in his hands. It turns out to be the photograph he lingered over so attentively earlier in the day – the one of the young woman who has just opened the door of what appears to be a New York apartment.

You were much thinner then, he says.

Middle age, Mr. Blank. It tends to do funny things to a girl's figure.

Tell me, Mr. Blank says, tapping the photo with his index finger. What's going on here? Who's the person standing in the hallway, and why do you look like that? Apprehensive, somehow, but at the same time pleased. If not, you wouldn't be smiling.

Sophie crouches down beside Mr. Blank, who is still sitting in the chair, and studies the photo in silence for several moments.

It's my second husband, she says, and I think it's the second time he came to see me. The first time, I was holding my baby in my arms when I opened the door, I remember that distinctly – so this must be the second time.

Why so apprehensive?

Because I wasn't sure how he felt about me.

And the smile?

I'm smiling because I was happy to see him.

Your second husband, you say. And what about the first? Who was he?

A man named Fanshawe.

Fanshawe . . . Fanshawe . . . Mr. Blank mutters to himself. I think we're finally getting somewhere.

With Sophie still crouching beside him, with the black-and-white photograph of her younger self still on his lap, Mr. Blank abruptly begins to waddle forward in the chair, moving as quickly as he can in the direction of the desk. Once he arrives, he tosses the picture of Sophie on top of Anna's portrait, reaches for the small pad, and opens it to the first page. Running his finger down the list of names, he stops when he comes to *Fanshawe* and then swivels around in the chair to face Sophie, who has climbed to her feet by now and is slowly walking toward him.

Aha, Mr. Blank says, tapping the pad with his finger. I knew it. Fanshawe is implicated in all this, isn't he?

I don't know what you mean, Sophie says, stopping at the foot of the bed and then sitting down in more or less the same spot occupied earlier by James P. Flood. Of course he's implicated. We're all implicated in this, Mr. Blank. I thought you understood that.

Confused by her response, the old man nevertheless struggles to stick to his train of thought. Have you ever heard of someone called Flood? James P. Flood. English fellow. Ex-policeman. Talks with a cockney accent.

Wouldn't you rather eat your lunch now? Sophie asks. The food is getting cold.

In a minute, Mr. Blank snaps back at her, peeved that she has changed the subject. Just give me a minute. Before we talk about eating, I want you to tell me everything you know about Flood.

I don't know anything. I heard he was around here this morning, but I've never met him.

But your husband . . . your first husband, I mean . . . this Fanshawe . . . He wrote books, didn't he? In one of them, one of them called . . . damn it . . . I can't remember the title. *Never . . . Never* something . . .

*Neverland.*

That's it. *Neverland.* He used Flood as one of the characters in that book, and in chapter . . . chapter thirty I think it was, or maybe it was chapter seven, Flood has a dream.

I don't remember, Mr. Blank.

Are you saying that you didn't read your husband's novel?

No, I read it. But it was such a long time ago, and I haven't looked at it since. You probably won't understand, but for my own peace of mind I've made a conscious decision not to think about Fanshawe and his work.

What ended the marriage? Did he die? Were you divorced?

I married him when I was very young. We lived together for a few years, I got pregnant, and then he vanished.

Did something happen, or did he leave you on purpose?

On purpose.

The man must have been insane. Walking out on a beautiful young thing like you.

Fanshawe was an extremely troubled person. So many good qualities, so many fine things in him, but at bottom he wanted to destroy himself, and in the end he managed to do it. He turned against me, he turned against his work, and then he walked out of his life and disappeared.

His work. You mean he stopped writing?

Yes. He gave up everything. He had great talent, Mr. Blank, but he came to despise that part of himself, and one day he just stopped, he just quit.

It was my fault, wasn't it?

I wouldn't go that far. You played a part in it, of course, but you were only doing what you had to do.

You must hate me.

No, I don't hate you. I went through a tough period for a while, but everything worked out pretty well after that. I got married again, remember, and it's been a good marriage, a long and good marriage. And then there are my two boys, Ben and Paul. They're all grown up now. Ben is a doctor, and Paul's studying to become an anthropologist. Not too bad, if I do say so myself. I hope you get to meet them one day. I think you'll be very proud.

Now Sophie and Mr. Blank are sitting beside each other on the bed, facing the stainless steel cart with the various dishes of Mr. Blank's lunch lying on the surface, each plate hidden by a round metal cover with a hole in the center. Mr. Blank has worked up an appetite and is eager to begin, but before he is allowed to touch a morsel of food, Sophie tells him, he must first take his afternoon pills. In spite of the understanding that has developed between them over the past several minutes, and in spite of the pleasure Mr. Blank feels at being so close to Sophie's warm

and ample body, he balks at this demand and refuses to swallow the medication. Whereas the pills he ingested that morning were green, purple, and white, the ones now sitting on the surface of the stainless steel cart are pink, red, and orange. Sophie explains that they are indeed different pills, designed to produce different effects from the ones he took earlier, and that the treatment will fail unless he takes these in conjunction with the others. Mr. Blank follows the argument, but that in no way convinces him to change his mind, and as Sophie picks up the first pill between her thumb and middle finger and tries to give it to him, Mr. Blank stubbornly shakes his head.

Please, Sophie implores him. I know you're hungry, but one way or another these pills are going into your system before you take a bite of food.

Fuck the food, Mr. Blank says, with bitterness in his voice.

Sophie sighs with exasperation. Look, old-timer, she says, I only want to help you. I'm one of the few people around here who's on your side, but if you won't cooperate, I can think of at least a dozen men who'd be happy to come in here and force these pills down your throat.

All right, Mr. Blank says, beginning to relent somewhat. But only on one condition.

Condition? What are you talking about?

I'll swallow the pills. But first you have to take off your clothes and let me run my hands over your body.

Sophie finds the proposition so ludicrous, she bursts out in a fit of laughter – little realizing that this is exactly how the other Sophie responded under similar circumstances all those many years ago at the frozen pond of Mr. Blank's boyhood. And then, to add insult to injury, she delivers the fatal words: *Don't be silly.*

Ah, says Mr. Blank, tipping backward as if someone has just smacked him across the face. Ah, he groans. Say anything you want, woman. But not that. Please. Not that. Say anything but that.

Within seconds, Mr. Blank's eyes have filled with tears, and before he knows what is happening, the tears are rolling down his cheeks and the old man is crying in earnest.

I'm sorry, Sophie says. I didn't mean to hurt your feelings.

What's wrong with wanting to look at you? Mr. Blank asks, choking through his sobs. You have such beautiful breasts. I just want to see them and touch them. I want to put my hands on your skin, to run my fingers through your pubic hair. What's so terrible about that? I'm not going to

hurt you. I just want a little tenderness, that's all. After everything that's been done to me in this place, is that too much to ask?

Well, Sophie says thoughtfully, doubtless feeling some compassion for Mr. Blank's plight, maybe we can come up with a compromise.

Such as? Mr. Blank asks, as he wipes away the tears with the back of his hand.

Such as . . . Such as, you take the pills, and each time you swallow one, I'll let you touch my breasts.

Bare breasts?

No. I'd rather keep my blouse on.

That's not good enough.

All right. I'll take off the blouse. But the bra stays where it is. Understood?

It's not quite paradise, but I suppose I'll have to accept it.

And in that way the matter is resolved. Sophie sheds the blouse, and as she does so Mr. Blank is heartened to see that the bra she is wearing is of the flimsy, lacy variety and not some drab piece of equipment worn by elderly matrons and others who have thrown in the towel on physical love. The upper halves of Sophie's round and abundant breasts are uncovered, and even lower down, the material of the bra is so thin as to allow him a clear view of her nipples jutting against the fabric. Not quite paradise, Mr. Blank says to himself as he downs the first pill with a sip of water, but rather satisfying all the same. And then his hands are upon them – his left hand on the right breast, his right hand on the left breast – and as he savors the bulk and softness of Sophie's somewhat pendulous but noble mammaries, he is further gladdened to observe that she is smiling. Not from pleasure, perhaps, but at least from amusement, thereby demonstrating that she bears him no ill will and is taking the adventure in her stride.

You're a dirty old man, Mr. Blank, she says.

I know, he answers. But I was a dirty young man, too.

They work their way through the process twice more – the downing of a pill followed by another delicious encounter with the breasts – and then Sophie puts on her blouse again, and the moment for lunch has arrived.

Unfortunately, the repeated fondling of a desirable woman's flesh has wrought a predictable change in the flesh of the fondler himself. Mr. Blank's old friend is acting up again, and because our hero is no longer wearing the cotton trousers and underpants and is quite naked

under the pajama bottoms, there is no barrier to prevent Mr. Bigshot from bounding out through the slit and poking his head into the light of day. This happens at the precise moment Sophie leans forward to begin removing the metal covers from the plates, and as she bends down to store the covers on the lower shelf of the cart, her eyes are just inches from the offending culprit.

Look at you, Sophie says, addressing her words to Mr. Blank's erect penis. Your master squeezes my tits a few times, and now you're all ready for action. Forget it, pal. The fun is over.

I'm sorry, Mr. Blank says, for once truly embarrassed by his behavior. It just kind of popped out on its own. I wasn't expecting it.

No apologies necessary, Sophie replies. Just stick that thing back in your pants, and we'll get down to business.

Business in this case is Mr. Blank's lunch, which consists of a small bowl of now tepid vegetable soup, a club sandwich on white toast, a tomato salad, and a cup of red Jell-o. We will not give an exhaustive account of the consumption of this meal, but one event nevertheless bears mentioning. As was the case after Mr. Blank took his pills in the morning, his hands begin to tremble uncontrollably the instant he tries to eat his food. These might be different pills, designed for different purposes and swathed in different colors, but in the matter of the trembling hands their effect is identical. Mr. Blank begins the meal by attacking the soup. As one might imagine, the inaugural journey of the spoon as it departs from the bowl toward Mr. Blank's mouth is a difficult one, and not a single drop makes it to the intended destination. Through no fault of his own, everything in the spoon comes raining down on Mr. Blank's white shirt.

Good God, he says. I've done it again.

Before the meal can continue, or, more exactly, before the meal can begin, Mr. Blank is obliged to remove the shirt, which is the last article of white clothing he has on, and replace it with the pajama top, thus reverting to the same attire he was discovered in at the beginning of this report. It is a sad moment for Mr. Blank, for now there is not a single trace left of Anna's gentle and meticulous efforts to dress him and prepare him for the day. Even worse, he has now entirely reneged on his promise to wear white.

As Anna did before her, Sophie now takes it upon herself to feed Mr. Blank. Although she is no less kind and patient with him than Anna was, Mr. Blank does not love Sophie in the way he loves Anna, and therefore he looks over her left shoulder at a spot on the far wall as she brings the

various spoons and forks to his mouth, pretending it is Anna who is sitting beside him and not Sophie.

Do you know Anna well? he asks.

I met her only a few days ago, Sophie replies, but we've already had three or four long talks. We're very different in all sorts of ways, but we see eye to eye on the stuff that really counts.

Like what?

You, for one thing, Mr. Blank.

Is that why she asked you to fill in for her this afternoon?

I think so.

I've had a pretty awful day so far, but finding her again has done me a lot of good. I don't know what I'd do without her.

She feels the same way about you.

Anna . . . But Anna what? I've spent hours trying to remember her last name. I think it begins with a *B*, but I can't get any further than that.

Blume. Her name is Anna Blume.

Of course! shouts Mr. Blank, striking his forehead with the palm of his left hand. What the hell is wrong with me? I've known that name all my life. Anna Blume. Anna Blume. Anna Blume . . .

Now Sophie is gone. The stainless steel cart is gone, the soup-splattered white shirt is gone, the wet and dirty clothes from the tub are gone, and once again, having taken a proper, uneventful pee in the bathroom with Sophie's help, Mr. Blank is alone, sitting on the edge of the narrow bed, palms spread out on his knees, head down, staring at the floor. He ponders the details of Sophie's recent visit, chastising himself for not having asked her any questions about the things that concern him most. Where he is, for example. Whether he is allowed to walk in the park without supervision. Where the closet is, if indeed there is a closet, and why he hasn't been able to find it. Not to mention the eternal enigma of the door – and whether it is locked from the outside or not. Why did he hesitate to bare his soul to her, he wonders, she who is nothing if not a sympathetic person who holds no grudge against him? Is it simply a question of fear, he asks himself, or does it have something to do with the treatment, the noxious, debilitating treatment that has slowly robbed him of the power to stand up for himself and fight his own battles?

Not knowing what to think, Mr. Blank shrugs, slaps his hands on his knees, and rises from the bed. Several seconds later, he is sitting at the desk, the ballpoint pen in his right hand, the little pad in front of him,

opened to the first page. He searches the list for Anna's name, discovers it on the second line directly below James P. Flood, and prints out the letters B-l-u-m-e, thus changing the entry from *Anna* to *Anna Blume.* Then, because all the lines on the first page have been filled, he turns to the second page and adds two more entries to the list:

John Trause
Sophie

As he closes the pad, Mr. Blank is dumbfounded to realize that Trause's name returned to him with no effort at all. After so many struggles, so many failures to remember names and faces and events, he considers this to be a triumph of the first magnitude. He rocks back and forth in the chair to celebrate his accomplishment, wondering if the afternoon pills aren't responsible in some way for counteracting his memory loss of the previous hours, or if it isn't just a lucky fluke, one of those unexpected things that happen to us for no apparent reason. Whatever the cause, he decides to go on thinking about the story now, in anticipation of a visit from the doctor that evening, since Farr told him he would do everything possible to allow him to go on telling the story to the end – not tomorrow, when Mr. Blank will no doubt have forgotten the bulk of what he has recounted so far, but today. As the old man goes on tipping back and forth in the chair, however, his eyes fall upon the strip of white tape affixed to the surface of the desk. He has looked at that piece of tape no fewer than fifty or a hundred times during the course of the day, and each time he did so the white strip was clearly marked with the word DESK. Now, to his astonishment, Mr. Blank sees that it is marked with the word LAMP. His initial response is to think that his eyes have fooled him in some way, so he stops rocking back and forth in order to take a closer look. He leans forward, lowers his head until his nose is nearly touching the tape, and carefully studies the word. To his immense chagrin, he discovers that it still reads LAMP.

With a growing sense of alarm, Mr. Blank clambers out of the chair and begins shuffling around the room, stopping at each strip of white tape attached to an object in order to find out if any other words have been altered. After a thorough investigation, he is horrified to discover that not a single label occupies its former spot. The wall now reads CHAIR. The lamp now reads BATHROOM. The chair now reads DESK. Several possible explanations flare up in Mr. Blank's mind at once. He has suffered a

stroke or brain injury of some kind; he has lost the ability to read; someone has played a nasty trick on him. But if he is the victim of a prank, he asks himself, who can be responsible for it? Several people have visited his room in the past few hours: Anna, Flood, Farr, and Sophie. He finds it inconceivable that either one of the women would have done such a thing to him. It's true, however, that his mind was elsewhere when Flood came in, and it's also true that he was in the bathroom flushing the toilet when Farr entered, but he can't imagine how either one of those men could have pulled off such an elaborate switching operation in the short period of time they were not in his field of vision – several seconds at most, scarcely any time at all. Mr. Blank knows that he is not in top form, that his mind is not working as well as it ought to, but he also knows that he is no worse now than he was when the day began, which would dispense with the stroke theory, and if he has lost the ability to read, how could he have made the two recent additions to his list of names? He sits down on the edge of the narrow bed and wonders if he didn't doze off for a few minutes after Sophie left the room. He doesn't remember having fallen asleep, but in the end that is the only explanation that makes sense. A fifth person entered the room, a person who was not Anna or Flood or Farr or Sophie, and switched the labels during Mr. Blank's brief, now-forgotten plunge into oblivion.

An enemy is stalking the premises, Mr. Blank says to himself, perhaps several or many of them working in league with one another, and their only intention is to frighten him, to disorient him, to make him think he is losing his mind, as if they were trying to persuade him that the shadow-beings lodged in his head had transformed themselves into living phantoms, bodiless souls conscripted to invade his little room and cause as much havoc as possible. But Mr. Blank is a man of order, and he is offended by the childish mischief-making of his captors. From long experience, he has come to appreciate the importance of precision and clarity in all things, and during the years when he was sending out his charges on their various missions around the world, he always took great pains to write up his reports on their activities in a language that would not betray the truth of what they saw and thought and felt at each step along the way. It will not do, then, to call a chair a desk or a desk a lamp. To indulge in such infantile whimsy is to throw the world into chaos, to make life intolerable for all but the mad. Mr. Blank has not reached the point where he cannot identify objects that do not have their names affixed to them, but there is no question that

he is in decline, and he understands that a day might come, perhaps soon, perhaps even tomorrow, when his brain will erode still further and it will become necessary for him to have the name of the thing on the thing in order for him to recognize it. He therefore decides to reverse the damage created by his unseen enemy and return each one of the scrambled labels to its proper spot.

The job takes longer to complete than he thinks it will, for Mr. Blank soon learns that the strips of tape on which the words have been written are endowed with almost supernatural powers of adhesion, and to peel one of them off the surface to which it is attached requires unstinting concentration and effort. Mr. Blank begins by using his left thumbnail to pry the first strip loose (the word WALL, which has landed on the oak board at the foot of the bed), but no sooner does he manage to slide his nail under the lower right-hand corner of the tape than the tip of the nail snaps. He tries again with the nail of his middle finger, which is somewhat shorter and therefore less frangible, and diligently hacks away at the stubborn right-hand corner until enough tape has detached itself from the bed for Mr. Blank to put a small section between his thumb and middle finger and, tugging gently so as not to cause a tear, pull the whole strip from the oak board. A satisfying moment, yes, but one that has required a good two minutes of laborious preparation. Considering that there are twelve strips of tape to be removed in all, and considering that Mr. Blank breaks three more fingernails in the process (thus diminishing the number of usable fingers to six), the reader will understand why it takes him more than half an hour to finish the job.

These strenuous activities have worn out Mr. Blank, and instead of pausing to look around the room and admire his work (which, however small and insignificant it might appear to be, is for him nothing short of a symbolic undertaking to restore harmony to a broken universe), he shuffles off into the bathroom to rinse the sweat from his face. The old dizziness has returned, and he clutches the sink with his left hand as he splashes water onto himself with his right. By the time he turns off the spigot and begins to reach for a towel, he is suddenly feeling worse, worse than he has felt at any moment of the day so far. The trouble seems to be located somewhere in his stomach, but before he can pronounce the word *stomach* to himself, it is traveling up his windpipe, accompanied by an unpleasant tingling in his jaws. He instinctively clutches the sink with both hands and lowers his head, bracing himself against the attack of nausea that has inexplicably overcome him. He fights against it for a

second or two, praying that he can ward off the coming explosion, but it is a hopeless cause, and an instant later he is vomiting into the sink. They've poisoned me! Mr. Blank shouts, once the onslaught is over. The monsters have poisoned me!

When the action resumes, Mr. Blank is stretched out on the bed, looking up at the white, freshly painted ceiling. Now that the murderous toxins have been flushed from his system, he feels drained of energy, half-dead from the savage bout of puking, retching, and weeping that took place in the bathroom just minutes ago. And yet, if such a thing is possible, he also feels better, more tranquil in the core of his debilitated self, more prepared to face the trials that no doubt lie ahead.

As Mr. Blank continues to study the ceiling, its whiteness gradually conjures up an image to him, and instead of looking at a ceiling he fancies that he is staring at a sheet of blank paper. Why this should be so he cannot say, but perhaps it has something to do with the dimensions of the ceiling, which is rectilinear and not square, meaning that the room is rectilinear and not square as well, and although the ceiling is much larger than a sheet of paper, its proportions are roughly similar to those of the standard eight-and-a-half-by-eleven-inch page. As Mr. Blank pursues this thought, something stirs inside him, some distant memory he cannot fix in his mind, that keeps breaking apart the closer he gets to it, but through the murk that is blocking him from seeing the thing clearly in his head, he can dimly make out the contours of a man, a man who is undoubtedly himself, sitting at a desk and rolling a sheet of paper into an old manual typewriter. It's probably one of the reports, he says out loud, speaking in a soft voice, and then Mr. Blank wonders how many times he must have repeated that gesture, how many times over the years, understanding now that it was no fewer than thousands of times, thousands upon thousands of times, more sheets of paper than a man could possibly count in a day or a week or a month.

Thinking about the typewriter recalls the typescript he read earlier in the day, and now that he has more or less recovered from the exasperating job of peeling off the strips of white tape and returning them to their correct spots in the room, and now that the battle that flared up so violently in his stomach has been quelled, Mr. Blank remembers that he was planning to go on with the story, to map out the tale to its conclusion in order to prepare himself for the supplementary visit from the doctor that evening. Still stretched out on the bed with his eyes open, he considers

for a moment whether to carry on in silence, that is, to tell the story to himself in his mind, or else to continue improvising the events out loud, even if there is no one in the room to follow what he is saying. Because he is feeling particularly alone just now, fairly crushed by the weight of his enforced solitude, he decides to pretend that the doctor is in the room with him and to proceed as before, that is, to tell the story with his voice rather than merely think it in his head.

Let's get on with it, shall we? he says. The Confederation. Sigmund Graf. The Alien Territories. Ernesto Land. What year is it in this imaginary place? About eighteen-thirty, I'd guess. No trains, no telegraph. You travel by horse, and you can wait as long as three weeks for a letter to arrive. Much like America, but not identical. No black slaves, for one thing, at least none mentioned in the text. But more ethnic variety than here for that moment in history. German names, French names, English names, Spanish names. All right, where were we? Graf is in the Alien Territories, looking for Land, who might or might not be a double agent, who might or might not have absconded with Graf's wife and daughter. Let's back up a little bit. I think I went too fast before, jumped to too many hasty conclusions. According to Joubert, Land is a traitor to the Confederation who's formed his own private army to help lead the Primitives in an invasion of the western provinces. I detest that word, by the way. Primitives. It's too flat, too blunt, has no flair. Let's try to think of something more colorful. Hmmm . . . I don't know . . . Maybe something like . . . the Spirit People. No. No good. The Dolmen. The Olmen. The Tolmen. Awful. What's wrong with me? The Djiin. That's it. The Djiin. Sounds a little like Injun, but with other connotations mixed in as well. All right, the Djiin. Joubert thinks Land is in the Alien Territories to lead the Djiin in an attack on the western provinces. But Graf thinks it's more complicated than that. Why? For one thing, he believes Land is loyal to the Confederation. For another, how could Land have crossed the border accompanied by a hundred men without Colonel De Vega's knowledge? De Vega claims to know nothing about it, but Carlotta has told Graf that Land entered the Territories more than a year ago, and unless she's lying, De Vega is in on the plot. Or else – and this is something I didn't think of before – Land bribed De Vega with a large sum of money, and the Colonel isn't involved at all. But that has nothing to do with Graf, who never suspects the possibility of a bribe. According to his reasoning, Land, De Vega, and the entire military are planning to hatch a phony war with the Djiin in order to hold the Confederation

together. Maybe they intend to wipe out the Djiin in the process, maybe not. For the moment, there are only two possibilities: Joubert's position and Graf's position. If this story is going to add up to anything, though, there has to be a third explanation, something no one ever would have expected. Otherwise, it's just too damned predictable.

All right, Mr. Blank continues, after a short pause to focus his thoughts. Graf has come to two Gangi villages, and the inhabitants of both have been massacred. He's buried the raving white soldier, and now he doesn't know what to think. For the time being, as he slowly wends his way toward Land, let's separate the two main questions he's confronted with. The professional question and the private question. What is Land doing in the Territories, and where are his wife and daughter? To be perfectly honest, this domestic issue bores me. It can be resolved in any one of several ways, but each solution is an embarrassment: too trite, too hackneyed, not worth thinking about. One: Beatrice and Marta have run away with Land. If Graf finds them together, he's vowed to kill Land. Either he'll succeed or he won't, but at that point the story devolves into a simple melodrama of a cuckold trying to defend his honor. Two: Beatrice and Marta have run away with Land, but Beatrice has died – either from the effects of the cholera epidemic or from the hardships of living in the Territories. Assume that Marta, now sixteen, has grown into a woman and is traveling with Land as his lover. What does Graf do then? Does he still try to kill Land, murdering his old friend while his only daughter begs him to spare the life of the man she loves? Oh Daddy, please, Daddy, don't do it! Or does Graf let bygones be bygones and forget the whole thing? One way or the other, it won't wash. Three: Beatrice and Marta have run away with Land, but both of them have died. Land won't mention their names to Graf, and that element of the story turns into a defunct red herring. Trause was apparently quite young when he wrote this piece, and it doesn't surprise me that he never published it. He worked himself into a corner with the two women. I don't know what solution he came up with, but I'd bet good money that it was the second one – which is just as bad as the first and the third. As far as I'm concerned, I'd just as soon forget about Beatrice and Marta. Let's say they died in the cholera epidemic and leave it at that. Poor Graf, of course, but if you want to tell a good story, you can't show any pity.

Okay, Mr. Blank says, clearing his throat as he tries to pick up the thread of the narrative, where were we? Graf. Graf alone. Graf wandering

around the desert on his horse, the good steed Whitey, searching for the elusive Ernesto Land . . .

Mr. Blank stops. A new idea has entered his head, a fiendish, devastating illumination that sends a wave of pleasure shuddering through his body, from the very toes on his feet to the nerve cells in his brain. In a single instant, the whole business has been made clear to him, and as the old man contemplates the shattering consequences of what he now knows is the inevitable choice, the only choice available to him from a horde of contending possibilities, he begins to pound his chest and kick his feet and shake his shoulders as he lets out a whoop of wild, convulsive laughter.

Hold on, Mr. Blank says, raising a hand to his imaginary interlocutor. Scratch everything. I've got it now. Back to the beginning. Part two, that is. Back to the beginning of part two, when Graf slips across the border and enters the Alien Territories. Forget the massacre of the Gangi. Forget the second massacre of the Gangi. Graf steers clear of all Djiin villages and settlements. The No-Entrance Decrees have been in force for ten years, and he knows the Djiin will not take kindly to his presence. A white man traveling alone in the Territories? Impossible. If they find him, he's as good as dead. So he keeps a wide berth, confining himself to the vast wilderness areas that separate the different nations from one another, looking for Land and his men, yes, encountering the raving soldier, yes, but once he finds what he's looking for, it's altogether the opposite of what he was expecting. On a barren plain in the north central region of the Territories, a stretch of country similar to the salt flats in Utah, he chances upon a mound of a hundred and fifteen corpses, some of them mutilated, some of them intact, all of them rotting and decomposing in the sun. Not Gangi bodies, not the bodies of any members of the Djiin nations, but white men, white men in soldiers' uniforms, at least those who weren't stripped naked and hacked to pieces, and as Graf stumbles around this putrid, nauseating mass of the slaughtered dead, he discovers that one of the victims is his old friend Ernesto Land – lying on his back with a bullet hole in his forehead and a swarm of flies and maggots crawling over his half-eaten face. We won't dwell on Graf's response to this horror: the puking and weeping, the howling, the rending of his garments. What matters is this. Because his encounter with the raving soldier took place only two weeks earlier, Graf knows the massacre must be fairly recent. But most of all, what matters is this: he has no doubt that Land and his men were murdered by the Djiin.

Mr. Blank pauses to emit another laugh, more restrained than the last one, perhaps, but nevertheless a laugh that manages to express both joy and bitterness at the same time, for even if Mr. Blank is happy to have reshaped the story according to his own design, he knows that it is a gruesome story for all that, and a part of him recoils in terror from what he has yet to tell.

But Graf is wrong, he says. Graf knows nothing about the sinister scheme he's been drawn into. He's the fall guy, as they say in the movies, the patsy who's been set up by the government to put the machinery in motion. They're all in on it – Joubert, the Ministry of War, De Vega, the whole lot of them. Yes, Land was sent into the Territories as a double agent, with instructions to stir up the Djiin into invading the western provinces, which would unleash the war the government so desperately wants. But Land fails in his mission. A year goes by, and when nothing happens after all that time, the men in power conclude that Land has betrayed them, that for one reason or another his conscience has gotten the better of him and he's made peace with the Djiin. So they cook up a new plan and send a second army into the Territories. Not from Ultima, but from another garrison several hundred miles to the north, and this contingent is much larger than the first, at least ten times larger, and with a thousand troops against a hundred, Land and his ragtag bunch of idealists don't have a chance. Yes, you heard me correctly. The Confederation sends in a second army to wipe out the first army. All in secret, of course, and if a man such as Graf should be sent out to look for Land, he would naturally conclude that the Djiin are responsible for that pile of stinking, mutilated corpses. At this point, Graf becomes the key figure in the operation. Without knowing it, he's the person who's going to get the war started. How? By being allowed to write his story in that crummy little cell in Ultima. De Vega works him over in the beginning, beats him constantly for a whole week, but that's only to put the fear of God into him and convince him that he's about to be executed. And when a man thinks he's about to die, he's going to spill his guts on paper the moment he's allowed to write. So Graf does what they want him to do. He tells about his mission to track down Land, and when he comes to the massacre he discovered in the salt flats, he omits nothing, describes the whole abomination down to the last gory detail. That's the crucial point: a vivid, eyewitness account of what happened, with all the blame put on the Djiin. When Graf finishes his story, De Vega takes possession of the manuscript and releases him from prison. Graf is stunned. He

was expecting to be shot, and here he is being paid a large bonus for his work and given a free ride back to the capital in a first-class carriage. By the time he makes it home, the manuscript has been skillfully edited and released to every newspaper in the country. CONFEDERATION SOLDIERS MASSACRED BY DJIIN. A Firsthand Report by Sigmund Graf, Deputy Assistant Director of the Bureau of Internal Affairs.

Graf returns to find the entire population of the capital up in arms, clamoring for an invasion of the Alien Territories. He understands now how cruelly he's been tricked. War on this scale could potentially destroy the Confederation, and it turns out that he, and he alone, was the match that ignited this deadly fire. He goes to Joubert and demands an explanation. Now that things have worked out so well, Joubert is all too happy to give it to him. Then he offers Graf a promotion with a large increase in salary, but Graf counters with an offer of his own: I resign, he says, and then he marches out of the room, slamming the door behind him. That evening, in the darkness of his empty house, he picks up a loaded revolver and fires a bullet through his skull. And that's it. End of story. *Finità, la commedia.*

Mr. Blank has been talking steadily for nearly twenty minutes, and he is tired now, and not only from the exertions of his vocal cords, for his throat was irritated to begin with (brought on by the upchuck binge in the bathroom just minutes before), and he delivers the final sentences of his tale with a noticeable rasp in his voice. He closes his eyes, forgetting that such an action is likely to bring back the procession of figment beings blundering through the wilderness, the mob of the damned, the faceless ones who will eventually surround him and tear his body apart, but this time luck spares Mr. Blank from the demons, and when he closes his eyes he is once again in the past, sitting in a wooden chair of some kind – an Adirondack chair he believes it is called – on a lawn somewhere in the country, some remote and rustic spot he cannot identify, with green grass all around him and bluish mountains in the distance, and the weather is warm, warm in the way summer is warm, with a cloudless sky above and the sun pouring down on his skin, and there is Mr. Blank, many years ago now it would seem, back in the days of his early manhood, sitting in the Adirondack chair and holding a small child in his arms, a one-year-old girl child dressed in a white T-shirt and a white diaper, and Mr. Blank is looking into the eyes of the little girl and talking to her, what words he cannot say, for this excursion into the past

is unfolding in silence, and as Mr. Blank talks to the little girl, she is looking back at him with an intent and serious expression in her eyes, and he wonders now, lying on the bed with his eyes closed, if this small person isn't Anna Blume at the beginning of her life, his beloved Anna Blume, and if it isn't Anna, whether the child might not be his daughter, but what daughter, he asks himself, what daughter and what is her name, and if he is the father of a child, where is the mother and what is her name, he asks himself, and then he makes a mental note to inquire about these matters the next time a person enters the room, to find out if he has a home somewhere with a wife and children, or once had a wife, or once had a home, or if this room is not the place where he has always lived, but Mr. Blank is about to forget this mental note and therefore will forget to ask these questions, for he is extremely tired now, and the image of himself in the Adirondack chair with the young child in his arms has just vanished, and Mr. Blank has fallen asleep.

Because of the camera, which has gone on taking one picture per second throughout this report, we know for certain that Mr. Blank's nap lasts for exactly twenty-seven minutes and twelve seconds. He might have gone on sleeping much longer than that, but a man has now entered the room, and he is tapping Mr. Blank on the shoulder in an effort to wake him. When the old man opens his eyes, he feels entirely refreshed by his brief sojourn in the Land of Nod, and he sits up immediately, alert and ready for the encounter, with no trace of grogginess clouding his mind.

The visitor appears to be in his late fifties or early sixties, and like Farr before him, he is dressed in a pair of blue jeans, but whereas Farr was wearing a red shirt, this man's shirt is black, and while Farr came into the room empty-handed, the man in the black shirt is carrying a thick bundle of files and folders in his arms. His face is deeply familiar to Mr. Blank, but as with so many of the faces he has seen today, whether in photographs or in the flesh, he is at a loss to attach a name to it.

Are you Fogg? he asks. Marco Fogg?

The visitor smiles and shakes his head. No, he says, I'm afraid not. Why would you think I'm Fogg?

I don't know, but when I woke up just now I suddenly remembered that Fogg stopped by around this time yesterday. A minor miracle, actually, now that I think about it. Remembering, I mean. But Fogg came in. I'm certain of that. For afternoon tea. We played cards for a while. We talked. And he told me a number of funny jokes.

Jokes? the visitor asks, walking over to the desk, swiveling the chair

by a hundred and eighty degrees, and sitting down with the pile of dossiers on his lap. As he does so, Mr. Blank stands up, shuffles forward for several feet, and then sits down on the bottom edge of the mattress, settling into roughly the same spot that Flood occupied earlier in the day.

Yes, jokes, Mr. Blank continues. I can't remember them all, but there was one that struck me as especially good.

You wouldn't mind telling it to me, would you? the visitor asks. I'm always on the lookout for good jokes.

I can try, Mr. Blank answers, and then he pauses for a few moments to collect his thoughts. Let's see, he says. Hmmm. Let me see. I think it begins like this. A man walks into a bar in Chicago at five o'clock in the afternoon and orders three scotches. Not one after the other, but all three at once. The bartender is a little puzzled by this unusual request, but he doesn't say anything and gives the man what he wants – three scotches, lined up on the bar in a row. The man drinks them down one by one, pays the bill, and leaves. The next day, he comes back at five o'clock and orders the same thing. Three scotches all at once. And the day after that, and every day after that for two weeks. Finally, curiosity gets the better of the barman. I don't mean to be nosy, he says, but you've been in here every day for the past two weeks ordering your three scotches, and I'd just like to know why. Most people take them one at a time. Ah, the man says, the answer is very simple. I have two brothers. One of them lives in New York, one lives in San Francisco, and the three of us are very close. As a way of honoring our friendship, we all go into a bar at five in the afternoon and order three scotches, silently toasting one another's health, pretending that we're all together in the same place. The barman nods, finally understanding the reason for this strange ritual, and thinks no more about it. The business goes on for another four months. The man comes in every day at five o'clock, and the bartender serves him the three drinks. Then something happens. The man shows up at his regular hour one afternoon, but this time he orders only two scotches. The bartender is worried, and after a while he plucks up his courage and says: I don't mean to be nosy, but every day for the past four and a half months you've come in here and ordered three scotches. Now you order two. I know it's none of my business, but I just hope nothing's gone wrong with your family. Nothing's wrong, the man says, as bright and chipper as ever. What is it, then? the bartender asks. The answer is very simple, the man says. I've stopped drinking.

The visitor erupts in a prolonged fit of laughter, and while Mr. Blank

does not join in, since he already knew the punch line, he nevertheless smiles at the man in the black shirt, pleased with himself for having pulled off the joke so well. When the hilarity at last dies down, the visitor looks at Mr. Blank and says: Do you know who I am?

I'm not sure, the old man replies. Not Fogg, in any case. But there's no question that I've met you before – many times, I think.

I'm your lawyer.

My lawyer. That's good . . . very good. I was hoping I'd see you today. We have a lot to talk about.

Yes, says the man in the black shirt, patting the bundle of files and folders on his lap. A great deal to talk about. But before we get down to that, I want you to take a good look at me and try to remember my name.

Mr. Blank looks carefully at the man's thin, angular face, peers into his large gray eyes, studies his jaw and forehead and mouth, but in the end he can do no more than let out a sigh and shake his head in defeat.

I'm Quinn, Mr. Blank, the man says. Daniel Quinn. Your first operative.

Mr. Blank groans. He is mortified with shame, embarrassed to such a point that a part of him, the innermost part of him, wants to crawl into a hole and die. Please forgive me, he says. My dear Quinn – my brother, my comrade, my loyal friend. It's these rotten pills I've been swallowing. They've screwed up my head, and I can't tell if I'm coming or going anymore.

You sent me on more missions than anyone else, Quinn says. Do you remember the Stillman case?

A little, Mr. Blank replies. Peter Stillman. Junior and Senior, if I'm not mistaken. One of them wore white clothes. I forget which now, but I think it was the son.

Exactly right. The son. And then there was that strange business with Fanshawe.

Sophie's first husband. The madman who disappeared.

Right again. But we mustn't forget the passport either. A small point, I suppose, but it was tough work just the same.

What passport?

My passport. The one that Anna Blume found when you sent her on her mission.

Anna? Do you know Anna?

Of course. Everyone knows Anna. She's something of a legend around here.

She deserves to be. There's no woman like her in the world.

And then, last but not least, there was my aunt, Molly Fitzsimmons, the woman who married Walt Rawley. I helped him write his memoirs.

Walt who?

Rawley. Once known as Walt the Wonder Boy.

Ah, yes. That was a long time ago, wasn't it?

Correct. A very long time ago.

And then?

That's it. You retired me after that.

Why would I do such a thing? What was I thinking?

I'd put in all those years, and the time came for me to go. Operatives don't last forever. It's the nature of the business.

When was that?

Nineteen ninety-three.

And what year is it now?

Two thousand and five.

Twelve years. What have you been doing with yourself since . . . since I retired you?

Traveling, mostly. By now, I've visited nearly every country in the world.

And now you're back, working as my lawyer. I'm glad it's you, Quinn. I always felt I could trust you.

You can, Mr. Blank. That's why I was given the job. Because we go so far back together.

You have to get me out of here. I don't think I can take it anymore.

That won't be easy. So many charges have been filed against you, I'm drowning in paperwork. You have to be patient. I wish I could give you an answer, but I have no idea how long it will take to sort things out.

Charges? What kind of charges?

The whole gamut, I'm afraid. From criminal indifference to sexual molestation. From conspiracy to commit fraud to negligent homicide. From defamation of character to first-degree murder. Shall I go on?

But I'm innocent. I've never done any of those things.

That's a debatable point. It all depends on how you look at it.

And what happens if we lose?

The nature of the punishment is still open to question. One group is advocating clemency, an across-the-board pardon on every count. But others are out for blood. And not just one or two of them. There's a whole gang, and they're becoming more and more vociferous.

Blood. I don't understand. You mean blood as in *death*?

Instead of answering, Quinn reaches into the pocket of his black shirt and pulls out a piece of paper, which he then unfolds in order to share what is written on it with Mr. Blank.

There was a meeting just two hours ago, Quinn says. I don't want to scare you, but someone got up and actually proposed this as a possible solution. I quote:

*He shall be drawn through the streets to the place of his execution, there to be hanged and cut down alive, and his body shall be opened, his heart and bowels plucked out, and his privy members cut off and thrown into the fire before his eyes. Then his head shall be stricken off from his body, and his body shall be divided into four quarters, to be disposed of at our discretion.*

Lovely, Mr. Blank sighs. And what gentle soul came up with that plan?

It doesn't matter, Quinn says. I just want you to get a sense of what we're dealing with. I'll fight for you to the bitter end, but we have to be realistic. The way it looks now, we're probably going to have to work out some compromises.

It was Flood, wasn't it? Mr. Blank asks. That odious little man who came in here and insulted me this morning.

No, as a matter of fact it wasn't Flood, but that doesn't mean he isn't a dangerous person. You were very wise to refuse his invitation to go to the park. Later on, we discovered that he'd concealed a knife in his jacket. Once he got you out of the room, he was planning to kill you.

Ah. I figured as much. That lousy, good-for-nothing piece of shit.

I know it's hard being cooped up in this room, but I would suggest you stay here, Mr. Blank. If someone else invites you out for a walk in the park, invent some excuse and say no.

So there really is a park?

Yes, there really is a park.

And the birds. Are they in my head, or can I really hear them?

What kind of birds?

Crows or seagulls, I can't tell which.

Seagulls.

Then we must be near the ocean.

You picked the spot yourself. In spite of everything that's been going on here, you've gathered us all in a beautiful place. I'm thankful to you for that.

Then why don't you let me see it? I can't even open the goddamned window.

It's for your own protection. You wanted to be on the top floor, but we can't take any chances, can we?

I'm not going to commit suicide, if that's what you mean.

I know that. But not everyone shares my opinion.

Another one of your compromises, huh?

By way of response, Quinn shrugs his shoulders, glances down, and looks at his watch.

Time is running short, he says. I've brought along the files of one case, and I think we should get to it now. Unless you're feeling too tired, of course. If you prefer, I could always come back tomorrow.

No, no, Mr. Blank answers, waving his arm in disgust. Let's get it over with now.

Quinn opens the top folder and removes four eight-by-ten black-and-white photographs. Wheeling himself forward in the chair, he hands them to Mr. Blank and says: Benjamin Sachs. Does the name ring any bells?

I think so, the old man replies, but I'm not sure.

It's a bad one. One of the worst, as a matter of fact, but if we can mount a compelling defense against this charge, we might be able to set a precedent for the others. Do you follow me, Mr. Blank?

Mr. Blank nods in silence, already beginning to look through the pictures. The first one shows a tall, gangly man of about forty, perched on the railing of a fire escape in what appears to be Brooklyn, New York, looking out into the night in front of him – but then Mr. Blank moves on to the second photo, and suddenly that same man has lost his grip on the railing and is falling through the darkness, a silhouette of splayed limbs caught in midair, plunging toward the ground below. That is disturbing enough, but once Mr. Blank comes to the third picture, a shudder of recognition passes through him. The tall man is on a dirt road somewhere out in the country, and he is swinging a metal softball bat at a bearded man who is standing in front of him. The image is frozen at the precise instant the bat makes contact with the bearded man's head, and from the look on his face it is clear that the blow will kill him, that within a matter of seconds he will fall to the ground with his skull crushed as blood pours from the wound and gathers in a puddle around his corpse.

Mr. Blank clutches his face, tearing at the skin with his fingers. He is finding it difficult to breathe now, for he already knows the subject of the fourth picture, even if he can't remember how or why he knows it, and because he can anticipate the explosion of the homemade bomb that will

tear the tall man apart and cast his mangled body to the four winds, he does not have the strength to look at it. Instead, he lets the four photographs slip out of his hands and fall to the floor, and then, bringing those same hands up to his face, he covers his eyes and begins to weep.

Now Quinn is gone, and once again Mr. Blank is alone in the room, sitting at the desk with the ballpoint pen in his right hand. The onrush of tears stopped more than twenty minutes ago, and as he opens the pad and turns to the second page, he says to himself: I was only doing my job. If things turned out badly, the report still had to be written, and I can't be blamed for telling the truth, can I? Then, applying himself to the task at hand, he adds three more names to his list:

John Trause
Sophie
Daniel Quinn
Marco Fogg
Benjamin Sachs

Mr. Blank puts down the pen, closes the pad, and pushes both articles aside. He realizes now that he was hoping for a visit from Fogg, the man with all the funny stories, but even though there is no clock in the room and no watch on his wrist, meaning that he has no idea of the time, not even an approximate one, he senses that the hour for tea and light conversation has passed. Perhaps, before long, Anna will be coming back to serve him dinner, and if by chance it isn't Anna who comes, but another woman or man sent in as a substitute, then he means to protest, to misbehave, to rant and shout, to cause such a ruckus that it will blow the very roof clear into the sky.

For want of anything better to do just now, Mr. Blank decides to go on with his reading. Directly below Trause's story about Sigmund Graf and the Confederation there is a longer manuscript of some one hundred and forty pages, which, unlike the previous work, comes with a cover page that announces the title of the piece and the author's name:

Travels in the Scriptorium
by
N.R. Fanshawe

Aha, Mr. Blank says out loud. That's more like it. Maybe we're finally getting somewhere, after all.

Then he turns to the first page and begins to read:

The old man sits on the edge of the narrow bed, palms spread out on his knees, head down, staring at the floor. He has no idea that a camera is planted in the ceiling directly above him. The shutter clicks silently once every second, producing eighty-six thousand four hundred still photos with each revolution of the earth. Even if he knew he was being watched, it wouldn't make any difference. His mind is elsewhere, stranded among the figments in his head as he searches for an answer to the question that haunts him.

Who is he? What is he doing here? When did he arrive and how long will he remain? With any luck, time will tell us all. For the moment, our only task is to study the pictures as attentively as we can and refrain from drawing any premature conclusions.

There are a number of objects in the room, and on each one a strip of white tape has been affixed to the surface, bearing a single word written out in block letters. On the bedside table, for example, the word is TABLE. On the lamp, the word is LAMP. Even on the wall, which is not strictly speaking an object, there is a strip of tape that reads WALL. The old man looks up for a moment, sees the wall, sees the strip of tape attached to the wall, and pronounces the word *wall* in a soft voice. What cannot be known at this point is whether he is reading the word on the strip of tape or simply referring to the wall itself. It could be that he has forgotten how to read but still recognizes things for what they are and can call them by their names, or, conversely, that he has lost the ability to recognize things for what they are but still knows how to read.

He is dressed in blue-and-yellow striped cotton pajamas, and his feet are encased in a pair of black leather slippers. It is unclear to him exactly where he is. In the room, yes, but in what building is the room located? In a house? In a hospital? In a prison? He can't remember how long he has been here or the nature of the circumstances that precipitated his removal to this place. Perhaps he has always been here; perhaps this is where he has lived since the day he was born. What he knows is that his heart is filled with an implacable sense of guilt. At the same time, he can't escape the feeling that he is the victim of a terrible injustice.

There is one window in the room, but the shade is drawn, and as far as he can remember he has not yet looked out of it. Likewise with the door and its white porcelain knob. Is he locked in, or is he free to come and

go as he wishes? He has yet to investigate this matter – for, as stated in the first paragraph above, his mind is elsewhere, adrift in the past as he wanders among the phantom beings that clutter his head, struggling to answer the question that haunts him.

The pictures do not lie, but neither do they tell the whole story. They are merely a record of time passing, the outward evidence. The old man's age, for example, is difficult to determine from the slightly out-of-focus black-and-white images. The only fact that can be set down with any certainty is that he is not young, but the word *old* is a flexible term and can be used to describe a person anywhere between sixty and a hundred. We will therefore drop the epithet *old man* and henceforth refer to the person in the room as Mr. Blank. For the time being, no first name will be necessary.

Mr. Blank stands up from the bed at last, pauses briefly to steady his balance, and then shuffles over to the desk at the other end of the room. He feels tired, as if he has just woken from a fitful, too-short night of sleep, and as the soles of his slippers scrape along the bare wood floor, he is reminded of the sound of sandpaper. Far off in the distance, beyond the room, beyond the building in which the room is located, he hears the faint cry of a bird – perhaps a crow, perhaps a seagull, he can't tell which . . .

By now, Mr. Blank has read all he can stomach, and he is not the least bit amused. In an outburst of pent-up anger and frustration, he tosses the manuscript over his shoulder with a violent flick of the wrist, not even bothering to turn around to see where it lands. As it flutters through the air and then thuds to the floor behind him, he pounds his fist on the desk and says in a loud voice: When is this nonsense going to end?

It will never end. For Mr. Blank is one of us now, and struggle though he might to understand his predicament, he will always be lost. I believe I speak for all his charges when I say he is getting what he deserves – no more, no less. Not as a form of punishment, but as an act of supreme justice and compassion. Without him, we are nothing, but the paradox is that we, the figments of another mind, will outlive the mind that made us, for once we are thrown into the world, we continue to exist forever, and our stories go on being told, even after we are dead.

Mr. Blank might have acted cruelly toward some of his charges over the years, but not one of us thinks he hasn't done everything in his power

to serve us well. That is why I plan to keep him where he is. The room is his world now, and the longer the treatment goes on, the more he will come to accept the generosity of what has been done for him. Mr. Blank is old and enfeebled, but as long as he remains in the room with the shuttered window and the locked door, he can never die, never disappear, never be anything but the words I am writing on this page.

In a short while, a woman will enter the room and feed him his dinner. I haven't yet decided who that woman will be, but if all goes well between now and then, I will send in Anna. That will make Mr. Blank happy, and when all is said and done, he has probably suffered enough for one day. Anna will feed Mr. Blank his dinner, then wash him and put him to bed. Mr. Blank will lie awake in the dark for some time, listening to the cries of birds in the far distance, but then his eyes will at last grow heavy, and his lids will close. He will fall asleep, and when he wakes up in the morning, the treatment will begin again. But for now it is still the day it has always been since the first word of this report, and now is the moment when Anna kisses Mr. Blank on the cheek and tucks him in, and now is the moment when she stands up from the bed and begins walking toward the door. Sleep well, Mr. Blank.

Lights out.

[2005]

# MAN IN THE DARK

I am alone in the dark, turning the world around in my head as I struggle through another bout of insomnia, another white night in the great American wilderness. Upstairs, my daughter and granddaughter are asleep in their bedrooms, each one alone as well, the forty-seven-year-old Miriam, my only child, who has slept alone for the past five years, and the twenty-three-year-old Katya, Miriam's only child, who used to sleep with a young man named Titus Small, but Titus is dead now, and Katya sleeps alone with her broken heart.

Bright light, then darkness. Sun pouring down from all corners of the sky, followed by the black of night, the silent stars, the wind stirring in the branches. Such is the routine. I have been living in this house for more than a year now, ever since they released me from the hospital. Miriam insisted that I come here, and at first it was just the two of us, along with a day nurse who looked after me when Miriam was off at work. Then, three months later, the roof fell in on Katya, and she dropped out of film school in New York and came home to live with her mother in Vermont.

His parents named him after Rembrandt's son, the little boy of the paintings, the golden-haired child in the red hat, the daydreaming pupil puzzling over his lessons, the little boy who turned into a young man ravaged by illness and who died in his twenties, just as Katya's Titus did. It's a doomed name, a name that should be banned from circulation forever. I think about Titus's death often, the horrifying story of that death, the images of that death, the pulverizing consequences of that death on my grieving granddaughter, but I don't want to go there now, I can't go there now, I have to push it as far away from me as possible. The night is still young, and as I lie here in bed looking up into the darkness, a darkness so black that the ceiling is invisible, I begin to remember the story I started last night. That's what I do when sleep refuses to come. I lie in bed and tell myself stories. They might not add up to much, but as long as I'm inside them, they prevent me from thinking about the things I would prefer to forget. Concentration can be a problem, however, and more often than not my mind eventually drifts away from the story I'm trying to tell to the things I don't want to think about. There's nothing

to be done. I fail again and again, fail more often than I succeed, but that doesn't mean I don't give it my best effort.

I put him in a hole. That felt like a good start, a promising way to get things going. Put a sleeping man in a hole, and then see what happens when he wakes up and tries to crawl out. I'm talking about a deep hole in the ground, nine or ten feet deep, dug in such a way as to form a perfect circle, with sheer inner walls of dense, tightly packed earth, so hard that the surfaces have the texture of baked clay, perhaps even glass. In other words, the man in the hole will be unable to extricate himself from the hole once he opens his eyes. Unless he is equipped with a set of mountaineering tools – a hammer and metal spikes, for example, or a rope to lasso a neighboring tree – but this man has no tools, and once he regains consciousness, he will quickly understand the nature of his predicament.

And so it happens. The man comes to his senses and discovers that he is lying on his back, gazing up at a cloudless evening sky. His name is Owen Brick, and he has no idea how he has landed in this spot, no memory of having fallen into this cylindrical hole, which he estimates to be approximately twelve feet in diameter. He sits up. To his surprise, he is dressed in a soldier's uniform made of rough, dun-colored wool. A cap is on his head, and a pair of sturdy, well-worn black leather boots are on his feet, laced above the ankles with a firm double knot. There are two military stripes on each sleeve of the jacket, indicating that the uniform belongs to someone with the rank of corporal. That person might be Owen Brick, but the man in the hole, whose name is Owen Brick, cannot recall having served in an army or fought in a war at any time in his life.

For want of any other explanation, he assumes he has received a knock on the head and has temporarily lost his memory. When he puts his fingertips against his scalp and begins to search for bumps and gashes, however, he finds no traces of swelling, no cuts, no bruises, nothing to suggest that such an injury has occurred. What is it, then? Has he suffered some debilitating trauma that has blacked out large portions of his brain? Perhaps. But unless the memory of that trauma suddenly returns to him, he will have no way of knowing. After that, he begins to explore the possibility that he is asleep in his bed at home, trapped inside some supernaturally lucid dream, a dream so lifelike and intense that the boundary between dreaming and consciousness has all but melted away. If that is true, then he simply has to open his eyes, hop out of bed, and walk into the kitchen to prepare the morning coffee. But how can

you open your eyes when they're already open? He blinks a few times, childishly wondering if that won't break the spell – but there is no spell to be broken, and the magic bed fails to materialize.

A flock of starlings passes overhead, entering his field of vision for five or six seconds, and then vanishes into the twilight. Brick stands up to inspect his surroundings, and as he does so he becomes aware of an object bulging in the left front pocket of his trousers. It turns out to be a wallet, his wallet, and in addition to seventy-six dollars in American money, it contains a driver's license issued by the state of New York to one Owen Brick, born June 12, 1977. This confirms what Brick already knows: that he is a man approaching thirty who lives in Jackson Heights, Queens. He also knows that he is married to a woman named Flora and that for the past seven years he has worked as a professional magician, performing mostly at children's birthday parties around the city under the stage name of the Great Zavello. These facts only deepen the mystery. If he is so certain of who he is, then how did he wind up at the bottom of this hole, dressed in a corporal's uniform no less, without papers or dog tags or a military ID card to prove his status as a soldier?

It doesn't take long for him to understand that escape is out of the question. The circular wall is too high, and when he kicks it with his boot in order to dent the surface and create some kind of foothold that would help him climb up, the only result is a sore big toe. Night is falling rapidly, and there is a chill in the air, a damp vernal chill worming itself into his body, and while Brick has begun to feel afraid, for the moment he is still more baffled than afraid. Nevertheless, he can't stop himself from calling out for help. Until now, all has been quiet around him, suggesting that he is in some remote, unpopulated stretch of countryside, with no sounds other than an occasional bird cry and the rustling of the wind. As if on command, however, as if by some skewed logic of cause and effect, the moment he shouts the word *HELP*, artillery fire erupts in the distance, and the darkening sky lights up with streaking comets of destruction. Brick hears machine guns, exploding grenades, and under it all, no doubt miles away, a dull chorus of howling human voices. This is war, he realizes, and he is a soldier in that war, but with no weapon at his disposal, no way to defend himself against attack, and for the first time since waking up in the hole, he is well and truly afraid.

The shooting goes on for more than an hour, then gradually dissipates into silence. Not long after that, Brick hears the faint sound of sirens, which he takes to mean that fire engines are rushing to buildings

damaged during the assault. Then the sirens stop as well, and quiet descends on him once again. Cold and frightened as he is, Brick is also exhausted, and after pacing around the confines of his cylindrical jail until the stars appear in the sky, he stretches out on the ground and manages to fall asleep at last.

Early the next morning, he is woken by a voice calling to him from the top of the hole. Brick looks up and sees the face of a man jutting over the rim, and since the face is all he can see, he assumes the man is lying flat on his stomach.

Corporal, the man says. Corporal Brick, it's time to get moving.

Brick stands up, and now that his eyes are only three or four feet from the stranger's face, he can see that the man is a swarthy, square-jawed fellow with a two-day stubble of beard and that he is wearing a military cap identical to the one on his own head. Before Brick can protest that much as he'd like to get moving, he's in no position to do anything of the sort, the man's face disappears.

Don't worry, he hears him say. We'll have you out of there in no time.

Some moments later, there follows the sound of a hammer or iron mallet pounding on a metal object, and because the sound becomes increasingly muted with each successive blow, Brick wonders if the man isn't driving a stake into the ground. And if it's a stake, then perhaps a length of rope will soon be attached to it, and with that rope Brick will be able to climb out of the hole. The clanging stops, another thirty or forty seconds go by, and then, just as he predicted, a rope drops down at his feet.

Brick is a magician, not a bodybuilder, and even if climbing a yard or so of rope is not an inordinately strenuous task for a healthy man of thirty, he nevertheless has a good deal of trouble hoisting himself to the top. The wall is of no use to him, since the soles of his boots keep sliding off the smooth surface, and when he tries to clamp his boots onto the rope itself, he fails to gain a secure purchase, which means that he has to rely on the strength of his arms alone, and given that his are not muscular or powerful arms, and given that the rope is made of coarse material and therefore chafes his palms, this simple operation is turned into something of a battle. When he finally nears the rim and the other man takes hold of his right hand and pulls him onto level ground, Brick is both out of breath and disgusted with himself. After such a dismal performance, he is expecting to be mocked for his ineptitude, but by some miracle the man refrains from making any disparaging comments.

As Brick struggles slowly to his feet, he notes that his rescuer's uniform

is the same as his, with the single exception that there are three stripes on the sleeves of his jacket, not two. The air is dense with fog, and he has difficulty making out where he is. Some isolated spot in the country, as he suspected, but the city or town that was under attack last night is nowhere to be seen. The only things he can distinguish with any clarity are the metal stake with the rope tied around it and a mud-splattered jeep parked about ten feet from the edge of the hole.

Corporal, the man says, shaking Brick's hand with a firm, enthusiastic grip. I'm Serge Tobak, your sergeant. Better known as Sarge Serge.

Brick looks down at the man, who is a good six inches shorter than he is, and repeats the name in a low voice: Sarge Serge.

I know, Tobak says. Very funny. But the name stuck, and there's nothing I can do about it. If you can't lick 'em, join 'em, right?

What am I doing here? Brick asks, trying to suppress the anguish in his voice.

Get a grip on yourself, boy. You're fighting a war. What did you think this was? A trip to Fun World?

What war? Does that mean we're in Iraq?

Iraq? Who cares about Iraq?

America's fighting a war in Iraq. Everyone knows that.

Fuck Iraq. This is America, and America is fighting America.

What are you talking about?

Civil war, Brick. Don't you know anything? This is the fourth year. But now that you've turned up, it's going to end soon. You're the guy who's going to make it happen.

How do you know my name?

You're in my platoon, dumbbell.

And what about the hole? What was I doing down there?

Normal procedure. All new recruits come to us like that.

But I didn't sign up. I didn't enlist.

Of course not. No one does. But that's the way it is. One minute you're living your life, and the next minute you're in the war.

Brick is so confounded by Tobak's statements, he doesn't know what to say.

It's like this, the sergeant rattles on. You're the chump they've picked for the big job. Don't ask me why, but the general staff thinks you're the best man for the assignment. Maybe because no one knows you, or maybe because you have this . . . this what? . . . this bland look about you, and no one would suspect you're an assassin.

Assassin?

That's it, assassin. But I like to use the word *liberator*. Or *maker of the peace*. Whatever you want to call it, without you the war will never end.

Brick would like to run away on the spot, but because he's unarmed, he can't think of anything else to do but play along. And who am I supposed to kill? he asks.

It's not *who* so much as *what*, the sergeant replies enigmatically. We're not even sure of his name. It could be Blake. It could be Black. It could be Bloch. But we have an address, and if he hasn't slipped away by now, you shouldn't have any trouble. We'll set you up with a contact in the city, you'll go undercover, and in a few days it should all be over.

And why does this man deserve to die?

Because he owns the war. He invented it, and everything that happens or is about to happen is in his head. Eliminate that head, and the war stops. It's that simple.

Simple? You make him sound like God.

Not God, Corporal, just a man. He sits in a room all day writing it down, and whatever he writes comes true. The intelligence reports say he's racked with guilt, but he can't stop himself. If the bastard had the guts to blow his brains out, we wouldn't be having this conversation.

You're saying it's a story, that a man is writing a story, and we're all part of it.

Something like that.

And after he's killed, then what? The war ends, but what about us?

Everything goes back to normal.

Or maybe we just disappear.

Maybe. But that's the risk we have to take. Do or die, son. More than thirteen million dead already. If things go on like this much longer, half the population will be gone before you know it.

Brick has no intention of killing anyone, and the longer he listens to Tobak, the more certain he becomes that the man is a raving lunatic. For the time being, however, he has no choice but to pretend to understand, to act as if he's eager to carry out the assignment.

Sarge Serge walks over to the jeep, fetches a bulging plastic bag from the back, and hands it to Brick. Your new duds, he says, and right there in the open he instructs the magician to strip off his army uniform and put on the civilian clothes contained in the bag: a pair of black jeans, a blue oxford shirt, a red V-neck sweater, a belt, a brown leather jacket, and black leather shoes. Then he hands him a green nylon backpack filled

with more clothes, shaving equipment, a toothbrush and toothpaste, a hairbrush, a .38-caliber revolver, and a box of bullets. Finally, Brick is given an envelope with twenty fifty–dollar bills in it and a slip of paper with the name and address of his contact.

Lou Frisk, the sergeant says. A good man. Go to him as soon as you get to the city, and he'll tell you everything you need to know.

What city are we talking about? Brick asks. I have no idea where I am.

Wellington, Tobak says, swiveling to his right and pointing into the heavy morning fog. Twelve miles due north. Just stay on this road, and you'll be there by the middle of the afternoon.

I'm supposed to walk?

Sorry. I'd give you a lift, but I have to go in the other direction. My men are waiting for me.

And what about breakfast? Twelve miles on an empty stomach . . .

Sorry about that, too. I was supposed to bring you an egg sandwich and a thermos of coffee, but I forgot.

Before leaving to join his men, Sarge Serge pulls the rope up from the hole, yanks the metal stake out of the ground, and tosses them into the back of the jeep. Then he climbs in behind the steering wheel and starts the engine. Giving Brick a farewell salute, he says: Hang in there, soldier. You don't look like much of a killer to me, but what do I know? I'm never right about anything.

Without another word, Tobak presses his foot on the accelerator, and just like that he is gone, disappearing into the fog within a matter of seconds. Brick doesn't budge. He is both cold and hungry, both destabilized and frightened, and for more than a minute he just stands there in the middle of the road, wondering what to do next. Eventually, he starts to shiver in the frosty air. That decides it for him. He has to get his limbs moving, to warm himself up, and so, without the faintest notion of what lies ahead of him, he turns around, thrusts his hands into his pockets, and begins walking toward the city.

A door has just opened upstairs, and I can hear the sound of footsteps traveling down the hall. Miriam or Katya, I can't tell which. The bathroom door opens and shuts; faintly, very faintly, I detect the familiar music of pee hitting water, but whoever has done the peeing is thoughtful enough not to flush the toilet and risk waking the household, even if two-thirds of its members are already awake. Then the bathroom door opens, and once again the quiet tread down the hall and the closing of a

bedroom door. If I had to choose, I would say it was Katya. Poor, suffering Katya, as resistant to sleep as her immobilized grandfather. I would love to be able to walk up the stairs, go into her room, and talk to her for a while. Tell some of my bad jokes, maybe, or else just run my hand over her head until her eyes closed and she fell asleep. But I can't climb the stairs in a wheelchair, can I? And if I used my crutch, I would probably fall in the dark. Damn this idiot leg. The only solution is to sprout a pair of wings, giant wings of the softest white down. Then I'd be up there in a flash.

For the past couple of months, Katya and I have spent our days watching movies together. Side by side on the living room sofa, staring at the television set, knocking off two, three, even four films in a row, then breaking for dinner with Miriam, and once dinner has been eaten, returning to the sofa for another film or two before going to bed. I should be working on my manuscript, the memoir I promised to write for Miriam after I retired three years ago, the story of my life, the family history, a chronicle of a vanished world, but the truth is I'd rather be on the sofa with Katya, holding her hand, letting her rest her head on my shoulder, feeling my mind grow numb from the endless parade of images dancing across the screen. For over a year I went at it every day, building up a hefty pile of pages, about half the story I'd guess, perhaps a little more, but now I seem to have lost the stomach for it. Maybe it started when Sonia died, I don't know, the end of married life, the loneliness of it all, the fucking loneliness after I lost her, and then I cracked up that rented car, destroying my leg, nearly killing myself in the process, maybe that added to it as well: the indifference, the feeling that after seventy-two years on this earth, who gives a damn if I write about myself or not? It was never anything that interested me, not even when I was young, and I certainly never had any ambition to write a book. I liked to read them, that was all, to read books and then write about them afterward, but I was always a sprinter, never a long-distance man, a greyhound working on deadline for forty years, an expert at cranking out the seven-hundred-word piece, the fifteen-hundred-word piece, the twice-weekly column, the occasional magazine assignment, how many thousands of them did I vomit forth? Decades of ephemera, mounds of burned-up and recycled newsprint, and unlike most of my colleagues, I never had the slightest inclination to collect the good ones, assuming there were any, and republish them in books that no sane person would bother to read. Let my half-finished manuscript go on gathering dust for

now. Miriam is hard at it, coming to the end of her biography of Rose Hawthorne, squeezing in her hours at night, on the weekends, on the days when she doesn't have to drive to Hampton to teach her courses, and for the time being maybe one writer in the house is enough.

Where was I? Owen Brick . . . Owen Brick walking down the road to the city. The cold air, the confusion, a second civil war in America. A prelude to something, but before I figure out what to do with my befuddled magician, I need a few moments to reflect on Katya and the films, since I still can't decide if this is a good thing or a bad thing. When she started ordering the DVDs through the Internet, I took it as a sign of progress, a small step in the right direction. If nothing else, it showed me that she was willing to let herself be distracted, to think about something other than her dead Titus. She's a film student, after all, training to become an editor, and when the DVDs started pouring into the house, I wondered if she wasn't thinking about going back to school or, if not school, then furthering her education on her own. After a while, though, I began to see this obsessive movie watching as a form of self-medication, a homeopathic drug to anesthetize herself against the need to think about her future. Escaping into a film is not like escaping into a book. Books force you to give something back to them, to exercise your intelligence and imagination, whereas you can watch a film – and even enjoy it – in a state of mindless passivity. That said, I don't mean to suggest that Katya has turned herself into a stone. She smiles and sometimes even emits a small laugh during the funny scenes in comedies, and her tear ducts have frequently been active during the touching scenes in dramas. It has more to do with her posture, I think, the way she slumps back on the sofa with her feet stretched out on the coffee table, unmoving for hours on end, refusing to stir herself even to pick up the phone, showing little or no signs of life except when I'm touching or holding her. It's probably my fault. I've encouraged her to lead this flattened-out existence, and maybe I should put a stop to it – although I doubt she'd listen to me if I tried.

On the other hand, some days are better than others. Each time we finish a movie, we talk about it for a little while before Katya puts on the next one. I usually want to discuss the story and the quality of the acting, but her remarks tend to focus on the technical aspects of the film: the camera setups, the editing, the lighting, the sound, and so on. Just tonight, however, after we watched three consecutive foreign films – *Grand Illusion, The Bicycle Thief,* and *The World of Apu* – Katya delivered some sharp and

incisive comments, sketching out a theory of film-making that impressed me with its originality and acumen.

Inanimate objects, she said.

What about them? I asked.

Inanimate objects as a means of expressing human emotions. That's the language of film. Only good directors understand how to do it, but Renoir, De Sica, and Ray are three of the best, aren't they?

No doubt.

Think about the opening scenes of *The Bicycle Thief*. The hero is given a job, but he won't be able to take it unless he gets his bicycle out of hock. He goes home feeling sorry for himself. And there's his wife outside their building, lugging two heavy buckets of water. All their poverty, all the struggles of this woman and her family are contained in those buckets. The husband is so wrapped up in his own troubles, he doesn't bother to help her until they're halfway to the door. And even then, he only takes one of the buckets, leaving her to carry the other. Everything we need to know about their marriage is given to us in those few seconds. Then they climb the stairs to their apartment, and the wife comes up with the idea to pawn their bed linens so they can redeem the bicycle. Remember how violently she kicks the bucket in the kitchen, remember how violently she opens the bureau drawer. Inanimate objects, human emotions. Then we're at the pawnshop, which isn't a shop, really, but a huge place, a kind of warehouse for unwanted goods. The wife sells the sheets, and after that we see one of the workers carry their little bundle to the shelves where pawned items are stored. At first, the shelves don't seem very high, but then the camera pulls back, and as the man starts climbing up, we see that they go on and on and on, all the way to the ceiling, and every shelf and cubby is crammed full of bundles identical to the one the man is now putting away, and all of a sudden it looks as if every family in Rome has sold their bed linens, that the entire city is in the same miserable state as the hero and his wife. In one shot, Grandpa. In one shot we're given a picture of a whole society living at the edge of disaster.

Not bad, Katya. The wheels are turning . . .

It just hit me tonight. But I think I'm on to something, since I saw examples in all three films. Remember the dishes in *Grand Illusion*?

The dishes?

Right near the end. Gabin tells the German woman that he loves her, that he'll come back for her and her daughter when the war is over, but

the troops are closing in now, and he and Dalio have to try to cross the border into Switzerland before it's too late. The four of them have a last meal together, and then the moment comes to say good-bye. It's all very moving, of course. Gabin and the woman standing in the doorway, the possibility that they'll never see each other again, the woman's tears as the men vanish into the night. Renoir then cuts to Gabin and Dalio running through the woods, and I'd bet money that every other director in the world would have stayed with them until the end of the film. But not Renoir. He has the genius – and when I say *genius*, I mean the understanding, the depth of heart, the compassion – to go back to the woman and her little daughter, this young widow who has already lost her husband to the madness of war, and what does she have to do? She has to go back into the house and confront the dining room table and the dirty dishes from the meal they've just eaten. The men are gone now, and because they're gone, those dishes have been transformed into a sign of their absence, the lonely suffering of women when men go off to war, and one by one, without saying a word, she picks up the dishes and clears the table. How long does the scene last? Ten seconds? Fifteen seconds? No time at all, but it takes your breath away, doesn't it? It just knocks the stuffing out of you.

You're a brave girl, I said, suddenly thinking about Titus.

Stop it, Grandpa. I don't want to talk about him. Some other time, maybe, but not now. Okay?

Okay. Let's stick to the movies. There's still one to go. The Indian film. I think it's the one I liked best.

That's because it's about a writer, Katya said, cracking a brief, ironic smile.

Maybe. But that doesn't mean it isn't good.

I wouldn't have chosen it unless it was good. No junk. That's the rule, remember? All sorts of movies, from the wacky to the sublime, but no junk.

Agreed. But where's the inanimate object in *Apu*?

Think.

I don't want to think. It's your theory, so you tell me.

The curtains and the hairpin. A transition from one life into another, the turning point of the story. Apu has gone to the country to attend his friend's cousin's wedding. A traditional arranged marriage, and when the bridegroom shows up, he turns out to be an idiot, a blithering numskull. The wedding is called off, and the friend's cousin's parents begin

to panic, afraid their daughter will be cursed for life if she doesn't get married that afternoon. Apu is asleep somewhere under the trees, not a care in the world, happy to be out of the city for a few days. The girl's family approaches him. They explain that he's the only available unmarried man, that he's the only one who can solve the problem for them. Apu is appalled. He thinks they're nuts, a bunch of superstitious country bumpkins, and refuses to go along. But then he mulls it over for a while and decides to do it. As a good deed, as an altruistic gesture, but he has no intention of taking the girl back to Calcutta with him. After the wedding ceremony, when they're finally alone together for the first time, Apu learns that this meek young woman is a lot tougher than he thought she was. I'm poor, he says, I want to be a writer, I have nothing to offer you. I know, she says, but that makes no difference, she's determined to go with him. Exasperated, flummoxed, but also moved by her resolve, Apu reluctantly gives in. Cut to the city. A carriage pulls up in front of the ramshackle building where Apu lives, and he and his bride step out. All the neighbors come to gawk at the beautiful girl as Apu leads her up the stairs to his squalid little garret. A moment later, he's called away by someone and leaves. The camera stays on the girl, alone in this strange room, this strange city, married to a man she hardly knows. Eventually, she walks to the window, which has a cruddy piece of burlap hanging over it instead of a real curtain. There's a hole in the burlap, and she looks through the hole into the backyard, where a baby in diapers is toddling along through the dust and debris. The camera angle reverses, and we see her eye through the hole. Tears are falling from that eye, and who can blame her for feeling overwrought, scared, lost? Apu reenters the room and asks her what's wrong. Nothing, she says, shaking her head, nothing at all. Then we fade to black, and the big question is: what next? What's in store for this unlikely couple who wound up marrying each other by pure accident? With a few deft and decisive strokes, everything is revealed to us in less than a minute. Object number one: the window. We fade in, it's early morning, and the first thing we see is the window the girl was looking through in the previous scene. But the ratty burlap is gone, replaced by a pair of clean checkered curtains. The camera pulls back a little, and there's object number two: potted flowers on the windowsill. These are encouraging signs, but we can't be sure what they mean yet. Domesticity, homeyness, a woman's touch, but this is what wives are supposed to do, and just because Apu's wife has carried out her duties well doesn't prove that she cares for him. The

camera continues pulling back, and we see the two of them asleep in bed. The alarm clock rings, and the wife climbs out of bed as Apu groans and buries his head in the pillow. Object number three: her sari. After she gets out of bed and starts walking off, she suddenly can't move – because her clothes are tied to Apu's. Very odd. Who could have done this – and why? The expression on her face is both peeved and amused, and we instantly know that Apu was responsible. She returns to the bed, thwacks him gently on the butt, and then unties the knot. What does this moment say to me? That they're having good sex, that a sense of playfulness has developed between them, that they're really married. But what about love? They seem to be contented, but how strong are their feelings for each other? That's when object number four appears: the hairpin. The wife leaves the frame to prepare breakfast, and the camera closes in on Apu. He finally manages to open his eyes, and as he yawns and stretches and rolls around in bed, he sees something in the crevice between the two pillows. He reaches in and pulls out one of his wife's hairpins. That's the crowning moment. He holds up the hairpin and studies it, and when you look at Apu's eyes, the tenderness and adoration in those eyes, you know beyond a doubt that he's madly in love with her, that she's the woman of his life. And Ray makes it happen without using a single word of dialogue.

Same with the dishes, I said. Same with the bundle of sheets. No words.

No words needed, Katya replied. Not when you know what you're doing.

There's another thing about those three scenes. I wasn't aware of it while we were watching the films, but listening to you describe them now, it jumped right out at me.

What?

They're all about women. How women are the ones who carry the world. They take care of the real business while their hapless men stumble around making a hash of things. Or else just lie around doing nothing. That's what happens after the hairpin. Apu looks across the room at his wife, who's crouching down over a pot making breakfast, and he doesn't make a move to help her. In the same way the Italian guy doesn't notice how hard it is for his wife to carry those water buckets.

At last, Katya said, giving me a small poke in the ribs. A man who gets it.

Let's not exaggerate. I'm just adding a footnote to your theory. Your very astute theory, I might add.

And what kind of husband were you, Grandpa?

Just as distracted and lazy as the jokers in those films. Your grandmother did everything.

That's not true.

Yes, it is. When you were with us, I was always on my best behavior. You should have seen us when we were alone.

I pause for a moment to shift my position in bed, to adjust the pillow, to take a sip of water from the glass on the bedside table. I don't want to start thinking about Sonia. It's still too early, and if I let myself go now, I'll wind up brooding about her for hours. Stick to the story. That's the only solution. Stick to the story, and then see what happens if I make it to the end.

Owen Brick. Owen Brick on his way to the city of Wellington, in which state he doesn't know, in which part of the country he doesn't know, but because of the dampness and chill in the air, he suspects that he's in the north, perhaps New England, perhaps New York State, perhaps somewhere in the Upper Midwest, and then, remembering Sarge Serge's talk about a civil war, he wonders what the fighting is about and who is fighting whom. Is it North against South again? East against West? Red against Blue? White against Black? Whatever caused the war, he tells himself, and whatever issues or ideas happen to be at stake, none of it makes any sense. How can this be America if Tobak knows nothing about Iraq? Utterly at a loss, Brick reverts to his earlier speculation that he is trapped in a dream, that in spite of the physical evidence around him, he is lying next to Flora in his bed at home.

Visibility is poor, but through the fog Brick can dimly apprehend that he is flanked by woods on both sides, that there are no houses or buildings anywhere in sight, no telephone poles, no traffic signs, no indication of human presence except the road itself, a badly paved stretch of tar and asphalt with numerous cracks and potholes, no doubt unrepaired for years. He walks on for a mile, then another mile, and still no cars drive past, no people emerge from the emptiness. Finally, after twenty minutes or so, he hears something approaching him, a clanking, whooshing sound that he is at pains to identify. Out of the fog, a man on a bicycle comes pedaling toward him. Brick raises his hand to catch the man's attention, calls out *Hello, Please, Sir*, but the cyclist ignores him and scoots on past. After a while, more people on bicycles start showing up, some riding in one direction, some in the other, but for all the notice they pay

to Brick as he urges them to stop, he might as well be invisible.

Five or six miles farther down the road, signs of life begin to appear – or rather signs of former life: burned-out houses, collapsed food markets, a dead dog, several exploded cars. An old woman dressed in tattered clothes and pushing a shopping cart filled with her possessions suddenly looms up in front of him.

Excuse me, Brick says. Could you tell me if this is the road to Wellington?

The woman stops and looks at Brick with uncomprehending eyes. He notes a small tuft of whiskers sprouting from her chin, her wrinkled mouth, her gnarled, arthritic hands. Wellington? she says. Who asked you?

No one asked me, Brick says. I'm asking you.

Me? What do I have to do with it? I don't even know you.

And I don't know you. All I'm asking is if this is the road to Wellington.

The woman scrutinizes Brick for a moment and says, It'll cost you five bucks.

Five bucks for a yes or no? You must be crazy.

Everyone's crazy around here. Are you trying to tell me you're not?

I'm not trying to tell you anything. I just want to know where I am.

You're standing on a road, nitwit.

Yes, fine, I'm standing on a road, but what I want to know is if this road leads to Wellington.

Ten bucks.

Ten bucks?

Twenty bucks.

Forget it, Brick says, by now at the limit of his patience. I'll figure it out for myself.

Figure out what? the woman asks.

Instead of answering her, Brick starts walking again, and as he strides off through the fog, he hears the woman burst out laughing behind him, as if someone has just told her a good joke . . .

The streets of Wellington. It's past noon by the time he enters the city, exhausted and hungry, his feet aching from the rigors of the long trek. The sun has burned off the early morning fog, and as he wanders around in the fine, sixty-degree weather, Brick is heartened to discover that the place is still more or less intact, not some bombed-out war zone heaped with rubble and the bodies of dead civilians. He sees a number of destroyed buildings, some cratered streets, a few demolished

barricades, but otherwise Wellington appears to be a functioning city, with pedestrians walking to and fro, people going in and out of shops, and no imminent threat hanging in the air. The only thing that distinguishes it from your normal American metropolis is the fact that there are no cars, trucks, or buses. Nearly everyone is moving around on foot, and those who aren't walking are mounted on bicycles. It's impossible for Brick to know yet if this is a result of a gasoline shortage or municipal policy, but he has to admit that the quiet has a pleasant effect, that he prefers it to the clamor and chaos of the streets in New York. Beyond that, however, Wellington has little to recommend it. It's a shabby, down-at-the-heels kind of place, with ugly, poorly constructed buildings, nary a tree in sight, and mounds of uncollected garbage littering the sidewalks. A glum burg, perhaps, but not the out-and-out hellhole Brick was expecting.

His first order of business is to fill his stomach, but restaurants seem to be scarce in Wellington, and he prowls around for some time before spotting a small diner on a side street off one of the main avenues. It's almost three o'clock, long past lunch hour, and the place is empty when he walks in. To his left is a counter with six vacant stools in front of it; to his right, running along the opposite wall, are four narrow booths, also vacant. Brick decides to sit at the counter. A few seconds after he settles onto one of the stools, a young woman emerges from the kitchen and slaps down a menu in front of him. She's in her mid-to-late twenties, a thin, pale blonde with a weary look in her eyes and the hint of a smile on her lips.

What's good today? Brick asks, not bothering to open the menu.

More like, what do we *have* today, the waitress replies.

Oh? Well, what are the choices?

Tuna salad, chicken salad, and eggs. The tuna's from yesterday, the chicken's from two days ago, and the eggs came in this morning. We'll cook them any way you like. Fried, scrambled, poached. Hard, medium, soft. Whatever, however.

Any bacon or sausage? Any toast or potatoes?

The waitress rolls her eyes in mock disbelief. Dream on, honey, she says. Eggs are eggs. Not eggs with something else. Just eggs.

All right, Brick says, feeling disappointed but nevertheless trying to keep up a good front, let's go for the eggs.

How do you want them?

Let's see . . . How do I want them? Scrambled.

How many?

Three. No, make that four.

Four? That'll cost you twenty bucks, you know. The waitress narrows her eyes, and she looks at Brick as if seeing him for the first time. Shaking her head, she adds: What are you doing in a dump like this with twenty dollars in your pocket?

Because I want eggs, Brick answers. Four scrambled eggs, served to me by . . .

Molly, the waitress says, giving him a smile. Molly Wald.

. . . by Molly Wald. Any objections to that?

None that I can think of.

So Brick orders his four scrambled eggs, struggling to maintain a light, bantering tone with the skinny, not unfriendly Molly Wald, but underneath it all he's calculating that with prices like these – eggs going at five dollars a pop in a no-account greasy spoon – the money Tobak gave him that morning isn't going to last very long. As Molly turns around and calls out the order into the kitchen behind her, Brick wonders if he should start questioning her about the war or play it closer to the vest and keep his mouth shut. Still undecided, he asks for a cup of coffee.

Sorry, no can do, Molly says, we're all out. Hot tea. I can give you some hot tea if you like.

Okay, Brick says. A pot of tea. After a moment's hesitation, he plucks up his courage and asks: Just out of curiosity, how much is it?

Five bucks.

Five bucks? It seems that everything in here costs five bucks.

Clearly thrown by his comment, Molly leans forward, plants her arms on the counter, and shakes her head. You're kind of dumb, aren't you?

Probably, Brick says.

We stopped using singles and coins six months ago. Where have you been, pal? Are you a foreigner or something?

I don't know. I'm from New York. Does that make me a foreigner or not?

New York City?

Queens.

Molly lets out a sharp little laugh, which seems to convey both contempt and pity for her know-nothing customer. That's rich, she says, really rich. A guy from New York who can't tell his ass from his elbow.

I . . . uh . . ., Brick stammers, I've been sick. Out of commission. You know, in a hospital, and I haven't kept up with what's been going on.

Well, for your information, Mr. Stupid, Molly says, we're in a war, and New York started it.

Oh?

Yes, *oh*. Secession. Maybe you've heard of it. When a state declares independence from the rest of the country. There are sixteen of us now, and God knows when it will end. I'm not saying it's a bad thing, but enough is enough. It wears you out, and pretty soon you're just sick of the whole business.

There was a lot of gunfire last night, Brick says, finally daring to ask a direct question. Who won?

The Federals attacked, but our troops fought them off. I doubt they'll try that again anytime soon.

Which means that things are going to be fairly quiet in Wellington.

At least for now, yeah. Or so they say. But who knows?

A voice from the kitchen announces: *Four scrambled*, and a moment later a white plate appears on the shelf behind Molly. She pivots, takes hold of Brick's meal, and sets it down in front of him. Then she begins preparing the tea.

The eggs prove to be dry and overcooked, and not even some healthy doses of salt and pepper can draw much flavor from them. Half-starved after his twelve-mile walk, Brick shovels one forkful of food into his mouth after another, chewing diligently on the rubbery eggs and washing them down with frequent sips of tea – which isn't hot as advertised, but tepid. No matter, he says to himself. With so many unanswered questions to be dealt with, the quality of the food is the least of his worries. Pausing for a moment about midway through his combat with the eggs, Brick looks over at Molly, who is still standing behind the counter, watching him eat with her arms folded across her chest, shifting the weight of her body now onto her left leg, now onto her right, her green eyes flickering with what appears to be a kind of suppressed mirth.

What's so funny? he asks.

Nothing, she says, shrugging her shoulders. It's just that you're eating so fast, you remind me of a dog we used to have when I was a kid.

Sorry, Brick says. I'm hungry.

So I gathered.

You also might have gathered that I'm new around here, he says. I don't know a soul in Wellington, and I need a place to stay. I was wondering if you had any ideas.

For how long?

I don't know. Maybe a night, maybe a week, maybe forever. It's too soon to tell.

You're pretty vague about it, aren't you?

It can't be helped. I'm in a situation, you see, an odd situation, and I'm kind of stumbling around in the dark. The fact is, I don't even know what day it is.

Thursday, April nineteenth.

April nineteenth. Good. That's just what I would have said. But what year?

Are you kidding?

No, unfortunately not. What year is it?

Two thousand and seven.

Strange.

Why strange?

Because it's the right year, but everything else is wrong. Listen to me, Molly . . .

I'm listening, friend. I'm all ears.

Good. Now, if I said the words *September eleventh* to you, would they have any special meaning?

Not particularly.

And *the World Trade Center*?

The twin towers? Those tall buildings in New York?

Exactly.

What about them?

They're still standing?

Of course they are. What's wrong with you?

Nothing, Brick says, muttering to himself in a barely audible voice. Then, looking down at his half-eaten eggs, he whispers: One nightmare replaces another.

What? I didn't hear you.

Lifting his head and looking Molly straight in the eyes, Brick asks her a final question: And there's no war in Iraq, is there?

If you already know the answer, why ask me?

I just had to be sure. Forgive me.

Look, mister—

Owen. Owen Brick.

All right, Owen. I don't know what your problem is, and I don't know what happened to you in that hospital, but if I were you, I'd finish those

eggs before they get cold. I'm going back into the kitchen to make a call. One of my cousins is the night manager of a little hotel around the corner. There could be a vacancy.

Why are you being so nice? You don't even know me.

I'm not being nice. My cousin and I have a deal. Whenever I bring him a new customer, he gives me a ten percent cut on the first night. It's strictly business, spaceman. If he has a room for you, you don't owe me a thing.

It turns out that he does. By the time Brick has swallowed the last of his food (with the aid of yet another gulp of the now cold tea), Molly has come back from the kitchen to give him the good news. There are three rooms available, she says, two of them for three hundred a night and the third for two hundred. Not knowing how much he can afford, she's taken it upon herself to book him the room for two hundred, a clear indication, Brick thankfully notes, that despite her tough talk about *strictly business*, Molly has reduced her finder's fee by ten dollars as a favor to him. Not such a bad girl, he thinks, no matter how hard she works at hiding it. Brick is feeling so lonely, so discombobulated by the events of the past twenty hours, he wishes she would abandon her post behind the counter and accompany him to the hotel, but he knows she can't, and he's too timid to ask her to make an exception for him. Instead, Molly sketches a diagram on a paper napkin, indicating the route he should follow to reach the Exeter Hotel, which is only one block away. Then he settles the tab, insisting that she accept a ten-dollar tip, and shakes her hand good-bye.

I hope I see you again, he says, suddenly and moronically on the verge of tears.

I'm always around, she replies. From eight to six, Monday through Friday. If you ever want another lousy meal, you know where to come.

The Exeter Hotel is a six-story limestone building in the middle of a block of discount shoe stores and dimly lit bars. It might have been an attractive place sixty or seventy years ago, but one look at the lobby, with its sagging, moth-eaten velvet chairs and dead potted palms, and Brick understands that two hundred dollars doesn't buy you much in Wellington. He's a bit stunned when the clerk behind the front desk insists that he pay for the night in advance, but since he's unfamiliar with local customs, he doesn't bother to protest. The clerk, who could pass for Serge Tobak's twin brother, counts out the four fifty-dollar bills, sweeps them into a drawer below the cracked marble counter, and hands

Brick the key to room 406. No signature or proof of identity required. When Brick asks where he can find the elevator, the clerk informs him that it's broken.

Somewhat winded after climbing the four flights of stairs, Brick unlocks the door and enters his room. He observes that the bed has been made, that the white walls look and smell as if they've been freshly painted, that everything is relatively clean, but once he begins to look around in earnest, he is gripped by a pulverizing sense of dread. The room is so bleak and unwelcoming, he imagines that dozens of desperate people have checked into this place over the years with no other purpose than to commit suicide. Where has this impression come from? Is it his own state of mind, he wonders, or can it be borne out by the facts? The sparseness of the furniture, for example: just one bed and one battered wardrobe stranded in an overly large space. No chair, no phone. The absence of any pictures on the walls. The blank, cheerless bathroom, with a single miniature bar of soap lying in its wrapper on the white sink, a single white hand towel hanging on the rack, the rusted enamel in the white tub. Pacing around in an ever-spiraling funk, Brick decides to turn on the old black-and-white television next to the window. Maybe that will calm him down, he thinks, or, if luck is with him, maybe a newscast will be on and he can learn something about the war. A hollow, echoing ping emerges from the box as he pushes the button. A promising sign, he says to himself, but then, after a long wait as the machine slowly warms up, no image appears on the screen. Nothing but snow, and the strident hiss of static. He changes the channel. More snow, more static. He goes around the dial, but each stop produces the same result. Rather than simply turn off the television, Brick yanks the cord out of the wall. Then he sits down on the ancient bed, which groans under the weight of his body.

Before he has a chance to slump into a miasma of useless self-pity, someone knocks on the door. No doubt an employee of the hotel, Brick thinks, but secretly he's hoping it's Molly Wald, that somehow or other she's managed to dash out of the diner for a couple of minutes to check on him and make sure he's all right. Not very probable, of course, and no sooner does he unlock the door than his fleeting hope is crushed. His visitor isn't Molly, but neither is it an employee of the hotel. Instead, he finds himself standing in front of a tall, attractive woman with dark hair and blue eyes dressed in black jeans and a brown leather jacket – clothes similar to the ones Sarge Serge gave him that morning. As Brick studies

her face, he is convinced they have met before, but his mind refuses to conjure up a memory of where or when.

Hi there, Owen, the woman says, flashing him a bright, brittle smile, and as he looks at her mouth, he notices that she's wearing an intense shade of red lipstick.

I know you, don't I? Brick answers. At least I think I do. Or maybe you just remind me of someone.

Virginia Blaine, the woman announces cheerfully, triumph ringing in her voice. Don't you remember? You had a crush on me in the tenth grade.

Good God, Brick mutters, more lost than ever now. Virginia Blaine. We sat next to each other in Miss Blunt's geometry class.

Aren't you going to let me in?

Of course, of course, he says, stepping out of the doorway and watching her stride across the threshold.

Once she has cast her eyes around the grim, barren room, Virginia turns to him and says: What a horrible place. Why on earth did you check in here?

It's a long story, Brick replies, not wanting to go into it.

This won't do, Owen. We'll have to find you something better.

Maybe tomorrow. I've already paid up for tonight, and I doubt they'd give me my money back now.

There isn't even a chair to sit in.

I realize that. You can sit on the bed if you want to.

Thanks, Virginia says, glancing over at the worn-out green bedspread, I think I'll stand.

What are you doing here? Brick asks, abruptly changing the subject.

I saw you walk into the hotel, and I came up to –

No, no, I don't mean that, he says, cutting her off in mid-sentence. I'm talking about *here*, in Wellington, a city I've never even heard of. In this country, which is supposed to be America but isn't America, at least not the America I know.

I can't tell you. Not yet, anyway.

I go to bed with my wife in New York. We make love, we fall asleep, and when I wake up I'm lying in a hole in the middle of goddamned nowhere, dressed in a fucking army uniform. What the hell is going on?

Calm down, Owen. I know it's a bit disorienting at first, but you'll get used to it, I promise.

I don't want to get used to it. I want to go back to my life.

You will. And a lot sooner than you think.

Well, at least that's something, Brick says, not sure whether he should believe her or not. But if I'm able to go back, what about you?

I don't want to go back. I've been here a long time now, and I like it better than where I used to be.

A long time . . . So when you stopped coming to school, it wasn't because you and your parents had moved away.

No.

I missed you a lot. For about three months, I'd been screwing up my courage to ask you out on a date, and then, just when I was ready to do it, you were gone.

It couldn't be helped. I didn't have any choice.

What keeps you here? Are you married? Do you have any kids?

No kids, but I used to be married. My husband was killed at the beginning of the war.

I'm sorry.

I'm sorry, too. And I'm also a little sorry to hear that you're married. I haven't forgotten you, Owen. I know it was a long time ago, but I wanted to go out on that date just as much as you did.

Now you tell me.

It's the truth. I mean, whose idea do you think it was to bring you here?

You're joking. Come on, Virginia, why would you do something that awful to me?

I wanted to see you again. And I also thought you'd be the perfect man for the job.

What job?

Don't be coy, Owen. You know what I'm talking about.

Tobak. The clown who calls himself Sarge Serge.

And Lou Frisk. You were supposed to go to him straight away, remember?

I was tired. I'd been walking all day on an empty stomach, and I needed to eat something and take a nap. I was about to climb into bed when you knocked on the door.

Bad luck. We're working on a tight schedule, and we have to go to Frisk now.

I can't. I'm just too exhausted. Let me sleep for a couple of hours, and then I'll go with you.

I really shouldn't. . .

Please, Virginia. For old times' sake.

All right, she says, looking down at her wristwatch. I'll give you an hour. It's four-thirty now. Expect a knock on your door at five-thirty sharp.

Thank you.

But no funny business, Owen. Okay?

Of course not.

After giving him a warm, affectionate smile, Virginia opens her arms and hugs Brick good-bye. It's so good to see you again, she whispers into his ear. Brick remains mute, his arms at his sides, a hundred thoughts darting through his head. Finally, Virginia lets go of him, pats him on the cheek, and makes her way to the door, which she opens with a quick, downward thrust on the handle. Before letting herself out, she turns and says: Five-thirty.

Five-thirty, Brick echoes, and then the door bangs shut, and Virginia Blaine is gone.

Brick already has a plan – and a set of principles. Under no circumstances does he want to meet Frisk or carry out the job they've assigned him. He is not going to murder anyone, he will not do anyone's bidding, he will keep himself out of sight for as long as necessary. Since Virginia knows where he is, he will have to leave the hotel at once and never return. Where to go next is the most immediate problem, and he can think of only three possible solutions. Return to the diner and ask Molly Wald for help. If she isn't willing to give it, then what? Roam the streets and look for another hotel, or else wait for nightfall and then slip out of Wellington.

He gives himself ten minutes, more than enough time for Virginia to get down the four flights of stairs and leave the Exeter. She could be waiting in the lobby, of course, or keeping watch on the hotel entrance from across the street, but if she isn't in the lobby, he will make his exit through a back door, assuming there is a back door and he can find it. And what if she happens to be in the lobby, after all? He will make a run for it, pure and simple. Brick might not be the fastest man in the world, but during his conversation with Virginia he noticed that she was wearing high-heeled boots, and surely a man in flat shoes can outrun a woman in high-heeled boots any day of the week.

As for the hug and the affectionate smile, as for professing to want to see him again and her regret at not having gone out with him in high school, Brick is nothing if not skeptical. Virginia Blaine, the heartthrob of his fifteen-year-old self, was the prettiest girl in the class, and every

boy swooned with lust and silent longing whenever she walked by. He wasn't telling the truth when he said he was about to ask her out on a date. There was no question that he wanted to ask, but at that point in his life, he never would have dared.

Leather jacket zipped, backpack slung over his right shoulder, down Brick goes, taking the rear stairwell, the fire exit, which mercifully allows him to bypass the lobby altogether and leads to a metal door that opens onto a street parallel to the front entrance of the hotel. No sign of Virginia anywhere, and so heartened is our frazzled hero by his successful escape, he feels a momentary surge of optimism, sensing that he can finally add the word *hope* to the lexicon of his miseries. He walks along quickly, sliding past knots of pedestrians, dodging a boy on a pogo stick, slackening his pace briefly at the approach of four soldiers carrying rifles, listening to the ever–present clank of bicycles rolling down the street. A turn, another turn, and then one more, and there he is, standing in front of the Pulaski Diner, the restaurant where Molly works.

Brick goes in, and once again the place is empty. Now that he understands the circumstances, this hardly comes as a surprise to him, since why would anyone bother to go to a restaurant that has no food? Not a customer to be seen, therefore, but more distressing is the absence of Molly as well. Wondering if she hasn't gone home early, Brick calls out her name, and when she fails to appear, he calls it out again. After several anxious seconds, he is relieved to see her walk into the room, but once she recognizes him, the boredom in her face instantly turns to worry, perhaps even anger.

Is everything okay? she asks, her voice sounding tight and defensive.

Yes and no, Brick says.

What does that mean? Did they give you any trouble at the hotel?

No trouble. They were expecting me. I paid for one night in advance and went upstairs.

What about the room? Any problem with that?

Let me tell you, Molly, Brick says, unable to suppress the smile that is spreading across his lips, I've traveled all over the world, and when it comes to first-class accommodations, I mean top-of-the-line comfort and elegance, nothing comes close to room four-oh-six at the Exeter Hotel in Wellington.

Molly smiles broadly at his facetious remark, and all at once she looks like a different person. Yeah, I know, she says. It's a classy place, isn't it?

Seeing that smile, Brick suddenly understands the cause of her alarm.

Her initial assumption was that he marched back here to complain, to accuse her of having swindled him, but now that she knows otherwise, she has let down her guard, relaxed into a more amiable attitude.

It has nothing to do with the hotel, he says. It's about that situation I mentioned to you before. A bunch of people are after me. They want me to do something I don't want to do, and now they know I'm staying at the Exeter. Which means I can't stay there anymore. That's why I came back. To ask for your help.

Why me?

Because you're the only person I know.

You don't know me, Molly says, shifting the weight of her body from her right leg to her left. I served you some eggs, I found a room for you, we talked for about five minutes. I hardly call that knowing me.

You're right. I don't know you. But I couldn't think of anywhere else to go.

Why should I stick my neck out for you? You're probably in some kind of trouble. Police trouble or army trouble. Or maybe you escaped from that hospital. The loony bin would be my guess. Give me one good reason why I should help you.

I can't. Not a single one, Brick says, dismayed at how badly he misjudged this girl, how foolish he was to think he could count on her. The only thing I can offer you is money, he adds, remembering the envelope of fifties in the backpack. If you know of a place where I could hide out for a while, I'll be glad to pay you.

Ah, well, that's different, isn't it? says the transparent, not-so-cunning Molly. How much money are we talking about?

I don't know. You tell me.

I suppose I could put you up in my apartment for a night or two. The sofa's long enough to hold that body of yours, I think. But no hanky-panky. My boyfriend lives with me, and he has a bad temper, if you know what I mean, so don't get any dumb ideas.

I'm married. I don't go in for stuff like that.

That's a good one. There isn't a married man in this world who'd pass up some extra nooky if it came his way.

Maybe I don't live in this world.

Yeah, maybe you don't at that. That would explain a lot of things, wouldn't it?

So, how much are you going to charge? Brick asks, eager to complete the transaction.

Two hundred bucks.

Two hundred? That's pretty steep, don't you think?

You don't know crap, mister. Around here, that's rock bottom, as low as it gets. Take it or leave it.

All right, Brick says, bowing his head and letting out a long, mournful sigh. I'll take it.

*

Suddenly, an urgent need to empty my bladder. I shouldn't have drunk that last glass of wine, but the temptation was too strong, and the fact is I like going to bed a little tipsy. The apple juice bottle is sitting on the floor next to the bed, but as I reach out and grope for it in the dark, I can't seem to find it. The bottle was Miriam's idea – to spare me the pain and difficulty of having to get out of bed and hobble off to the bathroom in the middle of the night. An excellent idea, but the whole point is to have the bottle close at hand, and on this particular night my waving, extended fingers make no contact with the glass. The only solution is to turn on the bedside lamp, but once that happens, any chance I have of falling asleep will be gone for good. The bulb is just fifteen watts, but in the ink-black dark of this room, switching it on will be like exposing myself to a searing blast of fire. I'll go blind for a few seconds, and then, as my pupils gradually expand, I'll be wide awake, and even after I turn off the lamp, my brain will go on churning until dawn. I know this from long experience, a lifetime of battling against myself in the trenches of night. Oh well, nothing to be done, not one bloody thing. I switch on. I go blind. I blink slowly as my eyes adjust, and then I catch sight of the bottle, standing on the floor a mere two inches from its usual spot. I lean over, extend my body a little farther, and take hold of the damn thing. Then, throwing back the covers, I inch myself into a sitting position – carefully, carefully, so as not to rouse the ire of my shattered leg – twist off the top of the bottle, stick my pecker into the hole, and let the pee come pouring out. It never fails to satisfy, that moment when the gush begins, and then watching the bubbling yellow liquid cascade into the bottle as the glass grows warm in my hand. How many times does a person urinate over the course of seventy-two years? I could do the calculations, but why bother now that the job is nearly done? As I remove my penis from the hole, I look down at my old comrade and wonder if I'll ever have sex again, if I'll ever run across another woman who will want to go to bed with me and spend a night in my arms. I push down the thought, tell myself to

desist, for therein lies the way to madness. Why did you have to die, Sonia? Why couldn't I have gone first?

I recap the bottle, return it to its proper place on the floor, and pull the blankets over me. What now? To turn off the light or not to turn off the light? I want to go back to my story and discover what happens to Owen Brick, but the latest installments of Miriam's book are lying on the lower shelf of the bedside table, and I promised to read them and give her my comments. After all the movie watching with Katya, I've fallen behind, and it irks me to think I've let her down. Just for a while, then, another chapter or two – for Miriam's sake.

Rose Hawthorne, the youngest of Nathaniel Hawthorne's three children, born in 1851, just thirteen when her father died, redheaded Rose, known to the family as Rosebud, a woman who lived two lives, the first one sad, tormented, failed, the second one remarkable. I've often asked myself why Miriam chose to take on this project, but I think I'm beginning to understand now. Her last book was a life of John Donne, the crown prince of poets, the genius of geniuses, and then she embarks on an investigation of a woman who floundered through the world for forty-five years, a truculent and difficult person, a confessed "stranger to herself," trying her hand first at music, then at painting, and after getting nowhere with either of those pursuits, turning to poetry and short stories, some of which she managed to publish (no doubt on the strength of her father's name), but the work was heavy and awkward, mediocre at best – excluding one line from a poem quoted in Miriam's manuscript, which I like enormously: *As the weird world rolls on.*

Add to the public portrait the private facts of her elopement at twenty with young writer George Lathrop, a man of talent who never fulfilled his promise, the bitter conflicts of that marriage, the separation, the reconciliation, the death of their only child at the age of four, the final separation, Rose's protracted squabbles with her brother and sister, and one begins to think: why bother, why spend your time exploring the soul of such an insignificant, unhappy person? But then, in midlife, Rose underwent a transformation. She became a Catholic, took holy vows, and founded an order of nuns called the Servants of Relief for Incurable Cancer, devoting her last thirty years to caring for the terminally ill poor, a passionate defender of every person's right to die with dignity. *The weird world rolls on.* In other words, as with Donne, Rose Hawthorne's life was a story of conversion, and that must have been the attraction, the thing that sparked Miriam's interest in her. Why that should interest

her is another question, but I believe it comes directly from her mother: a fundamental conviction that people have the power to change. That was Sonia's influence, not mine, and Miriam is probably a better person for it, but brilliant as my daughter is, there's also something naïve and fragile about her, and I wish to God she would learn that the rotten acts human beings commit against one another are not just aberrations – they're an essential part of who we are. She would suffer less that way. The world wouldn't collapse every time something bad happened to her, and she wouldn't be crying herself to sleep every other night.

I'm not going to pretend that divorce isn't a cruel business. Unspeakable suffering, crippling despair, demonic rage, and the constant cloud of sorrow in the head, which gradually turns into a kind of mourning, as if one were grieving a death. But Richard walked out on Miriam five years ago, and you'd think by now that she would have adjusted to her new circumstances, put herself back in circulation, attempted to reconfigure her life. But all her energy has gone into her teaching and writing, and whenever I bring up the subject of other men, she bristles. Luckily, Katya was already eighteen and off at college when the breakup happened, and she was old enough and strong enough to absorb the shock without going to pieces. Miriam had a much harder time of it when Sonia and I split up. She was just fifteen, a far more vulnerable age, and even though Sonia and I got back together nine years later, the damage had already been done. It's hard enough for grown-ups to live through a divorce, but it's worse for the kids. They're entirely powerless, and they bear the brunt of the pain.

Miriam and Richard made the same mistake that Sonia and I did: they married too young. In our case, we were both twenty-two – not such an uncommon occurrence back in 1957. But when Miriam and Richard walked down the aisle a quarter of a century later, she was the same age her mother had been. Richard was a little older, twenty-four or twenty-five, I think, but the world had changed by then, and they were little more than babies, two crackerjack baby students doing postgraduate work at Yale, and within a couple of years they had a baby of their own. Didn't Miriam understand that Richard might eventually grow restless? Didn't she realize that a forty-year-old professor standing in front of a room of female undergraduates could become entranced by those young bodies? It's the oldest story in the world, but the hardworking, loyal, high-strung Miriam wasn't paying attention. Not even with her own mother's story burned deeply in her mind – that awful moment

when her wretch of a father, after eighteen years of marriage, ran off with a woman of twenty-six. I was forty then. Beware of men in their forties.

Why am I doing this? Why do I persist in traveling down these old, tired paths; why this compulsion to pick at old wounds and make myself bleed again? It would be impossible to exaggerate the contempt I sometimes feel for myself. I was supposed to be looking at Miriam's manuscript, but here I am staring at a crack in the wall and dredging up remnants from the past, broken things that can never be repaired. Give me my story. That's all I want now – my little story to keep the ghosts away. Before switching off the lamp, I turn at random to another page in the manuscript and fall upon this: the final two paragraphs of Rose's memoir of her father, written in 1896, describing the last time she ever saw him.

*It seemed to me a terrible thing that one so peculiarly strong, sentient, luminous as my father should grow feebler and fainter, and finally ghostly still and white. Yet when his step was tottering and his frame that of a wraith, he was as dignified as in the days of greater pride, holding himself, in military self-command, even more erect than before. He did not omit to come in his very best black coat to the dinner-table, where the extremely prosaic fare had no effect on the distinction of the meal. He hated failure, dependence, and disorder, broken rules and weariness of discipline, as he hated cowardice. I cannot express how brave he seemed to me. The last time I saw him, he was leaving the house to take the journey for his health which led suddenly to the next world. My mother was to go to the station with him – she who, at the moment when it was said that he died, staggered and groaned, though so far from him, telling us that something seemed to be sapping all her strength; I could hardly bear to let my eyes rest upon her shrunken, suffering form on this day of farewell. My father certainly knew, what she vaguely felt, that he would never return.*

*Like a snow image of an unbending but old, old man, he stood for a moment gazing at me. My mother sobbed as she walked beside him to the carriage. We have missed him in the sunshine, in the storm, in the twilight, ever since.*

I switch off, and once again I'm in the dark, engulfed by the endless, soothing dark. Somewhere in the distance, I hear the sounds of a truck driving down an empty country road. I listen to the air rushing in and out of my nostrils. According to the clock on the bedside table, which I checked before turning off the lamp, the time is twenty past twelve. Hours and hours until daybreak, the bulk of the night still in front of me . . . Hawthorne didn't care. If the South wanted to secede from the country, he

said, let them go and good riddance. The weird world, the battered world, the weird world rolling on as wars flame all around us: the chopped-off arms in Africa, the chopped-off heads in Iraq, and in my own head this other war, an imaginary war on home ground, America cracking apart, the noble experiment finally dead. My thoughts drift back to Wellington, and suddenly I can see Owen Brick again, sitting in one of the booths at the Pulaski Diner, watching Molly Wald wipe down the tables and counter as six o'clock approaches. Then they're outdoors, walking together in silence as she leads him toward her place, the sidewalks clogged with exhausted-looking men and women shuffling home from work, soldiers with rifles standing guard at the main intersections, a pinkish sky gloaming overhead. Brick has lost all confidence in Molly. Realizing that she can't be trusted, that no one can be trusted, he ducked into the men's room at the diner about twenty minutes before they left and transferred the envelope of fifty-dollar bills from the backpack to the right front pocket of his jeans. A smaller chance of being robbed that way, he felt, and when he goes to bed that night, he has every intention of keeping his pants on. In the men's room, he finally took the trouble to examine the money and was encouraged to see the face of Ulysses S. Grant engraved on the front of each bill. That proved to him that this America, this other America, which hasn't lived through September 11 or the war in Iraq, nevertheless has strong historical links to the America he knows. The question is: at what point did the two stories begin to diverge?

Molly, Brick says, breaking the silence ten minutes into their walk, do you mind if I ask you something?

It depends on what it is, she answers.

Have you ever heard of the Second World War?

The waitress lets out a short, ill-tempered grunt. What do you think I am? she says. A retard? Of course I've heard of it.

And what about Vietnam?

My grandfather was one of the first soldiers they shipped out.

If I said *the New York Yankees*, what would you say?

Come on, everybody knows that.

What would you say? Brick repeats.

With an exasperated sigh, Molly turns to him and announces in a sardonic voice: The New York Yankees? They're those girls who dance at Radio City Music Hall.

Very good. And the Rockettes are a baseball team, right?

Exactly.

Okay. One last question, and then I'll stop.

You're a real pain in the ass, you know that?

Sorry. I know you think I'm stupid, but it isn't my fault.

No, I guess not. You just happened to be born that way.

Who's the president?

President? What are you talking about? We don't have a president.

No? Then who's in charge of the government?

The prime minister, birdbrain. Jesus Christ, what planet do you come from?

I see. The independent states have a prime minister. But what about the Federals? Do they still have a president?

Of course.

What's his name?

Bush.

George W.?

That's right. George W. Bush.

Sticking to his word, Brick refrains from asking any more questions, and once again the two of them walk through the streets in silence. A couple of minutes later, Molly points to a four-story wood-frame building on a low-rent residential block lined with similar four-story wooden buildings, all of them in need of a paint job. 628 Cumberland Avenue. Here we are, she says, extracting a key from her purse and unlocking the front door, and then Brick follows her up two flights of wobbly stairs to the apartment she occupies with her unnamed boyfriend. It's a small but tidy flat, consisting of one bedroom, a living room, a kitchen, and a bathroom with a shower but no tub. Looking around the place, Brick is struck by the fact that there's no television or radio either. When he remarks on this to Molly, she tells him that all the transmission towers in the state were blown up in the first weeks of the war, and the government doesn't have enough money to rebuild them.

Maybe after the war is over, Brick says.

Yeah, maybe, Molly answers, sitting down on the living room sofa and lighting up a cigarette. But the thing is, nobody seems to care anymore. It was hard at first – *my God, no TV!* – but then you kind of get used to it, and after another year or two, you begin to like it. The stillness, I mean. No more voices shouting at you twenty-four hours a day. It's an old-fashioned sort of life now, I guess, the way things must have been a hundred years ago. You want news, you read the paper. You want to see a movie, you go to the theater. No more couch potatoes. I know a lot

of people have died, and I know things are really tough out there, but maybe it's all been worth it. *Maybe*. Just maybe. If the war doesn't end soon, everything will turn to shit.

Brick is at a loss to explain it, but he realizes that Molly is no longer talking to him as if he were a dunce. How to account for this unexpected shift in tone? The fact that her job is done for the day and she's sitting comfortably in her apartment puffing on a cigarette? The fact that she's begun to feel sorry for him? Or, conversely, the fact that he's made her two hundred dollars richer and she's decided to stop poking fun at him? In any case, Brick thinks, a girl of many moods, perhaps not as crass as she seems to be, but not so terribly bright either. There are a hundred more questions he would like to ask her, but he decides not to push his luck.

Stubbing out her cigarette, Molly stands up and tells Brick that she's meeting her boyfriend for dinner across town in less than an hour. She walks over to a closet between the bedroom and the kitchen, pulls out two sheets, two blankets, and a pillow, then carries them into the living room and plops them down on the sofa.

There you are, she says. Bedding for your bed, which isn't a real bed. I hope it's not too lumpy.

I'm so tired, Brick answers, I could sleep on a pile of rocks.

If you get hungry, there's some stuff to eat in the kitchen. A can of soup, a loaf of bread, some sliced turkey. You can make yourself a sandwich.

How much?

What do you mean?

How much will it cost me?

Cut it out. I'm not going to charge you for a little food. You've already paid me enough.

And what about breakfast tomorrow morning?

Fine by me. We don't have a lot, though. Just coffee and toast.

Without waiting for Brick to answer, Molly rushes off to the bedroom to change her clothes. The door slams shut, and Brick begins making the bed that isn't a bed. When he's finished, he walks around the room looking for newspapers and magazines, hoping to find something that will tell him about the war, something that will give him a clue about where he is, some scrap of information that will help him understand a little more about the bewildering country he's landed in. But there are no magazines or newspapers in the living room – only a small bookcase crammed with paperback mysteries and thrillers, which he has no desire to read.

He returns to the sofa, sits down, leans his head against the upholstered backrest, and promptly dozes off.

When he opens his eyes thirty minutes later, the bedroom door is ajar, and Molly is gone.

He searches the bedroom for newspapers and magazines – with no success.

Then he walks into the kitchen to heat up a can of vegetable soup and fix himself a turkey sandwich. He notes that the brands are familiar to him: Progresso, Boar's Head, Arnold's. Washing the dishes after eating this *prosaic fare*, he looks at the white telephone attached to the wall and wonders what would happen if he tried to call Flora.

He takes the receiver off the hook, dials the number of his apartment in Jackson Heights, and quickly learns the answer. The number is out of service.

He dries the dishes and puts them back in the cupboard. Then, after turning off the kitchen light, he walks into the living room and thinks about Flora, his dark-haired Argentinian bedmate, his little spitfire, his wife of the past three years. What she must be going through, he says to himself.

He turns off the lights in the living room. He undoes the laces of his shoes. He crawls under the covers. He falls asleep.

Some hours later, he is woken by the sound of a key entering the lock of the apartment door. Keeping his eyes shut, Brick listens to the scraping of footsteps, the low-pitched rumble of a male voice, the sharper, more metallic voice of his female companion, no doubt Molly, yes, indeed Molly, who addresses the man as Duke, and then a light goes on, which registers as a crimson glare undulating on the surface of his eyelids. They both sound a bit drunk, and as the light goes off and they clomp into the bedroom – where another light immediately goes on – Brick gathers that they're quarreling about something. Before the door shuts, he catches the words *don't like it, two hundred, risky, harmless*, and understands that he is the subject of the argument and that Duke is none too happy about his presence in the house.

Managing to fall asleep again after the ruckus in the bedroom dies down (sounds of copulation: a grunting Duke, a yelping Molly, squeaking mattress and springs), Brick then floats off into a complex dream about Flora. At first, he's talking to her on the telephone. It isn't Flora's voice, however, with its thick, rolling *r*'s and singsong lilt, but the voice of Virginia Blaine, and Virginia/Flora is begging him to fly – not walk,

but fly – to a certain corner in Buffalo, New York, where she'll be standing naked under a transparent raincoat, holding a red umbrella in one hand and a white tulip in the other. Brick begins to weep, telling her that he doesn't know how to fly, at which point Virginia/Flora shouts angrily into the phone that she never wants to see him again and hangs up. Stunned by her vehemence, Brick shakes his head and mutters to himself: But I'm not in Buffalo today, I'm in Worcester, Massachusetts. Then he's walking down a street in Jackson Heights, dressed in his Great Zavello costume with the long black cape, looking for his apartment building. But the building is gone, and in its place there is a one-story wooden cottage with a sign above the door that reads: ALL-AMERICAN DENTAL CLINIC. He walks in, and there's Flora, the real Flora, dressed in a white nurse's uniform. I'm so glad you could come, Mr. Brick, she says, apparently not recognizing him, and then she's leading him into an office and gesturing for him to sit down in a dental chair. It's such a shame, she says, picking up a pair of large, gleaming pliers, it's such a shame, but it looks like we're going to have to pull out all your teeth. All of them? Brick asks, suddenly terrified. Yes, Flora answers, all of them. But don't worry. After we're done, the doctor will give you a new face.

The dream stops there. Someone is shaking Brick's shoulder and barking words at him in a loud voice, and as the groggy dreamer at last opens his eyes, he sees a large man with broad shoulders and muscular arms towering above him. One of those bodybuilder types, Brick thinks, Duke the boyfriend, the guy with the bad temper, dressed in a tight-fitting black T-shirt and blue boxer shorts, telling him to get the fuck out of the apartment.

I paid good money—Brick begins.

For one night, Duke shouts. The night's up now, and out you go.

Just a minute, just a minute, Brick says, raising his right hand as a sign of his peaceful intentions. Molly promised me breakfast. Coffee and toast. Just let me have some coffee, and then I'll be on my way.

No coffee. No toast. No nothing.

What if I paid you for it? A little extra, I mean.

Don't you understand English?

And with those words, Duke bends down, grabs hold of Brick's sweater, and yanks him to his feet. Now that he's standing, Brick has a clear view of the bedroom door, and the moment he catches sight of it, out comes Molly, securing the sash of her bathrobe and then running her hands through her hair.

Stop it, she says to Duke. You don't have to play rough.

Pipe down, he answers. You made this mess, and now I'm cleaning it up.

Molly shrugs, then looks at Brick with a small, apologetic smile. Sorry, she says. I guess you'd better be going now.

Slipping his feet into his shoes without bothering to tie the laces, then retrieving his leather jacket from the foot of the sofa and putting it on, Brick says to her: I don't get it. I give you all that money, and now you throw me out. It doesn't make sense.

Rather than answer him, Molly looks down at the floor and shrugs again. That apathetic gesture carries all the force of a defection, a betrayal. With no ally to stand up for him, Brick decides to leave without further protest. He bends down and picks up the green backpack from the floor, but no sooner does he turn to go than Duke snatches it out of his hands.

What's this? he asks.

My stuff, Brick says. Obviously.

*Your* stuff? Duke replies. I don't think so, funny man.

What are you talking about?

It's mine now.

Yours? You can't do that. Everything I own is in there.

Then try and get it back.

Brick understands that Duke is itching for a fight – and that the bag is merely a pretext. He also knows that if he tangles with Molly's boyfriend, there is every chance he will be ripped apart. Or so his mind tells him the instant he hears Duke issue his challenge, but Brick is no longer thinking with his mind, for the outrage surging through him has overwhelmed all reason, and if he allows this bully to get his way without offering some form of resistance, he will lose whatever respect he still has for himself. So Brick takes his stand, unexpectedly wrenching the bag out of Duke's grasp, and immediately after that the drubbing begins, an assault so one-sided and short-lived that the big man floors Brick with just three blows: a left to the gut, a right to the face, and a knee to the balls. Pain floods into every corner of the magician's body, and as he rolls around on the tattered rug gasping for breath, one hand clutching his stomach and the other clamped over his scrotum, he sees blood dripping from the wound that has opened on his cheek, and then, lying in the gathering puddle of red, a fragment of a tooth – the lower half of one of his left incisors. He is only dimly aware of Molly's

screams, which sound as if they are coming from ten blocks away. A moment after that, he is aware of nothing.

When he picks up the thread of his own story, Brick finds himself on his feet, maneuvering his body down the stairs as he clings to the banister with both hands, slowly descending to the ground floor, a single step at a time. The backpack is gone, which means that the gun and the bullets are also gone, not to speak of everything else that was in the bag, but as Brick pauses to reach into the right front pocket of his jeans, the trace of a smile flits across his bruised mouth – the bitter smile of the not quite vanquished. The money is still there. No longer the thousand that Tobak gave him the previous morning, but five hundred and sixty-five dollars is better than nothing, he thinks, more than enough to get him a room somewhere and a bite to eat. That's as far as his thoughts can take him now. To hide, to wash the blood off his face, to fill his stomach if and when his appetite returns.

However modest these plans might be, they are thwarted the moment he leaves the building and steps onto the sidewalk. Directly in front of him, standing with her arms folded and her back resting against the door of a military jeep, Virginia Blaine is eyeing Brick with a disgusted look on her face.

No monkey business, she says. You promised me.

Virginia, Brick replies, doing his best to play dumb, what are you doing here?

Ignoring his remark, the former queen of Miss Blunt's geometry class shakes her head and snaps back: We were supposed to meet at five-thirty yesterday afternoon. You stood me up.

Something happened, and I had to leave at the last minute.

You mean *I* happened, and you ran away.

Unable to think of an answer, Brick says nothing.

You don't look so good, Owen, Virginia continues.

No, I don't suppose I do. I just got the shit kicked out of me.

You should watch the company you keep. That Rothstein's a tough fellow.

Who's Rothstein?

Duke. Molly's boyfriend.

You know him?

He works with us. He's one of our best men.

He's an animal. A sadistic creep.

It was all an act, Owen. To teach you a lesson.

Oh? Brick snorts, indignation rising within him. And what lesson is that? The son of a bitch knocked out one of my teeth.

Just be glad it wasn't all of them.

Very nice, Brick mumbles, with a sarcastic edge to his voice, and then, all of a sudden, the final chapter of the dream comes rushing back to him: the All-American Dental Clinic, Flora and the pliers, the new face. Well, Brick thinks, as he touches the wound on his cheek, I got my new face, didn't I? Thanks to Rothstein's fist.

You can't win, Virginia says. Everywhere you go, someone is watching you. You'll never get away from us.

According to you, Brick says, not yet willing to give in, but knowing in his heart that Virginia is right.

Ergo, my dear Owen, this little interlude of dawdling and hide-and-seek has come to an end. Hop into the jeep. It's time for you to talk to Frisk.

No dice, Virginia. I can't hop, and I can't run, and I can't go anywhere yet. My face is bleeding, my balls are on fire, and every muscle in my stomach is torn to shreds. I have to patch myself up first. Then I'll talk to your man. But at least let me take a goddamn bath.

For the first time since the conversation began, Virginia smiles. Poor baby, she says, simpering with compassion, but whether this new concern for him is real or false is far from clear to Brick.

Are you with me or not? he asks.

Climb in, she says, patting the door of the jeep. Of course I'm with you. I'll take you back to my house, and we'll fix you up there. It's still early. Lou can wait a little while. As long as you see him before dark, we'll be okay.

With that reassurance, Brick hobbles over to the jeep and hoists his sorry carcass into the passenger seat as Virginia slips in behind the wheel. Once she starts the engine, she launches into a long, meandering account of the civil war, no doubt feeling an obligation to fill him in on the historical background of the conflict, but the problem is that Brick is in no condition to follow what she's saying, and as they lurch along over the potholed streets of Wellington, every jolt and bump sends a fresh attack of pain coursing through his body. To compound the trouble, the noise of the engine is so loud that it nearly swallows up Virginia's voice, and in order to hear anything at all, Brick must strain himself to the limit of his powers, which are diminished at best, if not entirely obliterated. Clutching the bottom of the seat with his two hands, pressing the soles of his shoes onto

the floor to brace himself against the next bounce of the chassis, he keeps his eyes shut throughout the twenty-minute drive, and from the ten thousand facts that come tumbling down on him between Molly's apartment and Virginia's house, this is what he manages to retain:

The election of 2000 . . . just after the Supreme Court decision . . . protests . . . riots in the major cities . . . a movement to abolish the Electoral College . . . defeat of the bill in Congress . . . a new movement . . . led by the mayor and borough presidents of New York City . . . secession . . . passed by the state legislature in 2003 . . . Federal troops attack . . . Albany, Buffalo, Syracuse, Rochester . . . New York City bombed, eighty thousand dead . . . but the movement grows . . . in 2004, Maine, New Hampshire, Vermont, Massachusetts, Connecticut, New Jersey, and Pennsylvania join New York in the Independent States of America . . . later that year, California, Oregon, and Washington break off to form their own republic, Pacifica . . . in 2005, Ohio, Michigan, Illinois, Wisconsin, and Minnesota join the Independent States . . . the European Union recognizes the existence of the new country . . . diplomatic relations are established . . . then Mexico . . . then the countries of Central and South America . . . Russia follows, then Japan . . . Meanwhile, the fighting continues, often horrendous, the toll of casualties steadily mounting . . . U.N. resolutions ignored by the Federals, but until now no nuclear weapons, which would mean death to everyone on both sides . . . Foreign policy: no meddling anywhere . . . Domestic policy: universal health insurance, no more oil, no more cars or planes, a fourfold increase in teachers' salaries (to attract the brightest students to the profession), strict gun control, free education and job training for the poor . . . all in the realm of fantasy for the moment, a dream of the future, since the war drags on, and the state of emergency is still in force.

The jeep slows down and gradually comes to a stop. As Virginia turns off the ignition, Brick opens his eyes and discovers that he is no longer in the heart of Wellington. They have come to a wealthy suburban street of large Tudor houses with pristine front lawns, tulip beds, forsythia and rhododendron bushes, the myriad trappings of the good life. As he climbs out of the jeep and looks down the block, however, he notices that several houses are standing in ruins: broken windows, charred walls, gaping holes in the facades, abandoned husks where people once lived. Brick assumes that the neighborhood was shelled during the war, but he doesn't ask any questions about it. Instead, pointing to the house they are about to enter, he blandly remarks: This is quite a place,

Virginia. You seem to have done pretty well for yourself.

My husband was a corporate lawyer, she says flatly, in no mood to talk about the past. He made a lot of money.

Virginia opens the door with a key, and they walk into the house . . .

A warm bath, lying in water up to his neck for twenty minutes, thirty minutes, inert, tranquil, alone. After which he puts on the white terry-cloth robe of Virginia's dead husband, walks into the bedroom, and sits down in a chair as Virginia patiently applies an antibacterial astringent to the gash on his cheek and then covers the wound with a small bandage. Brick is beginning to feel somewhat better. The wonders of water, he says to himself, realizing that the pain in his stomach and nether parts has all but vanished. His cheek still smarts, but eventually that discomfort will abate as well. As for the broken tooth, there is nothing to be done until he can visit a dentist and have a cap put on it, but he doubts that will happen anytime soon. For now (as confirmed when he studied his face in the bathroom mirror), the effect is altogether repulsive. A few centimeters of missing enamel and he looks like a broken-down bum, a pea-brained yokel. Fortunately, the gap is visible only when he smiles, and in Brick's present state, the last thing he wants to do is smile. Unless the nightmare ends, he thinks, there's a good chance he'll never smile again for the rest of his life.

Twenty minutes later, now dressed and sitting in the kitchen with Virginia – who has prepared him toast and coffee, the same minimal breakfast that nearly cost him his life earlier that morning – Brick is answering the tenth question she has asked him about Flora. He finds her curiosity puzzling. If she is the person responsible for bringing him to this place, then it would seem likely that she already knows everything about him, including his marriage to Flora. But Virginia is insatiable, and now Brick begins to wonder if all this questioning isn't simply a ploy to hold him in the house, to make him lose track of the time so that he won't try to run off again before Frisk shows up. He wants to run, that's certain, but after the long soak in the tub and the terry-cloth robe and the gentleness of her fingers as she put the bandage on his face, something in him has begun to soften toward Virginia, and he can feel the old flames of his adolescence slowly igniting again.

I met her in Manhattan, he says. About three and a half years ago. A fancy birthday party for a kid on the Upper East Side. I was the magician, and she was one of the caterers.

Is she beautiful, Owen?

To me she is. Not beautiful in the way you are, Virginia, with your incredible face and long body. Flora's little, not even five-four, just a slip of a thing, really, but she has these big burning eyes and all this tangly dark hair and the best laugh I've ever heard.

Do you love her?

Of course.

And she loves you?

Yes. Most of the time, anyway. Flora has a huge temper, and she can fly off into these maniacal tirades. Whenever we fight, I begin to think the only reason she married me was because she wanted her American citizenship. But it doesn't happen very often. Nine days out of ten, we're good together. We really are.

What about babies?

They're on the agenda. We started trying a couple of months ago.

Don't give up. That was my mistake. I waited too long, and now look at me. No husband, no children, nothing.

You're still young. You're still the prettiest girl on the block. Someone else will come along, I'm sure of it.

Before Virginia can answer him, the doorbell rings. She stands up, muttering *Shit* under her breath as if she means it, as if she honestly resents the intrusion, but Brick knows that he's cornered now, and any chance of escape is gone. Before leaving the kitchen, Virginia turns to him and says: I called while you were taking your bath. I told him to come between four and five, but I guess he couldn't wait. I'm sorry, Owen. I wanted to have those hours with you and charm your pants off. I really did. I wanted to fuck your brains out. Just remember that when you go back.

Back? You mean I'm going back?

Lou will explain. That's his job. I'm just a personnel officer, a little cog in a big machine.

Lou Frisk turns out to be a dour-looking man in his early fifties, somewhat on the short side, with narrow shoulders, wire-rimmed glasses, and the marred skin of someone who once suffered from acne. He's dressed in a green V-neck sweater with a white shirt and plaid tie, and in his left hand he's carrying a black satchel that resembles a doctor's bag. The moment he enters the kitchen, he puts down the bag and says: You've been avoiding me, Corporal.

I'm not a corporal, Brick answers. You know that. I've never been a soldier in my life.

Not in your world, Frisk says, but in this world you're a corporal in the Massachusetts Seventh, a member of the armed forces of the Independent States of America.

Putting his head in his hands, Brick groans softly as another element of the dream comes back to him: Worcester, Massachusetts. He looks up, watches Frisk settle into a chair across from him at the table, and says: I'm in Massachusetts, then. Is that what you're telling me?

Wellington, Massachusetts, Frisk nods. Formerly known as Worcester.

Brick pounds his fist on the table, finally giving vent to the rage that has been building inside him. I don't like this! he shouts. Someone's inside my head. Not even my dreams belong to me. My whole life has been stolen. Then, turning to Frisk and looking him directly in the eye, he yells at the top of his voice: Who's doing this to me?

Take it easy, Frisk says, patting Brick on the hand. You have every right to be confused. That's why I'm here. I'm the one who explains it to you, who sets things straight. We don't want you to suffer. If you'd come to me when you were supposed to, you never would have had that dream. Do you understand what I'm trying to tell you?

Not really, Brick says, in a more subdued voice.

Through the walls of the house, he catches the faint sound of the jeep's engine being turned on, and then the distant squeal of shifting gears as Virginia drives away.

Virginia? he asks.

What about her?

She just left, didn't she?

She has a lot of work to do, and our business doesn't concern her.

She didn't even say good-bye, Brick adds, reluctant to drop the matter. There is hurt in his voice, as if he can't quite believe that she would ditch him in such an offhanded way.

Forget Virginia, Frisk says. We have more important things to talk about.

She said I was going back. Is that true?

Yes. But first I have to tell you why. Listen carefully, Brick, and then give me an honest answer. Putting his arms on the table, Frisk leans forward and says: Are we in the real world or not?

How should I know? Everything looks real. Everything sounds real. I'm sitting here in my own body, but at the same time I can't be here, can I? I belong somewhere else.

You're here, all right. And you belong somewhere else.

It can't be both. It has to be one or the other.

Is the name Giordano Bruno familiar to you?

No. Never heard of him.

A sixteenth-century Italian philosopher. He argued that if God is infinite, and if the powers of God are infinite, then there must be an infinite number of worlds.

I suppose that makes sense. Assuming you believe in God.

He was burned at the stake for that idea. But that doesn't mean he was wrong, does it?

Why ask me? I don't know the first thing about any of this. How can I have an opinion about something I don't understand?

Until you woke up in that hole the other day, your entire life had been spent in one world. But how could you be sure it was the only world?

Because . . . because it was the only world I ever knew.

But now you know another world. What does that suggest to you, Brick?

I don't follow.

There's no single reality, Corporal. There are many realities. There's no single world. There are many worlds, and they all run parallel to one another, worlds and anti-worlds, worlds and shadow-worlds, and each world is dreamed or imagined or written by someone in another world. Each world is the creation of a mind.

You're beginning to sound like Tobak. He said the war was in one man's head, and if that man was eliminated, the war would stop. That's about the most asinine thing I've ever heard.

Tobak might not be the brightest soldier in the army, but he was telling you the truth.

If you want me to believe a crazy thing like that, you'll have to prove it to me first.

All right, Frisk says, slapping his palms on the table, what about this? Without another word, he reaches under his sweater with his right hand and pulls out a three-by-five photograph from his shirt pocket. This is the culprit, he says, sliding the photo across the table to Brick.

Brick does no more than glance at the picture. It's a color snapshot of a man in his late sixties or early seventies sitting in a wheelchair in front of a white country house. A perfectly sympathetic-looking man, Brick notes, with spiky gray hair and a weathered face.

This doesn't prove anything, he says, thrusting the photo back at Frisk. It's just a man. Any man. For all I know, he could be your uncle.

His name is August Brill, Frisk begins, but Brick cuts him off before he can say anything else.

Not according to Tobak. He said his name was Blake.

Blank.

Whatever.

Tobak isn't up on the latest intelligence reports. For a long time, Blank was our leading suspect, but then we crossed him off the list. Brill is the one. We're sure of that now.

Then show me the story. Reach into that bag of yours and pull out his manuscript and point to a sentence where my name is mentioned.

That's the problem. Brill doesn't write anything down. He's telling himself the story in his head.

How can you possibly know that?

A military secret. But we know, Corporal. Trust me.

Bullshit.

You want to go back, don't you? Well, this is the only way. If you don't accept the job, you'll be stuck here forever.

All right. Just for the sake of argument, imagine I shoot this man . . . this Brill. Then what happens? If he created your world, then the moment he's dead, you won't exist anymore.

He didn't invent this world. He only invented the war. And he invented you, Brick. Don't you understand that? This is your story, not ours. The old man invented you in order to kill him.

So now it's a suicide.

In a roundabout way, yes.

Once again, Brick puts his head in his hands and begins to moan. It's all too much for him, and after struggling to hold his ground against Frisk's demented assertions, he can feel his mind dissolving, whirling madly through a universe of disconnected thoughts and amorphous dreads. Only one thing is clear to him: he wants to go back. He wants to be with Flora again and return to his old life. In order to do that, he must accept a command to murder someone he has never met, a total stranger. He will have to accept, but once he gets to the other side, what is to prevent him from refusing to carry out the job?

Still looking down at the table, he forces the words out of his mouth: Tell me something about the man.

Ah, that's better, Frisk says. Coming to our senses at last.

Don't patronize me, Frisk. Just tell me what I need to know.

A retired book critic, seventy-two years old, living outside Brattleboro,

Vermont, with his forty-seven-year-old daughter and twenty-three-year-old granddaughter. His wife died last year. The daughter's husband left her five years ago. The granddaughter's boyfriend was killed. It's a house of grieving, wounded souls, and every night Brill lies awake in the dark, trying not to think about his past, making up stories about other worlds.

Why is he in a wheelchair?

A car accident. His left leg was shattered. They nearly had to amputate.

And if I agree to kill this man, you'll send me back.

That's the bargain. But don't try to wriggle out of it, Brick. If you break your promise, we'll come after you. Two bullets. One for you and one for Flora. Bang, bang. No more you. No more her.

But if you get rid of me, the war goes on.

Not necessarily. It's still just a hypothesis at this point, but some of us think that getting rid of you would produce the same result as eliminating Brill. The story would end, and the war would be over. Don't think we wouldn't be willing to take the risk.

How do I get back?

In your sleep.

But I've already gone to sleep here. Twice. And both times I woke up in the same place.

That's normal sleep. What I'm talking about is pharmacologically induced sleep. You'll be given an injection. The effect is similar to anesthesia – when they put a person under before surgery. The black void of oblivion, a nothingness as deep and dark as death.

Sounds like fun, Brick says, so unnerved by what is facing him that he can't help cracking a feeble joke.

Are you willing to give it a shot, Corporal?

Do I have a choice?

I feel a cough gathering in my chest, a faint rattle of phlegm buried deep in my bronchia, and before I can suppress it, the detonation comes blasting through my throat. Hack it up, propel the gunk northward, dislodge the slimy leftovers trapped in the tubes, but one try isn't enough, nor two, nor three, and here I am in a full-blown spasm, my whole body convulsing from the onslaught. It's my own fault. I stopped smoking fifteen years ago, but now that Katya is in the house with her ubiquitous American Spirits, I've begun to lapse into the old, dirty pleasures, cadging butts off her while we plunge through the entire corpus of world

cinema, side by side on the sofa, blowing smoke in tandem, two locomotives chugging away from the loathsome, intolerable world, but without regret, I might add, without a second thought or single pang of remorse. It's the companionship that counts, the conspiratorial bond, the fuck-you solidarity of the damned.

Thinking about the films again, I realize that I have another example to add to Katya's list. I must remember to tell her first thing tomorrow morning – in the dining room over breakfast – since it's bound to please her, and if I can manage to coax a smile out of that glum face of hers, I'll consider it a worthy accomplishment.

The watch at the end of *Tokyo Story*. We saw the film a few days ago, the second time for both of us, but my first viewing goes decades back, the late sixties or early seventies, and other than remembering that I'd liked it, most of the story had vanished from my mind. Ozu, 1953, eight years after the Japanese defeat. A slow, stately film that tells the simplest of stories, but executed with such elegance and depth of feeling that I had tears in my eyes at the end. Some films are as good as books, as good as the best books (yes, Katya, I'll grant you that), and this is one of them, no question about it, a work as subtle and moving as a Tolstoy novella.

An aging couple travels to Tokyo to visit their grown-up children: a struggling doctor with a wife and children of his own, a married hairdresser who runs a beauty salon, and a daughter-in-law who was married to another son killed in the war, a young widow who lives alone and works in an office. From the beginning, it's clear that the son and daughter consider the presence of their old parents something of a burden, an inconvenience. They're busy with their jobs, with their families, and they don't have time to take proper care of them. Only the daughter-in-law goes out of her way to show them any kindness. Eventually, the parents leave Tokyo and return to the place where they live (never mentioned, I believe, or else I blinked and missed it), and some weeks after that, without warning, without any premonitory illness, the mother dies. The action of the film then shifts to the family house in that unnamed city or town. The grown-up children from Tokyo come for the funeral, along with the daughter-in-law, Norika or Noriko, I can't remember, but let's say Noriko and stick with that. Then a second son shows up from somewhere else, and finally there's the youngest child of the group, who still lives at home, a woman in her early twenties who works as an elementary school teacher. One quickly understands that not only does she adore and admire Noriko, she prefers her to her own siblings. After the

funeral, the family is sitting around a table eating lunch, and once again the son and daughter from Tokyo are busy, busy, busy, too wrapped up in their own preoccupations to offer their father much support. They begin looking at their watches and decide to return to Tokyo on the night express. The second brother decides to leave as well. There is nothing overtly cruel about their behavior – this should be emphasized; it's in fact the essential point Ozu is making. They're merely distracted, caught up in the business of their own lives, and other responsibilities are pulling them away. But the gentle Noriko stays on, not wanting to abandon her grieving father-in-law (a walled-off, stone-faced grief, to be sure, but grief for all that), and on the last morning of her extended visit, she and the schoolteacher daughter have breakfast together.

The girl is still irritated by the hasty departure of her brothers and sister. She says they should have stayed longer and calls them selfish, but Noriko defends what they did (even if she would never do it herself), explaining that all children drift away from their parents in the end, that they have their own lives to look after. The girl insists that she'll never be like that. What's the point of a family if you act that way? she says. Noriko reiterates her previous comment, trying to comfort the girl by telling her that these things happen to children, that they can't be helped. A long pause follows, and then the girl looks at her sister-in-law and says: Life is disappointing, isn't it? Noriko looks back at the girl, and with a distant expression on her face, she answers: Yes, it is.

The teacher goes off to work, and Noriko begins straightening up the house (reminding me of the women in the other films Katya talked about tonight), and then comes the scene with the watch, the moment the entire film has been building up to. The old man walks into the house from the garden, and Noriko tells him she's leaving on the afternoon train. They sit down and talk, and if I can more or less remember the gist and flow of their conversation, it's because I asked Katya to play the scene again after the movie was finished. I was that impressed by it, and I wanted to study the dialogue more closely to see how Ozu managed to pull it off.

The old man begins by thanking her for everything she's done, but Noriko shakes her head and says she hasn't done anything. The old man presses on, telling her that she's been a great help and that his wife had talked to him about how kind she'd been to her. Again, Noriko resists the compliment, shrugging off her actions as unimportant, negligible. Not to be deterred, the old man says that his wife told him that being with Noriko was the happiest time she had in Tokyo. She was so worried

about your future, he continues. You can't go on like this. You have to get married again. Forget about X (his son, her husband). He's dead.

Noriko is too upset to respond, but the old man isn't about to give up and let the conversation end. Referring to his wife again, he adds: She said you were the nicest woman she'd ever met. Noriko holds her ground, claiming that his wife overestimated her, but the old man bluntly tells her that she's wrong. Noriko is beginning to grow unhinged. I'm not the nice woman you think I am, she says. Really, I'm quite selfish. And then she explains that she isn't always thinking about the old man's son, that days go by and he doesn't even cross her mind once. After a little pause, she confesses how lonely she is and how, when she can't sleep at night, she lies in bed wondering what will become of her. My heart seems to be waiting for something, she says. I'm selfish.

OLD MAN: No, you're not.

NORIKO: Yes. I am.

OLD MAN: You're a good woman. An honest woman.

NORIKO: Not at all.

At that point, Noriko finally breaks down and begins to cry, sobbing into her hands as the floodgates open – this young woman who has suffered in silence for so long, this good woman who refuses to believe she's good, for only the good doubt their own goodness, which is what makes them good in the first place. The bad know they are good, but the good know nothing. They spend their lives forgiving others, but they can't forgive themselves.

The old man stands up, and a few seconds later he returns with the watch, an old-fashioned timepiece with a metal cover protecting the face. It belonged to his wife, he tells Noriko, and he wants her to have it. Accept it for her sake, he says. I'm sure she'd be glad.

Moved by the gesture, Noriko thanks him as the tears continue to roll down her cheeks. The old man studies her with a thoughtful look on his face, but those thoughts are impenetrable to us, since all his emotions are hidden behind a mask of somber neutrality. Watching Noriko cry, he then makes a simple declaration, delivering his words in such a forthright, unsentimental manner that they cause her to collapse in a fresh outburst of sobbing – prolonged, wrenching sobs, a cry of misery so deep and painful, it's as if the innermost core of her self has been cracked open.

I want you to be happy, the old man says.

One brief sentence, and Noriko falls apart, crushed by the weight of

her own life. *I want you to be happy.* As she goes on crying, the father-in-law makes one more comment before the scene ends. It's strange, he says, almost in disbelief. We have children of our own, and yet you're the one who's done the most for us.

Cut to the school. We hear children singing, and a moment later we are in the daughter's classroom. The sound of a train is heard in the distance. The young woman looks at her watch and then walks to the window. A train roars by: the afternoon express, carrying her beloved sister-in-law back to Tokyo.

Cut to the train itself – and the thunderous noise of the wheels as they charge along the tracks. We are hurtling forward into the future.

A few moments after that, we are inside one of the carriages. Noriko is sitting alone, staring blankly into space, her mind elsewhere. Several more moments pass, and then she lifts her mother-in-law's watch off her lap. She opens the cover, and suddenly we can hear the second hand ticking around the dial. Noriko goes on examining the watch, the expression on her face at once sad and contemplative, and as we look at her with the watch in the palm of her hand, we feel that we are looking at time itself, time speeding ahead as the train speeds ahead, pushing us forward into life and then more life, but also time as the past, the dead mother-in-law's past, Noriko's past, the past that lives on in the present, the past we carry with us into the future.

The shriek of a train whistle resounds in our ears, a cruel and piercing noise. *Life is disappointing, isn't it?*

*I want you to be happy.*

And then the scene abruptly ends.

Widows. Women living alone. An image of the sobbing Noriko in my head. Impossible not to think of my sister now – and the luckless hand she was dealt by marrying a man who died young. It's been brewing in me ever since I started thinking about my civil war: the fact that in my own life I've been spared from all things military. An accident of birth, the fluke of entering the world in 1935, which made me too young for Korea and too old for Vietnam, and then the further good fortune to have been rejected by the army when I was drafted in 1957. They said I had a heart murmur, which turned out not to be true, and classified me as 4-F. No wars, then, but the time I came closest to something that resembled one, I happened to be with Betty and her second husband, Gilbert Ross. It was 1967, exactly forty years ago this summer, and the three of us

were having dinner together on the Upper East Side, Lexington Avenue I think it was, Sixty-sixth or Sixty-seventh Street, in a long-gone Chinese restaurant called Sun Luck. Sonia had gone off to France to visit her parents outside Lyon with the seven-year-old Miriam. I was supposed to join them later, but for the time being I was holed up in our shoe box of an apartment off Riverside Drive, sweating out a long piece for *Harper's* on recent American poetry and fiction inspired by the Vietnam war – with no air conditioner, just a cheap plastic fan, scribbling and typing in my underwear as my pores gushed through another New York heat wave. Money was tight for us back then, but Betty was seven years older than I was and living comfortably, as they say, and therefore she was in a position to invite her kid brother out for a free dinner every now and then. After a bad first marriage that had lasted too long, she had married Gil about three years earlier. A wise choice, I felt – or at least it looked that way at the time. Gil earned his money as a labor lawyer and strike mediator, but he had also joined the Newark city government as corporation counsel in the early sixties, and when he and my sister came to New York that night forty years ago, he was driving a city car, which was equipped with a two-way radio. I can't remember a thing about the dinner itself, but when we walked back to the car and Gil started up the engine to drive me home, frantic voices came pouring through the radio – police calls, I presume, reporting that the Central Ward of Newark was in chaos. Without bothering to go uptown to drop me at my apartment, Gil headed straight for the Lincoln Tunnel, and that was how I came to witness one of the worst race riots in American history. More than twenty people killed, more than seven hundred people injured, more than fifteen hundred people arrested, more than ten million dollars in property damage. I remember these numbers because when Katya was in high school a few years ago, she wrote a paper on racism for her American history class, and she interviewed me about the riot. Odd that those figures should have stuck, but with so many other things slipping away from me now, I cling to them as proof that I'm not quite finished.

Driving into Newark that night was like entering one of the lower circles of hell. Buildings in flames, hordes of men running wildly through the streets, the noise of shattering glass as one store window after another was broken, the noise of sirens, the noise of gunshots. Gil drove to City Hall, and once the three of us were inside the building, we went directly to the mayor's office. Sitting at his desk was Hugh Addonizio, a bald, bulging, pear-shaped man in his mid-fifties, ex-war hero, six-time

congressman, in his second term as mayor, and the big man was utterly lost, sitting at his desk with tears pouring down his face. What am I going to do? he said, looking up at Gil. What the hell am I going to do?

An indelible picture, undimmed after all these years: the sight of that pathetic figure paralyzed by the pressure of events, a man gone rigid with despair as the city exploded around him. Meanwhile, Gil calmly went about his business, calling the governor in Trenton, calling the chief of police, doing his best to get a grip on the situation. At one point, he and I left the room and went downstairs to the jail on the bottom floor of the building. The cells were crammed with prisoners, every one of them a black man, and at least half of them stood there with their clothes torn, blood trickling from their heads, their faces swollen. It wasn't difficult to guess what had caused these wounds, but Gil asked the question anyway. Man by man, the answer never varied: each one had been beaten by the cops.

Not long after we returned to the mayor's office, in walked a member of the New Jersey State Police, a certain Colonel Brand or Brandt, a man of around forty with a razor-sharp crew cut, a square, clenched jaw, and the hard eyes of a marine about to embark on a commando mission. He shook hands with Addonizio, sat down in a chair, and then pronounced these words: We're going to hunt down every black bastard in this city. I probably shouldn't have been shocked, but I was. Not by the statement, perhaps, but by the chilling contempt of the voice that uttered it. Gil told him not to use that kind of language, but the colonel merely sighed and shook his head, dismissing my brother-in-law's remark as if he considered him to be an ignorant fool.

That was my war. Not a real war, perhaps, but once you witness violence on that scale, it isn't difficult to imagine something worse, and once your mind is capable of doing that, you understand that the worst possibilities of the imagination are the country you live in. Just think it, and chances are it will happen.

That fall, when Gil was put in the untenable position of having to defend the city of Newark against scores of lawsuits from shopkeepers whose businesses had been destroyed in the riot, he quit his post and never worked in government again. Fifteen years later, two months short of his fifty-third birthday, he was dead.

I want to think about Betty, but in order to do that I have to think about Gil, and to think about Gil I have to go back to the beginning. And yet, how much do I know? Not a lot, finally, no more than a few pertinent

facts, gleaned from stories he and Betty told me. The first of three children born to a Newark saloonkeeper who supposedly could have passed as Babe Ruth's double. At some point, Dutch Schultz muscled in on Gil's father and stole the business, how or why I can't say, and a few years after that his father dropped dead of a heart attack. Gil was eleven at the time, and since his father died broke, the only thing he inherited from him was chronic high blood pressure and heart disease – which was first diagnosed at age eighteen and then blossomed into a full-blown coronary when he was just thirty-four, followed by another one two years later. Gil was a tall, powerful man, but he spent his whole life with a death sentence circulating in his veins.

His mother remarried when he was thirteen, and while his stepfather had no objections to raising the two younger kids, he wanted no part of Gil and kicked him out of the house – with the mother's consent. Talk about the unimaginable: to be exiled by your own mother and sent off to live with relatives in Florida for the rest of your childhood.

After high school, he came back north and started college at NYU, strapped for money, forced to work several part-time jobs to keep himself afloat. Once, when he was reminiscing about how hard up he was in those days, he described how he used to go to Ratner's, the old Jewish dairy restaurant on the Lower East Side, sit down at a table, and tell the waiter that he was expecting his girlfriend to show up at any minute. One of the chief lures of the place was the celebrated Ratner's dinner roll. The moment you took your seat, a waiter would come over and plunk down a basket of those rolls in front of you, accompanied by an ample supply of butter. Roll by buttered roll, Gil would eat his way through the basket, glancing at his watch from time to time, pretending to be upset by the lateness of his nonexistent girlfriend. Once the first basket was empty, it would automatically be replaced by a second, and then the second by a third. Finally, the girlfriend would fail to appear, and Gil would leave the restaurant with a disappointed look on his face. After a while, the waiters caught on to the trick, but not before Gil achieved a personal record of twenty-seven free rolls consumed at a single sitting.

Law school, followed by the start of a successful practice and a growing involvement with the Democratic Party. Idealistic, left-wing liberalism, a supporter of Stevenson for the 1960 presidential nomination, Eleanor Roosevelt's escort at the convention in Atlantic City, and later a photograph (which I've owned since Betty's death) of Gil shaking hands with John F. Kennedy during a visit to Newark in 1962 or 1963 as Kennedy

said to him: We've been hearing great things about you. But all that turned sour after the Newark disaster, and once Gil left politics, he and Betty packed it in and moved to California. I didn't see much of them after that, but for the next six or seven years I gathered all was calm. Gil built up his law practice, my sister opened a store in Laguna Beach (kitchenware, table linens, top-quality grinders and gadgets), and even though Gil had to swallow more than twenty pills a day to keep himself alive, whenever they came east for family visits, he looked to be in good shape. Then his health turned. By the mid-seventies, a series of cardiac arrests and other debilitations made work all but impossible for him. I sent them whatever I could whenever I could, and with Betty working full-time to keep them going, Gil now spent most of his days alone in the house, reading books. My big sister and her dying husband, three thousand miles away from me. During those last years, Betty told me, Gil would plant love notes in the drawers of her bureau, hiding them among her bras and slips and panties, and every morning when she woke up and got dressed, she would find another billet-doux declaring that she was the most gorgeous woman in the world. Not bad, finally. Considering what they were up against, not bad at all.

I don't want to think about the end: the cancer, the final stay in the hospital, the obscene sunlight that flooded the cemetery on the morning of the funeral. I've already dredged up enough, but still, I can't let go of this without revisiting one last detail, one last ugly turn. By the time Gil died, Betty was so deeply in debt that paying for a burial plot was a genuine hardship. I was prepared to help, but she had already asked me for money so often that she couldn't bring herself to do it again. Rather than turn to me, she went to her mother-in-law, the infamous woman who had allowed Gil to be thrown out of the house when he was a boy. I can't remember her name (probably because I despised her so much), but by 1980 she was married to her third husband, a retired businessman who happened to be immensely rich. As for husband number two, I don't know if his departure was caused by death or divorce – but no matter. Rich husband number three owned a large family plot in a cemetery somewhere in southern Florida, and my sister managed to talk him into letting Gil be buried there. Less than a year after that, husband number three died, and a large, Balzacian inheritance war broke out between his children and Gil's mother. They took her to court, won their case, and in order for her to come out of the affair with any money at all, one of the conditions of the settlement

required that Gil's remains be removed from the family plot. Imagine. The woman evicts her son from his house when he's a child, and then, for a bag of silver, evicts him from his grave after he's dead. When Betty called to tell me what had happened, she was sobbing. She had held up through Gil's death with a kind of grim, stoic grace, but this was too much for her, and she broke down and lost it completely. By the time Gil was exhumed and buried again, she was no longer the same person.

She lasted another four years. Living alone in a small apartment in the New Jersey suburbs, she grew fat, then very fat, and before long came down with diabetes, clogged arteries, and a thick dossier of other ailments. She held my hand when Oona left me and our catastrophic five-year marriage ended, applauded when Sonia and I got back together, saw her son whenever he and his wife flew in from Chicago, attended family events, watched television from morning to night, could still tell a decent joke when the spirit moved her, and turned into the saddest person I have ever known. One morning in the spring of 1987, her housekeeper called me in a state of quasi-hysteria. She had just entered Betty's apartment, using the key she had been given for her weekly cleaning chores, and had found my sister lying on the bed. I borrowed a car from a neighbor, drove out to New Jersey, and identified her body for the police. The shock of seeing her like that: so still, so far away, so terribly, terribly dead. When they asked me if I wanted the hospital to conduct an autopsy, I told them not to bother. There were only two possibilities. Either her body had given out on her or she had taken pills, and I didn't want to know the answer, for neither one of them would have told the real story. Betty died of a broken heart. Some people laugh when they hear that phrase, but that's because they don't know anything about the world. People die of broken hearts. It happens every day, and it will go on happening to the end of time.

No, I haven't forgotten. The cough sent me spinning into another zone, but I'm back now, and Brick is still with me. Through thick and thin, in spite of that dismal excursion into the past, but how to stop the mind from charging off wherever it wants to go? The mind has a mind of its own. Who said that? Someone, or else I just thought of it myself, not that it makes any difference. Coining phrases in the middle of the night, making up stories in the middle of the night – we're moving on, my little darlings, and agonizing as this mess can be, there's poetry in it, too, as

long as you can find the words to express it, assuming those words exist. Yes, Miriam, life is disappointing. But I also want you to be happy.

Fret not. I'm treading water because I can see the story turning in any one of several directions, and I still haven't decided which path to take. Hope or no hope? Both options are available, and yet neither one is fully satisfying to me. Is there a middle way after such a beginning, after throwing Brick to the wolves and bending the poor sap's mind out of shape? Probably not. Think dark, then, and go down into it, see it through to the end.

The injection has already been given. Brick falls into the bottomless black of unconsciousness, and hours later he opens his eyes and discovers that he's in bed with Flora. It's early morning, seven-thirty or eight o'clock, and as Brick looks at the naked back of his sleeping wife, he wonders if he wasn't right all along, if the time he spent in Wellington wasn't part of some bad, nauseatingly vivid dream. But then, as he shifts his head on the pillow, he feels Virginia's bandage pressing into his cheek, and when he runs his tongue over the ragged edge of his chipped incisor, he has no choice but to face the facts: he was there, and everything that happened to him in that place was real. By now, there is only a single, improbable straw to clutch at: what if the two days that elapsed in Wellington were no more than a blink of the eyes in this world? What if Flora never knew he was gone? That would solve the problem of having to explain where he's been, for Brick knows the truth will be difficult to swallow, especially for a jealous woman like Flora, and yet even if the truth comes out sounding like a lie, he doesn't have the strength or the will to concoct a story that would seem more plausible, something that would appease her suspicions and make her understand that his two-day absence had nothing to do with another woman.

Unfortunately for Brick, the clocks in both worlds tell the same time. Flora knows that he's been missing, and when she turns over in her sleep and inadvertently touches his body, she is instantly jolted awake. His anxieties are stilled by the joy that comes rushing into her intense brown eyes, and suddenly he feels ashamed of himself, mortified that he ever could have doubted her love for him.

Owen? she asks, as if hardly daring to believe what has happened. Is it really you?

Yes, Flora, he says. I'm back.

She throws her arms around him, holding him tightly against her smooth, bare skin. I've been going *crazy,* she says, rolling the *r* with

an emphatic trilling of her tongue. Just *crazy* out of my head. Then, as she sees the bandage on his cheek and the bruises around his lips, her expression changes to one of alarm. What happened? she asks. You're all beat up, baby.

It takes him over an hour to give a full account of his mysterious journey to the other America. The only thing he leaves out is Virginia's last remark about wanting to charm his pants off and fuck his brains out, but that is a minor detail, and he sees no point in riling up Flora with matters that have little bearing on the story. The most daunting part comes toward the end, when he tries to recapitulate his conversation with Frisk. It barely made sense to him at the time, and now that he's back in his own apartment, sitting in the kitchen and drinking coffee with his wife, all that talk about multiple realities and multiple worlds dreamed and imagined by other minds strikes him as out-and-out gibberish. He shakes his head, as if to apologize for making such a botch of it. But the injection was real, he says. And the order to shoot August Brill was real. And if he doesn't carry out the job, he and Flora will be in constant danger.

Until now, Flora has listened in silence, patiently watching her husband tell his absurd and ridiculous story, which she considers to be the largest mound of crap ever built by human hands. Under normal circumstances, she would fly into one of her rages and accuse him of two-timing her, but these are not normal circumstances, and Flora, who knows every one of Brick's faults, who has criticized him countless times during the three years of their marriage, has never once called him a liar, and in the face of the nonsense she has just been told, she finds herself stunned, at a loss for words.

I know it sounds incredible, Brick says. But it's all true, every word of it.

And you expect me to believe you, Owen?

I can hardly believe it myself. But it all happened, Flora, exactly as I told it to you.

Do you think I'm an idiot?

What are you talking about?

Either you think I'm an idiot or you've gone insane.

I don't think you're an idiot, and I haven't gone insane.

You sound like one of those crackpots. You know, one of those guys who's been abducted by aliens. What did the Martians look like, Owen? Did they have a big spaceship?

Stop it, Flora. That isn't funny.

Funny? Who's trying to be funny? I just want to know where you've been.

I've already told you. Don't think I wasn't tempted to make up another story. Some stupid thing about getting mugged and losing my memory for two days. Or being run over by a car. Or falling down the stairs in the subway. Some drek like that. But I decided to tell you the truth.

Maybe that's it. You got beat up, after all. Maybe you've been lying in an alley for the past two days, and you dreamed the whole thing.

Then why would I have this on my arm? A nurse put it there after they gave me the shot. It's the last thing I remember before I opened my eyes this morning.

Brick rolls up his left sleeve, points to a small flesh-colored bandage on his upper arm, and tears it off with his right hand. Look, he says. Do you see this little scab? That's the spot where the needle went into my skin.

It doesn't mean anything, Flora replies, dismissing the one piece of solid evidence Brick can offer. There are a million different ways you could have gotten that scab.

True. But the fact is it happened just one way, the way I told you. From Frisk's needle.

All right, Owen, Flora says, trying not to lose her temper, maybe we should stop talking about it now. You're home. That's the only thing that matters to me. Christ, baby, you don't know what it was like for those two days. I went nuts, I mean one hundred percent nuts. I thought you were dead. I thought you'd left me. I thought you were with another girl. And now you're back. It's like a miracle, and if you want to know the truth, I don't really care what happened. You were gone, and now you're back. End of story, okay?

No, Flora, it's not okay. I'm back, but the story isn't over. I have to go up to Vermont and shoot Brill. I don't know how much time I have, but I can't sit around and wait too long. If I don't do it, they're going to come after us. A bullet for you and a bullet for me. That's what Frisk said, and he wasn't joking.

Brill, Flora grunts, pronouncing the name as if it were an insult in some foreign language. I bet he doesn't even exist.

I saw his picture, remember?

A picture doesn't prove anything.

That's exactly what I said when Frisk showed it to me.

Well, there's one way to find out, isn't there? If he's some kind of

hotshot writer, he has to be on the Internet. Let's turn on my computer and look him up.

Frisk said he won a Pulitzer Prize about twenty years ago. If his name isn't on the list, then we're home free. If it is, then watch out, little Flora. We're in for some big trouble.

It won't be, Owen. Count on it. Brill doesn't exist, so his name can't be there.

But it is there. August Brill, winner of the 1984 Pulitzer Prize for criticism. They look further, and within minutes they have uncovered vast amounts of information, including biographical data from *Who's Who in America* (born NYC, 1935; married Sonia Weil, 1957, divorced 1975; married Oona McNally, 1976, divorced 1981; daughter, Miriam, born 1960; B.A. from Columbia, 1957; honorary doctorates from Williams College and the Pratt Institute; member of the American Academy of Arts and Sciences; author of more than 1,500 articles, reviews, and columns for magazines and newspapers; book editor of the *Boston Globe*, 1972–1991), a Web site containing over four hundred of his pieces written between 1962 and 2003, as well as a number of photographs taken of Brill in his thirties, forties, and fifties, leaving no doubt that these are younger versions of the old man in the wheelchair parked in front of the white clapboard house in Vermont.

Brick and Flora are sitting side by side at a small desk in the bedroom, their eyes fixed on the screen in front of them, too afraid to look at each other as they watch their hopes turn to dust. At last, Flora switches off the laptop and says in a low, quavering voice: I guess I was wrong, huh?

Brick stands up and begins pacing around the room. Do you believe me now? he asks. This Brill, this goddamn August Brill . . . I'd never even heard of him until yesterday. How could I have made it up? I'm not smart enough to have thought of half the things I've told you, Flora. I'm just a guy who performs magic tricks for little kids. I don't read books, I don't know anything about book critics, and I'm not interested in politics. Don't ask me how, but I've just come from a place that's in the middle of a civil war. And now I have to kill a man.

He sits down on the edge of the bed, overwhelmed by the ferocity of his situation, by the sheer injustice of what has happened to him. Watching Brick with worried eyes, Flora walks across the room and sits down beside him. She puts her arms around her husband, leans her head against his shoulder, and says: You're not going to kill anyone.

I have to, Brick answers, staring down at the floor.

I don't know what to think or not to think, Owen, but I'm telling you now, you're not going to kill anyone. You're going to leave that man alone.

I can't.

Why do you think I married you? Because you're a sweet person, my love, a kind and honest person. I didn't marry a killer. I married you, my funny Owen Brick, and I'm not going to stand by and let you murder someone and spend the rest of your life in prison.

I'm not saying I want to do it. I just don't have any choice.

Don't talk like that. Everyone has a choice. And besides, what makes you think you'd be able to go through with it? Can you actually see yourself walking into that man's house, pointing a gun at his head, and shooting him in cold blood? Not in a hundred years, Owen. It's just not in you to do something like that. Thank God.

Brick knows that Flora is right. He could never kill an innocent stranger, not even if his own life depended on it – which it probably does. He lets out a long, shuddering breath, then runs his hand through Flora's hair and says: So what am I supposed to do?

Nothing.

What do you mean, *nothing*?

We start living again. You do your job, I do mine. We eat and sleep and pay the bills. We wash the dishes and vacuum the floor. We make a baby together. You put me in the bath and shampoo my hair. I rub your back. You learn new tricks. We visit your parents and listen to your mother complain about her health. We go on, baby, and live our little life. That's what I'm talking about. Nothing.

A month goes by. In the first week after Brick's return, Flora misses her period, and a home pregnancy test brings them the news that if all goes well, they will become parents by the following January. They celebrate the positive test result by going out to a fashionable Manhattan restaurant that is far beyond their means, consume an entire bottle of French champagne before placing their orders, and then gorge themselves on a gargantuan porterhouse for two, which Flora claims is almost as good as the meat in Argentina. The next day, on his second visit to the dentist, a cap is put on Brick's left incisor, and he resumes his career as the Great Zavello. Bolting around the city in his battered yellow Mazda, he dons his cape and performs at elementary school assemblies, retirement homes, community centers, and private parties, pulling doves and rabbits out of his top hat, making silk scarves disappear, snatching eggs

out of thin air, and transforming dull newspapers into colorful bouquets of pansies, tulips, and roses. Flora, who left her catering job two years earlier and is now working as a receptionist at a doctor's office on Park Avenue, asks her boss for a twenty-dollar raise and is turned down. She explodes in a tantrum of injured pride and storms out of the building, but when she talks it over with Brick that evening, he persuades her to return the next morning and apologize to Dr. Sontag, which she does, and because the doctor doesn't want to lose such a competent, hard-working employee, he rewards her with a ten-dollar increase in salary, which is all she was hoping for in the first place. Money is nevertheless an issue, and with a child now on the way, Brick and Flora wonder if they will be able to feed that third mouth with what they are earning now. On a grim Sunday afternoon toward the end of the month, they even discuss the possibility of Brick going to work for his cousin Ralph, who owns a high-powered real estate agency in Park Slope. Magic would have to become a part-time occupation, little more than a hobby to be pursued on his days off, and Brick is reluctant to take such a drastic step, vowing to land some higher-paying jobs that will give them the breathing room they need. Meanwhile, he has not forgotten his visit to the other America. Wellington is still burning inside him, and not a day goes by when he doesn't think of Tobak, Molly Wald, Duke Rothstein, Frisk, and, most disturbingly of all, Virginia Blaine. He can't help himself. Flora has been so much more tender with him since his return, metamorphosing herself into the loving companion he always longed for, and while there is no question that he loves her back, Virginia is always there, lurking in a corner of his mind, gently putting the bandage on his face and telling him how much she wanted to charm his pants off. By way of compensation, perhaps, he begins reading Brill's old reviews on the Internet – always in secret, of course, since he doesn't want Flora to know that he's still thinking about the man he was instructed to kill – and every time he comes across an article about a book that sounds interesting, he checks it out of the library. He used to spend his evenings watching television with Flora on a sofa in the living room. Now he lies on the bed and reads books. So far, his most important discoveries have been Chekhov, Calvino, and Camus.

In this way Brick and Flora swim along in their conjugal nothing, the little life she lured him back to with the good sense of a woman who doesn't believe in other worlds, who knows there is only this world and that numbing routines and brief squabbles and financial worries are an

essential part of it, that in spite of the aches and boredoms and disappointments, living in this world is the closest we will ever come to seeing paradise. After the horrific hours he spent in Wellington, Brick too wants only this, the jumbled grind of New York, the naked body of his little Floratina, his work as the Great Zavello, his unborn child growing invisibly as the days pass, and yet deep inside himself he knows that he has been contaminated by his visit to the other world and that sooner or later everything will come to an end. He contemplates driving up to Vermont and talking to Brill. Would it be possible to convince the old man to stop thinking about his story? He tries to imagine the conversation, tries to summon the words he would use to present his argument, but all he ever sees is Brill laughing at him, the incredulous laughter of a man who would take him for an imbecile, a mental defective, and promptly throw him out of the house. So Brick does nothing, and precisely one month after his return from Wellington, on the evening of May twenty-first, as he sits in the living room with Flora, demonstrating a new card trick to his laughing wife, someone knocks on the door. Without having to think about it, Brick already knows what has happened. He tells Flora not to open the door, to run into the bedroom and go down the fire escape as fast as she can, but willful, independent Flora, unaware of the fix they're in, scoffs at his panicked instructions and does exactly what he tells her not to do. Bounding off the sofa before he can grab her arm, she dances to the door with a mocking pirouette and yanks it open. Two men are standing on the threshold, Lou Frisk and Duke Rothstein, and since each one is holding a revolver in his hand and pointing it at Flora, Brick doesn't move from his spot on the sofa. Theoretically, he can still try to escape, but the moment he stood up, the mother of his child would be dead.

Who the fuck are you? Flora says, in a shrill, angry voice.

Sit down next to your husband, Frisk replies, waving his gun in the direction of the sofa. We have some business to discuss with him.

Turning to Brick with an anguished look on her face, Flora says: What's going on, baby?

Come here, Brick answers, patting the sofa with his right hand. Those guns aren't toys, and you have to do what they say.

For once, Flora doesn't resist, and as the two men enter the apartment and shut the door, she walks over to the sofa and sits down beside her husband.

These are my friends, Brick says to her. Duke Rothstein and Lou Frisk. Remember when I told you about them? Well, here they are.

Jesus holy Christ, Flora mutters, by now sick to death with fear.

Frisk and Rothstein settle into two chairs opposite the sofa. The cards that were used to demonstrate the trick are strewn across the surface of the coffee table in front of them. Taking hold of one of the cards and turning it over, Frisk says: I'm glad you remember us, Owen. We were beginning to have our doubts.

Don't worry, Brick says. I never forget a face.

How's the tooth? Rothstein asks, breaking into what looks like a cross between a grimace and a smile.

Much better, thank you, Brick says. I went to the dentist, and he put a cap on it.

I'm sorry I hit you so hard. But orders are orders, and I had to do my job. Scare tactics. I guess they didn't work too well, did they?

Have you ever had a gun pointed at you? Frisk asks.

Believe it or not, Brick says, this is the first time.

You seem to be handling it pretty well.

I've played it out in my head so often, I feel as if it's already happened.

Which means you've been expecting us.

Of course I've been expecting you. The only surprise is that you didn't show up sooner.

We figured we'd give you a month. It's a tough assignment, and it seemed only fair to give you a little time to work yourself up to it. But the month is over now, and we still haven't seen any results. Do you want to explain yourself?

I can't do it. That's all. I just can't do it.

While you've been twiddling your thumbs in Jackson Heights, the war has gone from bad to worse. The Federals launched a spring offensive, and nearly every town on the East Coast has been under attack. Operation Unity, they call it. A million and a half more dead while you sit here wrestling with your conscience. The Twin Cities were invaded three weeks ago, and half of Minnesota is under Federal control again. Huge parts of Idaho, Wyoming, and Nebraska have been turned into prison camps. Shall I go on?

No, no, I get the picture.

You have to do it, Brick.

I'm sorry. I just can't.

You remember the consequences, don't you?

Isn't that why you're here?

Not yet. We're giving you a deadline. One week from today. If Brill

isn't taken care of by midnight on the twenty-eighth, Duke and I will be back, and next time our guns will be loaded. Do you hear me, Corporal? One week from today, or else you and your wife die for nothing.

I don't know what time it is. The hands on the alarm clock aren't illuminated, and I'm not about to switch on the lamp again and subject myself to the blinding rays of the bulb. I keep intending to ask Miriam to buy me one of those glow-in-the-dark jobs, but every time I wake up in the morning, I forget. The light erases the thought, and I don't remember it again until I'm back in bed, lying awake as I am now, staring up at the invisible ceiling in my invisible room. I can't be certain, but I would guess it's somewhere between one-thirty and two o'clock. Inching along, inching along . . .

The Web site was Miriam's idea. If I had known what she was up to, I would have told her not to waste her time, but she kept it a secret from me (in collusion with her mother, who had saved nearly every scrap of writing I'd ever published), and when she came to New York for my seventieth-birthday dinner, she took me into my study, turned on my laptop, and showed me what she had done. The articles were hardly worth the trouble, but the thought of my daughter spending untold hours typing up all those ancient pieces of mine – *for posterity*, as she put it – more or less undid me, and I didn't know what to say. My usual impulse is to deflect emotional scenes with a dry quip or wiseacre remark, but that night I simply put my arms around Miriam and said nothing. Sonia cried, of course. She always cried when she was happy, but on that occasion her tears were especially poignant and terrible to me, since her cancer had been detected only three days earlier and the prognosis was cloudy, touch-and-go at best. No one said a word about it, but all three of us knew that she might not be around for my next birthday. As it turned out, a year was too much to hope for.

I shouldn't be doing this. I promised myself not to fall into the trap of Sonia-thoughts and Sonia-memories, not to let myself go. I can't afford to break down now and sink into a despond of grief and self-recrimination. I might start howling and wake the girls upstairs – or else spend the next several hours thinking of ever more artful and devious ways to kill myself. That task has been reserved for Brick, the protagonist of tonight's story. Perhaps that explains why he and Flora turn on her computer and look at Miriam's Web site. It seems important that my hero should get to know me a bit, to learn what kind of man he's up against, and now

that he's dipped into some of the books I've recommended, we've finally begun to establish a bond. It's turning into a rather complicated jig, I suppose, but the fact is that the Brill character wasn't in my original plan. The mind that created the war was going to belong to someone else, another invented character, as unreal as Brick and Flora and Tobak and all the rest, but the longer I went on, the more I understood how badly I was fooling myself. The story is about a man who must kill the person who created him, and why pretend that I am not that person? By putting myself into the story, the story becomes real. Or else I become unreal, yet one more figment of my own imagination. Either way, the effect is more satisfying, more in harmony with my mood – which is dark, my little ones, as dark as the obsidian night that surrounds me.

I'm blathering on, letting my thoughts fly helter-skelter to keep Sonia at bay, but in spite of my efforts, she's still there, the ever-present absent one, who spent so many nights in this bed with me, now lying in a grave in the Cimetière Montparnasse, my French wife of eighteen years, and then nine years apart, and then twenty-one more years together, thirty-nine years in all, forty-one counting the two years before our wedding, more than half my life, much more than half, and nothing left now but boxes of photographs and seven scratchy LPs, the recordings she made in the sixties and seventies, Schubert, Mozart, Bach, and the chance to listen to her voice again, that small but beautiful voice, so drenched in feeling, so much the essence of who she was. Photographs . . . and music . . . and Miriam. She left me our child, too, that mustn't be overlooked, the child who is no longer a child, and how strange to think that I'd be lost without her now, no doubt drunk every night, if not dead or on life support in some hospital. When she asked me to move in with her after the accident, I politely turned her down, explaining that she had enough burdens already without adding me to the list. She took hold of my hand and said: No, Dad, you don't get it. I need you. I'm so damned lonely in that house, I don't know how much longer I can take it. I need someone to talk to. I need someone to look at, to be there at dinner, to hold me every once in a while and tell me that I'm not an awful person.

*Awful person* must have come from Richard, an epithet that shot out of his mouth during an ugly row at the end of their marriage. People say the worst things in the flush of anger, and it pains me that Miriam allowed those words to stick to her like some ultimate judgment of her character, a condemnation of who and what she is. There are depths of goodness in that girl, the same kind of self-punishing goodness that

Noriko embodies in the film, and because of that, almost inevitably, even if Richard was the one who jumped ship, she continues to fault herself for what happened. I don't know if I've been of much help to her, but at least she isn't alone anymore. We were settling into a fairly comfortable routine before Titus was killed, and I just want you to remember this, Miriam: when Katya was in trouble, she didn't go to her father, she went to you.

By now, Frisk and Rothstein have left the apartment. The moment the door shuts behind them, Flora begins swearing in Spanish, reeling off a long spate of invective that Brick is unable to follow, since his knowledge of the language is limited to just a few words, principally *hello* and *goodbye*, and yet he doesn't interrupt her, withdrawing into himself during those thirty seconds of incomprehension to ponder the dilemma that is facing them and think of what to do next. He finds it odd, but all fear seems to have left him, and while just minutes earlier he was convinced that he and Flora were about to be killed, instead of shaking and trembling in the aftermath of that unexpected reprieve, a great calm has settled over him. He saw his death in the form of Frisk's gun, and even if that gun is no longer there, his death is still with him – as if it were the only thing that belonged to him now, as if whatever life remains in him has already been stolen by that death. And if Brick is doomed, then the first thing to be done is to protect Flora by sending her as far away from him as possible.

Brick is calm, but it seems to have no effect on his wife, who is growing more and more agitated.

What are we going to do? she says. My God, Owen, we can't just sit around here and wait for them to come back. I don't want to die. It's too stupid to die when you're twenty-seven years old. I don't know . . . maybe we can run away and hide somewhere.

It wouldn't do any good. Wherever we went, they're bound to track us down.

Then maybe you have to kill that old man, after all.

We've already been through that. You were against it, remember?

I didn't know anything then. Now I know.

I don't see how that makes any difference. I can't do it, and even if I could, I'd only wind up in prison.

Who says you'll be caught? If you think of a good plan, maybe you'll get away with it.

Leave it alone, Flora. You don't want me to do it any more than I do.

Okay. Then we hire someone to do it for you.

Stop it. We're not killing anyone. Do you understand me?

What then? If we don't do something, we'll be dead one week from tonight.

I'm going to send you away. That's the first step. Back to your mother in Buenos Aires.

But you just said they'd find us wherever we go.

They're not interested in you. I'm the one they're after, and once we're apart, they're not going to bother with you.

What are you saying, Owen?

Just that I want you to be safe.

And what about you?

Don't worry. I'll think of something. I'm not going to let myself be killed by those two maniacs, I promise. You'll go down and visit your mother for a while, and when you come back, I'll be waiting for you in this apartment. Understood?

I don't like it, Owen.

You don't have to like it. You just have to do it. For me.

That evening they book a round-trip flight to Buenos Aires, and the next morning Brick drives Flora to the airport. He knows it is the last time he will ever see her, but he struggles to maintain his composure and gives no hint of the anguish roiling inside him. As he kisses her good-bye at the security entrance, surrounded by throngs of travelers and uniformed airport personnel, Flora suddenly begins to cry. Brick gathers her into his arms and strokes the top of her head, but now that he can feel her body convulsing against his, and now that her tears are seeping through his shirt and dampening his skin, he no longer knows what to say.

Don't make me go, Flora begs.

No tears, he whispers back to her. It's only ten days. By the time you come home, everything will be finished.

And so it will, he thinks, as he climbs into his car and drives home to Jackson Heights from the airport. At that point, he has every intention of keeping his word: to avoid another encounter with Rothstein and Frisk, to be waiting for Flora in the apartment when she returns – but that doesn't mean he plans on being alive.

*So now it's a suicide,* he remembers saying to Frisk.

*In a roundabout way, yes.*

Brick is approaching his thirtieth birthday, and not once in his life has he ever thought of killing himself. Now it has become his sole preoccupation, and for the next two days he sits in the apartment trying to figure out the most painless and efficient method of leaving this world. He considers buying a gun and shooting himself in the head. He considers poison. He considers slitting his wrists. Yes, he says to himself, that's the old standard, isn't it? Drink half a bottle of vodka, pour twenty or thirty sleeping pills down your throat, slip into a warm tub, and then slash your veins with a carving knife. Rumor has it that you barely feel a thing.

The conundrum is that there are still five more days to go, and with each day that passes, the calm and certainty that descended over his mind as he looked into the barrel of Frisk's gun loosen their hold on him by several more degrees. Death was a foregone conclusion back then, a mere formality under the circumstances, but as his calm gradually turns into disquiet, and his certainty melts away into doubt, he tries to imagine the vodka and the pills, the warm bath and the blade of the knife, and suddenly the old fear returns, and once that happens, he understands that his resolve has vanished, that he will never find the courage to go through with it.

How much time has passed by then? Four days – no, five days – which means that only forty-eight hours are left. Brick has yet to stir from his apartment and venture outside. He has canceled all his Great Zavello performances for the week, claiming to be down with the flu, and has unplugged the phone from the wall. He suspects that Flora has been trying to reach him, but he can't bring himself to talk to her just now, knowing that the sound of her voice would upset him so much that he might lose control and start babbling inanities to her or, worse, start crying, which would only deepen her alarm. Nevertheless, on the morning of May 27, he finally shaves, showers, and puts on a fresh set of clothes. Sunlight is pouring through the windows, the beckoning radiance of the New York spring, and he decides that a walk in the air might do him some good. If his mind has failed to solve his problems for him, perhaps he will find the answer in his feet.

The instant he steps onto the sidewalk, however, he hears someone calling his name. It's a woman's voice, and because no other pedestrians are passing by at that moment, Brick is at a loss to identify where the voice is coming from. He looks around, the voice calls to him again, and behold, there is Virginia Blaine, sitting behind the wheel of a car parked

directly across the street. In spite of himself, Brick is inordinately glad to see her, but as he steps down from the curb and walks over to the woman who has haunted him for the past month, a wave of apprehension flutters through him. By the time he reaches the white Mercedes sedan, he can feel his pulse pounding inside his head.

Good morning, Owen, Virginia says. Do you have a minute?

I wasn't expecting to see you again, Brick replies, looking closely at her beautiful face, which is even more beautiful than he remembered, and her dark brown hair, which is shorter than it was the last time he saw her, and her delicate mouth with the red lipstick, and her blue eyes with the long lashes, and her thin, graceful hands resting on the wheel of the car.

I hope I'm not interrupting anything, she says.

Not at all. I was just going out for a walk.

Good. Let's make it a drive instead, okay?

Where to?

I'll tell you later. We have a lot to talk about first. By the time we get to where we're going, you'll understand why I took you there.

Brick hesitates, still uncertain whether Virginia can be trusted or not, but then he realizes that he doesn't care, that in all probability he's a dead man no matter what he does. If these are the last hours of his life, he thinks, then better to spend them with her than to wait it out alone.

So off they go into the brilliant May morning, leaving New York behind them and traveling along the southern rim of Connecticut on I-95, then veering onto 395 just before New London and heading north at seventy miles an hour. Brick pays little attention to the passing landscape, choosing instead to keep his eyes on Virginia, who is wearing a pale blue cashmere sweater and a pair of white linen slacks, sitting in her brown leather seat with an air of such confidence and self-sufficiency that he is reminded of her younger self, the one that used to leave him stammering whenever he tried to talk to her. Things are different now, he tells himself. He grew up, and he isn't intimidated by her anymore. He's a bit wary, perhaps, but not of Virginia the woman – rather, of the *little cog in the big machine*, the person in cahoots with Frisk.

You're looking a lot better, Owen, she begins. No more cuts, no more bandages. And I see you've had your tooth fixed. The miracles of dentistry, huh? From beat-up boxer to Mr. Handsome again.

The subject doesn't interest Brick, and instead of making small talk about the condition of his face, he comes right to the point. Did Frisk give you the injection? he asks.

It doesn't matter how I got here, she says. The important thing is why I came.

To finish me off, I suppose.

You're wrong. I came because I was feeling guilty. I got you into this mess, and now I want to try to get you out of it.

But you're Frisk's girl. If you work for him, then you're a part of it, too.

But I don't work for him. That's only a cover.

What does that mean?

Do I have to spell it out?

You're a double agent?

Sort of.

You're not going to tell me you're with the Federals.

Of course not. I hate those murdering bastards.

Then who is it?

Patience, Owen. You have to give me some time. First things first, okay?

All right. I'm listening.

Yes, I was the one who suggested you for the job. But I didn't know what it was. Something big, they said, something vital to the outcome of the war, but they never gave me any details. I wasn't told until you were already on the other side. I swear, I had no idea they were going to order you to kill someone. And then, even after I found out, I had no idea Frisk was going to threaten to kill you if you didn't carry out the job. I only learned about that last night. That's why I came. Because I wanted to help.

I don't believe a word you're saying.

Why should you? If I were in your place, I wouldn't believe me either. But it's the truth.

The funny thing is, Virginia, it doesn't bother me anymore. When you lie, I mean. I like you too much to get worked up about it. You might be a fake, you might even be the person who winds up killing me, but I'll never stop liking you.

I like you, too, Owen.

You're a strange person. Did anyone ever tell you that?

All the time. Ever since I was a little girl.

How long has it been since you've been back on this side?

Fifteen years. This is my first trip. It wasn't even possible until about three months ago. You were the first one to go back and forth. Did you know that?

No one ever told me anything.

It's like stepping into a dream, isn't it? The same place, but entirely different. America without war. It's hard to digest. You get so used to the fighting, it kind of creeps into your bones, and after a while, you can't imagine a world without it.

America's at war, all right. We're just not fighting it here. Not yet, anyway.

How's your wife, Owen? It's stupid of me, but I can't remember her name.

Flora.

That's right, Flora. Do you want to call and let her know you'll be gone for a couple of days?

She isn't in New York. I sent her back to her mother in Argentina.

Smart thinking. You did the right thing.

She's pregnant, by the way. I thought you'd like to know that.

Good work, kid. Congratulations.

Flora's pregnant, I love her more than ever, I'd rather cut off my right arm than do anything to hurt her, and still, the only thing I really want right now is to go to bed with you. Does that make any sense?

Absolutely.

One last roll in the hay.

Don't talk like that. You're not going to die, Owen.

Well, what do you think? Does the idea appeal to you?

Do you remember what I said the last time you saw me?

How could I forget?

Then you already have your answer, don't you?

They cross the border into Massachusetts, and a few minutes later they stop to fill the tank with gas, visit the ladies' and men's, and eat a pair of wretched, microwaved hot dogs on soggy buns, which they wash down with gulps of bottled water. As they walk back to the car, Brick takes Virginia in his arms and kisses her, driving his tongue deep into her mouth. It is a delicious moment for him, fulfilling the dream of half a lifetime, but one also marked by shame and regret, for this small prelude to further pleasures with his old love is the first time he has touched another woman since marrying Flora. But Brick, who is nothing less than a soldier now, a man engaged in fighting a war, justifies his infidelity by reminding himself that he could well be dead by tomorrow.

Once they hit the highway again, he turns to Virginia and asks her the

question he's been putting off for more than two hours: where are they going?

Two places, she says. The first one today, the next one tomorrow.

Well, that's a start, I guess. You wouldn't care to be a little more specific, would you?

I can't tell you about the first stop, because I want that to be a surprise. But tomorrow we're going to Vermont.

Vermont . . . That means Brill. You're taking me to Brill.

You catch on fast, Owen.

It won't do any good, Virginia. I've thought about going there a dozen times, but I have no idea what to say to him.

Just ask him to stop.

He'll never listen to me.

How do you know unless you try?

Because I do, that's all.

You're forgetting that I'll be with you.

What difference does that make?

I've already told you that I don't really work for Frisk. Who do you think I take my orders from?

How should I know?

Come on, Corporal. Think.

Not Brill.

Yes, Brill.

That's impossible. He's on this side, and you're on the other side. There's no way for you to communicate.

Did you ever hear of a telephone?

The phones don't work. I already tried to call when I was in Wellington. I dialed my apartment in Queens, and they said the number was out of service.

There are phones and there are phones, my friend. Given his part in all this, do you think Brill would have one that didn't work?

So you talk to him.

Constantly.

But you've never met.

No. Tomorrow is the big day.

And what about now? Why not go to him now?

Because the appointment is for tomorrow. And until then, you and I have other plans.

Your surprise . . .

Exactly.

How much longer to go?

Less than half an hour. In about two minutes, I'm going to ask you to close your eyes. You can open them again after we get there.

Brick plays along with the game, gladly submitting to Virginia's puerile whims, and for the last minutes of the journey he sits in his seat without saying a word, trying to guess what prank she has in store for him. If he were better versed in geography, he might have found a solution long before their arrival, but Brick has no more than a fuzzy understanding of maps, and since he has never actually set foot in Worcester, Massachusetts (having imagined himself there only in a dream), when the car stops and Virginia tells him to open his eyes, he is convinced he's back in Wellington. The car has pulled up in front of the suburban house they entered last month, the same brick-and-stucco manor with the luxuriant front lawn, the flower beds, and the tall, blooming bushes. When he glances down the street, however, all the neighboring houses are intact. No charred walls, no collapsed roofs, no broken windows. The war has not touched the block, and as Brick slowly turns around in a circle, trying to absorb the familiar but altered setting, the illusion finally bursts, and he knows where he is. Not Wellington but Worcester, the former name of the city in the other world.

Isn't it wonderful? Virginia says, raising her arms and gesturing to the undamaged houses. Her eyes have lit up, and a smile is spreading across her face. This is the way it used to be, Owen. Before the guns . . . before the attacks . . . before Brill started tearing everything apart. I never thought I'd live to see it again.

Let Virginia Blaine have her brief moment of joy. Let Owen Brick forget his little Flora and find comfort in the arms of Virginia Blaine. Let the man and the woman who met as children take mutual pleasure in their adult bodies. Let them climb into bed together and do what they will. Let them eat. Let them drink. Let them return to the bed and do what they will to every inch and orifice of their grown-up bodies. Life goes on, after all, even under the most painful circumstances, goes on until the end, and then it stops. And these lives will stop, since they must stop, since neither one of them can ever make it to Vermont to talk to Brill, for Brill might weaken then and give up, and Brill can never give up, since he must go on telling his story, the story of the war in that other world, which is also this world, and he can't allow anyone or anything to stop him.

It's the middle of the night. Virginia is lying under the covers asleep,

her sated flesh expanding and contracting as the cool air enters and exits her lungs, dreaming God knows what in the dim moonlight that filters through the half-open window. Brick is on his side, his body curled around hers, one hand cupping her left breast, the other hand poised on the rounded area where her hip and buttock merge, but the corporal is restless, unaccountably wakeful, and after struggling to fall asleep for close to an hour, he slips out of bed to go downstairs and pour himself a drink, wondering if a shot of whiskey might not quell the tremors that are rising within him as he contemplates tomorrow's meeting with the old man. Dressed in the dead husband's terry-cloth robe, he walks into the kitchen and turns on the light. Confronted by the dazzle of that elegant space, with its sleek surfaces and costly appliances, Brick begins to think about Virginia's marriage. Her husband must have been a good deal older than she was, he muses, a sharp operator with the wherewithal to afford a house like this one, and because Virginia has yet to say a word about him (except to mention that he was rich), the not-so-well-off magician from Queens asks himself if she cared about her departed spouse or simply married him for his money. The idle thoughts of an insomniac, searching the cupboards for a clean glass and a bottle of scotch: the endless banalities that flit through the mind as one notion mutates into the next. So it goes with all of us, young and old, rich and poor, and then an unexpected event comes crashing down on us to jolt us out of our torpor.

Brick hears the low-flying planes in the distance, then the noise of a helicopter engine, and an instant after that, the keening blast of an explosion. The windows in the kitchen shatter to bits, the floor shakes under his bare feet and then begins to tilt, as if the entire foundation of the house were shifting position, and when Brick runs into the front hall to mount the stairs and check on Virginia, he is met by large, writhing spears of flame. Wooden shards and slate roof tiles are falling down from above. Brick turns his eyes upward, and after several seconds of confusion he understands that he is looking at the night sky through clouds of billowing smoke. The top half of the house is gone, which means that Virginia is also gone, and while he knows it will serve no purpose, he desperately wants to mount the stairs and look for her body. But the stairs are on fire now, and he will burn to death if he gets any closer.

He runs outside onto the lawn, and all around him howling neighbors are pouring from their houses into the night. A contingent of Federal troops has massed in the middle of the street, fifty or sixty helmeted men,

all of them armed with machine guns. Brick raises his hands in a gesture of surrender, but it doesn't do him any good. The first bullet hits him in the leg, and he falls down, clutching the wound as blood spurts onto his fingers. Before he can inspect the damage and see how badly he is hurt, a second bullet goes straight through his right eye and out the back of his head. And that is the end of Owen Brick, who leaves the world in silence, with no chance to say a last word or think a last thought.

Meanwhile, seventy-five miles to the northwest, in a white wooden house in southern Vermont, August Brill is awake, lying in bed and staring into the dark. And the war goes on.

Does it have to end that way? Yes, probably yes, although it wouldn't be difficult to think of a less brutal outcome. But what would be the point? My subject tonight is war, and now that war has entered this house, I feel I would be insulting Titus and Katya if I softened the blow. Peace on earth, good will toward men. Piss on earth, good will toward none. This is the heart of it, the black center of the dead of night, a good four hours still to burn and all hope for sleep utterly smashed. The only solution is to leave Brick behind me, make sure that he gets a decent burial, and then come up with another story. Something low to the ground this time, a counterweight to the fantastical machine I've just built. Giordano Bruno and the theory of infinite worlds. Provocative stuff, yes, but there are other stones to be unearthed as well.

War stories. Let your guard down for a moment, and they come rushing in on you, one by one by one . . .

The last time Sonia and I went to Europe together, we wound up in Brussels for a couple of days to attend a reunion of some distant branch of her family. One afternoon, we had lunch with a second cousin of hers, an old gent pushing eighty, a former publisher who had grown up in Belgium and later moved to France, an affable, well-read person who spoke in complex, highly articulated paragraphs, a walking book in the shape of a man. The restaurant was in a narrow arcade somewhere in the center of the city, and before we went inside to have our meal, he took us to a small courtyard at the end of the walkway to show us a fountain and a bronze statue of a water nymph sitting in the pool. It wasn't an especially brilliant work – a somewhat smaller than life-size rendering of a nude girl in her mid-to-late teens – but in spite of its clumsiness, there

were touching qualities about it as well, something about the curve of the girl's back, I think, or else the tininess of her breasts and her slender hips, or else simply the smallish scale of the piece in general. As we stood there examining it, Jean-Luc told us that the model had grown up to become his high school literature teacher and was only seventeen when she posed for the artist. We turned around and went into the restaurant, and over lunch he told us more about his connection to that woman. She was the one who made him fall in love with books, he said, because when he was her student he developed an intense crush on her, and that love wound up changing the direction of his life. When the Germans occupied Belgium in 1940, Jean-Luc was just fifteen, but he joined an underground resistance cell as a courier, attending school by day and running messages at night. His teacher joined the resistance as well, and one morning in 1942 the Germans marched into the lycée and arrested her. Shortly after that, Jean-Luc's cell was infiltrated and destroyed. He had to go into hiding, he said, and for the last eighteen months of the war he lived alone in an attic and did nothing but read books – all books, every book, from the ancient Greeks to the Renaissance to the twentieth century, consuming novels and plays, poetry and philosophy, understanding that he never could have done this without the influence of his teacher, who had been arrested before his eyes and for whom he prayed every night. When the war finally ended, he learned that she hadn't made it home from the camp, but no one could tell him how or when she had died. She had been blotted out, expunged from the face of the earth, and not a single person knew what had happened to her.

Some years after that (late forties? early fifties?), he was eating alone in a restaurant in Brussels and overheard two men talking at the next table. One of them had spent time in a concentration camp during the war, and as he told the other man a story about one of his fellow inmates, Jean-Luc became more and more convinced that he was referring to his teacher, the little water nymph sitting in the fountain at the end of the arcade. All the details seemed to fit: a Belgian girl in her twenties, red hair, small body, extremely beautiful, a left-wing troublemaker who had defied an order from one of the camp guards. To set an example for the other prisoners and demonstrate what happens to people who disobey the guards, the commandant decided to execute her in public, with the entire population of the camp on hand to witness the killing. Jean-Luc was expecting the man to say that they hanged her or stood her up against a wall and shot her, but it turned out that the commandant

had something more traditional in mind, a method that had gone out of fashion several centuries earlier. Jean-Luc couldn't look at us when he spoke the words. He turned his head away and looked out the window, as if the execution were taking place just outside the restaurant, and in a quiet voice suddenly filled with emotion, he said: She was drawn and quartered. With long chains attached to both her wrists and both her ankles, she was led into the yard, made to stand at attention as the chains were attached to four jeeps pointing in four different directions, and then the commandant gave the order for the drivers to start their engines. According to the man at the next table, the woman didn't cry out, didn't make a sound as one limb after another was pulled off her body. Is such a thing possible? Jean-Luc was tempted to talk to the man, he said, but then he realized that he wasn't capable of talking. Fighting back tears, he stood up, tossed some money on the table, and left the restaurant.

Sonia and I returned to Paris, and within forty-eight hours I heard two more stories that hit me hard – not with the sickening violence of Jean-Luc's story, but hard enough to have left an enduring impact. The first one came from Alec Foyle, a British journalist who flew in from London to have dinner with us one night. Alec is in his late forties, a onetime boyfriend of Miriam's, and even if it's all water under the bridge now, Sonia and I were both a little surprised when our daughter chose Richard over him. We had been out of contact for a number of years, and there was a lot of catching up to do, which led to one of those hectic conversations that careen abruptly from one subject to the next. At a certain point we started talking about families, and Alec told us about a recent conversation he'd had with a friend, a woman who covered the arts for the *Independent* or the *Guardian*, I forget which. He said to her: At one time or another, every family lives through extraordinary events – horrendous crimes, floods and earthquakes, bizarre accidents, miraculous strokes of luck, and there isn't a family in the world without secrets and skeletons, trunkfuls of hidden material that would make your jaw drop if the lid were ever opened. His friend disagreed with him. It's true for many families, she said, maybe for most families, but not all. Her family, for example. She couldn't think of a single interesting thing that had ever happened to any of them, not one exceptional event. Impossible, Alec said. Just concentrate for a moment, and you're bound to come up with something. So his friend thought for a while, and eventually she said: Well, maybe there's one thing. My grandmother told it to me not long

before she died, and I suppose it's fairly unusual.

Alec smiled at us from across the table. Unusual, he said. My friend wouldn't have been born if this thing hadn't happened, and she called it *unusual*. As far as I'm concerned, it's bloody astonishing.

His friend's grandmother was born in Berlin in the early twenties, and when the Nazis took power in 1933, her Jewish family reacted in the same way so many others did: they believed that Hitler was nothing more than a passing upstart and made no effort to leave Germany. Even as conditions worsened, they went on hoping for the best and refused to budge. One day, when the grandmother was seventeen or eighteen, her parents received a letter signed by someone claiming to be a captain in the SS. Alec didn't mention what year it was, but 1938 would be a reasonable assumption, I think, perhaps a little earlier. According to Alec's friend, the letter read as follows: You don't know me, but I am well aware of you and your children. I could be court-martialed for writing this, but I feel it is my duty to warn you that you are in great danger. If you don't act soon, you will all be arrested and sent to a camp. Trust me, this is not idle speculation. I am willing to furnish you with exit visas that will allow you to escape to another country, but in exchange for my help, you must do me one important favor. I have fallen in love with your daughter. I have been watching her for some time now, and although we have never spoken, this love is unconditional. She is the person I have dreamed of all my life, and if this were a different world and we were ruled by different laws, I would propose marriage tomorrow. This is all I am asking: next Wednesday, at ten o'clock in the morning, your daughter will go to the park across the street from your house, sit down on her favorite bench, and stay there for two hours. I promise not to touch her, not to approach her, not to address a single word to her. I will remain hidden for the full two hours. At noon, she can stand up and return to your house. The reason for this request is no doubt evident to you by now. I need to see my darling girl one last time before I lose her forever . . .

It goes without saying that she did it. She had to do it, even though the family feared it was a hoax, not to mention the more dire possibilities of molestation, abduction, and rape. Alec's friend's grandmother was an inexperienced girl, and the fact that she had been turned into an adored Beatrice by some unknown Dante from the SS, that a stranger had been spying on her for the past several months, listening in on her conversations and following her around the city, threw her into an ever-mounting

panic as she waited for Wednesday to come. Nevertheless, when the appointed hour arrived she did what she had to do and marched off to the park with her yellow star wrapped around the sleeve of her sweater, sat down on a bench, and opened the book she had carried along as a prop to still her nerves. For two straight hours, she didn't look up once. She was that scared, she told her granddaughter, and pretending to read was her only defense, the only thing that kept her from jumping up and running away. Impossible to calculate how long those two hours must have felt to her, but noon crept around at last, and she went home. The next day, the exit visas were slipped under the door as promised, and the family left for England.

The last story came from one of Sonia's nephews, the oldest son of the oldest of her three older brothers, Bertrand, the only other member of her family who had become a musician, and therefore someone special to her, a violinist in the orchestra of the Paris Opera, a colleague and a pal. The afternoon following our dinner with Alec, we met him for lunch at Allard, and midway through the meal he started talking about a cellist in the orchestra who was planning to retire at the end of the season. Everyone knew her story, he said, she talked about it openly, and so he didn't feel he would be breaking any confidence if he told it to us. Françoise Duclos. I have no idea why her name is still with me, but there it is – Françoise Duclos, the cellist. She married her husband in the mid-sixties, Bertrand said, gave birth to a daughter in the early seventies, and two years after that the husband vanished. Not such an uncommon occurrence, as the police told her when she reported him missing, but Françoise knew that her husband loved her, that he was crazy about their little girl, and, unless she was the blindest, most obtuse woman on earth, that he wasn't involved with another woman. He earned a decent salary, which meant that money wasn't an issue, he enjoyed his work, and he had never shown any penchant for gambling or risky investments. So what happened to him, and why did he disappear? No one knew.

Fifteen years went by. The husband was declared legally dead, but Françoise never remarried or lived with another man. She raised her daughter on her own (with help from her parents), was hired by the orchestra, gave private lessons in her apartment, and that was it: a pared-down existence, with a handful of friends, summers in the country with her brother's family, and an unsolved mystery as her constant companion. Then, after all those years of silence, the telephone rang one

day, and she was asked to go to the morgue to identify a body. The person who accompanied her into the room where the corpse was waiting warned her that she was in for a rough experience: the deceased had been pushed from a sixth-floor window and had died on contact with the pavement. Shattered as the body was, Françoise recognized it at once. He was twenty pounds heavier than he had been, his hair was thinner and had turned gray, but there was no question that she was looking at the corpse of her missing husband.

Before she could leave, a man entered the room, took Françoise by the arm, and said: Please come with me, Madame Duclos. I have something to tell you.

He led her outside, took her to his car, which was parked in front of a bakery on an adjacent street, and asked her to climb in. Rather than put the key in the ignition, the man rolled down the window and lit up a cigarette. Then, for the next hour, he told Françoise the story of the past fifteen years as she sat next to him in his little blue car, watching people walk out of the bakery carrying loaves of bread. That was one detail Bertrand remembered – the loaves of bread – but he couldn't tell us anything about the man. His name, his age, what he looked like – all a blank, but finally that's of scant importance.

Duclos was an agent for the DGSE, he told her. She couldn't have known that, of course, since agents are under strict orders not to talk about their work, and all those years when she thought her husband was writing economic studies for the Ministry of Foreign Affairs, he was actually operating as a spy under the Direction Générale de la Sécurité Extérieure. Just after the birth of their daughter seventeen years ago, he was given an assignment that turned him into a double agent: ostensibly acting in support of the Soviets but in fact feeding information to the French. After two years, the Russians found out what he was up to and tried to kill him. Duclos managed to escape, but from that point on returning home was no longer possible. The Russians were keeping watch on Françoise and her daughter, the phone in the apartment was tapped, and if Duclos tried to call or visit, all three of them would have been murdered instantly.

So he stayed away to protect his family, hidden by the French for fifteen years as he moved from one Paris apartment to another, a hunted man, a haunted man, stealing out to catch an occasional glimpse of his daughter, watching her grow up from afar, never able to talk to her, to know her, observing his wife as her youthful looks slowly vanished and

she lapsed into middle age, and then, because of carelessness, or because someone informed on him, or because of sheer dumb luck, the Russians finally caught up with Duclos. The capture . . . the blindfold . . . the ropes around his wrists . . . the punches to his face and body . . . and then the plunge from the sixth-floor window. Death by defenestration. Another classic method, the execution of choice among spies and policemen for hundreds of years.

There were numerous gaps in Bertrand's account, but he couldn't answer any of the questions Sonia and I asked him. How had Duclos occupied himself during all those years? Did he live under a false name? Had he gone on working for the DGSE in some capacity or other? How often was he able to go out? Bertrand shook his head. He simply didn't know.

What year did Duclos die? I asked. You must remember that.

Nineteen eighty-nine. The spring of eighty-nine. I'm sure of it, because that's when I joined the orchestra, and the thing with Françoise happened just a few weeks later.

The spring of eighty-nine, I said. The Berlin Wall came down in November. The Eastern bloc threw out their governments, and then the Soviet Union fell apart. That makes Duclos one of the last casualties of the Cold War, doesn't it?

I clear my throat, and a second later I'm coughing again, retching up gobs of sputum as I cover my mouth to stifle the noise. I want to spit into my handkerchief, but when I reach out and search for it with my fingers, I brush against the alarm clock, which falls off the night table and clatters onto the floor. Still no handkerchief. Then I remember that all my handkerchiefs are in the wash, so I swallow hard and let the goo slide down my throat, telling myself for the fiftieth time in the past fifty days to stop smoking, which I know will never happen, but I say it anyway, just to torture myself with my own hypocrisy.

I start thinking about Duclos again, wondering if I might not be able to tease a story out of that awful business, not necessarily Duclos and Françoise, not the fifteen years of hiding and waiting, not what I already know, but something I can make up as I go along. The daughter, for instance, thrust forward from 1989 to 2007. What if she grows up to become a journalist or a novelist, a scribbler of some sort, and after her mother's death she decides to write a book about her parents? But the man who betrayed her father to the Russians is still alive, and when he

gets wind of what she's up to, he tries to stop her – or even kill her . . .

That's as far as I get. A moment later, I hear footsteps on the second floor again, but this time they aren't heading for the bathroom, they're coming down the stairs, and as I imagine Miriam or Katya going into the kitchen to look for a drink or a cigarette or a snack from the refrigerator, I realize that the steps are coming in this direction, that someone is approaching my room. I hear a knock on the door – no, not exactly a knock, but a faint scratching of fingernails against the wood – and then Katya whispers, Are you awake?

I tell her to come in, and as the door opens I can make out her silhouette against the dim, bluish light behind her. She seems to be wearing her Red Sox T-shirt and gray sweatpants, and her long hair is tied back in a ponytail.

Are you all right? she asks. I heard something fall on the floor, and then a lot of terrible coughing.

I'm right as rain, I answer. Whatever that means.

Have you slept at all?

Not a wink. What about you?

In and out, but not much.

Why don't you close the door? It's better in here when it's completely dark. I'll give you one of my pillows, and you can lie down next to me.

The door shuts, I slide a pillow over to Sonia's old spot, and a few moments later Katya is stretched out on her back beside me.

It reminds me of when you were little, I say. When your grandmother and I came to visit, you always crawled into bed with us.

I miss her like crazy, you know. I still can't get it into my head that she isn't around anymore.

You and everyone else.

Why did you stop writing your book, Grandpa?

I decided it was more fun to watch movies with you.

That's recent. You stopped writing it a long time ago.

It got too sad. I enjoyed working on the early parts, but then I came to the bad times, and I started to struggle with it. I've done such stupid things in my life, I didn't have the heart to live through them again. Then Sonia got sick. After she died, the thought of going back to it revolted me.

You shouldn't be so hard on yourself.

I'm not. I'm just being honest.

The book was supposed to be for me, remember?

For you and your mother.

But she already knows everything. I don't. That's why I was looking forward to reading it so much.

You probably would have been bored.

You can be a real fathead sometimes, Grandpa. Did you know that?

Why do you still call me *Grandpa*? You stopped calling your mother *Mom* years ago. You must have been in high school, and suddenly *Mom* became *Mother*.

I didn't want to sound like a baby anymore.

I call you Katya. You could call me August.

I never liked that name very much. It looks good on paper, but it's hard to get it out of your mouth.

Something else, then. How about *Ed*?

Ed? Where did that come from?

I don't know, I say, doing my best to imitate a Cockney accent. It just popped into me little ole 'ed.

Katya lets out a brief, sarcastic groan.

I'm sorry, I continue. I can't help myself. I was born with the bad joke gene, and there's nothing I can do about it.

You never take anything seriously, do you?

I take everything seriously, my love. I just pretend not to.

August Brill, my grandfather, currently known as Ed. What did they call you when you were little?

Augie, mostly. On my good days I was Augie, but people called me a lot of other things, too.

It's hard to imagine it. You as a child, I mean. You must have been a weird kid. Reading books all the time, I'll bet.

That came later. Until I was fifteen, the only thing I cared about was baseball. We used to play it nonstop, all the way into November. Then it was football for a few months, but by the end of February we'd start in on baseball again. The old gang from Washington Heights. We were so nuts, we even played baseball in the snow.

What about girls? Do you remember the name of your first big love?

Of course. You never forget a thing like that.

Who was she?

Virginia Blaine. I fell for her when I was a sophomore in high school, and suddenly baseball didn't matter anymore. I started reading poetry, I took up smoking, and I fell in love with Virginia Blaine.

Did she love you back?

I was never sure. She went hot and cold on me for about six months,

and then she skipped off with someone else. It felt like the end of the world, my first real heartbreak.

Then you met Grandma. You were only twenty, right? Younger than I am now.

You're asking a lot of questions . . .

If you're not going to finish your book, how else am I going to find out what I need to know?

Why the sudden interest?

It's not sudden. I've been thinking about it for a long time. When I heard you were awake just now, I said to myself, Here's my chance, and I came down and knocked on your door.

Scratched on my door.

All right, scratched. But here we are now, lying in the dark, and if you don't answer my questions, I'm not going to let you watch movies with me anymore.

Speaking of which, I came up with another example to support your theory.

Good. But we're not talking about films now. We're talking about you.

It's not such a pleasant story, Katya. There are a lot of depressing things in it.

I'm a big girl, Ed. I can handle anything you dish out.

I wonder.

As far as I know, the only depressing thing you're talking about is the fact that you cheated on your wife and left her for another woman. I'm sorry, chum, but that's pretty standard practice around here, isn't it? You think I can't handle that? I already have, with my own father and mother.

When did you speak to him last?

Who?

Your father.

*Who?*

Come on, Katya. Your father, Richard Furman, your mother's ex-husband, my ex-son-in-law. Talk to me a little, sweetheart. I promise to answer your questions, but just let me know when you last heard from your father.

About two weeks ago, I guess.

Did you make any arrangements to see each other?

He invited me to come to Chicago, but I told him I wasn't feeling up to it. When the semester's over next month, he said he'd come to New York for a weekend and we could stay at a hotel somewhere and eat lots

of good food. I'll probably go, but I haven't decided yet. His wife's pregnant, by the way. Pretty Suzie Woozy is with child.

Does your mother know?

I didn't tell her. I thought she might be upset.

She's bound to find out eventually.

I know. But she seems to be doing a little better now, and I didn't want to rock the boat.

You're one tough cookie, kid.

No, I'm not. I'm a big soft jelly doughnut. All ooze and mush.

I take hold of Katya's hand, and for the next half minute or so we look up into the dark without saying a word. I wonder if she might not drift off to sleep if I don't resume the conversation, but a moment after I think that thought she breaks the silence by asking me another question:

When was the first time you saw her?

April fourth, nineteen fifty-five – at two-thirty in the afternoon.

For real?

For real.

Where were you?

Broadway. Broadway and One Hundred-fifteenth Street, walking uptown on my way to Butler Library. Sonia went to Juilliard, which was near Columbia at the time, and she was walking downtown. I must have spotted her about half a block away, probably because she was wearing a red coat – red jumps out at you, especially on a city street, with nothing but drab bricks and stones in the background. So I catch sight of the red coat coming toward me, and then I see that the person wearing the coat is a short girl with dark hair. Quite promising from a distance, but still too far away to be sure of anything. That's how it is with boys, you know that. Always looking at girls, always sizing them up, always hoping to run into the knockout beauty who will suck the breath out of you and make your heart stop beating. So I've seen the red coat, and I've seen that it's worn by a girl with short dark hair who stands approximately five feet five inches tall, and the next thing I notice is that her head is bobbing around a little bit, as if she's humming to herself, and that there's a certain bounce to her step, a lightness in the way she moves, and I say to myself, This girl is happy, happy to be alive and walking down the street in the crisp, sun-drenched air of early spring. A few seconds later, her face begins to acquire more definition, and I see that she's wearing bright red lipstick, and then, as the distance between us continues to narrow, I simultaneously absorb two important facts. One: that she is indeed

humming to herself – a Mozart aria, I think, but can't be certain – and not only is she humming, she has the voice of a real singer. Two: that she's sublimely attractive, perhaps even beautiful, and that my heart is about to stop beating. By now, she's only four or five feet away, and I, who have never stopped to talk to an unknown girl on the street, who have never in my life had the audacity to address a good-looking stranger in public, open my mouth and say hello, and because I'm smiling at her, no doubt smiling in a way that carries no threat or hint of aggression, she stops humming, smiles back at me, and returns my greeting with one of her own. And that's it. I'm too nervous to say anything more, and so I keep on walking, as does the pretty girl in the red coat, but after six or seven steps I regret my lack of boldness and turn around, hoping there's still time to initiate a conversation, but the girl is walking too quickly and is already out of range, and so, with my eyes on her back, I watch her cross the street and disappear into the crowd.

Frustrating – but understandable. I hate it when men try to pick me up on the street. If you'd acted more boldly, Sonia probably would have been turned off, and you wouldn't have gotten anywhere with her.

That's a generous way of looking at it. After she disappeared, I felt I'd blown the opportunity of a lifetime.

How long did it take before you saw her again?

Almost a month. The days dragged on, and I couldn't stop thinking about her. If I had known she was a student at Juilliard, I might have been able to track her down, but I didn't know anything. She was just a beautiful apparition who had looked into my eyes for a couple of seconds and then vanished. I was convinced I would never see her again. The gods had tricked me, and the girl I was destined to fall in love with, the one person who had been put on this earth to give my life meaning, had been snatched away and thrown into another dimension – an inaccessible place, a place I would never be allowed to enter. I remember writing a long, ridiculous poem about parallel worlds, lost chances, the tragic shittiness of fate. Twenty years old, and already I felt cursed.

But fate was on your side.

Fate, luck, whatever you want to call it.

Where did it happen?

On the subway. The Seventh Avenue IRT. Heading downtown on the evening on April twenty-seventh, nineteen fifty-five. The car was crowded, but the seat next to mine was empty. We stopped at Sixty-sixth

Street, the doors opened, and in she walked. Since there were no other seats available, she sat down beside me.

Did she remember you?

A vague recollection. I reminded her of our little encounter on Broadway earlier that month, and then it came back to her. We didn't have much time. I was on my way to the Village to meet some friends, but Sonia was getting off at Forty-second Street, so we were together for only three stops. We managed to introduce ourselves and exchange phone numbers. I learned that she was studying at Juilliard. I learned that she was French but had spent the first twelve years of her life in America. Her English was perfect, no accent at all. When I tried out some of my mediocre French on her, her French turned out to be perfect as well. We probably talked for seven minutes, ten minutes at the most. Then she got off, and I knew that something monumental had happened. For me, in any case. I couldn't know what Sonia was thinking or feeling, but after those seven or ten minutes, I knew that I had met the one.

First date. First kiss. First . . . you know what.

I called her the next afternoon. Trembling hands . . . I must have picked up the receiver and put it down three or four times before I found the courage to dial. An Italian restaurant in the West Village, I can't remember the name anymore. Inexpensive, I didn't have much money, and this was the first time – it's hard to believe – the first time I'd ever asked a girl out to *dinner*. I can't see myself. I have no idea what kind of impression I made, but I can see her sitting across from me in her white blouse, her steady green eyes, watchful, alert, amused, and that superb mouth with the rounded lips, smiling, smiling often, and her low voice, a resonant voice that came from somewhere deep in her diaphragm, an extremely sexy voice, I found, always did, and then her laugh, which was much higher, almost squeaky at times, a laugh that seemed to emerge from her throat, even her head, and whenever something tickled her funny bone – I'm talking about later now, not that night – she would go into these wild giggling fits, laughing so hard that tears would come streaming from her eyes.

I remember. I never saw anyone laugh like her. When I was little, I sometimes got scared by it. She would go on for so long, I thought it would never stop, that she would actually die laughing. Then I grew to love it.

So there we were, two twenty-year-old kids in that restaurant on Bank Street, Perry Street, wherever it was, out on our first date. We talked

about a lot of things, most of which I've forgotten, but I remember how taken I was when she told me about her family, her background. My own story seemed so dull by comparison, with my furniture-salesman father and fourth-grade schoolteacher mother, the Brills of upper Manhattan, who had never gone anywhere or done anything but work and pay the rent. Sonia's father was a research biologist, a professor, one of the top scientists in Europe. Alexandre Weil – a distant relative of the composer – born in Strasbourg, a Jew (as you already know), and therefore what a fortunate turn when Princeton offered him a job in 1935 and he had the good sense to accept it. If the family had stayed in France during the war, who knows what would have happened to them? Sonia's mother, Marie-Claude, was born in Lyon. I forget what her father did, but both of her grandfathers were Protestant ministers, which means that Sonia was hardly your typical French girl. No Catholics anywhere in sight, no Hail Marys, no visits to the confession box. Marie-Claude met Alexandre when they were students in Paris, and the marriage took place sometime in the early twenties. Four kids in all: three boys and then, five years after the last one was born, along came Sonia, the baby of the bunch, the little princess, who was only one month old when the family left for America. They didn't go back to Paris until nineteen forty-seven. Alexandre was given an important position at the Pasteur Institute – *directeur* was his title, I think – and Sonia wound up going to the Lycée Fénelon. She had already made up her mind to become a singer and didn't want to finish her *bac*, but her parents insisted. That's why she went to Juilliard instead of the conservatory in Paris. She was pissed off at her parents for bearing down on her so hard and more or less ran away. But all was forgiven in the end, and by the time I met Sonia, peace had broken out among the Weils. The family welcomed me in. I think they were touched by the fact that I came from a mixed family, too – in my case a Jewish mother and an Episcopalian father – and so, according to some mystical, unwritten code about clans and tribal loyalties, they figured that Sonia and I would be a good match.

You're getting ahead of yourself. Go back to nineteen fifty-five. The first kiss. The moment when you realized that Sonia cared about you.

A clear memory, because physical contact occurred that same night, in front of the door of her apartment. She shared a place on One Hundred-fourteenth Street with two other girls from Juilliard, and after riding back uptown on the subway, I walked her to her building. Two short blocks, from One Hundred-sixteenth to One Hundred-fourteenth, but

during that brief trajectory, very close to the beginning, with perhaps the tenth or twelfth step we took, your grandmother slipped her arm around mine, and the thrill of that moment has lingered in your grandfather's heart to this day. Sonia made the first move. There was nothing overtly erotic about it – merely a silent declaration that she liked me, that she had enjoyed our evening together, and that she had every intention of seeing me again – but that gesture meant so much . . . and made me so happy, I nearly fell to the ground. Then the door. Saying good night at the door, the classic scene of every budding courtship. To kiss or not to kiss? To nod or shake hands? To brush your fingers against her cheek? To take her in your arms and hug her? So many possibilities, so little time to choose. How to read someone else's desires, how to enter the thoughts of someone you barely know? I didn't want to scare her off by acting too forward, but neither did I want her to think I was some timid soul who didn't know his own mind. The middle road, then, which I improvised as follows: I put my hands on her shoulders, leaned forward and down (down because she was shorter than I was), and pressed my lips against hers – rather hard. No tongue involved, no enveloping hug, but a good solid buss for all that. I heard a quiet rumbling in Sonia's throat, a low-pitched *m*-sound, mmmm, and then a slight catch to her breath, a drop to another register, and something that resembled a laugh. I backed away, saw that she was smiling, and put my arms around her. An instant later, her arms were around me, and then I dove in for a real kiss, a French kiss, a French kiss with the French girl who was suddenly the only person who counted anymore. Just one, but a long one, and then, not wanting to overplay my hand, I said good night and headed for the stairs.

*Pas mal, mon ami.*

A kiss for the ages.

Now I need a sociology lesson. We're talking about nineteen fifty-five, and from all I've heard and read, the fifties weren't the best time for young people. I'm talking about young people and sex. These days, most kids start screwing in their teens, and by the time they've hit twenty, they're old pros at it. So there you are at twenty. Your first date with Sonia has just ended with a triumphant, slobbering kiss. You clearly have the hots for each other. But the prevailing wisdom of the period says: no sex before marriage, at least if you're a girl. You didn't get married until nineteen fifty-seven. You're not going to tell me you held back for two years, are you?

Of course not.

That's a relief.

Horniness is a human constant, the engine that drives the world, and even back then, in the dark age of the mid-twentieth century, students were fucking like rabbits.

Such language, Grandpa.

I thought you'd appreciate it.

That's just it. I do.

On the other hand, I'm not going to pretend there weren't a lot of girls who believed in the myth of the virgin bride, middle-class girls mostly, the so-called good girls, but we mustn't exaggerate either. The obstetrician who delivered your mother in nineteen sixty had been a doctor for almost twenty years. As she was stitching up Sonia's episiotomy after Miriam was born, she assured me that she was going to do a terrific job. She was an expert with the needle, she said, because she'd had so much practice: sewing up girls for their wedding nights to make the husbands think they'd married a virgin.

The things I never knew . . .

That was the fifties. Sex everywhere, but people closed their eyes and made believe it wasn't happening. In America anyway. What made things different for me and your grandmother was the fact that she was French. There are countless hypocrisies in French life, but sex isn't one of them. Sonia moved back to Paris when she was twelve and stayed there until she was nineteen. Her education was far more advanced than mine, and she was prepared to do things that would have sent most American girls shrieking from the bed.

Such as?

Use your imagination, Katya.

You're not going to shock me, you know. I went to Sarah Lawrence, remember? The sex capital of the Western world. I've been all around the block, believe me.

The body has a limited number of orifices. Let's just say that we explored every one of them.

In other words, Grandma was good in bed.

That's a blunt way of putting it, but yes, she was good. Uninhibited, comfortable in her body, sensitive to the shifts and swerves of her own feelings. Every time we did it, it seemed to be different from the time before. Fierce and dramatic one day, slow and languid the next, the surprise of it all, the endless nuances . . .

I remember her hands, the gentleness of her hands when she touched me.

Gentle hands, yes. But strong hands, too. Wise hands. That's how I used to think of them. Hands that could speak.

Did you live together before you were married?

No, no, that was out of the question. We had to sneak around a lot. It had its exciting aspects, but most of the time it was frustrating. I was still living with my parents in Washington Heights, so I didn't have a place of my own. And Sonia had her two roommates. We'd go there whenever they were gone, but that didn't happen often enough to satisfy us.

What about hotels?

Off-limits. Even if we could have afforded them, it was too dangerous. There were laws in New York that made it illegal for unmarried couples to be alone together in the same room. Every hotel had a detective – the house dick – and if he caught you, you'd be thrown in jail.

Lovely.

So what to do? Sonia had lived in Princeton as a child, and she still had friends there. There was one couple – the Gontorskis, I'll never forget them – a physics professor and his wife, refugees from Poland who loved Sonia and didn't give a damn about American sexual customs. They let us stay in their guest room on the weekends. And then there was the outdoor sex, the warm-weather sex in fields and meadows outside the city. A large element of risk. Someone finally found us naked in the bushes, and we got cold feet after that and stopped taking chances. Without the Gontorskis, we would have been in hell.

Why didn't you just get married? Right then, while you were still students.

The draft. The minute I graduated from college, I was going to be called up for my physical, and we figured I'd have to spend two years in the army. Sonia was already singing professionally by my senior year, and what if they shipped me off to West Germany or Greenland or South Korea? I couldn't have asked her to follow me. It wouldn't have been fair.

But you never were in the army, were you? Not if you were married in nineteen fifty-seven.

I flunked the exam. A false diagnosis, as it turned out – but no matter, I was free, and a month later we were married. We didn't have much money, of course, but the situation wasn't quite desperate. Sonia had dropped out of Juilliard and started her career, and by the time I left college I had already published about a dozen articles and reviews. We

sublet a railroad flat in Chelsea, sweated out one New York summer, and then Sonia's oldest brother, Patrice, a civil engineer, was hired to build a dam somewhere in Africa and offered us his Paris apartment rent-free. We jumped. The minute his telegram arrived, we started packing our bags.

I'm not interested in real estate, and I already know about your careers. I want you to tell me about the important things. What was she like? How did it feel being married to her? How well did you get along? Did you ever fight? The nuts and bolts, Grandpa, not just a string of superficial facts.

All right, let me change gears and think for a moment. What was Sonia like? What did I discover about her after we were married that I hadn't known before? Contradictions. Complexities. A darkness that revealed itself slowly over time and made me reassess who she was. I loved her madly, Katya, you have to understand that, and I'm not criticizing her for being who she was. It's just that as I got to know her better, I came to realize how much suffering she carried around inside her. In most ways, your grandmother was an extraordinary person. Tender, kind, loyal, forgiving, full of spirit, with a tremendous capacity for love. But she would drift off every now and then, sometimes right in the middle of a conversation, and start staring into space with this dreamy expression in her eyes, and it was as if she didn't know me anymore. At first, I imagined she was thinking some profound thought or remembering something that had happened to her, but when I finally asked her what was going through her head at those moments, she smiled at me and said, Nothing. It was as if her whole being would empty out, and she'd lose contact with herself and the world. All her instincts and impulses about other people were deep, uncannily deep, but her relation to herself was strangely shallow. She had a good mind, but essentially she was uneducated, and she had trouble following a train of thought, couldn't concentrate on anything for very long. Except her music, which was the most important thing in her life. She believed in her talent, but at the same time she knew her limits and refused to tackle pieces she felt were beyond her ability to perform well. I admired her honesty, but there was also something sad about it, as if she thought of herself as second-rate, doomed always to be a notch or two below the best. That's why she never did any opera. Lieder, ensemble work in choral pieces, undemanding solo cantatas – but she never pushed herself beyond that. Did we fight? Of course we fought. All couples fight, but she was never vicious or cruel

when we argued. Most of the time, I have to admit, her criticisms of me were spot-on. For a Frenchwoman, she turned out to be a rather lousy cook, but she liked good food, so we ate in restaurants fairly often. An indifferent housekeeper, absolutely no interest in possessions – I say that as a compliment – and even though she was a beautiful young woman with an adorable body, she didn't dress very well. She loved clothes, but she never seemed to choose the right ones. To be frank, I sometimes felt lonely with her, lonely in my work, since all my time was spent reading and writing about books, and she didn't read much, and what she did read she found difficult to talk about.

I'm getting the impression that you felt disappointed.

No, not disappointed. Far from it. Two newlyweds gradually adjusting to each other's foibles, the revelations of intimacy. All in all, it was a happy time for me, for both of us, with no serious complaints on either side, and then the dam in Africa was finished, and we went back to New York with Sonia three months pregnant.

Where did you live?

I thought you weren't interested in real estate.

That's right, I'm not. Question withdrawn.

Several places over the years. But when your mother was born, our apartment was on West Eighty-fourth Street, just off Riverside Drive. One of the windiest streets in the city.

What kind of baby was she?

Easy and difficult. Screaming and laughing. Great fun and a terrible pain in the ass.

In other words, a baby.

No. The baby of babies. Because she was *our* baby, and *our* baby was like no other baby in the world.

How long did Grandma wait until she went back to performing?

She took a year off from traveling, but she was singing in New York again when Miriam was just three months old. You know what a good mother she was – your own mother must have told you that a hundred times – but she also had her work. It was what she was born to do, and I never would have dreamed of trying to hold her back. Still, she had her doubts, especially in the beginning. One day, when Miriam was about six months old, I walked into the bedroom, and there was Sonia on her knees by the bed, hands together, head raised, murmuring to herself in French. My French was quite good by then, and I understood everything she said. To my astonishment, it turned out that she was praying. Dear

God, give me a sign and tell me what to do about my little girl. Dear God, fill the emptiness inside me and teach me how to love, to forbear, to give myself to others. She looked and sounded like a child, a small, simpleminded child, and I have to say that I was a little thrown by it – but also moved, deeply, deeply moved. It was as if a door had opened, and I was looking at a new Sonia, a different person from the one I'd known for the past five years. When she realized I was in the room, she turned around and gave me an embarrassed smile. I'm sorry, she said, I didn't want you to know. I walked over to the bed and sat down. Don't be sorry, I told her. I'm just a little puzzled, that's all. We had a long talk after that, at least an hour, the two of us sitting side by side on the bed, discussing the mysteries of her soul. Sonia explained that it started toward the end of her pregnancy, in the middle of the seventh month. She was walking down the street one afternoon on her way home, when all of a sudden a feeling of joy rose up inside her, an inexplicable, overwhelming joy. It was as if the entire universe were rushing into her body, she said, and in that instant she understood that everything was connected to everything else, that everyone in the world was connected to everyone else in the world, and this binding force, this power that held everything and everyone together, was God. That was the only word she could think of. God. Not a Jewish or Christian God, not the God of any religion, but God as the presence that animates all life. She started talking to him after that, she said, convinced that he could hear what she was saying, and these monologues, these prayers, these supplications – whatever you wanted to call them – always comforted her, always put her on an even keel with herself again. It had been going on for months now, but she didn't want to tell me because she was afraid I would think she was stupid. I was so much smarter than she was, so superior to her when it came to intellectual matters – her words, not mine – and she was worried that I'd burst out laughing at my ignorant wife when she told me that she'd found God. I didn't laugh. Heathen that I am, I didn't laugh. Sonia had her own way of thinking and her own way of doing things, and who was I to make fun of her?

I knew her all my life, but she never spoke to me about God, not once.

That's because she stopped believing. When our marriage broke up, she felt that God had abandoned her. That was a long time ago, angel, long before you were born.

Poor Grandma.

Yes, poor Grandma.

I have a theory about your marriage. Mother and I have talked about it, and she tends to go along with me, but I need confirmation, the inside dope from the horse's mouth. How would you respond if I said: You and Grandma got divorced because of her career?

My answer would be: Nonsense.

All right, not her career per se. The fact that she traveled so much.

I would say you were getting warmer – but only as an indirect cause, a secondary factor.

Mother says she used to hate it when Grandma went on tour. She'd break down and cry, she'd scream, she'd beg her not to go. Hysterical scenes . . . unadulterated anguish . . . separation after separation . . .

That happened once or twice, but I wouldn't make too big an issue of it. When Miriam was very young, say from one to six, Sonia never left for more than a week at a time. My mother would move in with us to take care of her, and things went rather smoothly. Your great-grandmother had a knack with little kids, she adored Miriam – who was her only granddaughter – and Miriam couldn't wait for her to show up. It all comes back to me now . . . the funny things your mother used to do. When she was three or four, she became fascinated by her grandmother's breasts. They were quite huge, I have to say, since my mother had grown into a fairly chunky broad by then. Sonia was small on top, with little adolescent breasts that filled out only when she was nursing Miriam, but after your mother was weaned, they got even smaller than they'd been before the pregnancy. The contrast was utterly stark, and Miriam couldn't help noticing. My mother had a voluminous chest, twenty times the size of Sonia's. One Saturday morning, she and Miriam were sitting on the sofa together watching cartoons. A commercial for pizza came on, which ended with the words: Now, that's a pizza! A moment later, your mother turned to my mother, clamped her mouth on her grandmother's right breast, and then came up shouting: Now, *that's* a pizza! My mother laughed so hard, she let out a fart, a gigantic trumpet blast of a fart. That got Miriam laughing so wildly, she peed in her pants. She jumped off the sofa and started running around the room, yelling at the top of her lungs: Fart-pee, fart-pee, *oui, oui, oui!*

You're making this up.

No, it really happened, I swear it did. The only reason I mention it is to show you that it wasn't all gloom in the house when Sonia was gone. Miriam didn't mope around feeling like some neglected Oliver Twist. She was mostly fine.

And what about you?

I learned to live with it.

That sounds like an evasive answer.

There were different periods, different stages, and each one had its own texture. In the beginning, Sonia was relatively unknown. She'd done a little singing in New York before we moved to Paris, but she had to start all over again in France, and then, just when things seemed to be taking off a bit, we came back to America, and she had to make another start. In the end, it all worked to her advantage, since she was known both here and in Europe. But it took time for her to develop a reputation. The turning point came in sixty-seven or sixty-eight, when she signed the contract to make those records with Nonesuch, but until then she didn't go away that often. I was torn down the middle. On the one hand, I was happy for her whenever she got a booking to perform in a new city. On the other hand – just like your mother – I hated to see her go. The only choice was to learn to live with it. That's not an evasion, it's a fact.

You were faithful . . .

Totally.

And when did you start to slip?

*Stray* is probably the word to use in this context.

Or *lapse*. There's a spiritual connotation to it that seems fitting.

All right, lapse. Around nineteen seventy, I suppose. But there was nothing spiritual about it. It was all about sex, sex pure and simple. Summer came, and Sonia went off on a three-month tour of Europe – with your mother, by the way – and there I was by myself, still just thirty-five years old, hormones roaring at full tilt, womanless in New York. I worked hard every day, but the nights were empty, colorless, stagnant. I began hanging out with a bunch of sportswriters, most of them heavy drinkers, playing poker until three in the morning, going out to bars, not because I especially liked any of them, but it was something to do, and I needed a little company after being alone all day. One night, after another boozy session in a bar, I was walking home from midtown to the Upper West Side, and I spotted a prostitute standing in the doorway of a building. A very attractive girl, as it happened, and I was drunk enough to accept her offer of a good time. Am I upsetting you?

A little.

I wasn't planning to give you any details. Just the general drift.

That's okay. It's my fault. I've turned this into Truth Night at Castle Despair, and now that we've started, we might as well go all the way.

Onward, then?

Yes, keep telling the story.

So I had my good time, which wasn't a good time at all, but after fifteen years of sleeping with the same woman I found it fascinating to touch another body, to feel flesh that was different from the flesh I knew. That was the discovery of that night. The novelty of being with another woman.

Did you feel guilty?

No. I considered it an experiment. A lesson learned, so to speak.

So my theory is right. If Grandma had been home in New York, you never would have paid that girl to sleep with you.

In that particular case, yes. But there was more to our downfall than infidelity, more to it than Sonia's absences. I've thought about this for years, and the only half-reasonable explanation I've ever come up with is that there's something wrong with me, a flaw in the mechanism, a damaged part gumming up the works. I'm not talking about moral weakness. I'm talking about my mind, my mental makeup. I'm somewhat better now, I think, the problem seemed to diminish as I grew older, but back then, at thirty-five, thirty-eight, forty, I walked around with a feeling that my life had never truly belonged to me, that I had never truly inhabited myself, that I had never been real. And because I wasn't real, I didn't understand the effect I had on others, the damage I could cause, the hurt I could inflict on the people who loved me. Sonia was my ground, my one solid connection to the world. Being with her made me better than I actually was – healthier, stronger, saner – and because we started living together when we were so young, the flaw was masked for all those years, and I assumed I was just like everyone else. But I wasn't. The moment I began to wander away from her, the bandage dropped off my wound, and then the bleeding wouldn't stop. I went after other women because I felt I'd missed out on something and had to make up for lost time. I'm talking about sex now, nothing but sex, but you can't run around and act the way I did and expect your marriage to hold together. I deceived myself into thinking it would.

Don't hate yourself so much, Grandpa. She took you back, remember?

I know . . . but all those wasted years. It makes me sick to think about them. My dumb-ass flings and dalliances. What did they add up to? A few cheap thrills, nothing of any importance – but there's no question that they laid the groundwork for what happened next.

Oona McNally.

Sonia was so trusting, and I was so discreet, our life went on together without any crucial disturbances. She didn't know, and I didn't tell, and not for one second did I ever think of leaving her. Then, in nineteen seventy-four, I wrote a favorable review of a first novel by a young American author. *Anticipation*, by the aforementioned O.M. It was a startling book, I felt, highly original and written with great command, a strong, promising debut. I didn't know anything about the writer – only that she was twenty-six years old and lived in New York. I read the book in galleys, and since galleys didn't have author photos on them in the seventies, I didn't even know what she looked like. About four months later, I went to a poetry reading at the Gotham Book Mart (without Sonia, who was at home with Miriam), and when the reading was over and we all started walking down the stairs, someone grabbed me by the arm. Oona McNally. She wanted to thank me for the nice review I'd given her novel. That was the extent of it, but I was so impressed by her looks – tall and lithe, an exquisite face, the second coming of Virginia Blaine – that I asked her out for a drink. How many times had I betrayed Sonia by then? Three or four one-night stands, and one mini-affair that lasted roughly two weeks. Not such a gruesome catalogue when compared to some men, but enough to have taught me that I was prepared to seize opportunities whenever they presented themselves. But this girl was different. You didn't sleep with Oona McNally and say good-bye to her the next morning – you fell in love with her, you wanted her to be part of your life. I won't bore you with the tawdry incidentals. The clandestine dinners, the long talks in out-of-the-way bars, the slow mutual seduction. She didn't jump into my arms immediately. I had to go after her, win her confidence, persuade her that it was possible for a man to be in love with two women at the same time. I still had no intention of leaving Sonia, you understand. I wanted both of them. My wife of seventeen years, my comrade, my innermost heart, the mother of my only child – and this ferocious young woman with the burning intelligence, this new erotic charm, a woman I could finally share my work with and talk to about books and ideas. I began to resemble a character in a nineteenth-century novel: solid marriage in one box, lively mistress in another box, and I, the master magician, standing between them, with the skill and cunning never to open both boxes at the same time. For several months I managed to make it work, and I was no longer a mere magician, I was an aerialist as well, prancing along my high wire, shuttling between ecstasy and anguish every day, growing more and more certain that I would never fall.

And then?

December nineteen seventy-four, two days after Christmas.

You fell.

I fell. Sonia did a Schubert recital at the Ninety-second Street Y that night, and when she came home she told me she knew.

How did she find out?

She wouldn't say. But all her facts were correct, and I saw no point in denying them. The thing I remember best about that conversation was how composed she was – at least until the end, when she stopped talking. She didn't cry or shout, she didn't carry on, she didn't punch me or throw things across the room. You have to choose, she said. I'm willing to forgive you, but you have to go to that girl right now and break it off. I don't know what will happen to us, I don't know if we'll ever be the same again. Right now, I feel as if you've stabbed me in the chest and ripped out my heart. You've killed me, August. You're looking at a dead woman, and the only reason I'm going to pretend to be alive is because Miriam needs her mother. I've always loved you, I've always thought you were a man with a great soul, but it turns out that you're just another lying shit. How could you have done it, August? . . . Her voice broke then, and she put her face in her hands and started crying. I sat down beside her on the sofa and put my arm around her shoulder, but she pushed me away. Don't touch me, she said. Don't come near me until you've talked to that girl. If you don't come back tonight, don't bother to come back at all – not ever.

Did you come back?

I'm afraid not.

This is getting rather grim, isn't it?

I'll stop if you want me to. We could always talk about something else.

No, keep going. But let's skip ahead, all right? You don't have to tell me about your marriage to Oona. I know you loved her, I know you had a stormy time of it, and I know she left you for that German painter. Klaus Something.

Bremen.

Klaus Bremen. I know how hard it was for you, I know you went through a really bad period.

The alcohol period. Primarily scotch, single-malt scotch.

And you don't have to talk about your troubles with my mother. She's already told me about them. They're finished, and there's no reason to go over them again, is there?

If you say so.

The only thing I want to hear about is how you and Grandma got back together.

This is all about her, isn't it?

It has to be. Because she's the one who isn't here anymore.

Nine years apart. But I never turned against her. Regret and remorse, self-contempt, the corrosive poison of uncertainty, those were the things that undermined my years with Oona. Sonia was too much a part of me, and even after the divorce, she was still there, still talking to me in my head – the ever-present absent one, as I sometimes call her now. We were in contact, of course, we had to be because of Miriam, the logistics of shared custody, the weekend arrangements, the summer holidays, the high school and college events, and as we slowly adjusted to our new circumstances, I felt her anger against me turn to a kind of pity. Poor August, the champion of fools. She had men. That goes without saying, *n'est-ce pas*? She was only forty when I walked out on her, still radiant, still the same shining girl she'd always been, and one of her entanglements became quite serious, I think, although your mother probably knows more about it than I do. When Oona waltzed off with her German painter, I was shattered. Your tactful reference to *a bad period* doesn't begin to describe how bad it was. I'm not going to delve into those days now, I promise, but even then, at a time when I was absolutely alone, it never occurred to me to reach out to Sonia. That was nineteen eighty-one. In nineteen eighty-two, a couple of months before your parents' wedding, she wrote me a letter. Not about us, but about your mother, worried that Miriam was too young to be rushing into marriage, that she was about to make the same mistake we did in our early twenties. Very prescient, of course, but your grandmother always had a nose for such things. I wrote back and said she was probably right, but even if she was right, there was nothing we could do about it. You can't meddle with other people's feelings, least of all your own child's, and the truth is that kids learn nothing from their parents' mistakes. We have to leave them alone and let them thrash out into the world to make their own mistakes. That was my answer, and then I concluded the letter with a rather trite remark: The only thing we can do is hope for the best. On the day of the wedding, Sonia walked up to me and said: I'm hoping for the best. If I had to pinpoint the moment when our reconciliation began, I would choose that one, the moment when your grandmother said those words to me. It was an important day for both of us – our daughter's

wedding – and there was a lot of emotion in the air – happiness, anxiety, nostalgia, a whole range of feeling – and neither one of us was in a mood for bearing grudges. I was still a wreck at that point, by no means fully recovered from the Oona debacle, but Sonia was going through a hard time as well. She'd retired from singing earlier that year, and as I later found out from your mother (Sonia never shared any secrets with me about her private life), she had recently parted ways with a man. So, on top of everything else, we were both at a low ebb that day, and seeing each other somehow had a consoling effect. Two veterans who'd fought in the same war, watching their child march off to a new war of her own. We danced together, we talked about the old days, and for a few moments we even held hands. Then the party was over, and everyone went home, but I remember thinking when I was back in New York that being with her that day was the best thing that had happened to me in a long time. I never made a conscious decision about it, but one morning about a month later, I woke up and realized that I wanted to see her again. No, more than that. I wanted to win her back. I knew my chances were probably nil, but I also knew that I had to give it a try. So I called.

Just like that? You just picked up the phone and called?

Not without trepidation. Not without a lump in my throat and a knot in my stomach. It was an exact reprise of the first time I'd called her – twenty-seven years before. I was twenty again, a jittery, lovesick juvenile plucking up his courage to call his dream girl and ask her out on a date. I must have stared at the phone for ten minutes, but when I dialed the number at last, Sonia wasn't in. The answering machine clicked on, and I was so rattled by the sound of her voice that I hung up. Relax, I said to myself, you're behaving like an idiot, so I dialed the number again and left a message. Nothing elaborate. Just that I wanted to talk to her about something, that I hoped she was well, and that I would be in all day.

Did she call back – or did you have to try again?

She called. But that didn't prove anything. She had no idea what I wanted to talk about. For all she knew, it might have been about Miriam – or some trivial, practical matter. In any case, her voice sounded calm, a little reserved, but with no edge to it. I told her that I'd been thinking about her and wanted to know how she was. Hanging in there, she said, or words to that effect. It was good to see you at the wedding, I said. Yes, she answered, it was a remarkable day, she'd had a wonderful time. Back and forth we went, a bit tentatively on both sides, polite and cautious, not daring to say much of anything. Then I popped the question: would

she have dinner with me one night that week. *Dinner*? As she repeated the word, I could hear the disbelief in her voice. There was a long pause after that, and then she said she wasn't sure, she'd have to think it over. I didn't insist. The important thing was not to come on too strong. I knew her too well, and if I started to push, the odds were that she'd start pushing back. That's how we left it. I told her to take care of herself and said good-bye.

Not such a promising start.

No. But it could have been worse. She hadn't turned down the invitation, she just didn't know if she should accept it or not. Half an hour later, the phone rang again. Of course I'll have dinner with you, Sonia said. She apologized for having hesitated, but I'd caught her with her guard down, and she'd been entirely flustered. So we made our dinner date, and that was the beginning of a long and delicate dance, a minuet of desire, fear, and surrender that went on for more than eighteen months. It took that much time before we started living together, but even though we made it through another twenty-one years, Sonia refused to marry me again. I don't know if you were aware of that. Your grandmother and I lived in sin until the day she died. Marriage would have jinxed us, she said. We'd tried it once, and look what happened to us, so why not take another approach? After struggling so hard to get her back, I was happy to abide by her rules. I proposed to her every year on her birthday, but those declarations were no more than encrypted messages, a sign that she could trust me again, that she could go on trusting me for the duration. There was so much I never understood about her, so much she didn't understand about herself. That second courtship was a tough business, a man wooing his ex-wife, and the ex-wife playing hard to get, not giving an inch, not knowing what she wanted, going back and forth between temptation and revulsion until she finally gave in. It took half a year before we wound up in bed. The first time we made love, she laughed when it was over, collapsing into one of those crazy giggling jags of hers that went on so long I began to grow frightened. The second time we made love, she cried, sobbing into the pillow for more than an hour. So many things had changed for her. Her voice had lost the indefinable quality that had made it her voice, that fragile, crystalline ache of unbridled feeling, the hidden god who had spoken through her – all that was gone now, and she knew it, but giving up her career had been a difficult blow, and she was still coming to terms with it. She taught now, giving private singing lessons in her apartment, and there were many days when she had no interest in

seeing me. Other days, she would call in a fit of desperation: Come now, I have to see you now. We were lovers again, probably closer to each other than we'd ever been the first time around, but she wanted to keep our lives separate. I wanted more, but she wouldn't give in. That was the line she wouldn't cross and then, after a year and a half, something happened, and it all suddenly changed.

What was it?

You.

Me? What do you mean, *me*?

You were born. Your grandmother and I took the train to New Haven, and we were there when your mother went into labor. I don't want to exaggerate or sound overly sentimental about it, but when Sonia held you in her arms for the first time, she glanced over at me, and when I saw her face – I'm stumbling here, groping for the right words – her face . . . was illuminated. Tears were rolling down her cheeks. She was smiling, smiling and laughing, and it looked as if she'd been filled with light. A few hours later, after we'd gone back to our hotel, we were lying in bed in the dark. She took hold of my hand and said: I want you to move in with me, August. As soon as we get back to New York, I want you to move in and stay with me forever.

I did it.

You did it. You were the one who got us together again.

Well, at least I've accomplished one thing in my life. Too bad I was only five minutes old and didn't know what I was doing.

The first of many great deeds, with many more to come.

Why is life so horrible, Grandpa?

Because it is, that's all. It just is.

All those bad times with you and Grandma. All the bad times with my mother and father. But at least you loved each other and had your second chance. At least my mother loved my father enough to marry him. I've never loved anyone.

What are you talking about?

I tried to love Titus, but I couldn't. He loved me, but I couldn't love him back. Why do you think he joined that stupid company and went away?

To make money. He was going to put in a year and earn close to a hundred thousand dollars. That's an awful lot of cash for a twenty-four-year-old kid. I had a long talk with him before he left. He knew he was taking a risk, but he thought it was worth it.

He left because of me. Don't you understand that? I told him I didn't want to see him anymore, and so he went off and got himself killed. He died because of me.

You can't think that way. He died because he was in the wrong place at the wrong time.

And I put him there.

You had nothing to do with it. Stop beating yourself up, Katya. It's gone on long enough.

I can't help it.

You've been stuck here for nine months now, and it isn't doing you any good. I think it's time for a change.

I don't want anything to change.

Have you thought about going back to school in the fall?

Off and on. I'm just not sure I'm ready.

It doesn't start for another four months.

I know. But if I want to go back, I have to tell them by next week.

Tell them. If you're not feeling up to it, you can always change your mind at the last minute.

We'll see.

In the meantime, we have to shake things up around here. Does the thought of a trip interest you?

Where would we go?

Anywhere you like, for as long as you like.

What about Mother? We can't just leave her alone.

Her classes end next month. The three of us could go together.

But she's working on her book. She wanted to finish it this summer.

She can write while we're on the road.

The road? You can't ride around in a car. Your leg would hurt too much.

I was thinking more along the lines of a camper. I have no idea what those things cost, but I have a nice chunk of money in the bank. The proceeds from the sale of my New York apartment. I'm sure I could afford one. If not new, then secondhand.

What are you saying? That the three of us drive around in a camper all summer?

That's right. Miriam works on her book, and every day the two of us go off on a quest.

What are we looking for?

I don't know. Anything. The best hamburger in America. We make a

list of the top hamburger restaurants in the country and then go around from one to the next and rate them according to a complex list of criteria. Taste, juiciness, size, the quality of the bun, and so on.

If you ate a hamburger every day, you'd probably have a heart attack.

Fish, then. We'll look for the best fish joint in the Lower Forty-eight.

You're pulling my leg, right?

I don't pull legs. Men with bad legs don't do that. It's against our religion.

A camper would be pretty crowded. And besides, you're forgetting one important thing.

What's that?

You snore.

Ah. So I do, so I do. All right, we'll scrap the camper. What about going to Paris? You can see your cousins, practice your French, and gain a new perspective on life.

No thanks. I'd rather stay here and watch my movies.

They're turning into a drug, you know. I think we should cut down, maybe even stop for a while.

I can't do that. I need the images. I need the distraction of watching other things.

Other things? I don't follow. Other than what?

Don't be so dense.

I know I'm dumb, but I just don't get it.

Titus.

But we looked at that video only once – more than nine months ago.

Have you forgotten it?

No, of course not. I think about it twenty times a day.

That's my point. If I hadn't seen it, everything would be different. People go off to war, and sometimes they die. You get a telegram or a phone call, and someone tells you that your son or your husband or your ex-boyfriend has been killed. But you don't see how it happened. You make up pictures in your mind, but you don't know the real facts. Even if you're told the story by someone who was there, what you're left with is words, and words are vague, open to interpretation. We saw it. We saw how they murdered him, and unless I blot out that video with other images, it's the only thing I ever see. I can't get rid of it.

We'll never get rid of it. You have to accept that, Katya. Accept it, and try to start living again.

I'm doing my best.

You haven't stirred a muscle in close to a year. There are other distractions besides watching movies all day. Work, for one thing. A project, something to sink your teeth into.

Like what?

Don't laugh at me, but after looking at all those films with you, I've been thinking that maybe we should write one of our own.

I'm not a writer. I don't know how to make up stories.

What do you think I've been doing tonight?

I don't know. Thinking. Remembering.

As little as possible. I'm better off if I reserve my thinking and remembering for the daytime. Mostly, I've been telling myself a story. That's what I do when I can't sleep. I lie in the dark and tell myself stories. I must have a few dozen of them by now. We could turn them into films. Co-writers, co-creators. Instead of looking at other people's images, why not make up our own?

What kind of stories?

All kinds. Farces, tragedies, sequels to books I've liked, historical dramas, every kind of story you can imagine. But if you accept my offer, I think we should start with a comedy.

I'm not much into laughs these days.

Exactly. That's why we should work on something light – a frothy bagatelle, as frivolous and diverting as possible. If we really put our minds to it, we might have some fun.

Who wants fun?

I do. And you do, too, my love. We've turned into a couple of sad sacks, you and I, and what I'm proposing is a cure, a remedy to ward off the blues.

I launch into a story I sketched out last week – the romantic adventures of Dot and Dash, a chubby waitress and a grizzled short-order cook who work in a New York City diner – but less than five minutes into it, Katya falls asleep, and our conversation comes to an end. I listen to her slow, regular breathing, glad that she's finally managed to conk out, and wonder what time it is. Well past four, probably, perhaps even five. An hour or so until dawn, that incomprehensible moment when the blackness starts to thin out and the vireo who lives in the tree beside my window delivers his first chirp of the day. As I mull over the various things Katya has said to me, my thoughts gradually turn to Titus, and before long I'm inside his story again, reliving the disaster I've been struggling to avoid all night.

Katya blames herself for what happened, falsely linking herself to the chain of cause and effect that ultimately led to his murder. One mustn't allow oneself to think that way, but if I succumbed to her faulty logic, then Sonia and I would be responsible as well, since we were the ones who introduced her to Titus in the first place. Thanksgiving dinner five years ago, just after her parents' divorce. She and Miriam drove down to New York to spend the long weekend with us, and on Thursday Sonia and I cooked turkey for twelve people. Among the guests were Titus and his parents, David Small and Elizabeth Blackman, both painters, both old friends of ours. The nineteen-year-old Titus and the eighteen-year-old Katya seemed to hit it off. Did he die because he fell in love with our granddaughter? Follow that thought through to the end, and you could just as easily blame his parents. If David and Liz hadn't met, Titus never would have been born.

He was a bright boy, I thought, an open-hearted, undisciplined boy with wild red hair, long legs, and big feet. I met him when he was four, and since Sonia and I visited his parents' place fairly often, he felt comfortable around us, treating us not as family friends so much as a surrogate aunt and uncle. I liked him because he read books, a rare kid with a hunger for literature, and when he started writing short stories in his mid-teens, he would send them to me and ask for my comments. They weren't very good, but I was touched that he had turned to me for advice, and after a while he began coming to our apartment about once a month to talk about his latest efforts. I would suggest books for him to read, which he would plow through diligently with a kind of lunging, scattershot enthusiasm. His work gradually improved somewhat, but every month it was different, bearing the marks of whatever writer he happened to be reading at the moment – a normal trait in beginners, a sign of development. Flashes of talent began to glimmer through his ornate, overwritten prose, but it was still too early to judge whether he had any genuine promise. When he was a senior in high school and announced that he wanted to stay in the city to attend college at Columbia, I wrote a letter of recommendation for him. I don't know if that letter made any difference, but my alma mater accepted him, and his monthly visits continued.

He was in his second year when he showed up at that Thanksgiving dinner and met Katya. They made an odd and fetching duo, I thought. The floppy, grinning, arm-waving Titus and the small, slender, dark-haired daughter of my daughter. Sarah Lawrence was in Bronxville, just a short train ride into the city, and Katya stayed with us quite often

during her undergraduate days, most weekends in fact, escaping dormitory life for a comfortable bed in her grandparents' apartment and nights out in New York. She now claims that she didn't love Titus, but all during the years they were together, there were dozens upon dozens of dinners at our place, usually just the four of us, and I never felt anything but affection between them. Maybe I was blind. Maybe I took too much for granted, but except for an occasional intellectual disagreement and one breakup that lasted under a month, they struck me as a happy, thriving couple. When Titus came to see me on his own, he never hinted at any trouble with Katya, and Titus was a garrulous boy, a person who spoke whatever was on his mind, and if Katya had called it quits with him, surely he would have mentioned it to me. Or maybe not. It could be that I didn't know him as well as I thought I did.

When he started talking about going off to work in Iraq, his parents went into a tailspin of panic. David, normally the gentlest and most tolerant of men, screamed at his son and called him pathologically disturbed, a know-nothing dilettante, a suicidal maniac. Liz wept, took to her bed, and started gorging herself with heavy doses of tranquilizers. That was in February last year. Sonia had died the previous November, and I was in awful shape just then, drinking myself into oblivion every night, not fit for human contact, out of my mind with grief, but David was so distraught, he called me anyway and asked if I would talk some sense into the boy. I couldn't refuse. I had known Titus for too long, and the fact was that I felt concerned for him as well. So I pulled myself together and did the best I could – which was nothing, nothing at all.

I had lost touch with Titus after Sonia became ill, and he seemed to have changed in the intervening months. The talkative, goofy optimist had turned sullen, almost belligerent, and I knew from the start that my words would have no effect on him. At the same time, I don't think he was unhappy to see me, and when he spoke about Sonia and her death, there was true compassion in his voice. I thanked him for his words, poured us two glasses of neat scotch, and then led him into the living room, where we had had so many conversations in the past.

I'm not going to sit here and argue with you, I began. It's just that I'm a little confused, and I'd like you to clarify some things for me. Okay?

Okay, Titus said. No problem.

The war has been going on for close to three years now, I said. When the invasion started, you told me you were against it. *Appalled* was the word you used, I think. You said it was a phony, trumped-up war, the

worst political mistake in American history. Am I right, or have I mixed you up with someone else?

You're dead-on. That's exactly how I felt.

We haven't seen much of each other lately, but the last time you were here, I remember you said that Bush should be thrown in jail – along with Cheney, Rumsfeld, and the whole gang of fascist crooks who were running the country. When was that? Eight months ago? Ten months ago?

Last spring. April or May, I can't remember.

Have you changed your thinking since then?

No.

Not at all?

Not one bit.

Then why on earth do you want to go to Iraq? Why participate in a war you detest?

I'm not going there to help America. I'm going for myself.

The money. Is that it? Titus Small, mercenary-at-large.

I'm not a mercenary. Mercenaries carry weapons and kill people. I'm going to drive a truck, that's all. Transporting supplies from one place to another. Sheets and towels, soap, candy bars, dirty laundry. It's a shit job, but the pay is enormous. BRK – that's the name of the company. You sign up for a year, and you come home with ninety or a hundred thousand dollars in your pocket.

But you'll be supporting something you're opposed to. How can you justify that to yourself?

I don't look at it that way. For me, it's not a moral decision. It's about learning something, about starting a new kind of education. I know how horrible and dangerous it is over there, but that's just why I want to go. The more horrible, the better.

You're not making sense.

All my life, I've wanted to be a writer. You know that, August. I've been showing you my wretched little stories for years, and you've been kind enough to read them and give me your comments. You've encouraged me, and I'm very grateful to you for that, but we both know I'm no good. My stuff is dry and heavy and dull. Crap. Every word I've written so far is crap. I've been out of college for close to two years now, and I spend my days sitting in an office, answering the phone for a literary agent. What kind of life is that? It's so fucking safe, so fucking dreary, I can't stand it anymore. I don't *know* anything, August. I haven't *done* anything. That's why I'm going away. To experience something that isn't

about me. To be out in the big rotten world and discover what it feels like to be part of history.

Going off to war isn't going to turn you into a writer. You're thinking like a schoolboy, Titus. At best, you'll come back with your head full of unbearable memories. At worst, you won't come back at all.

I know there's a risk. But I have to take it. I have to change my life – *right now.*

Two weeks after that conversation, I climbed into a rented Toyota Corolla and set off for Vermont to spend some time with Miriam. The trip ended with the crash that put me in the hospital, and by the time I was released, Titus had already left for Iraq. There was no chance to say good-bye to him or wish him luck or beg him to reconsider his decision one last time. Such romantic claptrap . . . such childish drivel . . . but the kid was in despair over his ruined ambitions, facing up to the fact that he didn't have it in him to do the one thing he had always wanted to do, and he ran off in an impulsive attempt to redeem himself in his own eyes.

I moved in with Miriam in early April. Three months later, Katya called from New York, sobbing into the phone. Turn on the television, she said, and there was Titus on the evening news, sitting in a chair in some unidentified room with cinder-block walls, surrounded by four men with hoods over their heads and rifles in their hands. The quality of the video was poor, and it was difficult to read the expression on Titus's face. He looked more stunned than terrified, I felt, but apparently he had been beaten, for I could dimly make out what appeared to be a large bruise on his forehead. There was no sound, but over the images the newscaster was reading his prepared text, which went more or less as follows: *Twenty-four-year-old New Yorker Titus Small, a truck driver for the contracting company BRK, was abducted this morning en route to Baghdad. His captors, who have yet to identify themselves with any known terrorist organization, are demanding ten million dollars for his release, as well as the immediate cessation of all BRK activities in Iraq. They have vowed to execute their prisoner if these demands are not met within seventy-two hours. George Reynolds, a spokesman for BRK, said his company is doing everything in its power to ensure Mr. Small's safety.*

Katya arrived at her mother's house the following day, and two nights after that we switched on her laptop and looked at the second and last video shot by the kidnappers, the one that could be seen only on the Internet. We already knew that Titus was dead. BRK had made a

substantial offer on his behalf, but as expected (why think the unthinkable when profits are at stake?), they had refused to shut down their operations in Iraq. The slaughter was carried out as promised, precisely seventy-two hours after Titus was torn from his truck and thrown into that room with the cinder-block walls. I still don't understand why the three of us felt driven to watch the tape – as if it were an obligation, a sacred duty. We all knew it would go on haunting us for the rest of our lives, and yet somehow we felt we had to be there with Titus, to keep our eyes open to the horror for his sake, to breathe him into us and hold him there – in us, that lonely, miserable death, in us, the cruelty that was visited on him in those last moments, in us and no one else, so as not to abandon him to the pitiless dark that swallowed him up.

Mercifully, there is no sound.

Mercifully, a hood has been placed over his head.

He is sitting in a chair with his hands tied behind him, motionless, making no attempt to break free. The four men from the previous video are standing around him, three holding rifles, the fourth with a hatchet in his right hand. Without any signal or gesture from the others, the fourth man suddenly brings the blade down on Titus's neck. Titus jerks to his right, his upper body squirms, and then blood starts seeping through the hood. Another blow from the hatchet, this one from behind. Titus's head lolls forward, and by now blood is streaming down all over him. More blows: front and back, right and left, the dull blade chopping long past the moment of death.

One of the men puts down his rifle and clamps Titus's head firmly in his two hands to prop it up as the man with the hatchet continues to go about his business. They are both covered in blood.

When the head is finally severed from the body, the executioner lets the hatchet fall to the floor. The other man removes the hood from Titus's head, and then a third man takes hold of Titus's long red hair and carries the head closer to the camera. Blood is dripping everywhere. Titus is no longer quite human. He has become the idea of a person, a person and not a person, a dead bleeding thing: *une nature morte*.

The man holding the head backs away from the camera, and a fourth man approaches with a knife. One by one, working with great speed and precision, he stabs out the boy's eyes.

The camera rolls for a few more seconds, and then the screen goes black.

Impossible to know how long it has lasted. Fifteen minutes. A thousand years.

I hear the alarm clock ticking on the floor. For the first time in hours, I close my eyes, wondering if it might not be possible to sleep after all. Katya stirs, lets out a little groan, and then rolls onto her side. I consider putting my hand on her back and stroking it for a few seconds but then give up the idea. Sleep is such a rare commodity in this house, I don't want to risk disturbing her. Invisible stars, invisible sky, invisible world. I see Sonia's hands on the keyboard. She's playing something by Haydn, but I can't hear anything, the notes make no sound, and then she swivels around on the stool and Miriam runs into her arms, a three-year-old Miriam, an image from the distant past, perhaps real, perhaps imagined, I can barely tell the difference anymore. The real and the imagined are one. Thoughts are real, even thoughts of unreal things. Invisible stars, invisible sky. The sound of my breath, the sound of Katya's breath. Bedtime prayers, the rituals of childhood, the gravity of childhood. *If I should die before I wake*. How fast it all goes. Yesterday a child, today an old man, and from then until now, how many beats of the heart, how many breaths, how many words spoken and heard? Touch me, someone. Put your hand on my face and talk to me . . .

*

I can't be sure, but I think I might have dozed off for a while. No more than a few minutes, perhaps only seconds, but suddenly I've been interrupted by something, a sound, I believe, yes, several sounds in fact, a knocking on the door, a faint and persistent knocking, and then I open my eyes and tell Miriam to come in. As the door opens, I can see her face with a certain clarity, and I understand that it's no longer night, that we've come to the cusp of dawn. The world inside my room is gray now. Miriam has already put on some clothes (blue jeans and a baggy white sweater), and the moment she shuts the door behind her, the vireo lets out his first chirp of the day.

What a relief, she whispers, looking at the sleeping Katya. I just checked in on her, and when she wasn't in her bed, I got a little scared.

She came down a few hours ago, I whisper back to her. Another rough night, so we lay in the dark and talked.

Miriam walks over to the bed, plants a kiss on my cheek, and sits down beside me. Are you hungry? she asks.

A little.

Maybe I should start the coffee.

No, sit here and talk to me for a while. There's something I need to know.

About what?

Katya and Titus. She told me she broke up with him before he went away. Is that true? She seems to think he left because of her.

You had so many other things on your mind, I didn't want to bother you with it. Mommy's cancer . . . all those months . . . and then the car accident. But yes, they broke up.

When?

Let me think . . . Your seventieth birthday was in February, February two thousand and five. Mommy was already sick then. It was just a few months after that. Late spring or early summer.

But Titus didn't leave until the following February, two thousand and six.

Eight or nine months after they broke up.

So Katya is wrong. He didn't go to Iraq because of her.

She's punishing herself. That's what this is all about. She wants to implicate herself in what happened to him, but she really had nothing to do with it. You talked to him before he left. He explained his reasons to you.

And he didn't mention Katya's name. Not once.

You see?

It makes me feel a little better. And also a little worse.

She's coming along now. I can smell it. Bit by bit by bit. The next step is to talk her into going back to school.

She says she's considering it.

Which was out of the question just two months ago.

I grab hold of Miriam's hand and say, I almost forgot. I read some more of your manuscript last night . . .

And?

I think you've nailed it. No more doubts, all right? You're doing a first-rate job.

Are you sure?

I've told a lot of fibs in my day, but I never lie about books.

Miriam grins, aware of the two hundred and fifty-nine secret references buried in that remark, and I grin back at her. Keep on smiling, I say. You look beautiful when you smile.

Only when I smile?

All the time. Every minute of every day.

Another one of your fibs, but I'll take it. She pats me on the cheek and says: Coffee and toast?

No, not today. I think we should go all out this morning. Scrambled eggs and bacon, French toast, pancakes, the whole works.

A farmer's breakfast.

That's it, a farmer's breakfast.

I'll get your crutch, she says, standing up and walking over to the hook on the wall beside my bed.

I follow her with my eyes for a moment, and then I say: Rose Hawthorne wasn't much of a poet, was she?

No. Pretty awful, in fact.

But there's one line . . . one great line. I think it's as good as anything I've ever read.

Which one? she asks, turning to look at me.

*As the weird world rolls on.*

Miriam breaks into another big smile. I knew it, she says. When I was typing up the quote, I said to myself, He's going to like this one. It could have been written for him.

The weird world rolls on, Miriam.

Crutch in hand, she walks back to the bed and sits down beside me. Yes, Dad, she says, studying her daughter with a worried look in her eyes, the weird world rolls on.

[2007]

# INVISIBLE

# I

I shook his hand for the first time in the spring of 1967. I was a second-year student at Columbia then, a know-nothing boy with an appetite for books and a belief (or delusion) that one day I would become good enough to call myself a poet, and because I read poetry, I had already met his namesake in Dante's hell, a dead man shuffling through the final verses of the twenty-eighth canto of the *Inferno*. Bertran de Born, the twelfth-century Provençal poet, carrying his severed head by the hair as it sways back and forth like a lantern – surely one of the most grotesque images in that book-length catalogue of hallucinations and torments. Dante was a staunch defender of de Born's writing, but he condemned him to eternal damnation for having counseled Prince Henry to rebel against his father, King Henry II, and because de Born caused division between father and son and turned them into enemies, Dante's ingenious punishment was to divide de Born from himself. Hence the decapitated body wailing in the underworld, asking the Florentine traveler if any pain could be more terrible than his.

When he introduced himself as Rudolf Born, my thoughts immediately turned to the poet. Any relation to Bertran? I asked.

Ah, he replied, that wretched creature who lost his head. Perhaps, but it doesn't seem likely, I'm afraid. No *de*. You need to be nobility for that, and the sad truth is I'm anything but noble.

I have no memory of why I was there. Someone must have asked me to go along, but who that person was has long since evaporated from my mind. I can't even recall where the party was held – uptown or downtown, in an apartment or a loft – nor my reason for accepting the invitation in the first place, since I tended to shun large gatherings at the time, put off by the din of chattering crowds, embarrassed by the shyness that would overcome me in the presence of people I didn't know. But that night, inexplicably, I said yes, and off I went with my forgotten friend to wherever it was he took me.

What I remember is this: at one point in the evening, I wound up standing alone in a corner of the room. I was smoking a cigarette and looking out at the people, dozens upon dozens of young bodies crammed into

the confines of that space, listening to the mingled roar of words and laughter, wondering what on earth I was doing there, and thinking that perhaps it was time to leave. An ashtray was sitting on a radiator to my left, and as I turned to snuff out my cigarette, I saw that the butt-filled receptacle was rising toward me, cradled in the palm of a man's hand. Without my noticing them, two people had just sat down on the radiator, a man and a woman, both of them older than I was, no doubt older than anyone else in the room – he around thirty-five, she in her late twenties or early thirties.

They made an incongruous pair, I felt, Born in a rumpled, somewhat soiled white linen suit with an equally rumpled white shirt under the jacket and the woman (whose name turned out to be Margot) dressed all in black. When I thanked him for the ashtray, he gave me a brief, courteous nod and said *My pleasure* with the slightest hint of a foreign accent. French or German, I couldn't tell which, since his English was almost flawless. What else did I see in those first moments? Pale skin, unkempt reddish hair (cut shorter than the hair of most men at the time), a broad, handsome face with nothing particularly distinctive about it (a generic face, somehow, a face that would become invisible in any crowd), and steady brown eyes, the probing eyes of a man who seemed to be afraid of nothing. Neither thin nor heavy, neither tall nor short, but for all that an impression of physical strength, perhaps because of the thickness of his hands. As for Margot, she sat without stirring a muscle, staring into space as if her central mission in life was to look bored. But attractive, deeply attractive to my twenty-year-old self, with her black hair, black turtleneck sweater, black miniskirt, black leather boots, and heavy black makeup around her large green eyes. Not a beauty, perhaps, but a simulacrum of beauty, as if the style and sophistication of her appearance embodied some feminine ideal of the age.

Born said that he and Margot had been on the verge of leaving, but then they spotted me standing alone in the corner, and because I looked so unhappy, they decided to come over and cheer me up – just to make sure I didn't slit my throat before the night was out. I had no idea how to interpret his remark. Was this man insulting me, I wondered, or was he actually trying to show some kindness to a lost young stranger? The words themselves had a certain playful, disarming quality, but the look in Born's eyes when he delivered them was cold and detached, and I couldn't help feeling that he was testing me, taunting me, for reasons I utterly failed to understand.

I shrugged, gave him a little smile, and said: Believe it or not, I'm having the time of my life.

That was when he stood up, shook my hand, and told me his name. After my question about Bertran de Born, he introduced me to Margot, who smiled at me in silence and then returned to her job of staring blankly into space.

Judging by your age, Born said, and judging by your knowledge of obscure poets, I would guess you're a student. A student of literature, no doubt. NYU or Columbia?

Columbia.

Columbia, he sighed. Such a dreary place.

Do you know it?

I've been teaching at the School of International Affairs since September. A visiting professor with a one-year appointment. Thankfully, it's April now, and I'll be going back to Paris in two months.

So you're French.

By circumstance, inclination, and passport. But Swiss by birth.

French Swiss or German Swiss? I'm hearing a little of both in your voice.

Born made a little clucking noise with his tongue and then looked me closely in the eye. You have a sensitive ear, he said. As a matter of fact, I *am* both – the hybrid product of a German-speaking mother and a French-speaking father. I grew up switching back and forth between the two languages.

Unsure of what to say next, I paused for a moment and then asked an innocuous question: And what are you teaching at our dismal university?

Disaster.

That's a rather broad subject, wouldn't you say?

More specifically, the disasters of French colonialism. I teach one course on the loss of Algeria and another on the loss of Indochina.

That lovely war we've inherited from you.

Never underestimate the importance of war. War is the purest, most vivid expression of the human soul.

You're beginning to sound like our headless poet.

Oh?

I take it you haven't read him.

Not a word. I only know about him from that passage in Dante.

De Born was a good poet, maybe even an excellent poet – but deeply

disturbing. He wrote some charming love poems and a moving lament after the death of Prince Henry, but his real subject, the one thing he seemed to care about with any genuine passion, was war. He absolutely reveled in it.

I see, Born said, giving me an ironic smile. A man after my own heart.

I'm talking about the pleasure of seeing men break each other's skulls open, of watching castles crumble and burn, of seeing the dead with lances protruding from their sides. It's gory stuff, believe me, and de Born doesn't flinch. The mere thought of a battlefield fills him with happiness.

I take it you have no interest in becoming a soldier.

None. I'd rather go to jail than fight in Vietnam.

And assuming you avoid both prison and the army, what plans?

No plans. Just to push on with what I'm doing and hope it works out.

Which is?

Penmanship. The fine art of scribbling.

I thought as much. When Margot saw you across the room, she said to me: Look at that boy with the sad eyes and the brooding face – I'll bet you he's a poet. Is that what you are, a poet?

I write poems, yes. And also some book reviews for the *Spectator*.

The undergraduate rag.

Everyone has to start somewhere.

Interesting . . .

Not terribly. Half the people I know want to be writers.

Why do you say *want*? If you're already doing it, then it's not about the future. It already exists in the present.

Because it's still too early to know if I'm good enough.

Do you get paid for your articles?

Of course not. It's a college paper.

Once they start paying you for your work, then you'll know you're good enough.

Before I could answer, Born suddenly turned to Margot and announced: You were right, my angel. Your young man is a poet.

Margot lifted her eyes toward me, and with a neutral, appraising look, she spoke for the first time, pronouncing her words with a foreign accent that proved to be much thicker than her companion's – an unmistakable French accent. I'm always right, she said. You should know that by now, Rudolf.

A poet, Born continued, still addressing Margot, a sometime reviewer

of books, and a student at the dreary fortress on the heights, which means he's probably our neighbor. But he has no name. At least not one that I'm aware of.

It's Walker, I said, realizing that I had neglected to introduce myself when we shook hands. Adam Walker.

Adam Walker, Born repeated, turning from Margot and looking at me as he flashed another one of his enigmatic smiles. A good, solid American name. So strong, so bland, so dependable. Adam Walker. The lonely bounty hunter in a CinemaScope Western, prowling the desert with a shotgun and six-shooter on his chestnut-brown gelding. Or else the kindhearted, straight-arrow surgeon in a daytime soap opera, tragically in love with two women at the same time.

It sounds solid, I replied, but nothing in America is solid. The name was given to my grandfather when he landed at Ellis Island in nineteen hundred. Apparently, the immigration authorities found Walshinksky too difficult to handle, so they dubbed him Walker.

What a country, Born said. Illiterate officials robbing a man of his identity with a simple stroke of the pen.

Not his identity, I said. Just his name. He worked as a kosher butcher on the Lower East Side for thirty years.

There was more, much more after that, a good hour's worth of talk that bounced around aimlessly from one subject to the next. Vietnam and the growing opposition to the war. The differences between New York and Paris. The Kennedy assassination. The American embargo on trade with Cuba. Impersonal topics, yes, but Born had strong opinions about everything, often wild, unorthodox opinions, and because he couched his words in a half-mocking, slyly condescending tone, I couldn't tell if he was serious or not. At certain moments, he sounded like a hawkish right-winger; at other moments, he advanced ideas that made him sound like a bomb-throwing anarchist. Was he trying to provoke me, I asked myself, or was this normal procedure for him, the way he went about entertaining himself on a Saturday night? Meanwhile, the inscrutable Margot had risen from her perch on the radiator to bum a cigarette from me, and after that she remained standing, contributing little to the conversation, next to nothing in fact, but studying me carefully every time I spoke, her eyes fixed on me with the unblinking curiosity of a child. I confess that I enjoyed being looked at by her, even if it made me squirm a little. There was something vaguely erotic about it, I found, but I wasn't experienced enough back then to know if she was trying to send

me a signal or simply looking for the sake of looking. The truth was that I had never run across people like this before, and because the two of them were so alien to me, so unfamiliar in their affect, the longer I talked to them, the more unreal they seemed to become – as if they were imaginary characters in a story that was taking place in my head.

I can't recall whether we were drinking, but if the party was anything like the others I had gone to since landing in New York, there must have been jugs of cheap red wine and an abundant stock of paper cups, which means that we were probably growing drunker and drunker as we continued to talk. I wish I could dredge up more of what we said, but 1967 was a long time ago, and no matter how hard I struggle to find the words and gestures and fugitive overtones of that initial encounter with Born, I mostly draw blanks. Nevertheless, a few vivid moments stand out in the blur. Born reaching into the inside pocket of his linen jacket, for example, and withdrawing the butt of a half-smoked cigar, which he proceeded to light with a match while informing me that it was a Montecristo, the best of all Cuban cigars – banned in America then, as they still are now – which he had managed to obtain through *a personal connection* with someone who worked at the French embassy in Washington. He then went on to say a few kind words about Castro – this from the same man who just minutes earlier had defended Johnson, McNamara, and Westmoreland for their heroic work in battling the menace of communism in Vietnam. I remember feeling amused at the sight of the disheveled political scientist pulling out that half-smoked cigar and said he reminded me of the owner of a South American coffee plantation who had gone mad after spending too many years in the jungle. Born laughed at the remark, quickly adding that I wasn't far from the truth, since he had spent the bulk of his childhood in Guatemala. When I asked him to tell me more, however, he waved me off with the words *another time*.

I'll give you the whole story, he said, but in quieter surroundings. The whole story of my incredible life so far. You'll see, Mr. Walker. One day, you'll wind up writing my biography. I guarantee it.

Born's cigar, then, and my role as his future Boswell, but also an image of Margot touching my face with her right hand and whispering: Be good to yourself. That must have come toward the end, when we were about to leave or had already gone downstairs, but I have no memory of leaving and no memory of saying good-bye to them. All those things have been blotted out, erased by the work of forty years. They were two

strangers I met at a noisy party one spring night in the New York of my youth, a New York that no longer exists, and that was that. I could be wrong, but I'm fairly certain that we didn't even bother to exchange phone numbers.

I assumed I would never see them again. Born had been teaching at Columbia for seven months, and since I hadn't crossed paths with him in all that time, it seemed unlikely that I would run into him now. But odds don't count when it comes to actual events, and just because a thing is unlikely to happen, that doesn't mean it won't. Two days after the party, I walked into the West End Bar following my final class of the afternoon, wondering if I might not find one of my friends there. The West End was a dingy, cavernous hole with more than a dozen booths and tables, a vast oval bar in the center of the front room, and an area near the entrance where you could buy bad cafeteria-style lunches and dinners – my hangout of choice, frequented by students, drunks, and neighborhood regulars. It happened to be a warm, sun-filled afternoon, and consequently few people were present at that hour. As I made my tour around the bar in search of a familiar face, I saw Born sitting alone in a booth at the back. He was reading a German newsmagazine (*Der Spiegel*, I think), smoking another one of his Cuban cigars, and ignoring the half-empty glass of beer that stood on the table to his left. Once again, he was wearing his white suit – or perhaps a different one, since the jacket looked cleaner and less rumpled than the one he'd been wearing Saturday night – but the white shirt was gone, replaced by something red – a deep, solid red, midway between brick and crimson.

Curiously, my first impulse was to turn around and walk out without saying hello to him. There is much to be explored in this hesitation, I believe, for it seems to suggest that I already understood that I would do well to keep my distance from Born, that allowing myself to get involved with him could possibly lead to trouble. How did I know this? I had spent little more than an hour in his company, but even in that short time I had sensed there was something off about him, something vaguely repellent. That wasn't to deny his other qualities – his charm, his intelligence, his humor – but underneath it all he had emanated a darkness and a cynicism that had thrown me off balance, had left me feeling that he wasn't a man who could be trusted. Would I have formed a different impression of him if I hadn't despised his politics? Impossible to say. My father and I disagreed on nearly every

political issue of the moment, but that didn't prevent me from thinking he was fundamentally a good person – or at least not a bad person. But Born wasn't good. He was witty and eccentric and unpredictable, but to contend that war is the purest expression of the human soul automatically excludes you from the realm of goodness. And if he had spoken those words in jest, as a way of challenging yet another anti-militaristic student to fight back and denounce his position, then he was simply perverse.

Mr. Walker, he said, looking up from his magazine and gesturing for me to join him at his table. Just the man I've been looking for.

I could have invented an excuse and told him I was late for another appointment, but I didn't. That was the other half of the complex equation that represented my dealings with Born. Wary as I might have been, I was also fascinated by this peculiar, unreadable person, and the fact that he seemed genuinely glad to have stumbled into me stoked the fires of my vanity – that invisible cauldron of self-regard and ambition that simmers and burns in each one of us. Whatever reservations I had about him, whatever doubts I harbored about his dubious character, I couldn't stop myself from wanting him to like me, to think that I was something more than a plodding, run-of-the-mill American undergraduate, to see the promise I hoped I had in me but which I doubted nine out of every ten minutes of my waking life.

Once I had slid into the booth, Born looked at me across the table, disgorged a large puff of smoke from his cigar, and smiled. You made a favorable impression on Margot the other night, he said.

I was impressed by her too, I answered.

You might have noticed that she doesn't say much.

Her English isn't terribly good. It's hard to express yourself in a language that gives you trouble.

Her French is perfectly fluent, but she doesn't say much in French either.

Well, words aren't everything.

A strange comment from a man who fancies himself a writer.

I'm talking about Margot –

Yes, Margot. Exactly. Which brings me to my point. A woman prone to long silences, but she talked a blue streak on our way home from the party Saturday night.

Interesting, I said, not certain where the conversation was going. And what loosened her tongue?

You, my boy. She's taken a real liking to you, but you should also know that she's extremely worried.

Worried? Why on earth should she be worried? She doesn't even know me.

Perhaps not, but she's gotten it into her head that your future is at risk.

Everyone's future is at risk. Especially American males in their late teens and early twenties, as you well know. But as long as I don't flunk out of school, the draft can't touch me until after I graduate. I wouldn't want to bet on it, but it's possible the war will be over by then.

Don't bet on it, Mr. Walker. This little skirmish is going to drag on for years.

I lit up a Chesterfield and nodded. For once I agree with you, I said.

Anyway, Margot wasn't talking about Vietnam. Yes, you might land in jail – or come home in a box two or three years from now – but she wasn't thinking about the war. She believes you're too good for this world, and because of that, the world will eventually crush you.

I don't follow her reasoning.

She thinks you need help. Margot might not possess the quickest brain in the Western world, but she meets a boy who says he's a poet, and the first word that comes to her is *starvation*.

That's absurd. She has no idea what she's talking about.

Forgive me for contradicting you, but when I asked you at the party what your plans were, you said you didn't have any. Other than your nebulous ambition to write poetry, of course. How much do poets earn, Mr. Walker?

Most of the time nothing. If you get lucky, every now and then someone might throw you a few pennies.

Sounds like starvation to me.

I never said I planned to make my living as a writer. I'll have to find a job.

Such as?

It's difficult to say. I could work for a publishing house or a magazine. I could translate books. I could write articles and reviews. One of those things, or else several of them in combination. It's too early to know, and until I'm out in the world, there's no point in losing any sleep over it, is there?

Like it or not, you're in the world now, and the sooner you learn how to fend for yourself, the better off you'll be.

Why this sudden concern? We've only just met, and why should you care about what happens to me?

Because Margot asked me to help you, and since she rarely asks me for anything, I feel honor-bound to obey her wishes.

Tell her thank you, but there's no need for you to put yourself out. I can get by on my own.

Stubborn, aren't you? Born said, resting his nearly spent cigar on the rim of the ashtray and then leaning forward until his face was just a few inches from mine. If I offered you a job, are you telling me you'd turn it down?

It depends on what the job is.

That remains to be seen. I have several ideas, but I haven't made a decision yet. Maybe you can help me.

I'm not sure I understand.

My father died ten months ago, and it appears I've inherited a considerable amount of money. Not enough to buy a château or an airline company, but enough to make a small difference in the world. I could engage you to write my biography, of course, but I think it's a little too soon for that. I'm still only thirty-six, and I find it unseemly to talk about a man's life before he gets to fifty. What, then? I've considered starting a publishing house, but I'm not sure I have the stomach for all the long-range planning that would entail. A magazine, on the other hand, strikes me as much more fun. A monthly, or perhaps a quarterly, but something fresh and daring, a publication that would stir people up and cause controversy with every issue. What do you think of that, Mr. Walker? Would working on a magazine be of any interest to you?

Of course it would. The only question is: why me? You're going back to France in a couple of months, so I assume you're talking about a French magazine. My French isn't bad, but it isn't good enough for what you'd need. And besides, I go to college here in New York. I can't just pick up and move.

Who said anything about moving? Who said anything about a French magazine? If I had a good American staff to run things here, I could pop over every once in a while to check up on them, but essentially I'd stay out of it. I have no interest in directing a magazine myself. I have my own work, my own career, and I wouldn't have the time for it. My sole responsibility would be to put up the money – and then hope to turn a profit.

You're a political scientist, and I'm a literature student. If you're thinking of starting a political magazine, then count me out. We're on

opposite sides of the fence, and if I tried to work for you, it would turn into a fiasco. But if you're talking about a literary magazine, then yes, I'd be very interested.

Just because I teach international relations and write about government and public policy doesn't mean I'm a philistine. I care about art as much as you do, Mr. Walker, and I wouldn't ask you to work on a magazine if it wasn't a literary magazine.

How do you know I can handle it?

I don't. But I have a hunch.

It doesn't make any sense. Here you are offering me a job and you haven't read a word I've written.

Not so. Just this morning I read four of your poems in the most recent number of the *Columbia Review* and six of your articles in the student paper. The piece on Melville was particularly good, I thought, and I was moved by your little poem about the graveyard. *How many more skies above me / Until this one vanishes as well?* Impressive.

I'm glad you think so. Even more impressive is that you acted so quickly.

That's the way I am. Life is too short for dawdling.

My third-grade teacher used to tell us the same thing – with exactly those words.

A wonderful place, this America of yours. You've had an excellent education, Mr. Walker.

Born laughed at the inanity of his remark, took a sip of beer, and then leaned back to ponder the idea he had set in motion.

What I want you to do, he finally said, is draw up a plan, a prospectus. Tell me about the work that would appear in the magazine, the length of each issue, the cover art, the design, the frequency of publication, what name you'd want to give it, and so on. Leave it at my office when you're finished. I'll look it over, and if I like your ideas, we'll be in business.

Young as I might have been, I had enough understanding of the world to realize that Born could have been playing me for a dupe. How often did you wander into a bar, bump into a man you had met only once, and walk out with the chance to start a magazine – especially when the *you* in question was a twenty-year-old nothing who had yet to prove himself on any front? It was too outlandish to be believed. In all likelihood, Born had raised my hopes only in order to crush them, and I was fully expecting him to toss my prospectus into the garbage and tell me he

wasn't interested. Still, on the off chance that he meant what he'd said, that he was honestly intending to keep his word, I felt I should give it a try. What did I have to lose? A day of thinking and writing at the most, and if Born wound up rejecting my proposal, then so be it.

Bracing myself against disappointment, I set to work that very night. Beyond listing half a dozen potential names for the magazine, however, I didn't make much headway. Not because I was confused, and not because I wasn't full of ideas, but for the simple reason that I had neglected to ask Born how much money he was willing to put into the project. Everything hinged on the size of his investment, and until I knew what his intentions were, how could I discuss any of the myriad points he had raised that afternoon: the quality of the paper, the length and frequency of the issues, the binding, the possible inclusion of art, and how much (if anything) he was prepared to pay the contributors? Literary magazines came in numerous shapes and guises, after all, from the mimeographed, stapled underground publications edited by young poets in the East Village to the stolid academic quarterlies to more commercial enterprises like the *Evergreen Review* to the sumptuous *objets* backed by well-heeled angels who lost thousands with every issue. I would have to talk to Born again, I realized, and so instead of drawing up a prospectus, I wrote him a letter explaining my problem. It was such a sad, pathetic document – *We have to talk about money* – that I decided to include something else in the envelope, just to convince him that I wasn't the out-and-out dullard I appeared to be. After our brief exchange about Bertran de Born on Saturday night, I thought it might amuse him to read one of the more savage works by the twelfth-century poet. I happened to own a paperback anthology of the troubadours – in English only – and my initial idea was simply to type up one of the poems from the book. When I began reading through the translation, however, it struck me as clumsy and inept, a rendering that failed to do justice to the strange and ugly power of the poem, and even though I didn't know a word of Provençal, I figured I could turn out something better working from a French translation. The next morning, I found what I was looking for in Butler Library: an edition of the complete de Born, with the original Provençal on the left and literal prose versions in French on the right. It took me several hours to complete the job (if I'm not mistaken, I missed a class because of it), and this is what I came up with:

I love the jubilance of springtime
When leaves and flowers burgeon forth,
And I exult in the mirth of bird songs
Resounding through the woods;
And I relish seeing the meadows
Adorned with tents and pavilions;
And great is my happiness
When the fields are packed
With armored knights and horses.

And I thrill at the sight of scouts
Forcing men and women to flee with their belongings;
And gladness fills me when they are chased
By a dense throng of armed men;
And my heart soars
When I behold mighty castles under siege
As their ramparts crumble and collapse
With troops massed at the edge of the moat
And strong, solid barriers
Hemming in the target on all sides.

And I am likewise overjoyed
When a baron leads the assault,
Mounted on his horse, armed and unafraid,
Thus giving strength to his men
Through his courage and valor.
And once the battle has begun
Each of them should be prepared
To follow him readily,
For no man can be a man
Until he has delivered and received
Blow upon blow.

In the thick of combat we will see
Maces, swords, shields, and many-colored helmets
Split and shattered,
And hordes of vassals striking in all directions
As the horses of the dead and wounded
Wander aimlessly around the field.

And once the fighting starts
Let every well-born man think only of breaking
Heads and arms, for better to be dead
Than alive and defeated.

I tell you that eating, drinking, and sleeping
Give me less pleasure than hearing the shout
Of "Charge!" from both sides, and hearing
Cries of "Help! Help!," and seeing
The great and the ungreat fall together
On the grass and in the ditches, and seeing
Corpses with the tips of broken, streamered lances
Jutting from their sides.

Barons, better to pawn
Your castles, towns, and cities
Than to give up making war.

Late that afternoon, I slipped the envelope with the letter and the poem under the door of Born's office at the School of International Affairs. I was expecting an immediate response, but several days went by before he contacted me, and his failure to call left me wondering if the magazine project was indeed just a spur-of-the-moment whim that had already played itself out – or, worse, if he had been offended by the poem, thinking that I was equating him with Bertran de Born and thereby indirectly accusing him of being a warmonger. As it turned out, I needn't have worried. When the telephone rang on Friday, he apologized for his silence, explaining that he had gone to Cambridge to deliver a lecture on Wednesday and hadn't set foot in his office until twenty minutes ago.

You're perfectly right, he continued, and I'm perfectly stupid for ignoring the question of money when we spoke the other day. How can you give me a prospectus if you don't know what the budget is? You must think I'm a moron.

Hardly, I said. I'm the one who feels stupid – for not asking you. But I couldn't tell how serious you were, and I didn't want to press.

I'm serious, Mr. Walker. I admit that I have a penchant for telling jokes, but only about small, inconsequential things. I would never lead you along on a matter like this.

I'm happy to know that.

So, in answer to your question about money . . . I'm hoping we'll do well, of course, but as with every venture of this sort, there's a large element of risk, and so realistically I have to be prepared to lose every penny of my investment. What it comes down to is the following: How much can I afford to lose? How much of my inheritance can I squander away without causing problems for myself in the future? I've given it a good deal of thought since we talked on Monday, and the answer is twenty-five thousand dollars. That's my limit. The magazine will come out four times a year, and I'll put up five thousand per issue, plus another five thousand for your annual salary. If we break even at the end of the first year, I'll fund another year. If we come out in the black, I'll put the profits into the magazine, and that would keep us going for all or part of a third year. If we lose money, however, then the second year becomes problematical. Say we're ten thousand dollars in the red. I'll put up fifteen thousand, and that's it. Do you understand the principle? I have twenty-five thousand dollars to burn, but I won't spend a dollar more than that. What do you think? Is it a fair proposition or not?

Extremely fair, and extremely generous. At five thousand dollars an issue, we could put out a first-rate magazine, something to be proud of.

I could dump all the money in your lap tomorrow, of course, but that wouldn't really help you, would it? Margot is worried about your future, and if you can make this magazine work, then your future is settled. You'll have a decent job with a decent salary, and during your off-hours you can write all the poems you want, vast epic poems about the mysteries of the human heart, short lyric poems about daisies and buttercups, fiery tracts against cruelty and injustice. Unless you land in jail or get your head blown off, of course, but we won't dwell on those grim possibilities now.

I don't know how to thank you . . .

Don't thank me. Thank Margot, your guardian angel.

I hope I see her again soon.

I'm certain you will. As long as your prospectus satisfies me, you'll be seeing as much of her as you like.

I'll do my best. But if you're looking for a magazine that will cause controversy and stir people up, I doubt a literary journal is the answer. I hope you understand that.

I do, Mr. Walker. We're talking about quality . . . about fine, rarefied things. Art for the happy few.

Or, as Stendhal must have pronounced it: *ze appy foo*.

Stendhal and Maurice Chevalier. Which reminds me . . . Speaking of chevaliers, thank you for the poem.

The poem. I forgot all about it –

The poem you translated for me.

What did you think of it?

I found it revolting and brilliant. My faux ancestor was a true samurai madman, wasn't he? But at least he had the courage of his convictions. At least he knew what he stood for. How little the world has changed since eleven eighty-six, no matter how much we prefer to think otherwise. If the magazine gets off the ground, I think we should publish de Born's poem in the first issue.

I was both heartened and bewildered. In spite of my doleful predictions, Born had talked about the project as if it was already on the brink of happening, and at this point the prospectus seemed to be little more than an empty formality. No matter what plan I drew up, I felt he was prepared to give it his stamp of approval. And yet, pleased as I was by the thought of taking charge of a well-funded magazine, which on top of everything else would pay me a rather excessive salary, for the life of me I still couldn't fathom what Born was up to. Was Margot really the cause of this unexpected burst of altruism, this blind faith in a boy with no experience in editing or publishing or business who just one week earlier had been absolutely unknown to him? And even if that was the case, why would the question of my future be of any concern to her? We had barely talked to each other at the party, and although she had looked me over carefully and given me a pat on the cheek, she had come across as a cipher, an utter blank. I couldn't imagine what she had said to Born that would have made him willing to risk twenty-five thousand dollars on my account. As far as I could tell, the prospect of publishing a magazine left him cold, and because he was indifferent, he was content to turn the whole matter over to me. When I thought back to our conversation at the West End on Monday, I realized that I had probably given him the idea in the first place. I had mentioned that I might look for work with a publisher or a magazine after I graduated from college, and a minute later he was telling me about his inheritance and how he was considering starting up a publishing house or a magazine with his newfound money. What if I had said I wanted to manufacture toasters? Would he have answered that he was thinking about investing in a toaster factory?

It took me longer to finish the prospectus than I'd imagined it would –

four or five days, I think, but that was only because I did such a thorough job. I wanted to impress Born with my diligence, and therefore I not only worked out a plan for the contents of each issue (poetry, fiction, essays, interviews, translations, as well as a section at the back for reviews of books, films, music, and art) but provided an exhaustive financial report as well: printing costs, paper costs, binding costs, matters of distribution, print runs, contributors' fees, newsstand price, subscription rates, and the pros and cons of whether to include ads. All that demanded time and research, telephone calls to printers and binders, conversations with the editors of other magazines, and a new way of thinking on my part, since I had never bothered myself with questions of commerce before. As for the name of the magazine, I wrote down several possibilities, wanting to leave the choice to Born, but my own preference was the *Stylus* – in honor of Poe, who had tried to launch a magazine with that name not long before his death.

This time, Born responded within twenty-four hours. I took that as an encouraging sign when I picked up the phone and heard his voice, but true to form he didn't come right out and say what he thought of my plan. That would have been too easy, I suppose, too pedestrian, too straightforward for a man like him, and so he toyed with me for a couple of minutes in order to prolong the suspense, asking me a number of irrelevant and disjointed questions that convinced me he was stalling for time because he didn't want to hurt my feelings when he rejected my proposal.

I trust you're in good health, Mr. Walker, he said.

I think so, I replied. Unless I've contracted a disease I'm not aware of.

But no symptoms yet.

No, I'm feeling fine.

What about your stomach? No discomfort there?

Not at the moment.

Your appetite is normal, then.

Yes, perfectly normal.

I seem to recall that your grandfather was a kosher butcher. Do you still follow those ancient laws, or have you given them up?

I never followed them in the first place.

No dietary restrictions, then.

No. I eat whatever I want to.

Fish or fowl? Beef or pork? Lamb or veal?

What about them?

Which one do you prefer?

I like them all.

In other words, you aren't difficult to please.

Not when it comes to food. With other things yes, but not with food.

Then you're open to anything Margot and I choose to prepare.

I'm not sure I understand.

Tomorrow night at seven o'clock. Are you busy?

No.

Good. Then you'll come to our apartment for dinner. A celebration is in order, don't you think?

I'm not sure. What are we celebrating?

The *Stylus,* my friend. The beginning of what I hope will turn out to be a long and fruitful partnership.

You want to go ahead with it?

Do I have to repeat myself?

You're saying you liked the prospectus?

Don't be so dense, boy. Why would I want to celebrate if I hadn't liked it?

I remember dithering over what present to give them – flowers or a bottle of wine – and opting in the end for flowers. I couldn't afford a good enough bottle to make a serious impression, and as I thought the matter through, I realized how presumptuous it would have been to offer wine to a couple of French people anyway. If I made the wrong choice – which was more than likely to happen – then I would only be exposing my ignorance, and I didn't want to start off the evening by embarrassing myself. Flowers on the other hand would be a more direct way of expressing my gratitude to Margot, since flowers were always given to the woman of the house, and if Margot was a woman who liked flowers (which was by no means certain), then she would understand that I was thanking her for having pushed Born to act on my behalf. My telephone conversation with him the previous afternoon had left me in a state of semishock, and even as I walked to their place on the night of the dinner, I was still feeling overwhelmed by the altogether improbable good luck that had fallen down on me. I remember putting on a jacket and tie for the occasion. It was the first time I had dressed up in months, and there I was, Mr. Important himself, walking across the Columbia campus with an enormous bouquet of flowers in my right hand, on my way to eat and talk business with *my publisher*.

He had sublet an apartment from a professor on a yearlong sabbatical, a large but decidedly stuffy, overfurnished place in a building on Morningside Drive, just off 116th Street. I believe it was on the third floor, and from the French windows that lined the eastern wall of the living room there was a view of the full, downward expanse of Morningside Park and the lights of Spanish Harlem beyond. Margot answered the door when I knocked, and although I can still see her face and the smile that darted across her lips when I presented her with the flowers, I have no memory of what she was wearing. It could have been black again, but I tend to think not, since I have a vague recollection of surprise, which would suggest there was something different about her from the first time we had met. As we were standing on the threshold together, before she even invited me into the apartment, Margot announced in a low voice that Rudolf was in a foul temper. There was a crisis of some sort back home, and he was going to have to leave for Paris tomorrow and wouldn't return until next week at the earliest. He was in the bedroom now, she added, on the telephone with Air France arranging his flight, so he probably wouldn't be out for another few minutes.

As I entered the apartment, I was immediately hit by the smell of food cooking in the kitchen – a sublimely delicious smell, I found, as tempting and aromatic as any vapor I had ever breathed. The kitchen happened to be where we headed first – to hunt down a vase for the flowers – and when I glanced at the stove, I saw the large covered pot that was the source of that extraordinary fragrance.

I have no idea what's in there, I said, gesturing to the pot, but if my nose knows anything, three people are going to be very happy tonight.

Rudolf tells me you like lamb, Margot said, so I decided to make a *navarin* – a lamb stew with potatoes and *navets*.

Turnips.

I can never remember that word. It's an ugly word, I think, and it hurts my mouth to say it.

All right, then. We'll banish it from the English language.

Margot seemed to enjoy my little remark – enough to give me another brief smile, at any rate – and then she began to busy herself with the flowers: putting them in the sink, removing the white paper wrapper, taking down a vase from the cupboard, trimming the stems with a pair of scissors, putting the flowers in the vase, and then filling the vase with water. Neither one of us said a word as she went about these minimal tasks, but I watched her closely, marveling at how slowly and methodically she

worked, as if putting flowers in a vase of water were a highly delicate procedure that called for one's utmost care and concentration.

Eventually, we wound up in the living room with drinks in our hands, sitting side by side on the sofa as we smoked cigarettes and looked out at the sky through the French windows. Dusk ebbed into darkness, and Born was still nowhere to be seen, but the ever-placid Margot betrayed no concern over his absence. When we'd met at the party ten or twelve days earlier, I had been rather unnerved by her long silences and oddly disconnected manner, but now that I knew what to expect, and now that I knew she liked me and thought I was *too good for this world,* I felt a bit more at ease in her company. What did we talk about in the minutes before her man finally joined us? New York (which she found to be dirty and depressing); her ambition to become a painter (she was attending a class at the School of the Arts but thought she had no talent and was too lazy to improve); how long she had known Rudolf (all her life); and what she thought of the magazine (she was crossing her fingers). When I tried to thank her for her help, however, she merely shook her head and told me not to exaggerate: she'd had nothing to do with it.

Before I could ask her what that meant, Born entered the room. Again the rumpled white pants, again the unruly shock of hair, but no jacket this time, and yet another colored shirt – pale green, if I remember correctly – and the stump of an extinguished cigar clamped between the thumb and index finger of his right hand, although he seemed not to be aware that he was holding it. My new benefactor was angry, seething with irritation over whatever crisis was forcing him to travel to Paris tomorrow, and without even bothering to say hello to me, utterly ignoring his duties as host of our little celebration, he flew into a tirade that wasn't addressed to Margot or myself so much as to the furniture in the room, the walls around him, the world at large.

Stupid bunglers, he said. Sniveling incompetents. Slow-witted functionaries with mashed potatoes for brains. The whole universe is on fire, and all they do is wring their hands and watch it burn.

Unruffled, perhaps even vaguely amused, Margot said: That's why they need you, my love. Because you're the king.

Rudolf the First, Born replied, the bright boy with the big dick. All I have to do is pull it out of my pants, piss on the fire, and the problem is solved.

Exactly, Margot said, cracking the largest smile I'd yet seen from her.

I'm getting sick of it, Born muttered, as he headed for the liquor cabinet,

put down his cigar, and poured himself a full tumbler of straight gin. How many years have I given them? he asked, taking a sip of his drink. You do it because you believe in certain principles, but no one else seems to give a damn. We're losing the battle, my friends. The ship is going down.

This was a different Born from the one I had come to know so far – the brittle, mocking jester who exulted in his own witticisms, the displaced dandy who blithely went about founding magazines and asking twenty-year-old students to his house for dinner. Something was raging inside him, and now that this other person had been revealed to me, I felt myself recoil from him, understanding that he was the kind of man who could erupt at any moment, that he was someone who actually *enjoyed* his own anger. He swigged down a second belt of gin and then turned his eyes in my direction, acknowledging my presence for the first time. I don't know what he saw in my face – astonishment? confusion? distress? – but whatever it was, he was sufficiently alarmed by it to switch off the thermostat and immediately lower the temperature. Don't worry, Mr. Walker, he said, doing his best to produce a smile. I'm just letting off a little steam.

He gradually willed himself out of his funk, and by the time we sat down to eat twenty minutes later, the storm seemed to have passed. Or so I thought when he complimented Margot on her superb cooking and praised the wine she had bought for the meal, but it proved to be no more than a temporary lull, and as the evening progressed, further squalls and gales came swooping down on us to spoil the festivities. I don't know if the gin and Burgundy affected Born's mood, but there was no question that he packed away a good deal of alcohol – at least twice the amount that Margot and I downed together – or if he was simply out of sorts because of the bad news he had received earlier in the day. Perhaps it was both in combination, or perhaps it was something else, but there was scarcely a moment during that dinner when I didn't feel that the house was about to catch on fire.

It began when Born raised his glass to toast the birth of our magazine. It was a gracious little speech, I thought, but when I jumped in and started mentioning some of the writers I was planning to solicit work from for the first issue, Born cut me off in mid-sentence and told me never to discuss business while eating, that it was bad for the digestion and I should learn to start acting like an adult. It was a rude and unpleasant thing to say, but I hid my injured pride by pretending to agree with him and then took another bite of Margot's stew. A moment later, Born

put down his fork and said to me: You like it, Mr. Walker, don't you?

Like what? I asked.

The *navarin*. You seem to be eating it with relish.

It's probably the best meal I've had all year.

In other words, you're attracted to Margot's food.

Very much. I find it delicious.

And what about Margot herself? Are you attracted to her as well?

She's sitting right across the table from me. It seems wrong to talk about her as if she weren't here.

I'm sure she doesn't mind. Do you, Margot?

No, Margot said. Not in the least.

You see, Mr. Walker? Not in the least.

All right, then, I answered. In my opinion, Margot is a highly attractive woman.

You're avoiding the question, Born said. I didn't ask if you found her attractive, I want to know if *you* are attracted to *her*.

She's your wife, Professor Born. You can't expect me to answer that. Not here, not now.

Ah, but Margot isn't my wife. She's my special friend, as it were, but we aren't married, and we have no plans to marry in the future.

You live together. As far as I'm concerned, that's as good as being married.

Come, come. Don't be such a prude. Forget that I have any connection to Margot, all right? We're talking in the abstract here, a hypothetical case.

Fine. Hypothetically speaking, I would hypothetically be attracted to Margot, yes.

Good, Born said, rubbing his hands together and smiling. Now we're getting somewhere. But attracted to what degree? Enough to want to kiss her? Enough to want to hold her naked body in your arms? Enough to want to sleep with her?

I can't answer those questions.

You're not telling me you're a virgin, are you?

No. I just don't want to answer your questions, that's all.

Am I to understand that if Margot threw herself at you and asked you to fuck her, you wouldn't be interested? Is that what you're saying? Poor Margot. You have no idea how much you've hurt her feelings.

What are you talking about?

Why don't you ask her?

Suddenly, Margot reached across the table and took hold of my hand. Don't be upset, she said. Rudolf is only trying to have some fun. You don't have to do anything you don't want to do.

Born's notion of fun had nothing to do with mine, alas, and at that stage of my life I was ill-equipped to play the sort of game he was trying to drag me into. No, I wasn't a virgin. I had slept with a number of girls by then, had fallen in and out of love several times, had suffered through a badly broken heart just two years earlier and, like most young men around the world, thought about sex almost constantly. The truth was that I would have been delighted to sleep with Margot, but I refused to allow Born to goad me into admitting it. This wasn't a hypothetical case. He actually seemed to be propositioning me on her behalf, and whatever sexual code they lived by, whatever romps and twisted dalliances they indulged in with other people, I found the whole business ugly, off-kilter, sick. Perhaps I should have spoken up and told him what I thought, but I was afraid – not of Born exactly, but of causing a rift that might lead him to change his mind about our project. I desperately wanted the magazine to work, and as long as he was willing to back it, I was prepared to put up with any amount of inconvenience and discomfort. So I did what I could to hold my ground and not lose my temper, to absorb *blow upon blow* without falling from my horse, to resist him and appease him at the same time.

I'm disappointed, Born said. Until now, I took you for an adventurer, a renegade, a man who enjoys thumbing his nose at convention, but at bottom you're just another stuffed shirt, another bourgeois simpleton. How sad. You strut around with your Provençal poets and your lofty ideals, with your draft-dodger cowardice and that ridiculous necktie of yours, and you think you're something exceptional, but what I see is a pampered middle-class boy living off Daddy's money, a poseur.

Rudolf, Margot said. That's enough. Leave him alone.

I realize I'm being a bit harsh, Born said to her. But young Adam and I are partners now, and I need to know what he's made of. Can he stand up to an honest insult, or does he crumble to pieces when he's under attack?

You've had a lot to drink, I said, and from all I can gather you've had a rough day. Maybe it's time for me to be going. We can pick up the conversation when you're back from France.

Nonsense, Born replied, pounding the table with his fist. We're still working on the stew. Then there's the salad, and after the salad the

cheese, and after the cheese dessert. Margot has already been hurt enough for one night, and the least we can do is sit here and finish her remarkable dinner. In the meantime, maybe you can tell us something about Westfield, New Jersey.

Westfield? I said, surprised to discover that Born knew where I had grown up. How did you find out about Westfield?

It wasn't difficult, he said. As it happens, I've learned quite a bit about you in the past few days. Your father, for example, Joseph Walker, age fifty-four, better known as Bud, owns and operates the Shop-Rite supermarket on the main street in town. Your mother, Marjorie, a.k.a. Marge, is forty-six and has given birth to three children: your sister, Gwyn, in November nineteen forty-five; you in March nineteen forty-seven; and your brother, Andrew, in July nineteen fifty. A tragic story. Little Andy drowned when he was seven, and it pains me to think how unbearable that loss must have been for all of you. I had a sister who died of cancer at roughly the same age, and I know what terrible things a death like that does to a family. Your father has coped with his sorrow by working fourteen hours a day, six days a week, while your mother has turned inward, battling the scourge of depression with heavy doses of prescription pharmaceuticals and twice-weekly sessions with a psychotherapist. The miracle, to my mind, is how well you and your sister have done for yourselves in the face of such calamity. Gwyn is a beautiful and talented girl in her last year at Vassar, planning to begin graduate work in English literature right here at Columbia this fall. And you, my young intellectual friend, my budding wordsmith and translator of obscure medieval poets, turn out to have been an outstanding baseball player in high school, co-captain of the varsity team, no less. *Mens sana in corpore sano*. More to the point, my sources tell me that you're a person of deep moral integrity, a pillar of moderation and sound judgment who, unlike the majority of his classmates, does not dabble in drugs. Alcohol yes, but no drugs whatsoever – not even an occasional puff of marijuana. Why is that, Mr. Walker? With all the propaganda abroad these days about the liberating powers of hallucinogens and narcotics, why haven't you succumbed to the temptation of seeking new and stimulating experiences?

Why? I said, still reeling from the impact of Born's astounding recitation about my family. I'll tell you why, but first I'd like to know how you managed to dig up so much about us in such a short time.

Is there a problem? Were there any inaccuracies in what I said?

No. It's just that I'm a little stunned, that's all. You can't be a cop or an

FBI agent, but a visiting professor at the School of International Affairs could certainly be involved with an intelligence organization of some kind. Is that what you are? A spy for the CIA?

Born cracked up laughing when I said that, treating my question as if he'd just heard the funniest joke of the century. The CIA! he roared. The CIA! Why on earth would a Frenchman work for the CIA? Forgive me for laughing, but the idea is so hilarious, I'm afraid I can't stop myself.

Well, how did you do it, then?

I'm a thorough man, Mr. Walker, a man who doesn't act until he knows everything he needs to know, and since I'm about to invest twenty-five thousand dollars in a person who qualifies as little more than a stranger to me, I felt I should learn as much about him as I could. You'd be amazed how effective an instrument the telephone can be.

Margot stood up then and began clearing plates from the table in preparation for the next course. I made a move to help her, but Born gestured for me to sit back down in my chair.

Let's return to my question, shall we? he said.

What question? I asked, no longer able to keep track of the conversation.

About why no drugs. Even the lovely Margot has a joint now and then, and to be perfectly frank with you, I have a certain fondness for weed myself. But not you. I'm curious to know why.

Because drugs scare me. Two of my friends from high school are already dead from heroin overdoses. My freshman roommate went off the rails from taking too much speed and had to drop out of college. Again and again, I've watched people climb the walls from bad LSD trips – screaming, shaking, ready to kill themselves. I don't want any part of it. Let the whole world get stoned on drugs for all I care, but I'm not interested.

And yet you drink.

Yes, I said, lifting my glass and taking another sip of wine. With immense pleasure, too, I might add. Especially with stuff as good as this to keep me company.

We moved on to the salad after that, followed by a plate of French cheeses and then a dessert baked by Margot that afternoon (apple tart? raspberry tart?), and for the next thirty minutes or so the drama that had flared up during the first part of the meal steadily diminished. Born was being nice to me again, and although he continued to drink glass after glass of wine, I was beginning to feel confident that we would get to the

end of the dinner without another outburst or insult from my capricious, half-crocked host. Then he opened a bottle of brandy, lit up one of his Cuban cigars, and started talking about politics.

Fortunately, it wasn't as gruesome as it could have been. He was deep in his cups by the time he poured the cognac, and after an ounce or two of those burning, amber spirits, he was too far gone to engage in a coherent conversation. Yes, he called me a coward again for refusing to go to Vietnam, but mostly he talked to himself, lapsing into a long, meandering monologue on any number of disparate subjects as I sat there listening in silence and Margot washed pots and pans in the kitchen. Impossible to recapture more than a fraction of what he said, but the key points are still with me, particularly his memories of fighting in Algeria, where he spent two years with the French army interrogating *filthy Arab terrorists* and losing whatever faith he'd once had in the idea of justice. Bombastic pronouncements, wild generalizations, bitter declarations about the corruption of all governments – past, present, and future; left, right, and center – and how our so-called civilization was no more than a thin screen masking a never-ending assault of barbarism and cruelty. Human beings were animals, he said, and soft-minded aesthetes like myself were no better than children, diverting ourselves with hairsplitting philosophies of art and literature to avoid confronting the essential truth of the world. Power was the only constant, and the law of life was kill or be killed, either dominate or fall victim to the savagery of monsters. He talked about Stalin and the millions of lives lost during the collectivization movement in the thirties. He talked about the Nazis and the war, and then he advanced the startling theory that Hitler's admiration of the United States had inspired him to use American history as a model for his conquest of Europe. Look at the parallels, Born said, and it's not as far-fetched as you'd think: extermination of the Indians is turned into the extermination of the Jews; westward expansion to exploit natural resources is turned into eastward expansion for the same purpose; enslavement of the blacks for low-cost labor is turned into subjugation of the Slavs to produce a similar result. Long live America, Adam, he said, pouring another shot of cognac into both our glasses. Long live the darkness inside us.

As I listened to him rant on like this, I felt a growing pity for him. Horrible as his view of the world was, I couldn't help feeling sorry for a man who had descended into such pessimism, who so willfully shunned the possibility of finding any compassion, grace, or beauty in his fellow

human beings. Born was just thirty-six, but already he was a burnt-out soul, a shattered wreck of a person, and at his core I imagined that he must have suffered terribly, living in constant pain, lacerated by the jabbing knives of despair, disgust, and self-contempt.

Margot reentered the dining room, and when she saw the state Born was in – bloodshot eyes, slurred speech, body listing to the left as if he was about to fall off his chair – she put her hand on his back and gently told him in French that the evening was over and that he should toddle off to bed. Surprisingly, he didn't protest. Nodding his head and muttering the word *merde* several times in a flat, barely audible voice, he allowed Margot to help him to his feet, and a moment later she was guiding him out of the room toward the hall that led to the back of the apartment. Did he say good night to me? I can't remember. For several minutes, I remained in my chair, expecting Margot to return in order to show me out, but when she didn't come back after what seemed to be an inordinate length of time, I stood up and headed for the front door. That was when I saw her – emerging from a bedroom at the end of the hall. I waited as she walked toward me, and the first thing she did when we were standing next to each other was put her hand on my forearm and apologize for Rudolf's behavior.

Is he always like that when he drinks? I asked.

No, almost never, she said. But he's very upset right now and has many things on his mind.

Well, at least it wasn't dull.

You comported yourself with great discretion.

So did you. And thank you for the dinner. I'll never forget the *navarin*.

Margot gave me one of her small, fleeting smiles and said: If you want me to cook for you again, let me know. I'll be happy to give you another meal while Rudolf is in Paris.

Sounds good, I said, knowing I would never find the courage to call her but at the same time feeling touched by the invitation.

Again, another flicker of a smile, and then two perfunctory kisses, one on each cheek. Good night, Adam, she said. You will be in my thoughts.

I didn't know if I was in her thoughts or not, but now that Born was out of the country, she had entered mine, and for the next two days I could barely stop thinking about her. From the first night at the party, when Margot had trained her eyes on me and studied my face with such intensity, to the disturbing conversation Born had provoked at the dinner

about the degree of my attraction to her, a sexual current had been running between us, and even if she was ten years older than I was, that didn't prevent me from imagining myself in bed with her, from wanting to go to bed with her. Was the offer to give me another dinner a veiled proposition, or was it simply a matter of generosity, a desire to help out a young student who subsisted on the wretched fare of cheap diners and warmed-over cans of precooked spaghetti? I was too timid to find out. I wanted to call her, but every time I reached for the phone, I understood that it was impossible. Margot lived with Born, and even though he had insisted that marriage wasn't in their future, she was already claimed, and I didn't feel I had the right to go after her.

Then she called me. Three days after the dinner, at ten o'clock in the morning, the telephone rang in my apartment, and there she was on the other end of the line, sounding a little hurt, disappointed that I hadn't been in touch, in her own subdued way expressing more emotion than at any time since we'd met.

I'm sorry, I lied, but I was going to call you later today. You beat me to it by a couple of hours.

Funny boy, she said, seeing right through my fib. You don't have to come if you don't want to.

But I do, I answered, meaning every word of it. Very much.

Tonight?

Tonight would be perfect.

You don't have to worry about Rudolf, Adam. He's gone, and I'm free to do whatever I like. We all are. Nobody can own another person. Do you understand that?

I think so.

How do you feel about fish?

Fish in the sea or fish on a plate?

Grilled sole. With little boiled potatoes and *choux de Bruxelles* on the side. Does that appeal to you, or would you rather have something else?

No. I'm already dreaming about the sole.

Come at seven. And don't trouble yourself with flowers this time. I know you can't afford them.

After we hung up, I spent the next nine hours in a torment of anticipation, daydreaming through my afternoon classes, pondering the mysteries of carnal attraction, and trying to understand what it was about Margot that had worked me up to such a pitch of excitement. My first impression of her had not been particularly favorable. She had

struck me as an odd and vapid creature, sympathetic at heart, perhaps, intriguing to look at, but with no electricity in her, a woman lost in some murky inner world that shut her off from true engagement with others, as if she were some silent visitor from another planet. Two days later, I had run into Born at the West End, and when he told me about her reaction to our meeting at the party, my feelings for her began to shift. Apparently she liked me and was concerned about my welfare, and when you're informed that a person likes you, your instinctive response is to like that person back. Then came the dinner. The languor and precision of her gestures as she cut the flowers and put them in the vase had stirred something in me, and the simple act of watching her move had suddenly become fascinating, hypnotic. There were depths of sensuality in her, I discovered, and the bland, uninteresting woman who seemed not to have a thought in her head turned out to be far more astute than I had imagined. She had defended me against Born at least twice during the dinner, intervening at the precise moments when things had threatened to fly out of control. Calm, always calm, barely speaking above a whisper, but each time her words had produced the desired effect. Thrown by Born's prodding insinuations, convinced that he was trying to lure me into some voyeuristic mania of his – watching me make love to Margot? – I'd assumed that she was in on it as well, and therefore I had held back and refused to play along. But now Born was on the other side of the Atlantic, and Margot still wanted to see me. It could only be for one thing. I understood now that it had always been that one thing, right from the moment she'd spotted me standing alone at the party. That was why Born had behaved so testily at the dinner – not because he wanted to instigate an evening of depraved sexual antics, but because he was angry at Margot for telling him she was attracted to me.

She cooked us dinner for five straight nights, and for five straight nights we slept together in the spare bedroom at the end of the hall. We could have used the other bedroom, which was larger and more comfortable, but neither one of us wanted to go in there. That was Born's room, the world of Born's bed, and for those five nights we made it our business to create a world of our own, sleeping in that tiny room with the single barred window and the narrow bed, which came to be known as the love bed, although love finally had nothing to do with what happened to us during those five days. We didn't fall for each other, as the saying goes, but rather we fell into each other, and in the deeply intimate space we inhabited for that short, short time, our sole preoccupation

was pleasure. The pleasure of eating and drinking, the pleasure of sex, the pleasure of taking part in a wordless animal dialogue that was conducted in a language of looking and touching, of biting, tasting, and stroking. That doesn't mean we didn't talk, but talk was kept to a minimum, and what talk there was tended to focus on food – *What should we eat tomorrow night?* – and the words we exchanged over dinner were wispy and banal, of no real importance. Margot never asked me questions about myself. She wasn't curious about my past, she didn't care about my opinions on literature or politics, and she had no interest in what I was studying. She simply took me for what I represented in her own mind – her choice of the moment, the physical being she desired – and every time I looked at her, I sensed that she was drinking me in, as if just having me there within arm's reach was enough to satisfy her. What did I learn about Margot during those days? Very little, almost nothing at all. She had grown up in Paris, was the youngest of three children, and knew Born because they were second cousins. They had been together for two years now, but she didn't think it would last much longer. He seemed to be growing bored with her, she said, and she was growing bored with herself. She shrugged when she said that, and when I saw the distant expression on her face, I had the terrible intuition that she already considered herself to be half dead. After that, I stopped pressing her to open up to me. It was enough that we were together, and I cringed at the thought of accidentally touching on something that might cause her pain.

Margot without makeup was softer and more earthbound than the striking female object she presented to the public. Margot without clothes proved to be slight, almost meager, with small, pubescent-like breasts, slender hips, and sinewy arms and legs. A full-lipped mouth, a flat belly with a slightly protruding navel, tender hands, a nest of coarse pubic hair, firm buttocks, and extremely white skin that felt smoother than any skin I had ever touched. The particulars of a body, the irrelevant, precious details. I was tentative with her at first, not knowing what to expect, a bit awed to find myself with a woman so much more experienced than I was, a beginner in the arms of a veteran, a fumbler who had always felt shy and awkward in his nakedness, who until then had always made love in the dark, preferably under the blankets, coupling with girls who had been just as shy and awkward as he was, but Margot was so comfortable with herself, so knowledgeable in the arts of nibbling, licking, and kissing, so unreluctant to explore me with her hands

and tongue, to attack, to swoon, to give herself without coyness or hesitation that it wasn't long before I let myself go. If it feels good, it's good, Margot said at one point, and that was the gift she gave me over the course of those five nights. She taught me not to be afraid of myself anymore.

I didn't want it to end. Living in that strange paradise with the strange, unfathomable Margot was one of the best, most unlikely things that had ever happened to me, but Born was due to return from Paris the next evening, and we had no choice but to cut it off. At the time, I imagined it was only a temporary cease-fire. When we said good-bye on the last morning, I told her not to worry, that sooner or later we'd figure out a way to continue, but for all my bluster and confidence Margot looked troubled, and just as I was about to leave the apartment, her eyes unexpectedly filled with tears.

I have a bad feeling, she said. I don't know why, but something tells me this is the end, that this is the last time I'll ever see you.

Don't say that, I answered. I live just a few blocks from here. You can come to my apartment anytime you want.

I'll try, Adam. I'll do my best, but don't expect too much from me. I'm not as strong as you think I am.

I don't understand.

Rudolf. Once he comes back, I think he's going to throw me out.

If he does, you can move in with me.

And live with two college boys in a dirty apartment? I'm too old for that.

My roommate isn't so bad. And the place is fairly clean, all things considered.

I hate this country. I hate everything about it except you, and you aren't enough to keep me here. If Rudolf doesn't want me anymore, I'll pack up my things and go home to Paris.

You talk as if you want it to happen, as if you're already planning to break it off yourself.

I don't know. Maybe I am.

And what about me? Haven't these days meant anything to you?

Of course they have. I've loved being with you, but we've run out of time now, and the moment you walk out of here, you'll understand that you don't need me anymore.

That's not true.

Yes, it is. You just don't know it yet.

What are you talking about?

Poor Adam. I'm not the answer. Not for you – probably not for anyone.

It was a dismal end to what had been such a momentous time for me, and I left the apartment feeling shattered, perplexed, and perhaps a little angry as well. For days afterward, I kept going over that final conversation, and the more I analyzed it, the less sense it made to me. On the one hand, Margot had teared up at the moment of my departure, confessing that she was afraid she would never see me again. That would suggest she wanted our fling to go on, but when I proposed that we begin meeting at my apartment, she had become hesitant, all but telling me it wouldn't be possible. Why not? For no reason – except that she wasn't as strong as I thought she was. I had no idea what that meant. Then she had started talking about Born, which quickly devolved into a muddle of contradictions and conflicting desires. She was worried that he was going to kick her out, but a second later that seemed to be exactly what she wanted. Even more, perhaps she was going to take the initiative and leave him herself. Nothing added up. She wanted me and didn't want me. She wanted Born and didn't want Born. Each word that came out of her mouth subverted what she had said a moment earlier, and in the end there was no way to know what she felt. Perhaps she didn't know herself. That struck me as the most plausible explanation – Margot in distress, Margot pulled apart by equal and opposite forces – but after spending those five nights with her, I couldn't help feeling hurt and abandoned. I tried to keep my spirits up – hoping she would call, hoping she would change her mind and come rushing back to me – but deep down I knew it was finished, that her fear of never seeing me again was in fact a prophecy, and that she was gone from my life for good.

Meanwhile, Born was back in New York, but a full week had gone by and I still hadn't heard from him. The longer his silence went on, the more I realized how much I was dreading his call. Had Margot told him what she and I had been up to during his absence? Were the two of them still together, or was she already back in France? After three or four days, I found myself hoping that he had forgotten about me and that I would never have to see him again. There would be no magazine, of course, but I hardly cared about that now. I had betrayed him by sleeping with his girlfriend, and even if he had more or less encouraged me to do it, I wasn't proud of what I had done – especially after Margot had told me that I didn't need her anymore, which meant, I now understood, that she didn't need me anymore. I had created a mess for myself, and coward

that I probably was, I would have preferred to hide under my bed than have to face either one of them.

But Born hadn't forgotten me. Just when I was beginning to think the story was over, he called early one evening and asked me to drop by his apartment for a chat. That was the word he used – *chat* – and I was amazed by how chipper he sounded on the phone, positively bursting with energy and good cheer.

Sorry for the delay, he said. A thousand pardons, Walker, but I've been busy, busy, juggling this and that, a thousand things, for which I beg a thousand pardons, but time is a-wasting, and the moment has come to sit down and talk business. I owe you a check for the first issue, and after we've had our little chat, I'll take you out for dinner somewhere. It's been a while, and I believe we have some catching up to do.

I didn't want to go, but I went. Not without trepidation, not without a flutter of panic twitching in my stomach, but in the end I felt I had no choice. By some miracle, the magazine appeared to be alive, and if he wanted to talk to me about it, if he was in fact ready to start writing checks to support the cause, I didn't see how I could turn down his invitation. *I believe we have some catching up to do.* Like it or not, I was about to find out if Born knew what had been going on behind his back – and, if he did know, exactly what he had done about it.

He was dressed in white again: the full suit, the shirt open at the collar, but clean and unrumpled this time, the perfect hidalgo. Freshly shaven, his hair combed, looking nattier and more pulled together than I had ever seen him. A warm smile when he opened the door, a firm shake of the hand as I entered the apartment, a friendly pat on the shoulder as he led me toward the liquor cabinet and asked me what I wanted to drink, but no Margot, no sign of her anywhere, and while that didn't necessarily mean anything, I was beginning to suspect the worst. We sat down near the French windows overlooking the park, I on the sofa, he in a large chair opposite, facing each other across the coffee table, Born grinning with contentment, so pleased with himself, so terribly happy as he told me that his trip to Paris had been a resounding success and the knotty problem that had been bedeviling his colleagues was now untangled at last. Then, after a few desultory questions about my studies and the books I had been reading lately, he leaned back in his chair and said, apropos of nothing: I want to thank you, Walker. You've done me an important service.

Thank me? For what?

For showing me the light of truth. I feel greatly in your debt.

I still don't know what you're talking about.

Margot.

What about her?

She betrayed me.

How? I asked, trying to play dumb but feeling ridiculous, crumpling up with shame as Born continued to smile at me.

She slept with you.

She told you that?

Whatever her faults might be, Margot never lies. If I'm not mistaken, you spent five straight nights with her – right here in this apartment.

I'm sorry, I said, looking down at the floor, too embarrassed to meet Born's gaze.

Don't be sorry. I fairly pushed you into it, didn't I? If I had been in your shoes, I probably would have done the same thing. It was obvious that Margot wanted to sleep with you. Why would a healthy young man turn down an opportunity like that?

If you wanted her to do it, then why do you feel betrayed?

Ah, but I didn't want her to do it. I was only pretending.

And why would you pretend?

To test her loyalty, that's why. And the tramp fell for the bait. Don't worry, Walker. I'm well rid of her, and I have you to thank for getting her out the door.

Where is she now?

Paris, I presume.

Did you push her out, or did she leave because she wanted to?

That's difficult to say. Probably a little of both. Let's call it a separation by mutual consent.

Poor Margot . . .

A wonderful cook, a wonderful fuck, but at bottom just another mindless slut. Don't feel sorry for her, Walker. She isn't worth it.

Harsh words for someone who shared your life for two years.

Perhaps. As you've already noticed, my mouth tends to run away from me at times. But facts are facts, and the fact is I'm not getting any younger. It's time for me to think about marriage, and no sane man would consider marrying a girl like Margot.

Do you have someone in mind, or is that just a statement of future intentions?

I'm engaged. As of two weeks ago. Yet one more thing I accomplished

on my trip to Paris. That's why I'm in such a good mood tonight.

Congratulations. And when is the happy day?

It's still not clear. There are complicated issues involved, and the wedding can't take place until next spring at the earliest.

A pity to wait so long.

It can't be helped. Technically, she's still married to someone else, and we have to wait for the law to do its work. Not that it isn't worth it. I've known this woman since I was your age, and she's an exemplary person, the partner I've longed for all my life.

If you care about her so much, why have you been with Margot for the past two years?

Because I didn't know I was in love with her until I saw her again in Paris.

Exit Margot, enter wife. Your bed won't be empty for long, will it?

You underestimate me, young man. Much as I'd like to move in with her now, I'm going to hold off until we're married. It's a question of principle.

Chivalry in action.

That's it. Chivalry in action.

Like our old friend from Périgord, the ever-gentle, peace-loving Bertran.

The mention of the poet's name seemed to stop Born dead in his tracks. *Merde!* he said, thwacking his knee with the palm of his left hand, I almost forgot. I owe you money, don't I? Sit tight while I look for my checks. I won't be a minute.

With those words Born bounced out of his chair and began rushing toward the other end of the apartment. I stood up to stretch my legs, and by the time I reached the dining room table, which was no more than ten or twelve feet from the sofa, he had already returned. Brusquely pulling out a chair, he sat down, opened his checkbook, and started to write – using a speckled green fountain pen, I remember, with a thick nib and blue-black ink.

I'm giving you six thousand, two hundred and fifty dollars, he said. Five thousand to pay for the first issue, plus twelve fifty to cover a fourth of your annual salary. Take your time, Adam. If you can put the contents together by . . . let's see . . . by the end of August or the beginning of September, that will be soon enough. I'll be long gone by then, of course, but we can stay in contact through the post, and if something urgent comes up, you can call me and reverse the charges.

It was the largest check I had ever seen, and when he tore it out of the book and handed it to me, I looked down at the sum and felt dizzy with apprehension. Are you sure you want to go ahead with it? I asked. This is an awful lot of money, you know.

Of course I want to go ahead with it. We made a deal, and now it's up to you to assemble the best first issue you possibly can.

But Margot's out of the picture now. You're under no obligation to her anymore.

What are you talking about?

It was Margot's idea, remember? You gave me this job because of her.

Nonsense. It was my idea from the start. The only thing Margot ever wanted was to crawl into bed with you. She couldn't have cared less about jobs or magazines or the precarious state of your future. If I told you she was the one who put me up to it, that was only because I didn't want to embarrass you.

Why in the world would you do this for me?

To be perfectly honest, I don't know. But I see something in you, Walker, something I like, and for some inexplicable reason I find myself willing to take a gamble on you. I'm betting that you'll make a success of it. Prove me right.

It was a warm spring evening, a soft and beautiful evening with a cloudless sky overhead, the smell of flowers in the air, and no wind at all, not even the faintest hint of a breeze. Born was planning to take me to a Cuban restaurant on Broadway and 109th Street (the Ideal, a favorite spot of his), but as we walked westward across the Columbia campus, he proposed that we continue on past Broadway and head for Riverside Drive, where we could stop to look at the Hudson for a few moments, and then make our way downtown along the edge of the park. It was that kind of a night, he said, and since we weren't in any rush, why not prolong the journey a bit and take advantage of the good weather? So we took our little stroll in the pleasant spring air, talking about the magazine, about the woman Born was planning to marry, about the trees and shrubs in Riverside Park, about the geological composition of the New Jersey Palisades across the river, and I remember that I felt happy, awash in a sense of well-being, and whatever misgivings I might have had about Born were beginning to melt away, or at least had been put in abeyance for now. He hadn't blamed me for allowing myself to be seduced by Margot. He had just given me a check for an enormous

amount of money. He wasn't haranguing me with his warped political ideas. For once, he seemed to be relaxed and undefensive, and perhaps he really had fallen in love, perhaps his life was turning in a new and better direction, and for that one night, in any case, I was willing to give him every benefit of the doubt.

We crossed over to the eastern sidewalk of Riverside Drive and began walking downtown. Several streetlamps had burned out, and as we approached the corner of West 112th, we found ourselves entering a block-long stretch of murk and darkness. Night had fallen in earnest by then, and it was difficult to see anything more than a yard or two in front of us. I lit up a cigarette, and through the glow of the match burning near my mouth, I glimpsed the shadowy outline of a figure emerging from a blackened doorway. A second later, Born grabbed my arm and told me to stop. Just that one word: *Stop*. I let the match fall from my hand and tossed the cigarette into the gutter. The figure was coming toward us, unmistakably walking in our direction, and after a few more steps I saw that it was a black kid dressed in dark clothes. He was rather short, probably no more than sixteen or seventeen, but after another three or four steps, I finally understood why Born had grabbed my arm, finally saw what he had already seen. The kid was holding a gun in his left hand. The gun was pointed at us, and just like that, with a single tick of the clock, the entire universe had changed. The kid wasn't a person anymore. He was that gun and nothing else, the nightmare gun that lived in every New Yorker's imagination, the heartless, inhuman gun that was destined to find you alone one night on a darkened street and send you to an early grave. Fork it over. Empty your pockets. Shut up. A moment earlier, I had been on top of the world, and now, suddenly, I was more afraid than I had ever been in my life.

The kid stopped about two feet in front of us, pointed the gun at my chest, and said: Don't move.

He was close enough now for me to see his face, and as far as I could tell he looked scared, not at all confident about what he was doing. How could I have known this? Perhaps it was something in his eyes, or perhaps I had detected a slight tremor in his lower lip – I can't be sure. Fear made me blind, and whatever sense I had of him must have come to me through my pores, a subliminal osmosis, so to speak, knowledge without consciousness, but I was almost certain that he was a beginner, a novice thug out on his first or second job.

Born was standing to my left, and after a moment I heard him say:

What do you want from us? There was a small quiver in his voice, but at least he had managed to speak, which was more than I was capable of doing just then.

Your money, the kid said. Your money and your watch. Both of you. Wallets first. And be quick about it. I ain't got all night.

I reached into my pocket for my billfold, but Born unexpectedly chose to make a stand. A stupid move, I thought, an act of defiance that could wind up getting us both killed, but there wasn't a thing I could do about it.

And what if I don't want to give you my money? he asked.

Then I'll shoot you, mister, the kid said. I'll shoot you and take your wallet anyway.

Born let out a long, histrionic sigh. You're going to regret this, little man, he said. Why don't you just run along now and leave us alone?

Why don't you just shut your fucking mouth and give me your wallet? the kid answered, thrusting the gun into the air a couple of times for emphasis.

As you wish, Born replied. But don't say I didn't warn you.

I was still looking at the kid, which meant that I had only a vague, peripheral view of Born, but at the last second I turned my head slightly to the left and saw him reach into the inside breast pocket of his jacket. I assumed he was going for his billfold, but when his hand emerged from the pocket it was bunched up into a fist, as if he was hiding something, concealing some object in his closed palm. I couldn't begin to guess what that thing might have been. An instant later, I heard a click, and the blade of a knife jumped out of its sheath. With a hard, upward thrust, Born immediately stabbed the kid with the switchblade – straight in the stomach, a dead-center hit. The boy grunted as the steel tore through his flesh, grabbed his stomach with his right hand, and slowly sank to the ground.

Shit, man, he said. It ain't even loaded.

The gun fell out of his hand and clattered onto the sidewalk. I could barely absorb what I was seeing. Too many things had happened in too short a time, and none of them seemed quite real anymore. Born swept up the gun and dropped it into the side pocket of his jacket. The kid was moaning now, clutching his stomach with both hands and writhing around on the pavement. It was too dark to make out much of anything, but after a few moments I thought I saw blood oozing onto the ground.

We have to get him to a hospital, I finally said. There's a phone booth up on Broadway. You wait with him here and I'll run to make the call.

Don't be an idiot, Born said, grabbing hold of my jacket and giving me

a good hard shake. No hospitals. The boy is going to die, and we can't have anything to do with it.

He won't die if an ambulance gets here within ten or fifteen minutes.

And if he lives, then what? Do you want to spend the next three years of your life in court?

I don't care. Walk away from it if you like. Go home and drink another bottle of gin, but I'm running off to Broadway right now to call for an ambulance.

Fine. Have it your own way. We'll pretend to be good little Boy Scouts, and I'll sit here with this piece of garbage and wait for you to come back. Is that what you want? How stupid do you think I am, Walker?

I didn't bother to answer him. Instead, I turned on my heels and started running up 112th Street toward Broadway. I was gone for ten minutes, fifteen minutes at the most, but when I returned to the spot where I'd left Born and the wounded boy, they had both disappeared. Except for a patch of congealing blood on the sidewalk, there was no sign that either one of them had ever been there.

I went home. There was no point in waiting for the ambulance now, so I climbed back up the hill toward Broadway and headed downtown. My mind was blank, incapable of producing a single coherent thought, but as I unlocked the door of the apartment, I realized that I was sobbing, had in fact been sobbing for the past several minutes. Luckily, my roommate was out, which spared me the trouble of having to talk to him in that state. I went on crying in my room, and when the tears finally stopped, I tore up Born's check and put the pieces in an envelope, which I mailed to him early the next morning. There was no accompanying letter. I was confident that the gesture spoke for itself and that he would understand I was finished with him and wanted nothing more to do with his filthy magazine.

That afternoon, the late edition of the *New York Post* reported that the body of eighteen-year-old Cedric Williams had been discovered in Riverside Park with over a dozen knife wounds gouged into his chest and stomach. There was no doubt in my mind that Born was responsible. The moment I'd left him to call for the ambulance, he had picked up the bleeding Williams and carried him into the park to finish off the job he had started on the sidewalk. Considering the amount of traffic that moves along Riverside Drive, I found it incredible that no one had spotted Born crossing the street with the kid in his arms, but according

to the paper, the investigators working on the case had yet to establish any leads.

Knowing what I did, I clearly had an obligation to call the local precinct house and tell them about Born and the knife and the attempt by Williams to hold us up. I chanced upon the article while drinking a cup of coffee in the Lions Den, the snack bar on the ground floor of the undergraduate student center, and rather than use a public phone, I decided to walk to my apartment on 107th Street and make the call from there. I still hadn't told anyone about what had happened. I had tried to reach my sister in Poughkeepsie – the one person I was prepared to unburden myself to – but she hadn't been in. Once I arrived at my apartment building, I collected my mail in the lobby before taking the elevator upstairs. There was only one letter for me: a stampless, hand-delivered envelope with my name written across the front in block letters, folded up in thirds and then shoved through a narrow slot in the mailbox. I opened it in the elevator on my way up to the ninth floor. *Not a word, Walker. Remember: I still have the knife, and I'm not afraid to use it.*

There was no signature at the bottom, but that hardly seemed necessary. It was a vicious threat, and now that I had seen Born in action, now that I had witnessed the brutality he was capable of, I felt certain he wouldn't hesitate to carry it out. He would come after me if I tried to turn him in. If I did nothing, he would leave me alone. I still had every intention of calling the police, but the day passed, and then more days passed, and I couldn't bring myself to do it. Fear reduced me to silence, but the fact was that only silence could protect me from having to cross paths with him again, and that was all that mattered to me now: to keep Born out of my life forever.

This failure to act is far and away the most reprehensible thing I have ever done, the low point in my career as a human being. Not only did it allow a killer to walk free, but it also had the insidious effect of forcing me to confront my own moral weakness, to recognize that I had never been the person I had thought I was, that I was less good, less strong, less brave than I had imagined myself to be. Horrid, implacable truths. My cowardice sickened me, and yet how not to be afraid of that knife? Born had stuck it into Williams's belly without the slightest compunction or regret, and even if the first stab could have been justified as an act of self-defense, what about the twelve others he had delivered in the park, the cold-blooded decision to kill? After torturing myself for close to a week, I finally found the courage to call my sister again, and when

I heard myself spewing out the whole sordid business to Gwyn over the course of our two-hour conversation, I realized that I didn't have a choice. I had to step forward. If I didn't talk to the police, I would lose all respect for myself, and the shame of it would go on haunting me for the rest of my life.

I'm fairly certain they believed my story. I gave them Born's note, for one thing, and although it lacked a signature, the knife was mentioned, the threat was explicit, and if there was any doubt concerning the author's identity, a handwriting expert could easily confirm that it had been composed by Born. There was also the bloodstain on the sidewalk near the corner of Riverside Drive and West 112th Street. And then there was my emergency call for the ambulance, which tallied with their records, and the additional fact that I was able to tell them that no one had been present at the scene when the ambulance arrived. At first, they were reluctant to believe that a professor at Columbia University's School of International Affairs could commit such a nasty street crime, let alone that such a person would walk around with a switchblade in his pocket, but in the end they assured me they would look into it. I left the police station convinced that the matter would soon be closed. It was the end of May, which meant there were still two or three weeks to go before the semester ended, and because I had put off reporting to the police for six long days following the discovery of Williams's corpse, I figured that Born must have thought his threatening note had done its job. But I was wrong, miserably and tragically wrong. As promised, the police did go to question him, but they quickly learned from an administrator at the School of International Affairs that Professor Born had returned to Paris earlier in the week. His mother had died quite suddenly, they were told, and with so little time remaining in the semester, his final classes were going to be taught by a substitute. In other words, Professor Born would not be coming back.

He had been frightened of me, after all. In spite of the note, he had assumed I would ignore his threat and go to the police anyway. Yes, I did go – but not soon enough, not soon enough by half, and because I gave him that extra time, he had pounced at the opportunity and run, fleeing the country and escaping the jurisdiction of New York's laws. I knew for a fact that the story about his mother's death was a sham. During our first conversation at the party in April, he had told me that both his parents were dead, and unless his mother had been resurrected in the interim, I was hard-pressed to see how she could have died twice. When

the detective called to tell me what had happened, I felt crushed, humiliated, numb. Born had defeated me. He had shown me something about myself that filled me with revulsion, and for the first time in my life I understood what it was to hate someone. I could never forgive him – and I could never forgive myself.

# II

Back in the dark ages of our youth, Walker and I had been friends. We entered Columbia together in 1965, two eighteen-year-old freshmen from New Jersey, and over the next four years we moved in the same circles, read the same books, shared the same ambitions. Then our class graduated, and I lost contact with him. In the early seventies, I ran into someone who told me Adam was living in London (or maybe it was Rome, he wasn't sure), and that was the last time I heard anyone mention his name. For the next thirty-something years, he rarely entered my thoughts, but whenever he did, I would find myself wondering how he had managed to disappear so thoroughly. Of all the young misfits from our little gang at college, Walker was the one who had struck me as the most promising, and I figured it was inevitable that sooner or later I would begin reading about the books he had written or come across something he had published in a magazine – poems or novels, short stories or reviews, perhaps a translation of one of his beloved French poets – but that moment never came, and I could only conclude that the boy who had been destined for a life in the literary world had gone on to concern himself with other matters.

A little less than a year ago (spring 2007), a UPS package was delivered to my house in Brooklyn. It contained the manuscript of Walker's story about Rudolf Born (Part I of this book), along with a cover letter from Adam that read as follows:

Dear Jim,

Forgive the intrusion after such a long silence. If memory serves, it's been thirty-eight years since we last talked, but I recently came across an announcement that you'll be doing an event in San Francisco next month (I live in Oakland), and I was wondering if you might have some free time to spend with me – perhaps dinner at my house, for example – since I'm in urgent need of help, and I believe you're the only person I know (or knew) who can give it to me. I say this not to alarm you but because of the enormous admiration I have for the books you have written – which have made me so proud of you, so proud

to have once counted myself among your friends.

By way of anticipation, I enclose a still-not-finished draft of the first chapter of a book I am trying to write. I want to go on with it but seem to have hit a wall of struggle and uncertainty – *fear* might be the word I'm looking for – and I'm hoping that a talk with you might give me the courage to climb over it or tear it down. I should add (in case you're in doubt) that it is not a work of fiction.

At the risk of sounding melodramatic, I should also add that I am not well, am in fact slowly dying of leukemia, and will be lucky to hang on for another year. Just so you know what you're getting yourself into, in case you choose to get into it. I look a fright these days (no hair! thin as a twig!), but vanity has no place in my world anymore, and I have done my best to come to terms with the thing that has happened to me, even as I fight on with the treatments. A couple of centuries ago, sixty used to be considered old, and since none of us thought we would live past thirty, reaching the double of that isn't half bad, is it?

I could go on, but I don't want to take up any more of your time. Sending you this manuscript was not an easy decision (you must be inundated by countless letters from cranks and would-be novelists), but I'll be glad to fill you in on my comings and goings of the past four decades if you decide to accept my invitation – which I fervently hope you will. As for the ms., save it for the plane trip to California if you're too busy between now and then. It's short enough to be consumed in less than an hour.

Hoping for a response.

Yours in solidarity,

Adam Walker

It hadn't been a close friendship – no shared confidences, no long one-on-one talks, no letters exchanged – but there was no question that I admired Walker, and I had no doubt that he looked on me as an equal, since he never failed to show me anything but respect and goodwill. He was a bit timid, I remember, a trait that seemed odd in a person of such keen intelligence who also happened to be one of the best-looking boys on campus – *handsome as a movie star,* as a girlfriend of mine once put it. But better to be shy than arrogant, I suppose, better to blend in delicately than to intimidate everyone with your insufferable human perfection.

He was something of a loner, then, but amiable and droll whenever he emerged from his cocoon, with a sharp, offbeat sense of humor, and what I especially liked about him was the broad range of his interests, his ability to talk about Cavalcanti, say, or John Donne, and then, with the same acumen and knowledge, turn around and tell you something about baseball that had never occurred to you before. Concerning his inner life, however, I knew nothing. Beyond the fact that he had an older sister (a remarkable beauty, by the way, leading one to suspect that the entire Walker clan had been blessed with the genes of angels), I knew nothing about his family or background, and certainly nothing about the death of his little brother. Now Walker himself was dying, a month past his sixtieth birthday he was beginning to say his farewells, and after reading his hesitant, touching letter, I couldn't help thinking that this was the start, that the bright young men of yore were at last turning old, and before long our whole generation would be gone. Rather than follow Adam's advice and ignore his manuscript until I was on the plane to California, I sat down and read it immediately.

How to describe my response? Fascination, amusement, a growing sense of dread, and then horror. If I hadn't been told it was a true story, I probably would have plunged in and taken those sixty-plus pages for the beginning of a novel (writers do, after all, sometimes inject characters who bear their own names into works of fiction), and then I might have found the ending implausible – or perhaps too abrupt, which would have made it unsatisfying – but because I approached it as a piece of autobiography from the start, Walker's confession left me shaken and filled with sorrow. Poor Adam. He was so hard on himself, so contemptuous of his weakness in relation to Born, so disgusted with his petty aspirations and youthful strivings, so sick over his failure to recognize that he was dealing with a monster, but who can blame a twenty-year-old boy for losing his bearings in the blur of sophistication and depravity that surrounds a person like Born? *He had shown me something about myself that filled me with revulsion*. But what had Walker done wrong? He had called for an ambulance on the night of the stabbing, and then, after a momentary lapse of courage, he had gone and talked to the police. Under the circumstances, no one could have done more than that. Whatever revulsion Walker felt about himself could not have been caused by how he behaved at the end. It was the beginning that distressed him, the simple fact that he had allowed himself to be seduced, and he had gone on torturing himself about it for the rest of his life – to such an extent that

now, even as his life was ending, he felt driven to march back into the past and tell the story of his shame. According to his letter, this was only the first chapter. I wondered what could possibly come next.

I wrote back to Walker that evening, assuring him that I had received his package, expressing concern and sympathy over the state of his health, telling him that in spite of everything I was happy to have heard from him after so many years, was moved by his kind words about the books I had published, and so on. Yes, I promised, I would adjust my schedule to make sure I could go to his house for dinner and would gladly discuss the problems he was having with the second chapter of his memoir. I don't have a copy of my letter, but I remember that I wrote it in a spirit of encouragement and support, calling the chapter he had sent me both *excellent* and *disturbing,* or words to that effect, and telling him I felt the project was well worth seeing through to the end. I needn't have said anything more, but curiosity got the better of me, and I concluded with what might have been an impertinence. Forgive me for asking, I wrote, but I'm not sure I can wait until next month to find out what happened to you after we last saw each other. If you're feeling up to it, I would welcome another letter before I head for your neck of the woods. Not a blow-by-blow account, of course, but the gist, whatever you care to tell me.

Not wanting to entrust my letter to the vagaries of the U.S. Postal Service, I shipped it by express mail the following morning. Two days later, I received Walker's express mail response.

> Gratified, thankful, looking forward to next month.
>
> In answer to your question, I'm more than happy to oblige you, although I'm afraid you'll find my story rather dull. June 1969. We shook hands, I remember, vowed to stay in touch, and then walked off in opposite directions, never to meet again. I went back to my parents' house in New Jersey, planning to visit for a couple of days, got drunk with my sister that night, tripped, fell down the stairs, and broke my leg. Bad luck, it would seem, but in the end it was the best thing that could have happened to me. Ten days later, *Greetings!,* and an invitation from the federal government to show up for my army physical. I hobbled into the draft board on crutches, was given a I-Y deferment because of the broken leg, and by the time the break mended, the Selective Service had instituted the lottery. I wound up drawing a high number, an obscenely high

number (346), and all of a sudden, literally in a single flash, the confrontation I had been dreading for so long was permanently erased from my future.

Beyond that early gift from the gods, I mostly bumped along, struggling to keep my balance, lurching fitfully between bouts of optimism and blinding stretches of despair. Unaccountable, perplexing, perplexed. In the fall of 1969 I moved to London – not because England attracted me, but because I couldn't stand living in America anymore. The poison of Vietnam, the tears of Vietnam, the blood of Vietnam. We were all out of our minds back then, weren't we? All driven to madness by a war we detested and couldn't stop. So I left our fair country, found myself a shithole flat in Hammersmith, and spent the next four years toiling in the sewers of Grub Street – cranking out countless freelance book reviews and accepting any translation that came my way, French books mostly, one or two in Italian, regurgitating into English everything from a dull academic history of the Middle East to an anthropological study of voodoo to crime fiction. Meanwhile, I continued writing my crabbed, gnostic poems. In 1972, a book was published by an obscure small press based in Manchester, an edition of three or four hundred copies, one review in an equally obscure little magazine, sales in the neighborhood of fifty – echoing those hilarious lines from *Krapp's Last Tape* (which I remember you were so fond of): "Seventeen copies sold, of which eleven at trade price to free circulating libraries beyond the seas. Getting known." Getting known indeed.

I pushed on with it for another year, and then, after a bitter, anguished debate with myself, I concluded that I wasn't making sufficient progress and stopped. It's not that I thought my work was bad. There were occasional sparks, a few poems that seemed to have something fresh and urgent about them, lines I felt genuinely proud of, but by and large the results were mediocre, and the prospect of living out my life as a mediocrity frightened me into quitting.

The London years. The somber revelations of dashed hopes, loveless sex in the beds of prostitutes, one serious liaison with an English girl named Dorothy that crashed to a sudden halt when she found out I was Jewish. But, believe it or not, in spite of how grim all this must sound to you, I think I was growing stronger,

finally beginning to grow up and take charge of my life. I finished my last poem in June 1973, ceremoniously burned it in the kitchen sink, and went back to America. I had sworn not to return until the last U.S. soldier had left Vietnam, but I had a new plan now, and I didn't have time for such high-minded claptrap anymore. I was going to throw myself into the trenches and fight it out with my bare fists. Good-bye, literature. Welcome to the thing-in-itself, the sensorium of the real.

Berkeley, California. Three years of law school. The idea was to do some good, to work with the poor, the downtrodden, to involve myself with the spat-upon and the invisible and see if I couldn't defend them against the cruelties and indifference of American society. More high-minded claptrap? Some might think so, but it never felt that way to me. From poetry to justice, then. Poetic justice, if you will. For the sad fact remains: there is far more poetry in the world than justice.

Now that my illness has forced me to stop working, I've had ample time to ponder my motives for choosing the life I did. In a very concrete way, I think it started that night in 1967 when I saw Born stab Cedric Williams in the belly – and then, after I had run off to call for an ambulance, carry him into the park and murder him. For no reason, no reason whatsoever, and then, even worse, for him to have gotten away with it, to have skipped the country and never to have been judged for his crime. It would be impossible to overstate how terribly this grieved me, has continued to grieve me. Justice betrayed. The anger and frustration have not diminished, and if that is how I feel, if this sense of justice is what burns most brightly in me, then I'm certain I chose the correct path for myself.

Twenty-seven years of legal aid work, community activism in the black neighborhoods of Oakland and Berkeley, rent strikes, class action suits against various corporations, police brutality cases, the list goes on. In the long run, I don't think I've accomplished much. A number of satisfying victories, yes, but this country is no less cruel now than it was then, perhaps more cruel than ever, and yet to have done nothing would have been impossible for me. I would have felt that I was living in a fraudulent relation with myself.

Am I starting to sound like a self-righteous prig? I hope not.

Income was meager, of course. The kind of work I did does not

a rich man make. But there were family resources that fell into my lap – my lap and my sister's lap – following the deaths of our parents (mother in 1974, father in 1976). We sold the house and our father's supermarket for a considerable sum, and because Gwyn is a clever and practical woman, she invested the money well, which meant that I always had enough to live on (modestly, but comfortably) without worrying too much about what my work brought in. Playing the system in order to beat the system. A fine little twist of hypocrisy, I suppose, but everyone has to put food on the table, everyone needs a roof over his head. Alas, medical bills have made a severe dent in my savings these past two years, but I think I'll have enough to carry me through to the end – assuming I don't last too long, which doesn't appear likely.

As for matters of the heart, I staggered along in my clumsy, retarded way for a good many years, too many years, crawling in and out of various beds, falling in and out of love with various women, but never felt any temptation to settle down and marry until I was thirty-six, when I met the one person who ever really counted for me, a social worker by the name of Sandra Williams – yes, the same last name that belonged to the murdered boy, a slave name, a common slave name borne by hundreds of thousands if not millions of African-Americans – and although an interracial marriage can pose numerous social problems for the couple (from both camps), I never considered it to be an impediment, for the truth was that I loved Sandra, loved her from the first day to the last. A wise woman, a brave woman, a spirited and beautiful woman, just six months younger than I was, already married and divorced when we met, with a twelve-year-old girl, Rebecca, my stepdaughter, herself now married and the mother of two, and the nineteen years I spent with Sandra turned me into someone better than I had been, better than I would have been alone or with anyone else, and now that she is dead (of cervical cancer, five years ago), not a day goes by when I don't long for her. My only regret is that we never managed to have children together, but making a family is beyond the power of a man who turns out to have been born sterile.

What more to say? I am well cared for by my housekeeper (who will cook dinner for us on the night of your visit), I see Rebecca and her family often, I talk to my sister on the telephone nearly

> every day, I have many friends. When health permits, I continue to devour books (poems, history, novels, among them yours – the instant they are published), still take an active interest in baseball (an incurable disease), and fitfully indulge in the escapism of watching films (thanks to a DVD player, loyal friend to the solitaries and shut-ins of this world). But mostly I think about the past, the old days, that long-ago year (1967) when so much happened to me, happened in me and around me, the unexpected turns and discoveries of that year, the madness of that year, which pushed me toward the life I wound up living, for both good and bad. Nothing like a fatal illness to sharpen one's thoughts, to make one want to tote up the accounts, to produce a final reckoning.
> The plan is to write the book in three parts, three chapters. Not a long book, not a complicated book, but it has to be done right, and to be stuck in the second part has become a source of terrible discombobulation. Rest assured, I am not expecting you to solve the problem for me. But I have a suspicion, perhaps a groundless suspicion, that a talk with you would give me the kick in the pants I need. Beyond that – and before that – that is, above and beyond my minuscule travails, there will be the tremendous pleasure of seeing you again . . .

I had been hoping for a word from him, but it never occurred to me that he would write more than a couple of paragraphs, that he would be willing to put in the time and effort to share such a full account of himself with me – I, who was hardly more than a stranger to him at that point. *Many friends* or not, he must have been lonely, I thought, he must have been more than a little desperate, and while I still couldn't grasp why I was the person he had chosen to be his confessor, he had latched on to me in such a way as to make it all but unthinkable not to do everything I could for him. How swiftly the weather changes. A dying friend had reentered my life after an absence of close to forty years, and suddenly I felt an obligation not to let him down. But what kind of help could I give him? He was having trouble with his book, and for some inexplicable reason he had deluded himself into thinking I had the power to say the magic words that would get him started again. Did he expect me to hand him a prescription for a pill that cured struggling authors of their writer's block? Was that all he wanted from me? It seemed so paltry, so painfully beside the point. Walker was an intelligent man, and if his

book needed to be written, he would find a way to do it.

That was more or less what I told him in my next letter. Not straight off, since there were other subjects to be addressed first (my sadness over his wife's death, my surprise over his choice of profession, my admiration for the work he had done and the battles he had fought), but once those matters had been dispensed with, I said quite bluntly and simply that I believed he would figure it out on his own. Fear is a good thing, I continued, repeating the word he had used in his first letter, fear is what drives us to take risks and extend ourselves beyond our normal limits, and any writer who feels he is standing on safe ground is unlikely to produce anything of value. As for the wall he had mentioned, I said that everyone hits those walls, and more often than not the condition of being stuck arises from a flaw in the writer's thinking – i.e., he doesn't fully understand what he is trying to say or, more subtly, he has taken a wrong approach to his subject. By way of example, I told him about the problems I had encountered while working on an early book of mine – also a memoir (of sorts), which had been divided into two parts. Part One was written in the first person, and when I began Part Two (which was more directly about myself than the previous part), I continued writing in the first person, grew more and more dissatisfied with the results, and eventually stopped. The pause lasted several months (difficult months, anguished months), and then one night the solution came to me. My approach had been wrong, I realized. By writing about myself in the first person, I had smothered myself and made myself invisible, had made it impossible for me to find the thing I was looking for. I needed to separate myself from myself, to step back and carve out some space between myself and my subject (which was myself), and therefore I returned to the beginning of Part Two and began writing it in the third person. *I* became *He*, and the distance created by that small shift allowed me to finish the book. Perhaps he (Walker) was suffering from the same problem, I suggested. Perhaps he was too close to his subject. Perhaps the material was too wrenching and personal for him to write about it with the proper objectivity in the first person. What did he think? Was there a chance that a new approach might get him up and running again?

When I sent the letter, my trip to California was still six weeks off. Walker and I had already set the date and time of our dinner, he had furnished me with directions to his house, and I wasn't anticipating another letter from him before my departure. A month went by, perhaps a little longer than that, and then, when I was least expecting it, he contacted

me again. Not by mail this time, but by telephone. Years had passed since our last conversation, but I recognized his voice at once – and yet (how to express this?) it wasn't quite the same voice I remembered, or else it was the same but with something added to it or subtracted from it, the same voice in a slightly different register: Walker at one remove from himself and the world, incapacitated, ill, speaking softly, slowly, with a barely perceptible flutter embedded in each word that escaped from his mouth, as if he were summoning all his strength to push the air up through his windpipe and into the phone.

Hi there, Jim, he said. I hope I'm not interrupting your dinner.

Not at all, I replied. We won't be eating for another twenty or thirty minutes.

Good. It must be cocktail hour, then. Assuming you still drink.

I still drink. Which is exactly what we're doing now. My wife and I just opened a bottle of wine, and we're gradually swilling ourselves into a stupor as a chicken roasts in the oven.

The pleasures of domestic life.

And what about you? How are things on your end?

Couldn't be better. A minor setback last month, but all is well again, and I've been working my head off. I wanted you to know that.

Working on the book?

Working on the book.

Which means you're unstuck.

That's why I called. To thank you for your last letter.

A new approach, then?

Yes, and it helped enormously.

This is good news.

I hope so. Rather brutal stuff, I'm afraid. Ugly things I haven't had the heart or the will to look at in years, but I'm past it now and furiously mapping out the third chapter.

You mean the second chapter is finished?

A draft. I came to the end about ten days ago.

Why didn't you send it to me?

I don't know. Too nervous, I guess. Too unsure of myself.

Don't be ridiculous.

I was thinking it might be better to wait until the whole thing was done before showing it to you.

No, no, send me the second part now. We can talk about it when I see you in Oakland next week.

After you read it, you might not want to come.

What are you talking about?

It's disgusting, Jim. Every time I think about it, it makes me want to puke.

Send it anyway. No matter what my reaction is, I promise I won't back out of the dinner. I want to see you again.

And I want to see you.

Good. Then it's settled. The twenty-fifth at seven o'clock.

You've been very kind to me.

I haven't done anything.

More than you know, good sir, more than you know.

Try to take care of yourself, all right?

I'll do my best.

See you on the twenty-fifth, then.

Yes, the twenty-fifth. At the stroke of seven.

It was only after we hung up that I realized how unsettling this conversation had been for me. For one thing, I felt certain that Walker was lying about the state of his health – which was not good, not good at all, and no doubt growing worse by the minute – and while it was perfectly understandable that he should want to hide the truth from me, to deflect any impulse on my part to pity him by toughing it out with a stoic's false cheerfulness (*Couldn't be better!*), I nevertheless felt (and this is something of a paradox) a tone of *self*-pity running through his words, as if from the beginning to the end of our talk he had been fighting back tears, willing himself not to lose his grip and start weeping into the phone. His physical condition was already a cause for grave concern, but now I was just as worried about the condition of his mind. At certain points during our conversation, he had sounded like a man on the brink of a mental breakdown, a man holding himself together with nothing more than a few frayed pieces of string and wire. Was it possible that writing the new chapter of his book had depleted him to such an extent? Or was that only one element among several, among many? Walker was dying, after all, and perhaps the mere fact of his impending death, the corrosive horror of that impending death, had become too much for him to face anymore. And yet, the trembling, tearful catch in his voice could just as easily have been caused by an adverse reaction to a medicine he was taking, a side effect of some drug that was helping to keep him alive. I didn't know. I didn't know anything, but after the lucid, forthright depiction of himself

in the first part of his book, along with the two articulate and courageous letters he had sent me, I found myself a bit thrown by how different he sounded in person. I wondered what it would be like to spend an evening in his company, enclosed in the private world of his dwindling, devastated self, and for the first time since accepting his invitation I was beginning to dread our encounter.

Two days after the phone call, the second part of his book arrived at my house in a FedEx envelope. A brief cover letter informed me that he had at last come up with a title, *1967*, and that each chapter would be headed by the name of a season. The first part was *Spring*, the part I had just been sent was *Summer*, and the part he was working on now was *Fall*. I had already heard him describe the new pages to me over the phone, and with the words *brutal*, *ugly*, and *disgusting* still fresh in my mind, I braced myself for something unbearable, a story that would be even more harsh and troubling than *Spring*.

## SUMMER

Spring turns into summer. For you it is the summer after the spring of Rudolf Born, but for the rest of the world it is the summer of the Six-Day War, the summer of race riots in more than one hundred American cities, the Summer of Love. You are twenty years old and have just finished your second year of college. When war breaks out in the Middle East, you think about joining the Israeli army and becoming a soldier, even though you are an avowed pacifist and have never shown any interest in Zionism, but before you can come to a decision and make any plans, the war suddenly ends, and you remain in New York.

Nevertheless, you feel a strong urge to quit the country, to be anywhere but where you are now, and therefore you have already gone to the dean of students and told him that you want to sign up for the Junior Year Abroad Program (after a lengthy consultation with your father, who has grudgingly given his approval). You have chosen Paris. You are not going there simply because you are fond of Paris, which you visited for the first time two summers ago, but because you are keen to perfect your French, which is adequate now but could be better. You are aware that Born is in Paris, or at least you assume he is, but you weigh the odds in your mind and figure your chances of running into him are slight. And if such an event should occur, you feel prepared to handle it in a manner appropriate to the circumstances. How difficult would it be to turn your

head and walk on past him? That is what you tell yourself, in any case, but in your innermost heart of hearts you play out scenes in which you do not turn your head, in which you confront him in the middle of the street and strangle him to death with your bare hands.

You live in a two-bedroom apartment in a building on West 107th Street between Broadway and Amsterdam Avenue. Your roommate has just graduated and is leaving the city, and because you need someone else to share the place with you, you have already invited your sister to occupy the other bedroom – for, as luck would have it, her years at Vassar have come to an end, and she is about to begin graduate work in the English Department at Columbia. You and your sister have always been close – best friends, co-conspirators, obsessed guardians of your dead brother's memory, fellow students of literature, confidants – and you are pleased with the arrangement. It is only for the summer, of course, since you will be winging off to Paris in September, but for part of June and all of July and August you will be together, dwelling under the same roof for the first time in years. After you are gone, your sister will take over the lease and find another person to live in the room you have vacated.

Your family is well-off, but not exceedingly well-off, not rich by the standards of the rich, and although your father is generous enough to provide you with an allowance to cover basic expenses, more money is needed for the books and records you want to buy, the films you want to see, the cigarettes you want to smoke, and so you begin looking for a summer job. Your sister has already found one for herself. She is just sixteen months older than you are, but her interactions with the world have always been more sensible and prudent than yours, and within days of learning that she would be studying at Columbia and sharing an apartment with you on West 107th Street, she set about looking for a job compatible with her interests and talents. Consequently, everything has been arranged in advance, and immediately after she arrives in New York, she begins working as an editorial assistant for a large commercial publisher in midtown. You, on the other hand, in your scattershot, haphazard way, put off the search until the last minute, and because you resist the idea of spending forty hours a week in an office with a tie around your neck, you jump at the first opportunity that presents itself. A friend has left town for the summer, and you apply to fill his spot as a page at Butler Library on the Columbia campus. The salary is less than half of what your sister earns, but you console yourself with the thought that you can walk to and from your job, which will exempt you from the ordeal of

having to cram yourself twice daily into a subway car filled with hordes of sweating commuters.

You are given a test before they hire you. A senior librarian hands you a stack of cards, perhaps eighty cards, perhaps a hundred cards, each one bearing the title of a book, the name of the author of that book, the year of the publication of that book, and a Dewey decimal number that indicates where that book must be shelved. The librarian is a tall, grim-faced woman of around sixty, a certain Miss Greer, and already she seems suspicious of you, determined not to give an inch. Because she has just met you and cannot possibly know who you are, you imagine that she is suspicious of all young people – as a matter of principle – and therefore what she sees when she looks at you is not you as yourself but you as yet one more guerrilla fighter in the war against authority, an unruly insurrectionist who has no business barging into the sanctum of her library and asking for work. Such are the times you live in, the times you both live in. She instructs you to put the cards in order, and you can sense how deeply she wants you to fail, how happy it will make her to reject your application, and because you want the job just as much as she doesn't want you to have it, you make sure that you don't fail. Fifteen minutes later, you hand her the cards. She sits down and begins looking through them, one by one, one after the other, all the way through to the end, and as you watch the skeptical expression on her face melt into a kind of bafflement, you know that you have done well. The stony face cracks a little smile. She says: No one ever gets it perfect. This is the first time I've seen it happen in thirty years.

You work from ten in the morning until four in the afternoon, Monday through Friday. You make it a habit to arrive promptly, entering the broad and pretentious faux-classical building designed by James Gamble Rogers with your lunch in a brown paper bag. Pomp and stuffiness aside, the building never fails to impress you with its bulk and grandeur, but the crowning touch of idiocy, you feel, the greatest embarrassment of all, are the names of the illustrious dead chiseled into the façade – Herodotus, Homer, Plato, along with numerous others – and every morning you imagine how different the library would look if it were adorned with other sets of names: the names of jazz musicians, for example (Fats Waller, Charlie Parker, Benny Goodman), or movie goddesses from the 1940s (Ingrid Bergman, Hedy Lamarr, Gene Tierney), or obscure, barely remembered baseball players (Gus Zernial, Wayne Terwilliger, Clyde Kluttz), or, quite simply, the names of your friends.

And so the day begins. You go in through the front door, the heavy front door with its polished brass fittings, walk up the marble staircase, glance at the portrait of Eisenhower (former university president, then the president who reigned over your childhood), and enter a small room to the right of the front desk, where you say good morning to Mr. Goines, your supervisor, a small man with owl glasses and a protruding belly, who doles out your chores for the day. Essentially, there are only two tasks to perform. Either you are putting books back on shelves or sending newly requested books to the main desk via dumbwaiter from one of the floors above. Each job has its advantages and disadvantages, and each can be carried out by anyone possessing the mental skills of a fruit fly.

When putting books onto the shelves, you must confirm and then reconfirm that the Dewey decimal number of the book you are shelving is one notch above the book to its left and one notch below the book to its right. The books are loaded onto a wooden cart equipped with four wheels, roughly fifty to a hundred books for each shelving session, and as you guide your little vehicle through the labyrinthine stacks, you are alone, always and everlastingly alone, since the stacks are off-limits to everyone but library personnel, and the only other person you will ever see is one of your fellow pages, manning the desk in front of the dumbwaiter. Each of the several floors is identical to all the others: an immense windowless space filled with row upon row of towering gray metal shelves, all of them stuffed to capacity with books, thousands of books, tens of thousands of books, hundreds of thousands of books, a million books, and at times even you, who love books as much as anyone on this earth, become stupefied, anxious, even nauseated when you consider how many billions of words, how many trillions of words those books contain. You are shut off from the world for hours every day, inhabiting what you come to think of as an airless bubble, even if there must be air because you are breathing, but it is dead air, air that has not stirred in centuries, and in that suffocating environment you often feel drowsy, drugged to the point of semiconsciousness, and have to fight off the urge to lie down on the floor and go to sleep.

Still, your shelving missions sometimes lead to unexpected discoveries, and the cloud of boredom that envelops you is momentarily lifted. Chancing upon a 1670 edition of *Paradise Lost,* for example. It is not the original printing from 1667, but very nearly so, a copy that came off the presses during Milton's lifetime, a book the poet conceivably could have held in his hands, and you marvel that this precious tome is not

locked away in some temperature-controlled vault for rare books but is sitting out in the open in the musty stacks. Why is this discovery so important to you, why do your hands tremble as you open the book and begin scanning its pages? Because you have spent the past several months immersed in John Milton, studying Milton more closely than any poet you have ever read. During the tormented spring of Rudolf Born, you were one of several undergraduates enrolled in Edward Tayler's class, the renowned Milton course taught by the finest professor you had all year, attending both lectures and seminars, carefully plowing your way through *Areopagitica, Paradise Lost, Paradise Regained, Samson Agonistes,* and a host of shorter works, and now that you have come to love Milton and rank him above all other poets of his time, you feel an instant surge of happiness when you stumble across this book, this three-hundred-year-old book, while making your lugubrious rounds as a shelver in the stacks of Butler Library.

Unfortunately, such moments of happiness do not come often. It is not that you are particularly unhappy with your job at the library, but as time goes by and the hours you spend there accumulate, it becomes increasingly difficult for you to keep your mind on what you are supposed to be doing, mindless as those tasks might be. A sense of unreality invades you each time you set foot in the silent stacks, a feeling that you are not truly there, that you are trapped in a body that has ceased to belong to you. And so it happens that one afternoon, just two weeks after you earned your job with the only perfect test score in the annals of pagedom, as you find yourself on yet another shelving foray, working in an aisle of medieval German history, you are half startled out of your wits when someone taps you on the shoulder from behind. You instinctively wheel around to confront the person who touched you – no doubt someone who has slipped unnoticed into this restricted area to attack and/or rob the first victim he can find – and there, much to your relief, is Mr. Goines, looking at you with a sad expression on his face. Without saying a word, he lifts his right hand into the air, crooks his forefinger at you, and with an impatient, wiggling gesture beckons you to follow him. The little man waddles down the aisle, turns right when he comes to the corridor, walks past one row of shelves, then a second, and makes another right turn into an aisle of medieval French history. You and your cart were in this aisle just twenty minutes earlier, shelving several books on life in tenth-century Normandy, and sure enough, Mr. Goines goes straight to the spot where you were working. He points to the shelf and

says, Look at this, and so you bend down and look. At first, you fail to notice anything out of the ordinary, but then Mr. Goines pulls two books off the shelf, two books separated by a distance of about twelve inches, with three or four books standing between them. Your supervisor shoves the two books close to your face, making it clear that he wants you to read the Dewey decimal numbers affixed to the spines, and it is only then that you become aware of your error. You have reversed the placement of the books, putting the first where the second should be and the second where the first should be. Please, Mr. Goines says, in a rather supercilious voice, don't ever do it again. If a book is put in the wrong place, it can be lost for twenty years or more, maybe forever.

It is a small matter, perhaps, but you feel humiliated by your negligence. Not that the two books in question could have been lost (they were on the same shelf, after all, just inches away from each other), but you understand the point Mr. Goines is trying to make, and although you bristle at the condescending tone he adopts with you, you apologize and promise to be more vigilant in the future. You think: Twenty years! Forever! You are astounded by the idea. Put something in the wrong place, and even though it is still there – quite possibly smack under your nose – it can vanish for the rest of time.

You return to your cart and continue shelving books of medieval German history. Until now, you have not known you are being spied upon. It puts a sickening taste in your mouth, and you tell yourself to be careful, to keep on your toes, to take nothing for granted ever again, not even in the benign, soporific precincts of a university library.

Shelving expeditions eat up approximately half your day. The other half is spent sitting behind a small desk on one of the upper floors, waiting for a pneumatic tube to come flying up through the intestines of the building with a withdrawal slip commanding you to retrieve this or that book for the student or professor who has just asked for it below. The pneumatic tube makes a distinctive, clattering noise as it speeds upward toward its destination, and you can hear it from the moment it begins its ascent. The stacks are distributed among several floors, and since you are just one of several pages sitting at desks on those several floors, you don't know if the pneumatic tube with the withdrawal slip rolled up inside it is headed for you or one of your colleagues. You don't find out until the last second, but if it is indeed meant for you, the metallic cylinder comes bursting out of an opening in the wall behind you and lands in the box with a propulsive thud, which instantly triggers a mechanism

that turns on the forty or fifty red lightbulbs that line the ceiling from one end of the floor to the other. These lights are essential, for it often happens that you are away from your desk when the tube arrives, in the process of searching for another book, and when you see the lights go on you are alerted to the fact that a new order has just come in. If you are not away from your desk, you pull the withdrawal slip out of the tube, go off to find the book or books that are wanted, return to your desk, tuck the withdrawal slips into the books (making sure that the top portion is sticking out by a couple of inches), load the books into the dumbwaiter in the wall behind your desk, and push the button for the second floor. To top off the operation, you return the empty tube by squeezing it into a little hole in the wall. You hear a pleasant *whoosh* as the cylinder is sucked into the vacuum, and more often than not you will go on standing there for a moment, following the sound of the clattering missile as it plunges through the pipe on its way downstairs. Then you return to your desk. You settle into your chair. You sit and wait for the next order.

On the surface, there is nothing to it. What could be simpler or less challenging than loading books into a dumbwaiter and pushing a button? After the drudgery of shelving, you would think your stints behind the desk would come as a welcome respite. As long as there are no books to retrieve (and there are many days when the pneumatic tube is sent to you just three or four times in as many hours), you can do whatever you want. You can read or write, for example, you can stroll around the floor and poke into arcane volumes, you can draw pictures, you can sneak an occasional nap. At one time or another, you manage to do all those things, or make an attempt to do them, but the atmosphere in the stacks is so oppressive, you find it difficult to focus your attention for any length of time on the book you are reading or the poem you are trying to write. You feel as if you are trapped inside an incubator, and little by little you come to understand that the library is good for one thing and one thing only: indulging in sexual fantasies. You don't know why it happens to you, but the more time you spend in that unbreathable air, the more your head fills with images of naked women, beautiful naked women, and the only thing you can think about (if *thought* is the appropriate word in this context) is fucking beautiful naked women. Not in some sensuously decked-out boudoir, not in some tranquil Arcadian meadow, but right here on the library floor, rolling around in sweaty abandon as the dust of a million books hovers in the air around you. You fuck Hedy Lamarr. You fuck Ingrid Bergman. You fuck Gene Tierney.

You couple with blondes and brunettes, with black women and Chinese women, with all the women you have ever lusted after, one by one, two by two, three by three. The hours inch along, and as you sit at your desk on the fourth floor of Butler Library, you feel your cock grow hard. It is always hard now, always hard with the hardest of hard-ons, and there are times when the pressure becomes so great that you leave your desk, dash down the corridor to the men's room, and wank into the toilet. You are disgusted with yourself. You are appalled by how quickly you give in to your desires. As you zip up you swear it will never happen again, which is exactly what you said to yourself twenty-four hours ago. Shame stalks you as you return to your desk, and you sit down wondering if there isn't something seriously wrong with you. You decide that you have never been more lonely, that you are the loneliest person in the world. You think you might be headed for a crack-up.

Your sister says to you: What do you think, Adam? Should we go home for the weekend or stay here and sweat it out in New York?

Let's stay, you answer, as you contemplate the bus ride to New Jersey and the long hours you would have to spend talking to your parents. If it gets too hot in the apartment, you say, we can always go to the movies. There are some good things playing at the New Yorker and the Thalia on Saturday and Sunday, and the air-conditioning will cool us off.

It is early July, and you and your sister have been living together for two weeks now. Since all your friends have vanished for the summer, Gwyn is the only person you have seen – not counting the people you work with at the library, but they don't count for much. You have no girlfriend at the moment (Margot was the last woman you slept with), and your sister has recently parted ways with the young professor she was involved with for the past year and a half. Therefore, you have only each other for company, but there is nothing wrong with that as far as you are concerned, and all in all you are more than satisfied with the way things have worked out since she moved in with you. You are entirely at ease in her company, you can talk more openly with her than anyone else you know, and your relations are remarkably free of conflict. Every now and then, she becomes annoyed with you for neglecting to wash the dishes or leaving a mess in the bathroom, but each time you fall down on the domestic front you promise to mend your lackadaisical habits, and little by little you have been improving.

It is a happy arrangement, then, just as you imagined it would be when

you proposed the idea in the first place, and now that you are slowly going to pieces at your job in the Castle of Yawns, you understand that living in the apartment with your sister is no doubt helping you keep your sanity, that more than anyone else she has the power to lighten the despair you carry around inside you. On the other hand, the fact that you are together again has produced some curious effects, consequences you did not foresee when the two of you discussed the possibility of joining forces back in the spring. Now you ask yourself how you could have been so blind. You and Gwyn are brother and sister, you belong to the same family, and therefore it is only natural, during the course of the long conversations you have with each other, that family matters should sometimes be mentioned – remarks about your parents, references to the past, memories of small details from the life you shared as children – and because these subjects have been unearthed so often during the weeks you have spent together, you find yourself thinking about them even when you are alone. You don't want to think about them, but you do. You have spent the past two years consciously trying to avoid your parents, doing everything you can to keep them at arm's length, and you have gone back to Westfield only when you were certain that Gwyn was going to be there as well. You still love your parents, but you don't particularly like them anymore. You came to this conclusion after your sister went off to college, leaving you alone with them for your last two years of high school, and when you finally went off to college yourself, you felt as if you had broken out of prison. It's not that you pride yourself for feeling the way you do – in fact, you are revolted by it, appalled by your coldness and lack of compassion – and you constantly berate yourself for accepting money from your father, who supports you and pays your tuition, but you need to be in college in order to stay away from him and your mother, and since you have no money of your own, and since your father earns too much for you to qualify for a scholarship, what choice do you have but to wallow in the ignominy of your two-faced position? So you run, and as you run you know you are running for your life, and unless you maintain the distance between you and your parents, you will begin to wither and die, just as surely as your brother Andy died when he drowned in Echo Lake on August 10, 1957, that small lake in New Jersey with its eerily appropriate name, for Echo too withered and died, and after her beloved Narcissus drowned, there was nothing left of her but a heap of bones and the wailing of her disembodied, inextinguishable voice.

You don't want to think about these things. You don't want to think about your parents and the eight years you spent walled up in a house of grief. You were ten at the time of Andy's death, and both you and Gwyn had been shipped off to a summer camp in New York State, which meant that neither one of you was present when the accident occurred. Your mother was alone with the seven-year-old Andy, planning to spend a week in the little lakeside bungalow your father bought in 1949 when you and your sister were no more than tots, the site of family summers, the site of smoky barbecues and mosquito-ridden sunsets, and the irony was that they were in the process of selling the place, this was to be the last summer at Echo Lake, just an hour's drive from home but no longer the calm retreat it had been now that all the new houses were going up, and so, with her two oldest kids away, your mother succumbed to a burst of nostalgia and decided to haul Andy out to the lake, even though your father was too busy to go with them. Andy wasn't much of a swimmer at that point, was still struggling to get the hang of it, but he had a daredevil streak in him, and he incited mischief with such hell-bent exuberance that everyone thought he was destined to earn an advanced degree in Practical Jokes. On the third day of the visit, sometime around six in the morning, with your mother still asleep in her room, Andy got it into his head to go for an unchaperoned swim. Before leaving, the seven-year-old adventurer sat down to write this short, semi-literate message – *Deere Mom Ime in the lake Lov Andy* – then tiptoed out of the bungalow, jumped into the water, and drowned. *Ime in the lake.*

You don't want to think about it. You have run away now, and you don't have the heart to return to that house of screams and silences, to listen to your mother howling in the bedroom upstairs, to reopen the medicine cabinet and count the bottles of tranquilizers and antidepressants, to think about the doctors and the breakdowns and the suicide attempt and the long stay in the hospital when you were twelve. You don't want to remember your father's eyes and how for years they seemed to look right through you, nor his robotic daily drill of waking at six sharp every morning and not returning from work until nine at night, or his refusal to mention the name of his dead son to you or your sister. You rarely saw him anymore, and with your mother all but incapable of tending the house and preparing meals, the ritual of the family dinner came to an end. The chores of cleaning and cooking were handled by a succession of so-called maids, principally worn-out black women in their fifties and sixties, and because on most nights your

mother preferred to eat alone in her room, it was usually just you and your sister, sitting face to face at the pink Formica table in the kitchen. Where your father ate his dinner was a mystery to you. You imagined that he went to restaurants, or perhaps the same restaurant every night, but he never said a word about it.

It is painful for you to think about these things, but now that your sister is with you again, you can't help yourself, the memories come rushing in on you against your will, and when you sit down to work on the long poem you started in June, you often find yourself stopping in mid-phrase, staring out the window, and reminiscing about your childhood.

You realize now that you began running away from them much earlier than you suspected. If not for Andy's death, you probably would have remained a compliant, dutiful son until the hour you left home, but once the household began to fall apart – with your mother withdrawing into a state of permanent guilt-racked mourning and your father scarcely present anymore – you had to look elsewhere for some kind of sustainable existence. In the circumscribed world of childhood, elsewhere meant school and the ball fields you played on with your friends. You wanted to excel at everything, and because you were lucky enough to have been endowed with reasonable intelligence and a strong body, your grades were always near the top of your class and you stood out in any number of sports. You never sat down and thought any of this through (you were too young for that), but these successes helped to nullify some of the grimness that surrounded you at home, and the more you succeeded, the more you asserted your independence from your mother and father. They wished you well, of course, they were not actively against you, but a moment arrived (you could have been eleven) when you began to crave the admiration of your friends as much as you craved your parents' love.

Hours after your mother was carted off to the mental hospital, you swore an oath on your brother's memory to be a good person for the rest of your life. You were alone in the bathroom, you remember, alone in the bathroom fighting back tears, and by good you meant honest, kind, and generous, you meant never making fun of anyone, never feeling superior to anyone, and never picking a fight with anyone. You were twelve years old. When you were thirteen, you stopped believing in God. When you were fourteen, you spent the first of three consecutive summers working in your father's supermarket (bagging, shelving, manning the register, signing in deliveries, removing trash – thus perfecting the skills that

would lead to your exalted position as a page at the Columbia library). When you were fifteen, you fell in love with a girl named Patty French. Later that year, you told your sister that you were going to become a poet. When you were sixteen, Gwyn left home and you went into internal exile.

Without Gwyn, you never would have made it that far. Much as you wanted to forge a life for yourself beyond the grasp of your family, home was where you lived, and without Gwyn to protect you in that home, you would have been smothered, annihilated, driven to the edge of madness. Early memories nonexistent, but you first see her as a five-year-old as the two of you sit naked in the bathtub, your mother washing Gwyn's hair, the shampoo foaming up in frothy white spikes and bizarre undulations as your sister throws back her head, laughing, and you look on in rapt wonder. Already, you loved her more than anyone else in the world, and until you were six or seven you assumed that you would always live with her, that you would end up as man and wife. Needless to add that you sometimes squabbled and played nasty tricks on each other, but not habitually, not half as often as most siblings do. You looked so much alike, with your dark hair and gray-green eyes, with your elongated bodies and smallish mouths, so alike that you could have passed for male and female versions of the same person, and then in jumped the fair-skinned Andy with his blond curls and short, chubby frame, and right from the start you both found him a comical personage, a clever midget in soggy diapers who had joined the family for the sole purpose of entertaining you. For the first year of his life, you treated him like a toy or pet dog, but then he began to talk, and you reluctantly decided that he must be human. A real person, then, but contrary to you and your sister, who tended to be restrained and well mannered, your little brother was a dervish of fluctuating moods, alternately boisterous and sulky, prone to sudden, uncontrollable crying fits and long spurts of jungle-crazy laughter. It couldn't have been easy for him – trying to crack into the inner circle, trying to keep up with his big sister and brother – but the gap narrowed as he grew older, the frustrations gradually diminished, and near the end the crybaby was developing into a good kid – more than a little daft at times (*Ime in the lake*) but nevertheless a good kid.

Just before Andy was born, your parents moved you and your sister into adjoining bedrooms on the third floor. It was a separate realm up there under the eaves, a small principality cut off from the rest of the house, and after the cataclysm of Echo Lake in August 1957, it became

your refuge, the only spot in that fortress of sorrow where you and your sister could escape your grieving parents. You grieved too, of course, but you grieved in the way children do, more selfishly, perhaps more solemnly, and for many months you and your sister tortured yourselves by recounting all the less-than-kind things you had ever done to Andy – the taunts, the cutting remarks, the teasing insults, the slaps and shoves, the too hard punches – as if compelled by some shadowy sense of guilt to do penance, to grovel in your wickedness by endlessly rehearsing the slew of misdemeanors you had committed over the years. These recitations always took place at night, in the dark after you had gone to bed, the two of you talking through the open door between your rooms, or else one of you in the other's bed, lying side by side on your backs, looking up at the invisible ceiling. You felt like orphans then, with the ghosts of your parents haunting the floor below, and sleeping together became a natural reflex, an abiding comfort, a remedy to ward off the shakes and tears that came so often in the months after Andy's death.

Intimacies of this sort were the unquestioned ground of your relations with your sister. It went all the way back to the beginning, to the very edge of conscious memory, and you cannot recall a single moment when you felt shy or afraid in her presence. You took baths with her when you were small children, you eagerly explored each other's bodies in games of "doctor," and on stormy afternoons when you were confined to the house, Gwyn's preferred activity was jumping on the bed together stark naked. Not just for the pleasure of the jumping, as she put it, but because she liked to see your penis flopping up and down, and diminutive as that organ must have been at that point in your life, you readily obliged her, since it always made her laugh, and nothing made you happier than to see your sister laugh. How old were you then? Four years old? Five years old? Eventually, children begin to recoil from the rowdy, Caliban nudism of toddlerhood, and by the time they reach the age of six or seven the barriers of modesty have already gone up. For some reason, this failed to happen with you and Gwyn. No more splashing in the tub, perhaps, no more doctor games, no more jumping on the bed, but still, an altogether un-American casualness as far as your bodies were concerned. The door of the bathroom you shared was often left open, and how many times did you walk past that door and catch sight of Gwyn peeing into the toilet, how many times did she glimpse you stepping from the shower without a stitch of clothing on? It felt perfectly natural to see each other naked, and now, in the summer of 1967, as you put

down your pen and look out the window to think about your childhood, you ponder this lack of inhibition and conclude that it must have been because you felt your body belonged to her, that each of you belonged to the other, and therefore it would have been unimaginable to act differently. It's true that as time went on you both became somewhat more reserved, but even when your bodies began to change, you did not completely withdraw from each other. You remember the day Gwyn walked into your room, sat down on the bed, and lifted her blouse to show you the first, tiny swell of her nipples, the earliest sign of her incipient, growing breasts. You remember showing her your first pubic hair and one of your first adolescent erections, and you also remember standing next to her in the bathroom and looking at the blood run down her legs when she had her first period. Neither one of you thought twice about going to the other when these miracles occurred. Life-altering events demanded a witness, and what better person to serve that role than one of you?

Then came the night of the grand experiment. Your parents were going away for the weekend, and they had decided that you and your sister were old enough to take care of yourselves without supervision. Gwyn was fifteen and you were fourteen. She was nearly a woman, and you were just emerging from boyhood, but both of you were trapped in the throes of early teenage desperation, thinking about sex from morning to night, masturbating incessantly, out of your minds with desire, your bodies burning with lustful fantasies, longing to be touched by someone, to be kissed by someone, ravenous and unfulfilled, aroused and alone, damned. The week before your parents' departure, the two of you had openly discussed the dilemma, the great contradiction of being old enough to want it but too young to get it. The world had played a trick on you by forcing you to live in the mid-twentieth century, citizens of an advanced industrial nation no less, whereas if you had been born into a primitive tribe somewhere in the Amazon or the South Seas, you would no longer still be virgins. That was when you hatched your plan – immediately following that conversation – but you waited until your parents were gone before you put it into action.

You were going to do it once, just once. It was supposed to be an experiment, not a new way of life, and no matter how much you enjoyed it, you would have to stop after that one night, because if you went on with it after that, things could get out of hand, the two of you could easily get carried away, and then there would be the problem of having to account for bloody sheets, not to mention the grotesque possibility,

suddenly had your first ejaculation of the night, a ferocious spasm that wound up all over her stomach. Mercifully, whatever embarrassment you felt was short-lived, for even as the juices were pouring out of you, Gwyn had begun to laugh, and by way of toasting your accomplishment, she merrily rubbed her hand across her belly.

It went on for hours. You were both so young and inexperienced, both so charged up and indefatigable, both so crazy in your hunger for each other, and because you had promised that this would be the only time, neither one of you wanted it to end. So you kept at it. With the strength and stamina of your fourteen years, you quickly rebounded from your accidental discharge, and as your sister gently put her hand around your rejuvenated penis (sublime transport, inexpressible joy), you forged on with your anatomy lesson by roaming your hands and mouth over other areas of her body. You discovered the delicious, down-soft regions of nape and inner thigh, the indelible satisfactions of back hollow and buttocks, the almost unbearable delight of the licked ear. Tactile bliss, but also the smell of the perfume Gwyn had put on for the occasion, the ever more sweaty slickness of your two bodies, and the little symphony of sounds you both made throughout the night, singly and together: the moans and whimpers, the sighs and yelps, and then, when Gwyn came for the first time (rubbing her clitoris with the middle finger of her left hand), the sound of air surging in and out of her nostrils, the accelerating speed of those breaths, the triumphant gasp at the end. The first time, followed by two other times, perhaps even a third. In your own case, beyond the early solo bungle, there was the hand of your sister wrapped around your penis, the hand moving up and down as you lay on your back in a fog of mounting excitation, and then there was her mouth, also moving up and down, her mouth around your once-again hard penis, and the profound intimacy you both felt when you came into that mouth – the fluid of one body passing into another, the intermingling of one person with another, conjoined spirits. Then your sister fell back onto the bed, opened her legs, and told you to touch her. Not there, she said, here, and she took your hand and guided you to the place where she wanted you to be, the place where you had never been, and you, who had known nothing before that night, slowly began your education as a human being.

*

Six years later, you are sitting in the kitchen of the apartment you share with your sister on West 107th Street. It is early July 1967, and you have just told her that you would prefer to stay in New York for the weekend,

that you have no interest in trekking out to your parents' house on the bus. Gwyn is sitting across the table from you, dressed in blue shorts and a white T-shirt, her long dark hair pinned up on her head because of the heat, and you notice that her arms are tanned, that in spite of the office job that keeps her indoors for much of the day, she has been out in the sun often enough for her skin to have acquired a lovely ginger-brown cast, which somehow reminds you of the color of pancakes. It is six-thirty on a Thursday evening, and you are both home from work, drinking beer directly from the can and smoking unfiltered Chesterfields. In an hour or so, you will be going out to dinner at an inexpensive Chinese restaurant – more for the air-conditioning than the food – but for now you are content to sit and do nothing, to recompose yourself after another tedious day at the library, which you have begun referring to as the Castle of Yawns. After your comment about not wanting to go to New Jersey, you have no doubt that Gwyn will start talking about your parents. You are prepared for that, and talk you will if you must, but you nevertheless hope the conversation will not last too long. The nine millionth chapter in the saga of Marge and Bud. When did you and your sister start calling your parents by their first names? You can't remember precisely, but more or less around the time Gwyn left home for college. They are still Mom and Dad when you are with them, but Marge and Bud when you and your sister are alone. A slight affectation, perhaps, but it helps to separate them from you in your mind, to create an illusion of distance, and that is what you need, you tell yourself, that is what you need more than anything else.

I don't get it, your sister says to you. You never want to go there anymore.

I wish I did, you answer, shrugging defensively, but every time I set foot in that house, I feel I'm being sucked back into the past.

Is that so terrible? You're not going to tell me all your memories are bad. That would be ridiculous. Ridiculous and untrue.

No, no, not all bad. Good and bad together. But the strange thing is, whenever I'm there, it's the bad ones I think about. When I'm not there, I mostly think about the good.

Why don't I feel that way?

I don't know. Maybe because you're not a boy.

What difference does that make?

Andy was a boy. There were two of us once, and now there's only me – sole survivor of the shipwreck.

So? Better one than none, for God's sake.

It's their eyes, Gwyn, the expression on their faces when they look at me. One minute, I feel as if I'm being reproached. Why you? they seem to be asking me. Why did you get to live when your brother didn't? And the next minute, their eyes are drowning me with tenderness, a worried, nauseating, overprotective love. It makes me want to jump out of my shoes.

You're exaggerating. There's no reproach, Adam. They're so proud of you, you should hear them carry on when you're not there. Endless hymns to the wonder boy they created, the crown prince of the Walker dynasty.

Now you're the one who's exaggerating.

Not really. If I didn't like you so much, I'd feel jealous.

I don't know how you can stand it. Watching them together, I mean. Every time I look at them, I ask myself why they're still married.

Because they want to be married, that's why.

It makes no sense. They can't even talk to each other anymore.

They've been through fire together, and they don't have to talk now if they don't feel like it. As long as they want to stay together, it's none of our business how they manage their lives.

She used to be so beautiful.

She's still beautiful.

She's too sad to be beautiful. No one that sad can still be beautiful.

You stop for a moment to absorb what you have just said. Then, turning your eyes away from your sister, unable to look at her as you formulate the next sentence, you add:

I feel so sorry for her, Gwyn. I can't tell you how many times I've wanted to call the house and tell her that everything is okay, that she can stop hating herself now, that she's punished herself long enough.

You should do it.

I don't want to insult her. Pity is such an awful, useless emotion – you have to bottle it up and keep it to yourself. The moment you try to express it, it only makes things worse.

Your sister smiles at you, somewhat inappropriately, you feel, but when you study her face and see the grave and pensive look in her eyes, you understand that she has been hoping you would say something like this, that she is relieved to hear that you are not quite as walled off and coldhearted as you make yourself out to be, that there is some compassion in you, after all. She says: Okay, little brother. You'll sweat it out in

New York if you like. But, just for your information, a trip back home every now and then can lead to some rather interesting discoveries.

Such as?

Such as the box I found under my bed the last time I was there.

What was in it?

Quite a few things, actually. One of them happened to be the play we wrote together in high school.

I shudder to think . . .

*King Ubu the Second.*

Did you take a look at it?

I couldn't resist.

And?

Not too hot, I'm afraid. But there were some funny lines, and two of the scenes almost made me laugh. When Ubu arrests his wife for burping at the table, and the bit when Ubu declares war on America so he can give it back to the Indians.

Adolescent drivel. But we had a good time, didn't we? I can remember rolling around on the floor and laughing so hard that my stomach hurt.

We took turns writing sentences, I think. Or was it whole speeches?

Speeches. But don't make me swear to it in court. I could be wrong.

We were crazy back then, weren't we? Both of us – each one as crazy as the other. And no one ever guessed. They all thought we were successful, well-adjusted kids. People looked up to us, we were envied, and deep down we were both nuts.

Again you look into your sister's eyes, and you can sense that she wants to talk about the grand experiment, a subject neither one of you has mentioned in years. Is it worth going into now, you wonder, or should you deflect the conversation onto something else? Before you can decide what to do, she says:

I mean, what we did that night was absolutely insane.

Do you think so?

Don't you?

Not really. My dick was sore for a week afterward, but I still look back on it as the best night of my life.

Gwyn smiles, disarmed by your insouciant attitude toward what most people would consider to be a crime against nature, a mortal sin. She says: You don't feel guilty?

No. I felt blameless then, and I feel blameless now. I always assumed you felt the same way.

I want to feel guilty. I tell myself I should feel guilty, but the truth is that I don't. That's why I think we were insane. Because we walked away from it without any scars.

You can't feel guilty unless you think you've done something wrong. What we did that night wasn't wrong. We didn't hurt anyone, did we? We didn't force each other to do anything we didn't want to do. We didn't even go all the way. What we did was a little youthful experimenting, that's all. And I'm glad we did it. To be honest, my only regret is that we didn't do it again.

Ah. So you were thinking the same thing I was.

Why didn't you tell me?

I was too scared, I guess. Too scared that if we kept on doing it, we might find ourselves in real trouble.

So you found yourself a boyfriend instead. Dave Cryer, the king of the animals.

And you fell for Patty French.

Water under the bridge, comrade.

Yes, it's all water under the bridge now, isn't it?

You and your sister talk about the past, then, and your parents' silent marriage, and your dead brother, and the childish farce you wrote in tandem one spring vacation years ago, but these matters take up no more than a small fraction of the time you spend together. Another fraction is consumed in brief conversations concerning household maintenance (shopping, cleaning, cooking, paying the rent and utility bills), but the bulk of the words you exchange that summer are about the present and the future, the war in Vietnam, books and writers, poets, musicians, and filmmakers, as well as the stories you bring home from your respective jobs. You and your sister have always talked, the two of you have been engaged in a complex, ongoing dialogue since your earliest childhood, and this willingness to share your thoughts and ideas is probably what best defines your friendship. It turns out that you agree about most things, but by no means all things, and you enjoy duking it out over your differences. Your spats about the relative merits of various writers and artists have a somewhat comical aspect to them, however, since it rarely happens that either of you manages to persuade the other to change his or her opinion. Case in point: you both consider Emily Dickinson to be the supreme American poet of the nineteenth century, but whereas you have a soft spot for Whitman, Gwyn dismisses him as bombastic and

crude, a false prophet. You read one of the shorter lyrics out loud to her (*The Dalliance of the Eagles*), but she remains unconvinced, telling you she's sorry, but a poem about eagles fucking in midair leaves her cold. Case in point: she admires *Middlemarch* above all other novels, and when you confess to her that you never made it past page 50, she urges you to give it another try, which you do, and once again you give up before reaching page 50. Case in point: your positions on the war and American politics are nearly identical, but with the draft staring you in the face the instant you leave college, you are far more vociferous and hotheaded than she is, and whenever you launch into one of your apoplectic rants against the Johnson administration, Gwyn smiles at you, sticks her fingers in her ears, and waits for you to stop.

You both love Tolstoy and Dostoyevsky, Hawthorne and Melville, Flaubert and Stendhal, but at that stage of your life you cannot stomach Henry James, while Gwyn argues that he is the giant of giants, the colossus who makes all other novelists look like pygmies. You are in complete harmony about the greatness of Kafka and Beckett, but when you tell her that Céline belongs in their company, she laughs at you and calls him a fascist maniac. Wallace Stevens yes, but next in line for you is William Carlos Williams, not T. S. Eliot, whose work Gwyn can recite from memory. You defend Keaton, she defends Chaplin, and while you both howl at the sight of the Marx Brothers, your much-adored W. C. Fields cannot coax a single smile from her. Truffaut at his best touches you both, but Gwyn finds Godard pretentious and you don't, and while she lauds Bergman and Antonioni as twin masters of the universe, you reluctantly tell her that you are bored by their films. No conflicts about classical music, with J. S. Bach at the top of the list, but you are becoming increasingly interested in jazz, while Gwyn still clings to the frenzy of rock and roll, which has stopped saying much of anything to you. She likes to dance, and you don't. She laughs more than you do and smokes less. She is a freer, happier person than you are, and whenever you are with her, the world seems brighter and more welcoming, a place where your sullen, introverted self can almost begin to feel at home.

The conversation continues throughout the summer. You talk about books and films and the war, you talk about your jobs and your plans for the future, you talk about the past and the present, and you also talk about Born. Gwyn knows you are suffering. She understands that the experience still weighs heavily on you, and again and again she patiently listens to you tell the story, again and again the same story, the obsessive

story that has wormed itself into your soul and become an integral part of your being. She tries to reassure you that you acted well, that there was nothing else you could have done, and while you agree that you could not have prevented Cedric Williams's murder, you know that your cowardly hesitation before going to the police allowed Born to escape unpunished, and you cannot forgive yourself for that. Now it is Friday, the first evening of the early July weekend you have chosen to spend in New York, and as you and your sister sit at the kitchen table, drinking your postwork beers and smoking your cigarettes, the conversation once again turns to Born.

I've been mulling it over, Gwyn says, and I'm pretty sure the whole thing started because Born was sexually attracted to you. It wasn't just Margot. It was the two of them together.

Startled by your sister's theory, you pause for a moment to consider whether it makes any sense, painfully reviewing your tangled relations with Born from this altered perspective, but in the end you say no, you don't agree.

Think about it, Gwyn persists.

I am thinking about it, you answer. If it were true, then he would have made a pass at me. But he didn't. He never tried to touch me.

It doesn't matter. Chances are, he wasn't even aware of it himself. But a man doesn't fork over thousands of dollars to a twenty-year-old stranger because he's worried about his future. He does it out of a homoerotic attraction. Born fell in love with you, Adam. Whether he knew it himself is irrelevant.

I'm still not convinced, but now that you mention it, I wish he *had* made a pass at me. I would have punched him in the face and told him to fuck off, and then we never would have taken that walk down Riverside Drive, and the Williams kid never would have been killed.

Has anyone ever tried something like that with you?

Like what?

Another man. Has another man ever made a move on you?

I've gotten some curious stares, but no one's ever said anything to me.

So you've never done it.

Done what?

Have sex with another guy.

God no.

Not even when you were little?

What are you talking about? Little boys don't have sex. They can't

have sex – for the simple reason that they're little boys.

I don't mean little little. I'm talking about just after puberty. Thirteen, fourteen years old. I thought all boys that age liked to jerk each other off.

Not me.

What about the famous circle jerk? You must have taken part in one of those.

How old was I the last year I went to summer camp?

I can't remember.

Thirteen . . . It must have been thirteen, because I started working at the Shop-Rite when I was fourteen. Anyway, the last year I went to camp, some of the boys in my cabin did that. Six or seven of them, but I was too shy to join in.

Too shy or too put off?

A little of both, I guess. I've always found the male body somewhat repellent.

Not your own, I hope.

I mean other men's bodies. I have no desire to touch them, no desire to see them naked. To tell you the truth, I've often wondered why women are drawn to men. If I were a woman, I'd probably be a lesbian.

Gwyn smiles at the absurdity of your remark. That's because you're a man, she says.

And what about you? Have you ever been attracted to another girl?

Of course. Girls are always getting crushes on each other. It comes with the territory.

I mean sexually attracted. Have you ever felt the urge to sleep with a girl?

I just spent four years at an all-girls college, remember? Things are bound to happen in a claustrophobic atmosphere like that.

Really?

Yes, really.

You never told me.

You never asked.

Did I have to? What about the No-Secrets Pact of nineteen sixty-one?

It's not a secret. It's too unimportant to qualify as a secret. For the record – just so you don't get the wrong impression – it happened exactly twice. The first time, I was stoned on pot. The second time, I was drunk.

And?

Sex is sex, Adam, and all sex is good, as long as both people want it. Bodies like to be touched and kissed, and if you close your eyes, it hardly

matters who's touching and kissing you.

As a statement of principle, I couldn't agree with you more. I just want to know if you enjoyed it, and if you did enjoy it, why you haven't done it more often.

Yes, I enjoyed it. But not enormously, not as much as I enjoy having sex with men. Contrary to your view on the subject, I adore men's bodies, and I have a particular fondness for the thing they have that women's bodies don't. Being with a girl is pleasant enough, but it doesn't have the power of a good, old-fashioned two-sex tumble.

Less bang for your buck.

Exactly. Minor league.

Bush league, as it were.

Stifling a laugh, Gwyn flings her cigarette pack at you and shouts in pretend anger: You're impossible!

That is precisely what you are: impossible. The moment the word flies out of your sister's mouth, you regret your lewd and feeble joke, and for the rest of the evening and long into the following day, the word sticks to you like a curse, like some pitiless condemnation of who and what you are. Yes, you are impossible. You and your life are impossible, and you wonder how on earth you managed to find your way into this cul-de-sac of despair and self-loathing. Is Born alone responsible for what has happened to you? Can a single momentary lapse of courage have damaged your belief in yourself so badly that you no longer have faith in your future? Just months ago you were going to set the world on fire with your brilliance, and now you think of yourself as stupid and inept, a moronic masturbation machine trapped in the dead air of an odious job, a nobody. If not for Gwyn, you might think about checking yourself into a hospital. She is the only person you can talk to, the only person who makes you feel alive. And yet, happy as you are to be with her again, you know that you mustn't overburden her with your troubles, that you can't expect her to transform herself into the divine surgeon who will cut open your chest and mend your ailing heart. You must help yourself. If something inside you is broken, you must put it back together with your own two hands.

*

After twenty-four hours of bleak introspection, the agony slowly subsides. The turnaround begins on Saturday, the second evening of the early July weekend you have chosen to spend in Manhattan. After dinner, you and your sister ride the 104 bus down Broadway to the New

Yorker Theatre and walk into the coolness of that dark space to watch Carl Dreyer's 1955 film, *Ordet* (The Word). Normally, you would not be interested in a film about Christianity and matters of religious faith, but Dreyer's direction is so exact and piercing that you are quickly swept up into the story, which begins to remind you of a piece of music, as if the film were a visual translation of a two-part invention by Bach. The aesthetics of Lutheranism, you whisper into Gwyn's ear at one point, but since she has not been privy to your thoughts, she has no idea what you are talking about and returns your comment with a bewildered frown.

There is little need to rehash the intricacies of the story. Compelling as those twists and turns might be, they amount to just one story among an infinity of stories, one film among a multitude of films, and if not for the end, *Ordet* would not have affected you more than any other good film you have seen over the years. It is the end that counts, for the end does something to you that is wholly unexpected, and it crashes into you with all the force of an axe felling an oak.

The farm woman who has died in childbirth is stretched out in an open coffin as her weeping husband sits beside her. The mad brother who thinks he is the second coming of Christ walks into the room holding the hand of the couple's young daughter. As the small group of mourning relatives and friends looks on, wondering what blasphemy or sacrilege is about to be committed at this solemn moment, the would-be incarnation of Jesus of Nazareth addresses the dead woman in a calm and quiet voice. Rise up, he commands her, lift yourself out of your coffin and return to the world of the living. Seconds later, the woman's hands begin to move. You think it must be a hallucination, that the point of view has shifted from objective reality to the mind of the addled brother. But no. The woman opens her eyes, and just seconds after that she sits up, fully restored to life.

There is a large crowd in the theater, and half the audience bursts out laughing when they see this miraculous resurrection. You don't begrudge them their skepticism, but for you it is a transcendent moment, and you sit there clutching your sister's arm as tears roll down your cheeks. What cannot happen has happened, and you are stunned by what you have witnessed.

Something changes in you after that. You don't know what it is, but the tears you shed when you saw the woman come back to life seem to have washed out some of the poison that has been building up inside you. The days pass. At various moments, you think your small breakdown in the

balcony of the New Yorker Theatre might be connected to your brother, Andy, or, if not to Andy, then to Cedric Williams, or perhaps to both of them together. At other moments, you are convinced that by some strange, sympathetic overlapping of subject and object, you felt you were watching yourself rise from the dead. Over the next two weeks, your step gradually becomes less heavy. You still feel doomed, but you sense that when the day comes for you to be led to the scaffold, you might have it in you to crack a parting joke or exchange pleasantries with your hooded executioner.

Every year since your brother's death, you and your sister have celebrated his birthday. Just the two of you, with no parents, relatives, or other guests allowed. For the first three years, when you were both still young enough to spend your summers at sleepaway camp, you would hold the party in the open air, the two of you tiptoeing out of your cabins in the middle of the night and running across the darkened ball fields up to the meadow on the northern edge of the campgrounds and then bolting into the woods with flashlights illuminating your path through the trees and underbrush – each one of you holding a cupcake or cookie, which you had stolen from the mess hall after dinner that evening. For three consecutive summers after your camp days ended, you both worked in your father's supermarket, and therefore you were at home on the twenty-sixth of July and could celebrate the birth of your brother in Gwyn's bedroom on the third floor of the house. The next two years were the most difficult, since you both traveled during those summers and were far apart on the appointed day, but you managed to perform truncated versions of the ritual over the telephone. Last year, you took a bus to Boston, where Gwyn was shacked up with her then boyfriend, and the two of you went out to a restaurant to lift a glass in honor of the departed Andy. Now another July twenty-sixth is upon you, and for the first summer in a long while you are together again, about to throw your little fête in the kitchen of the apartment you share on West 107th Street.

It is not a party in the traditional sense of the word. Over the years, you and your sister have developed a number of strict protocols regarding the event, and with slight variations, depending on how old you have been, each July twenty-sixth is a reenactment of all the previous July twenty-sixths of the past ten years. In essence, the birthday dinner is a conversation divided into three parts. Food is served and eaten, and once the three-part talk is finished, a small chocolate cake appears,

ornamented by a single candle burning in the center. You do not sing the song. You mouth the words in unison, speaking softly, barely raising your voices above a whisper, but you do not sing them. Nor do you blow the candle out. You let it burn down to a stub, and then you listen to it sizzle as the flame is extinguished in the ooze of the chocolate frosting. After a slice of cake, you open a bottle of scotch. Alcohol is a new element, not introduced until 1963 (the last of the supermarket summers, when you were sixteen and Gwyn was seventeen), but for the next two years you were apart and drinkless, and last year you were in a public place, which meant you had to watch your consumption. This year, alone in your New York apartment, you both aim to get good and drunk.

Gwyn has put on lipstick and makeup for the dinner, and she comes to the table wearing gold hoop earrings and a pale green summer shift, which makes the green of her gray-green eyes appear even more vivid. You are in a white oxford shirt with short sleeves and a button-down collar, and around your neck is the only tie you own, the same tie Born ridiculed you for wearing last spring. Gwyn laughs when she sees you in that getup and says you look like a Mormon – one of those earnest young men who go around the world knocking on doors and giving out pamphlets, a proselytizer on a holy mission. Nonsense, you tell her. You don't have a crew cut, and your hair isn't blond, and therefore you could never be confused with a Mormon. Still and all, Gwyn says, you look mighty, mighty strange. If not a Mormon, she continues, then perhaps a fledgling accountant. Or a math student. Or a wannabe astronaut. No, no, you shoot back at her – a civil rights worker in the South. All right, she says, you win, and an instant later you remove both the tie and the shirt, leave the kitchen, and change into something else. When you return, Gwyn smiles but says nothing further about your clothes.

As usual, the weather is hot, and because you don't want to increase the temperature in the kitchen, you have refrained from using the oven and prepared a light summer meal that consists of chilled soup, a platter of cold cuts (ham, salami, roast beef), and a lettuce-and-tomato salad. There is also a loaf of Italian bread, along with a bottle of chilled Chianti encased in a straw covering (the cheap wine of choice among students of the period). After taking your first sips of the cold watercress soup, you begin the three-part conversation. That is the core of the experience for you, the single most important reason for staging this annual event. All the rest – the meal, the cake, the candle, the words of the happy birthday song, the booze – are mere trappings.

Step One: You talk about Andy in the past tense, dredging up everything you can recall about him while he was still alive. Invariably, this is the longest portion of the ritual. You remember your memories of past years, but additional ones always seem to spring forth from your unconscious as well. You try to keep the tone light and cheerful. This is not an exercise in morbidity, it is a celebration, and laughter is permitted at all times. You repeat some of his early mispronunciations of words: hangaburger for hamburger, human bean for human being, chuthers for each other – as in *They kissed their chuthers* – and the perfectly logical but demented *Mommy's Ami,* following a reference by your mother to the city of Miami. You talk about his bug collection, his Superman cape, and his bout with the chicken pox. You remember teaching him how to ride a bicycle. You remember his aversion to peas. You remember his first day of school (tears and torment), his skinned elbows, his hiccuping fits. Just seven years on this earth, but every year you and Gwyn come to the same conclusion: the list is inexhaustible. And yet, every year, you can't help feeling that a little more of him has vanished, that in spite of your best efforts, less and less of him is coming back to you, that you are powerless to stop him from fading away.

Step Two: You talk about him in the present tense. You imagine what kind of person he would have become if he were still alive today. For ten years now, he has been living this shadow existence inside you, a phantom being who has grown up in another dimension, invisible yet breathing, breathing and thinking, thinking and feeling, and you have followed him since the age of eight, for more years after death than he ever managed to live, and now that he is seventeen, the gap between you has become ever smaller, ever less significant, and it shocks you, it shocks you and your sister simultaneously, to realize that at seventeen he is probably no longer a virgin, that he has smoked pot and gotten drunk, that he shaves and masturbates, drives a car, reads difficult books, is thinking about what college to go to, and is on the brink of becoming your equal. Gwyn starts to cry, saying that she can't stand it anymore, that she wants to stop, but you tell her to hang on for a few more minutes, that the two of you never have to do this again, that this will be the last birthday party for the rest of your lives, but for Andy's sake you have to see this one through to the end.

Step Three: You talk about the future, about what will happen to Andy between now and his next birthday. This has always been the easiest part, the most enjoyable part, and in past years you and Gwyn have

sailed through the game of predictions with immense enthusiasm and brio. But not this year. Before you can begin the third and last part of the conversation, your overwrought sister clamps her hand over her mouth, gets up from her chair, and rushes out of the kitchen.

You find her in the living room, sobbing on the sofa. You sit down next to her, put your arm around her shoulders, and talk to her in a soothing voice. Calm down, you say. It's all right, Gwyn. I'm sorry . . . sorry I pushed you so hard. It's my fault.

You feel the thinness of her quaking shoulders, the delicate bones beneath her skin, her heaving rib cage pressing against your own ribs, her hip against your hip, her leg against your leg. In all the years you have known her, you doubt you have ever seen her so miserable, so crushed by sadness.

It's no good, she finally says, her eyes cast downward, addressing her words to the floor. I've lost contact with him. He's gone now, and we'll never find him again. In two weeks, it will have been ten years. That's half your life, Adam. Next year, it will be half of mine. That's too long. The space keeps growing. The time keeps growing, and every minute he drifts farther and farther away from us. Good-bye, Andy. Send us a postcard someday, all right?

You don't say anything. You sit there with your arm around your sister and let her go on crying, knowing that it would be useless to intervene, that you must allow the explosion to run its course. How long does it last? You haven't the faintest idea, but a moment eventually comes when you notice that the tears have stopped. With your left hand, the free hand that is not around her shoulders, you take hold of her chin and turn her face toward you. Her eyes are red and swollen. Rivulets of mascara have run down her cheeks. Mucus is dribbling from her nose. You withdraw your left hand, put it into the back pocket of your pants, and pull out a handkerchief. You begin dabbing her face with the cloth. Little by little, you wipe away the tears, the snot, and the black mascara, and throughout the long, meticulous procedure, your sister doesn't move. Looking at you intently, her eyes washed clean of any discernible emotion, she sits in absolute stillness as you repair the damage left by the storm. When the job is finished, you stand up and say to her: Time for a drink, Miss Walker. I'll go get the scotch.

You march off to the kitchen. A minute later, when you return to the living room with a bottle of Cutty Sark, two glasses, and a pitcher of ice cubes, she is exactly where she was when you left her – sitting on

the sofa, her head leaning against the backrest, eyes shut, breathing normally again, purged. You put down the drinking equipment on one of the three wooden milk crates that stand side by side in front of the sofa, the battered, upside-down boxes that you and your former roommate dragged off the street one day and which now serve as your excuse for a coffee table. Gwyn opens her eyes and gives you a wan, exhausted smile, as if asking you to forgive her for her outburst, but there is nothing to forgive, nothing to talk about, nothing you could ever hold against her, and as you set about pouring the drinks and putting ice into the glasses, you feel relieved that the business with Andy is over, relieved that there will be no more birthday celebrations for your absent brother, relieved that you and your sister have at last put this childish thing behind you.

You hand Gwyn her drink and then sit down beside her on the sofa. For several minutes, neither one of you says a word. Sipping your scotches and staring ahead at the wall in front of you, you both know what is going to happen tonight, you feel it as a certainty in your blood, but you also know that you have to be patient and give the alcohol time to do its work. When you lean forward to prepare the second round of drinks, Gwyn starts talking to you about her broken romance with Timothy Krale, the thirty-year-old assistant professor who entered her life more than eighteen months ago and left it this past April, at roughly the same moment you were shaking Born's hand for the first time. The teacher of her class on modernist poetry, of all things, the man risked his job by going after her, and she fell hard for him, especially in the beginning, during the first wild months of furtive assignations and weekend jaunts to distant motel rooms in forgotten towns across upstate New York. You yourself met him a number of times, and you understood what Gwyn saw in him, you concurred that Krale was an attractive and intelligent fellow, but you also sensed that there was something desiccated about the man, a detachment from others that made it difficult for you to warm up to him. It didn't surprise you when Gwyn turned down his proposal of marriage and put a stop to the affair. She told him that she felt too young, that she wasn't ready to commit herself over the long term, but that wasn't the real reason, she explains to you now, she left him because he wasn't a kind enough lover. Yes, yes, she says, she knows he loved her, loved her as much as he was capable of loving anyone, but she found him selfish in bed, inattentive, too driven by his own needs, and she couldn't imagine herself tolerating such a man for the rest of her life. She turns to you now, and with a look of utmost seriousness and conviction

in her eyes, she sets forth her definition of love, wanting to know if you share her opinion or not. Real love, she says, is when you get as much pleasure from giving pleasure as you do from receiving it. What do you think, Adam? Am I right or wrong? You tell her she is right. You tell her it is one of the most perceptive things she has ever said.

When does it start? When does the idea revolving in both your minds manifest itself as action in the physical world? Midway through the third drink, when Gwyn hunches forward and puts her glass down on the makeshift table. You have promised yourself that you will not make the first move, that you will hold back from touching her until she touches you, for only then will you know beyond all doubt that she wants what you want and that you have not misread her desires. You are a little drunk, of course, but not egregiously so, not so far gone that you have lost your wits, and you fully understand the import of what you are about to do. You and your sister are no longer the floundering, ignorant puppies you were on the night of the grand experiment, and what you are proposing now is a monumental transgression, a dark and iniquitous thing according to the laws of man and God. But you don't care. That is the simple truth of the matter: you are not ashamed of what you feel. You love your sister. You love her more than any person you have known or will ever know on the face of this wretched earth, and because you will be leaving the country in approximately one month, not to return for an entire year, this is your only chance, the only chance for both of you, since it is all but inevitable that a new Timothy Krale will walk into Gwyn's life while you are gone. No, you have not forgotten the vow you took when you were twelve years old, the promise you made to yourself to live your life as an ethical human being. You want to be a good person, and every day you struggle to follow the oath you swore on your dead brother's memory, but as you sit on the sofa watching your sister put her glass down on the table, you tell yourself that love is not a moral issue, desire is not a moral issue, and as long as you cause no harm to each other or anyone else, you will not be breaking your vow.

A moment later, you put down your glass as well. The two of you lean back on the sofa, and Gwyn takes hold of your hand, intertwining her fingers with yours. She asks: Are you afraid? You tell her no, you're not afraid, you're extremely happy. Me too, she says, and then she kisses you on the cheek, very gently, no more than the faintest nuzzle, the merest brush of her mouth against your skin. You understand that everything must go slowly, must build by the smallest of increments, that for a long

while it will be a halting, tentative dance of yes and no, and you prefer it that way, for if either one of you should have second thoughts, there will be time to back down and call it off. More often than not, what stirs the imagination is best kept in the imagination, and Gwyn is aware of that, she is wise enough to know that the distance between thought and deed can be enormous, a gulf as large as the world itself. So you test the waters cautiously, baby step by baby step, grazing your mouths against each other's necks, grazing your lips against each other's lips, but for many minutes you do not open your mouths, and although you have wrapped your arms around each other in a tight embrace, your hands do not move. A good half hour goes by, and neither one of you shows any inclination to stop. That is when your sister opens her mouth. That is when you open your mouth, and together you fall headfirst into the night.

There are no rules anymore. The grand experiment was a one-time-only event, but now that you are both past twenty, the strictures of your adolescent frolic no longer hold, and you go on having sex with each other every day for the next thirty-four days, right up to the day you leave for Paris. Your sister is on the pill, there are spermicidal creams and jellies in her bureau drawer, condoms are available to you, and you both know that you are protected, that the unmentionable will never come to pass, and therefore you can do anything and everything to each other without fear of destroying your lives. You don't discuss it. Beyond the brief exchange on the night of your brother's birthday (*Are you afraid? No, I'm not afraid*) you never say a word about what is happening, refuse to explore the ramifications of your monthlong affair, your monthlong marriage, for that is finally what it is, you are a young married couple now, a pair of newlyweds trapped in the throes of constant, overpowering lust – sex beasts, lovers, best friends: the last two people left in the universe.

Outwardly, your lives go on as before. Five days a week, the alarm clock wakes you early in the morning, and after a minimal breakfast of orange juice, coffee, and buttered toast, you both rush out of the apartment and head for your jobs, Gwyn to her office on the twelfth floor of a glass tower in the heart of Manhattan and you to your dreary clerk's post in the Palace of Null. You would prefer to have her within your sight at all times, would be perfectly content if she were never apart from you for a single minute, but if these unavoidable separations cause you a measure of pain, they also increase your longing for her, and perhaps that isn't a bad thing, you decide, for you spend your days in the thrall

of breathless anticipation, agitated and alert, counting the hours until you can see her and hold her again. Intense. That is the word you use to describe yourself now. You are intense. Your feelings are intense. Your life has become increasingly intense.

At work, you no longer sit behind your desk fantasizing about Ingrid Bergman and Hedy Lamarr. From time to time, an erection still threatens to burst through your pants, but you don't need to touch it anymore, and you have stopped running to the men's room at the end of the corridor. This is the library, after all, and thoughts about naked women are an inextricable part of working in the library, but the only naked body you think about now belongs to your sister, the real body of the real woman you share your nights with, and not some figment who exists only in your brain. There is no question that Gwyn is just as beautiful as Hedy Lamarr, perhaps even more beautiful – undoubtedly more beautiful. This is an objective fact, and you have spent the past seven years watching men stop dead in their tracks to stare at her as she walks past them on the street, have witnessed how many quick, astonished turns of the head, how many surreptitious glances on the subway, in restaurants, in theaters – hundreds and hundreds of men, and every one of them with the same leering, misty, dumbfounded look in his eyes. Yes, it is the face that launched a thousand hopes, the face that spawned a thousand dirty dreams, and as you wait at your desk for the next pneumatic tube to come rattling up from the second floor, you see that face in your head, you're looking into Gwyn's large, animated, gray-green eyes, and as those eyes look into yours, you watch her undo the back of her white summer dress and let it slide down the length of her tall, slender body.

You sit in baths together. That is the new postwork routine, and rather than spend that hour in the kitchen as you did before your brother's birthday party, you now hoist your beers and puff on your cigarettes while soaking in a lukewarm bath. Not only does it provide respite from the heaviness of the dog-day heat, but it gives you yet another chance to look at each other's naked bodies, which you never seem to tire of doing. Again and again, you tell your sister how much you love to look at her, that you adore every centimeter of her vibrant, luminous skin, and that beyond the overtly feminine places all men think about, you worship her elbows and knees, her wrists and ankles, the backs of her hands and her long, thin fingers (you could never be attracted to a woman with short thumbs, you tell her one day – an absurd but utterly sincere pronouncement), and that you are both mystified and enchanted by how a body as

delicate as hers can also be as strong as it is, that she is both a swan and a tiger, a mythological being. She is fascinated by the hair that has grown on your chest (a recent development of the past twelve months) and has an unflagging interest in the mutabilities of your penis: from the limp, dangling member depicted in biology textbooks to the full-bore phallic titan at the summit of arousal to the shrunken, exhausted little man in postcoital retreat. She calls your dick a variety show. She says it has multiple personalities. She claims she wants to adopt it.

Now that you are living on such intimate terms with her, Gwyn has emerged as a slightly different person from the one you have known all your life. She is both funnier and more salacious than you imagined, more vulgar and idiosyncratic, more passionate, more playful, and you are startled to learn how deeply she exults in filthy language and the bizarre slang of sex. Gwyn has rarely sworn in your presence. She is a literate, well-educated girl who speaks in full, grammatical sentences, but except for the night of the grand experiment long ago, you have known nothing about her sexuality, and therefore you could not have guessed that she would grow up into a woman who likes to talk about sex as well as have it. Common twentieth-century words do not interest her. She shuns the term *making love,* for example, in favor of older, more hilarious locutions, such as rumpty-rumpty, quaffing, and bonker bang. A good orgasm is referred to as a bone-shaker. Her ass is a rumdadum. Her crotch is a slittie, a quim, a quim-box, a quimsby. Her breasts are boobs and tits, boobies and titties, her twin girls. At one time or another, your penis is a bong, a blade, a slurp, a shaft, a drill, a quencher, a queller, a lancelot, a lightning rod, Charles Dickens, Dick Driver, and Adam Junior. The words excite and amuse her, and once you recover from your initial shock, you are excited and amused as well. In the grip of approaching orgasm, however, she tends to revert to the contemporary standbys, falling back on the simplest, crudest words in the English lexicon to express her feelings. Cunt, pussy, fuck. Fuck me, Adam. Again and again. Fuck me, Adam. For an entire month you are the captive of that word, the willing prisoner of that word, the embodiment of that word. You dwell in the land of flesh, and your cup runneth over. Surely goodness and mercy shall follow you all the days of your life.

Still, you and your sister never talk about what you are doing. You don't even have a conversation to discuss why you don't talk about it. You are living in the confines of a shared secret, and the walls of that space are built by silence, an insane silence that can be broken only at the

risk of bringing those walls down upon your heads. So you sit in your lukewarm bath, you slather each other with soap, you make love on the floor before dinner, you make love in Gwyn's bed after dinner, you sleep like stones, and early in the morning the alarm clock rousts you back to consciousness. On the weekends, you take long rambles through Central Park, resisting the temptation to hold hands, to kiss in public. You go to the movies. You go to plays. The poem you started in June has not advanced by a single line since the night of Andy's birthday, but you don't care, you have other things to absorb your attention now, and time is passing quickly, there are fewer and fewer days before your departure, and you want to spend every moment you can with her, to live out the mad thing you have done together to the very end of the time that is left.

The last day comes. For seventy-two hours, you have been living in a state of constant turmoil, of ever-mounting dread. You don't want to go. You want to cancel the trip and stay in New York with your sister, but at the same time you understand that this is out of the question, that the month you have lived with her in unholy matrimony was made possible only by the fact that it was for one month, that there was a limit to how long your incestuous rampage could go on, and because you can't bear to face the truth that it is over now, you feel broken and bereft, benumbed by sorrow.

To make matters worse, you have to spend your last day in New York with your parents. Bud and Marge drive their big car into the city to treat you and your sister to a farewell family lunch at an expensive midtown restaurant – and then on to the airport for last kisses, last hugs, last good-byes. Your nervous, overmedicated mother says little during the meal, but your father is in uncommonly good spirits that day. He keeps addressing you as *son* rather than by your name, and while you know that your father intends no harm, you find this verbal tic annoying, since it seems to deprive you of your personhood and transform you into an object, a thing. Not Adam but Son, as in my son, my creation, my heir. Bud says he envies you for the adventure that awaits you in Paris, meaning Paris as the capital of loose women and late-night naughtiness (ha ha, wink wink), and though he himself never had such an opportunity, could never even afford to go to college, much less spend a year studying in a foreign country, he is clearly proud of himself for having done well enough in the money department to be backing his offspring's trip to Europe, symbol of the

good life, the rich life, an emblem of middle-class American success, of which he is one of Westfield, New Jersey's shining examples. You cringe and endure, struggling not to lose your patience, wishing you could be alone with Gwyn. As usual, your sister is calm and composed, alert to the tensions underlying the occasion but stubbornly pretending not to notice them. On the way to the airport, you sit together in the backseat of the car. She takes hold of your hand and squeezes it hard, not loosening her grip throughout the entire forty-minute ride, but that is the only hint she gives of what she is feeling on this horrible day, this day of days, and somehow it is not enough, this hand squeezing your hand is not enough, and from this day forward you know that nothing will ever be enough again.

At the departure gate, your mother puts her arms around you and begins to cry. She can't stand the thought of not seeing you for a whole year, she says, she will miss you, she will worry about you day and night, and please remember to eat enough, send letters, call if you feel homesick, I will always be there for you. You hug her tightly, thinking, My poor mother, my poor wretched mother, and tell her that everything will be fine, but you are by no means certain of that, and your words lack conviction, you can hear your voice trembling as you speak. Over your mother's shoulder, you see your father observing you with that distant, shut-down look in his eyes, and you know he doesn't have the first idea what to make of you, that you have always been a mystery to your father, a person beyond understanding, but now, for once in your life, you find yourself in accord with him, for the truth of the matter is that you, too, have no idea what to make of yourself, and yes, even to yourself, you are a person beyond understanding.

A last look at Gwyn. There are tears in your sister's eyes, but you can't tell if they are meant for you or your mother, if they are an expression of private anguish or sympathy for the overwrought woman who has been weeping in her son's arms. Now that the end has come, you want Gwyn to suffer as much as you are suffering. Pain is the only thing that holds you together now, and unless her pain is as great as yours, there will be nothing left of the small, perfect universe you have lived in for the past month. It is impossible to know what she is thinking, and because your parents are standing less than three feet from you, you cannot ask. You take her in your arms and whisper: I don't want to go. You say it again: I don't want to go. And then you step back from her, put your head down, and go.

# III

One week after I read the text of *Summer,* I was in Oakland, California, ringing the doorbell of Walker's house. I hadn't written or called to tell him what I thought of the second part of his book, nor had he written or called to ask. I felt it would be better to hold back from giving any comments until I saw him in person, and with our scheduled dinner looming up on the immediate horizon, my chance would come soon enough. I couldn't explain why it was so important to me, but I wanted him to be looking into my eyes when I told him that I was not disgusted by what he had written, that I did not find it brutal or ugly (to quote his words back to him), and that my wife, who had now read the first and second parts of the book, felt the same as I did. That was the little speech I rehearsed in my head as the taxi took me across the bridge from San Francisco to Oakland, but I never managed to say what I wanted to say. It turned out that Walker had died just twenty-four hours after he'd sent me the manuscript, and by the time I reached the front door of his house, his ashes had been in the ground for three days.

Rebecca was the one who told me these things, the same Rebecca Adam had talked about in the second letter I received from him, his thirty-five-year-old stepdaughter, a tall, broad-shouldered woman with light brown skin, penetrating eyes, and an attractive if not conventionally pretty face, who referred to her mother's white husband not as her stepfather but as her father. I was glad to hear her use that word, glad to know that Walker had been capable of inspiring that degree of love and loyalty in a child who had not been born to him. That one word seemed to tell me everything about the sort of life he had built for himself in this small house in Oakland with Sandra Williams and her daughter, who eventually became his daughter, and who, even after her mother's death, had stayed by him until the end.

Rebecca broke the news to me just seconds after she opened the door and let me into the house. I shouldn't have been surprised, but I was. In spite of the weakness and fear I had detected in his voice when we talked on the phone, in spite of my certainty that he was coming to the end, I hadn't thought it would happen just yet, I had assumed there was still

some time left – enough time for us to have our dinner, at any rate, perhaps even enough time for him to finish his book. When Rebecca spoke the words *My father passed six days ago,* I felt so rattled, so unwilling to accept the finality of her statement that a sudden wave of dizziness rushed through my head, and I had to ask her if I could sit down. She walked me over to a chair in the living room, then went into the kitchen to fetch a glass of water. When she returned, she apologized for her stupidity, even though no apologies were necessary, and even though she was anything but stupid.

I didn't find out that you and my father were planning to have dinner tonight until less than an hour ago, she said. Ever since the funeral, I've been coming to the house and sorting through his things, and it didn't enter my fat little head until six o'clock this evening to open his date book and see if there were any appointments I had to cancel. When I saw the thing for seven o'clock, I immediately called your house in Brooklyn. Your wife gave me the number of your hotel in San Francisco, but when I called them, they said you weren't in your room. I figured you were already on your way here, so I called my husband, told him to feed the kids, and stuck around here waiting for you to show up. You might not be aware of it, but you rang the bell exactly on the dot of seven.

That was the deal, I said. I promised to be here at the stroke of seven. I thought your father would be amused by my punctuality.

I'm sure he would have been, she replied, with a touch of sadness in her voice.

Before I could say anything, she changed the subject and again apologized for something that needed no apology. I was planning to call you within the next few days, she said. Your name is on the list, and I'm sorry I didn't get around to it sooner. Dad had a lot of friends, a ton of friends. So many people to contact, and then there was the funeral to arrange, and a million other things to take care of, and I suppose you could say I've been a bit swamped. Not that I'm complaining. It's better to keep yourself busy at a time like this than to sit around and mope, don't you think? But I'm really sorry I didn't get in touch with you earlier. Dad was so happy when you wrote back to him last month. He's been talking about you ever since I can remember, I feel as if I've known you all my life. His friend from college, the one who went on to make a name for himself out in the big world. It's an honor to meet you at last. Not the best of circumstances, I know, but I'm glad you're here.

Me too, I said, feeling somewhat calmed by the patter of her resonant,

soothing voice. Your father was writing something, I continued. Did you know about that?

He mentioned it to me. A book called *1967*.

Have you read it?

No.

Not a word?

Not a single letter. A couple of months ago, he told me that if he died before he finished it, he wanted me to delete the text from his computer. Just wipe it out and forget it, he said, it's of no importance.

So you erased it?

Of course I did. It's a sin to disobey a person's dying wish.

Good, I thought to myself. Good that this woman won't have to set eyes on Walker's manuscript. Good that she won't have to learn about her father's secret, which surely would have hurt her deeply, confused her, devastated her. I could take it in my stride, but that was only because I didn't belong to Walker's family. But imagine his child having to read those fifty pages. Unthinkable.

We were sitting face to face in the living room, each one of us planted in a soft, tattered armchair. Minimal furnishings, a couple of framed posters on the wall (Braque, Miró), another wall lined with books from top to bottom, a cotton throw rug in the center of the room, and a warm California dusk hovering outside the windows, yellowish and dim: the comfortable but modest life Walker had referred to in his letter. I drank down the last of the water Rebecca had given me and put the glass on the round short-legged table that stood between us. Then I said: What about Adam's sister? I used to know her a little bit back in the sixties, and I've often wondered what happened to her.

Aunt Gwyn. She lives back east, so I never got to know her very well. But I've always liked her. A generous, funny woman, and she and my mom hit it off, they were solid together. She came out for the funeral, of course, stayed right here in the house, and went home just this morning. My dad's death really shook her up. We all knew he was sick, we all knew he wasn't going to last long, but she wasn't around at the end, she didn't see how he was slipping away from us, and so she wasn't expecting it to happen so soon. She cried her heart out at the funeral, I mean really broke down and sobbed, and all I could do was hold her and try not to break down myself. My little Adam, she kept saying. My poor little Adam.

Poor little Gwyn.

Poor little everyone, Rebecca said, as her own eyes suddenly began to glisten. A few seconds later, a single tear fell from her left eye and slid down her cheek, but she didn't bother to wipe it away.

Is she married?

To an architect named Philip Tedesco.

I've heard of him.

Yes, he's very well known. They've been married for a long time and have two grown-up daughters. One of them is exactly my age.

The last time I saw Gwyn, she was a graduate student in English literature. Did she ever get her PhD?

I'm not sure. What I do know is that she works in publishing. She's director of a university press in the Boston area. A big one, a prominent one, but for the life of me I can't remember the name of it just now. Dammit. Maybe it will come to me later.

Don't worry about it. It's not important.

Without thinking, I reached into my pocket and pulled out a tin of Schimmelpennincks, the tiny Dutch cigars I have smoked since my early twenties. I was about to open the lid, saw Rebecca looking at me, and hesitated. Before I could ask her if it was all right to smoke in the house, she sprang out of her chair and said: I'll get you an ashtray. Matter-of-fact, sympathetic, one of the last Americans who had not joined the ranks of the Tobacco Police. Then she added: I think there's one in my father's study – at which point she smacked the heel of her hand against her forehead and muttered angrily: Good God, I don't know what's wrong with me today.

Is there a problem? I asked, bewildered by how upset she had become.

I have something for you, she said. It's sitting on my father's desk, and I forgot all about it until this minute. I was going to mail it to you, but then, when I looked in the date book and saw you were coming here tonight, I told myself I could give it to you in person. But I swear, if I hadn't mentioned my father's study, I would have let you walk out of this house empty-handed. I think I must be going senile.

So I accompanied her into the study, a midsize room on the ground floor with a wooden desk, another wall packed with books, filing cabinets, a laptop computer, and a telephone – not so much a lawyer's miniature home office as a place to think, a vestige of Walker's early life as a poet. A nine-by-twelve manila envelope had been placed on top of the shut computer. Rebecca picked it up and handed it to me. My name was written out across the front in block letters, and just below

my name, in much smaller cursive, I read: Notes for *Fall*.

Dad gave this to me two days before he died, Rebecca said. It must have been around six o'clock, because I remember coming here straight from my job at the hospital to check in on him. He said he'd talked to you on the phone about two hours earlier, and that if and when, in the event of, I don't want to say the word anymore, in the event of his you-know-what, I was to get this to you as quickly as possible. He looked so drained . . . so worn out when he said that to me, I could see he'd taken a bad turn, that his strength was beginning to leave him. Those were his last two requests. To delete the *1967* file from his computer and give you the envelope. Here it is. I have no idea what Notes for *Fall* means. Do you?

No, I lied. Not the foggiest notion.

Back in my hotel room later that night, I opened the envelope and pulled out a short, handwritten letter from Walker and thirty-one single-spaced pages of notes that he had typed up on his computer and then printed out for me. The letter read as follows:

> Five minutes after our telephone conversation. Deepest thanks for the encouragement. First thing tomorrow morning, I will have my housekeeper send you the second chapter by express mail. If you find it repugnant, which I fear you will, please accept my apologies. As for the pages in this envelope, you will see that they are the outline for the third part. Written in great haste – telegraphic style – but working quickly helped bring back memories, a deluge of memories, and now that the outline is finished, I don't know if I have it in me to work it up into a proper piece of prose. I feel exhausted, frightened, perhaps a little deranged. I will put the printed-out ms. into an envelope and give it to my daughter, who will send it to you in case I don't hold on long enough to have our famous, much talked about dinner. So weak, so little left, time running out. I will be robbed of my old age. I try not to feel bitter about it, but sometimes I can't help myself. Life is shit, I know, but the only thing I want is more life, more years on this godforsaken earth. As for the enclosed pages, do with them what you will. You are a pal, the best of men, and I trust your judgment in all things. Wish me luck on my journey. With love, Adam.

Reading that letter filled me with an immense, uncontainable sadness. Just hours before, Rebecca had jolted me with the news that Walker was dead, and now he was talking to me again, a dead man was talking to me, and I felt that as long as I held the letter in my hand, as long as the words of that letter were still before my eyes, it would be as if he had been resurrected, as if he had been momentarily brought back to life in the words he had written to me. A strange response, perhaps, no doubt an embarrassingly doltish response, but I was too distraught to censor the emotions that were running through me, and so I read the letter six or seven more times, ten times, twelve times, enough times to have learned every word of it by heart before I found the courage to put it away.

I went to the minibar, poured two little bottles of scotch into a tall glass, and then returned to the bed, where I sat down with the résumé of the third and final part of Walker's book.

Telegraphic. No complete sentences. From beginning to end, written like this. Goes to the store. Falls asleep. Lights a cigarette. In the third person this time. Third person, present tense, and therefore I decided to follow his lead and render his account in exactly that way – third person, present tense. *As for the enclosed pages, do with them what you will.* He had given me his permission, and I don't feel that turning his encrypted, Morse-code jottings into full sentences constitutes a betrayal of any kind. Despite my editorial involvement with the text, in the deepest, truest sense of what it means to tell a story, every word of *Fall* was written by Walker himself.

## FALL

Walker arrives in Paris a month before his classes are scheduled to begin. He has already rejected the idea of living in a student dormitory and therefore must arrange for his own housing. On the first morning after crossing the Atlantic, he returns to the hotel he stayed in for several weeks during his first visit to Paris two years before. He plans to use it as a base while he searches for better lodgings elsewhere, but the half-drunk manager with the two-day stubble of beard remembers him from his earlier visit, and when Walker mentions that he will be staying for an entire year, the man offers him a monthly rate that averages out to less than two dollars a night. Nothing is expensive in the Paris of 1967, but even by the standards of that time this is an exceedingly low rent, almost an act of charity, and Walker impulsively decides to accept the

man's offer. They shake hands on it, and then the man ushers him into the back room for a glass of wine. It is ten o'clock in the morning. As Walker puts the glass to his mouth and takes his first sip of the acrid *vin ordinaire,* he says to himself: Good-bye, America. For better or worse, you are in Paris now. You must not allow yourself to fall apart.

The Hôtel du Sud is a decrepit, crumbling establishment on the rue Mazarine in the sixth arrondissement, not far from the Odéon metro station on the Boulevard Saint-Germain. In America, a building in such a state of disrepair would be condemned for demolition, but this is not America, and the broken-down eyesore Walker now inhabits is nevertheless a historic structure, erected in the seventeenth century, he thinks, perhaps even earlier, which means that in spite of its filthiness and dilapidation, in spite of the creaking, worn-out steps of the cramped circular staircase, his new digs are not entirely without charm. Granted, his room is a disaster area of brittle, peeling wallpaper and cracked wooden floor planks, the bed is an ancient spring contraption with a caved-in mattress and rock-hard pillows, the small desk wobbles, the desk chair is the least comfortable chair in all of Europe, and one door of the armoire is missing, but setting aside these disadvantages, the room is fairly spacious, light pours through the two sets of double windows, and no noise can be heard from the street. When the manager opens the door and lets him in for the first time, Walker instantly feels that this will be a good place for writing poems. In the long run, that is the only thing that counts. This is the kind of room poets are supposed to work in, the kind of room that threatens to break your spirit and forces you into constant battle with yourself, and as Walker deposits his suitcase and typewriter by the foot of the bed, he vows to spend no less than four hours a day on his writing, to bear down on his work with more diligence and concentration than ever before. It doesn't matter that there is no telephone, that the toilet is a communal toilet at the end of the hall, that there is nowhere to shower or bathe, that everything around him is old. Walker is young, and this is the room where he means to reinvent himself.

There is university business to be taken care of, the tedium of consulting with the director of the Junior Year Abroad Program, selecting courses, filling out forms, attending an obligatory luncheon to meet the other students who will be in Paris for the year. There are just six of them (three Barnard girls and three Columbia boys), and while they all seem earnest and friendly, more than willing to accept him as a member of the gang, Walker makes up his mind to have as little to do with them

as possible. He has no inclination to become part of a group, and he certainly doesn't want to waste his time speaking English. The whole point in coming to Paris is to perfect his French. In order to do that, the shy and reticent Walker will have to embolden himself to make contact with the natives.

On an impulse, he decides to call Margot's parents. He remembers that the Jouffroys live on the rue de l'Université in the seventh arrondissement, not terribly far from his hotel, and he hopes they will be able to tell him where he can find her. Why he should want to see Margot again is a difficult question to answer, but for now Walker doesn't even bother to ask it. He has been in Paris for six days, and the truth is that he is beginning to feel somewhat lonely. Rather than renege on his plan not to fraternize with his fellow students, he has steadfastly stuck to himself, spending every morning in his room, parked at his wobbly desk writing and rewriting his newest poems, and then, after hunger drives him down into the street to search for food (most often at the student cafeteria around the corner on the rue Mazet, where he can buy a tasteless but filling lunch for one or two francs), he has consumed the rest of the daylight hours by walking aimlessly around the city, browsing in bookstores, reading on park benches, alive to the world around him but not yet immersed in it, still feeling his way, not unhappy, no, but wilting a little from the constant solitude. Except for Born, Margot is the one person in all of Paris with whom he has shared anything in the past. If she and Born are together again, then he must and will avoid her, but if it turns out that they are well and truly separated, that the breakup has indeed continued for these past three-plus months, then what possible harm can come from seeing her for an innocent cup of coffee? He doubts she will have any interest in renewing physical relations with him, but if she does, he would welcome the chance to sleep with her again. After all, it was the reckless, unbridled Margot who unleashed the erotic maelstrom in him that led to the furies of late summer. He is certain of the connection. Without Margot's influence, without Margot's body to instruct him in the intricate workings of his own heart, the story with Gwyn never would have been possible. Margot the fearless, Margot the silent, Margot the cipher. Yes, he very much wants to see her again, even if it is only for an innocent cup of coffee.

He walks to the café on the corner, buys a telephone *jeton* from the barman, and then goes downstairs to look up the Jouffroys' number in the directory. He is heartened when the phone is answered on the first

ring – then shocked when the person on the other end proves to be Margot herself.

Walker insists on conducting the conversation in French. Back in the spring, they spoke to each other in French a number of times, but mostly they communicated in English, and even if Margot is a person of few words, Walker knows she can express herself more comfortably in her own language. Now that he is in Paris, he aims to give Margot's Frenchness back to her, wondering if she might not show herself to be a somewhat different person in her own country and her own tongue. The real Margot, as it were, at home in the city where she was born, and not some disaffected, hostile visitor stuck in an America she could barely tolerate.

They run through the common litany of questions and answers. What in the world is he doing in Paris? How are things? Was it pure luck that she picked up the phone or has she moved in with her parents? What is she doing now? Does she have time to join him for a cup of coffee? She hesitates for a moment and then surprises him by answering: Why not? They arrange to meet at La Palette in an hour.

It is four o'clock in the afternoon, and Walker arrives first, ten minutes in advance. He orders a cup of coffee and then sits there for half an hour, growing more and more convinced that she has stood him up, but just when he is about to leave, Margot wanders in. Moving in that slow, distracted way of hers, the flicker of a smile parting her lips, kissing him warmly on both cheeks, she settles into the chair across from him. She doesn't apologize for her lateness. Margot is not a person who would do that kind of thing, and he doesn't expect it from her, he would never dream of asking her to play by anyone's rules but her own.

*En français, alors?* she says.

Yes, he answers, speaking to her in French. That's why I'm here. To practice my French. Since you're the only French person I know, I was hoping I could practice with you.

Ah, so that's it. You want to use me to further your education.

In a manner of speaking, yes. But speaking is only part of it. That is, we don't have to talk every minute if you don't want to.

Margot smiles, then changes the subject by asking him for a cigarette. As he lights the Gauloise for her, Walker looks at Margot and suddenly understands that he will never be able to separate her in his mind from Born. It is a grotesque realization, and it utterly smashes the playful, seductive tone he was trying to initiate. He was foolish to call her, he

tells himself, foolish to think he could talk her into bed again by acting as if the horrors of the spring had never happened. Even if Margot is no longer a part of Born's life, she is tied to Born in Walker's memory, and to look at her is no different from looking at Born himself. Unable to stop himself, he begins telling her about the stroll down Riverside Drive on that May evening after she left New York. He describes the stabbing to her. He tells her point-blank that Born is without question the murderer of Cedric Williams.

He watches Margot's face carefully as he recounts the gruesome particulars of that night and the days that followed, and for once she looks like a normal human being to him, an undead fellow creature with a conscience and a capacity to feel pain, and in spite of his fondness for Margot, he discovers that he enjoys punching her like this, hurting her like this, destroying her faith in a man she lived with for two years, a man she supposedly loved. Margot is crying now. He wonders if he is doing this to her because of the way she treated him in New York. Is this his revenge for having been dumped without warning at the beginning of their affair? No, he doesn't think so. He is talking to her because he understands that he can no longer look at her without seeing Born, and therefore this is the last time he will ever see her, and he wants her to know the truth before they go their separate ways. When he finishes telling the story, she stands up from the table and rushes off in the direction of the toilets.

He can't be certain if she will be coming back. She has taken her purse with her to the women's room, and since the weather outdoors is warm and mild, she was not wearing a coat or jacket when she entered the café, which means that no coat or jacket is slung over the back of her chair. Walker decides to give her a quarter of an hour, and if she hasn't returned to the table by then, he will get up and leave. Meanwhile, he asks the waiter for another drink. No, not coffee this time, he says. Make it a beer.

Margot is gone for just under ten minutes. When she sits down in her chair again, Walker notices the puffiness around her lids, the glassy sheen in her eyes, but her makeup is intact, and her cheeks are no longer smudged with mascara. He thinks: Gwyn's mascara on the night of Andy's birthday; Margot's mascara on a September afternoon in Paris; the weeping mascara of death.

Forgive me, she says to him in a subdued voice. These things you've told me . . . I don't . . . I don't know what to think anymore.

But you believe me, don't you?

Yes, I believe you. No one would ever make up something like that.

I'm sorry. I didn't want to upset you, but I thought you should know what happened – just in case you ever felt tempted to go back to him.

The strange thing is, I'm not surprised . . .

Did Born ever hit you?

Just once. A slap across the face. A hard, angry slap across the face.

Just once?

Just once. But there's violence in him. Under all the charm and witty jokes, there's real anger, real violence. I hate to admit it now, but I think it excited me. Never knowing if I could trust him or not, never knowing what he was going to do next. He only hit me that one time, but he got into a couple of fights while we were together, fights with other men. You've seen his temper. You know what he's like when he's drunk. I think it goes back to his days in the army, the war, the awful things he did during the war. Torturing prisoners. He once confessed to me that he tortured prisoners in Algeria. He denied it the next day, but I didn't believe him, even though I pretended to. The first story was the truth, I know it.

What about the knife he carries in his pocket? Didn't that ever scare you?

I take people as they are, Adam. I don't ask a lot of questions. If he wanted to carry a knife, I figured that was his business. He said it was a dangerous world and a man had to protect himself. After what happened to you that night in New York, you can't really argue with him, can you?

My sister has a theory. I don't know if it's a good theory, but she thinks Born started talking to me at the party because he felt a sexual attraction. A homoerotic attraction, as she put it. What do you think? Is she on to something or not?

It's possible. Anything is possible.

Did he ever talk to you about being attracted to men?

No. But that's neither here nor there. I can't tell you what he did before I started living with him. I can't even account for all the things he did while we were together. Who knows what a person's secret desires are? Unless the person acts on them or talks about them, you don't have a clue. The only thing I can talk about is what I saw with my own eyes – and what I saw was this. Very early in our relationship, Rudolf and I had a threesome with another man. It was my idea. Rudolf went along

with it to please me, to prove that he was willing to do anything I asked him to do. The other man was an old friend of mine, someone I'd slept with before, an extremely good-looking guy. If Rudolf was attracted to this person, he would have kissed him, wouldn't he? He would have gone for his cock and sucked him off. But he didn't do those things. He liked watching me with François, I could see he was very hot when he saw François's cock go into me, but he didn't touch him in a sexual way. Does that prove anything? I don't know. All I can tell you is that when we saw you at the party in New York, I told Rudolf you were one of the most beautiful boys I had ever seen. He agreed with me. He said you looked like a tormented Adonis, Lord Byron on the verge of a nervous breakdown. Does that mean he was attracted to you? Maybe yes, maybe no. You're a special case, Adam, and what makes you special is that you have no idea of the effect you have on other people. It seems perfectly plausible to me that a straight man could get a crush on you. Maybe that's what happened to Rudolf. But I can't know for certain, because even if he did fall for you, he never said a word about it.

He's getting married. Did you know that? At least he said he was the last time I saw him.

Yes, I know. I know all about it. That was my exit visa out of the affair. Good-bye to the double-crossing slut Margot, hello to the angelic Hélène Juin.

You sound bitter . . .

No, not bitter. Confused. I know her, you see, I've known her for a long time, and it just doesn't make any sense to me. Hélène must be five or six years older than Rudolf, she has an eighteen-year-old daughter, and all I can say about her is that she's very dull, very ordinary, very proper. A nice person, of course, a nice, hardworking bourgeois person with a tragic story, but I don't understand what he sees in her. Crazy Rudolf will be bored out of his mind.

He said he loved her.

He probably does. But that doesn't mean he should marry her.

Tragic story. Something to do with her first husband, right? I didn't quite understand what he was talking about.

Juin is a close friend of Rudolf's. Six or seven years ago, he was in a bad car accident. Crushed to pieces, fractured skull, all sorts of internal injuries, but somehow he managed to survive. Or nearly survive. He's been in a coma ever since, more or less brain-dead, on life support in a hospital. For years, Hélène refused to give up hope, but his condition

never improved, it never will improve, and finally her friends and family persuaded her to file for a divorce. When it goes through next spring, she'll be free to marry again. Good for her, but the last person I thought she'd go for was Rudolf. I've sat through at least a dozen dinners with the two of them, and I never sensed any strong feeling on either side. Friendship, yes, but no . . . no . . . what's the word I'm looking for?

Sparks.

That's it. No sparks.

You still miss him, don't you?

Not anymore. Not after what you've told me today.

But you did.

I did. I didn't want to, but I did.

The man is a maniac, you know.

True. But what law says you can't love a maniac?

They both fall silent after that, at a loss for more words, more thoughts. Margot looks at her watch, and Walker imagines she is about to tell him she's late for another appointment, that she has to run. Instead, she asks him if he has plans for dinner tonight, and if he doesn't, would he care to go to a restaurant with her? She knows a good place on the rue des Grands Augustins and will gladly treat him if he is low on money. Walker wants to tell her that it won't be possible, that he doesn't think he can see her anymore, that he believes they should put a stop to their friendship, but he can't bring himself to say the words. He is too lonely to refuse her offer, too weak-minded to turn his back on the only person he knows in Paris. Yes, he says, he would love to have dinner with her, but it's still early, not even six o'clock, and what will they do in the meantime? Anything you want, Margot says, meaning, quite literally, anything he wants, and because the thing he wants most is to crawl into bed with her, he suggests they walk over to his hotel on the rue Mazarine so he can show her his ridiculously ugly hellhole of a room. Since thoughts of sex are never far from Margot's mind, she quickly understands Walker's intentions, then goes on to demonstrate that understanding by giving him a little smile.

I wasn't very nice to you in New York, was I? she says.

You were extremely nice to me. At least for a while. But then, no, not very nice.

I'm sorry I hurt you. It was a bad time for me. I didn't know what I was doing, and then, all of a sudden, the only thing I wanted was to get out of New York. Try not to hold it against me.

I don't. I admit that I felt angry for a few weeks, but it didn't last longer than that. I stopped blaming you a long time ago.

We can be friends now, can't we?

I hope so.

Nothing too intense, mind you. Not every minute, not every day. I'm not ready for that. I'm not sure I'll ever be ready for that again. But we can take care of each other a little bit. It might be good for both of us.

As they make their way to the hotel, Walker senses that the woman beside him is no longer the same Margot he met in New York last spring. He was right to think she would be somewhat different in her own language, in her own city, in the wake of her split-up with Born, and after the conversation in the café, he can only conclude that she is more forthright, more articulate, more vulnerable than he previously imagined. Still, even as he anticipates their imminent arrival at the hotel – the mounting of the circular stairs, the key entering the lock of his door, the shedding of their clothes, the sight of Margot's small, naked body, the feel of her body against his – he wonders if he hasn't committed a colossal mistake.

At first, things do not go well. Margot says nothing about his room, because she is either too polite or too indifferent to bother mentioning it, but Walker can't help seeing it through her eyes, and he is overcome with embarrassment, appalled at himself for having dragged her up to such a tawdry, dismal place. It puts him in a foul mood, and when the two of them sit down on the bed and begin to kiss, he feels absent, alarmingly disengaged. Margot pulls back and asks if anything is wrong. Don't get weird on me, Adam, she says. This is supposed to be fun, remember?

He can't tell her that he is thinking about Gwyn, that the moment their mouths touched he was seized by a memory of the last time his mouth touched the mouth of his sister, and as he struggles to kiss Margot now, the only thought in his mind is that he will never be able to hold his sister in this way again.

I don't know what's wrong with me, he says. I feel so sad . . . so bloody fucking sad.

Maybe I should go, Margot says, gently patting his back. Sex isn't compulsory, after all. We can try again another day.

No, don't leave. I don't want you to leave. Just give me a little time. I'll be all right, I promise.

Margot gives him the time, and eventually he begins to emerge from his melancholic funk, not fully perhaps, but enough to feel aroused when she slides out of her dress and he puts his arms around her bare

skin, enough to make love to her, enough to make love to her twice, and in the pause between couplings, as they drink from the bottle of red wine he carried up to his room earlier that day, Margot further arouses him with graphic stories about her sexual encounters with other women, her passion for touching and kissing large breasts (because hers are so small), for licking and fondling women's crotches, for thrusting her tongue deep into women's assholes, and while Walker can't tell if these are true stories or simply a ploy to get him hard again for their second go at it, he enjoys listening to this dirty talk, just as he enjoyed listening to Gwyn's dirty talk in the apartment on West 107th Street. He wonders if words aren't an essential element of sex, if talking isn't finally a more subtle form of touching, and if the images dancing in our heads aren't just as important as the bodies we hold in our arms. Margot tells him that sex is the one thing in life that counts for her, that if she couldn't have sex she would probably kill herself to escape the boredom and monotony of being trapped inside her own skin. Walker doesn't say anything, but as he comes into her for the second time, he realizes that he shares her opinion. He is mad for sex. Even in the grip of the most crushing despair, he is mad for sex. Sex is the lord and the redeemer, the only salvation on earth.

They never make it to the restaurant. After finishing off the bottle of wine, they both fall asleep and forget about dinner. Early the next morning, just before dawn, Walker opens his eyes and discovers that he is alone in bed. A piece of paper is lying on the pillow next to him, a note from Margot: *Sorry. The bed was too uncomfortable. Call me next week.*

He asks himself if he will have the courage to call. Then, more to the point, he asks himself if he will have the courage not to call, if he can resist seeing her again.

Two days later, he is sitting at an outdoor café on the place Saint-André des Arts, nursing a glass of beer and writing in a small notebook. It is six o'clock in the evening, the end of another workday, and now that Walker has begun to settle into the rhythms of Paris, he understands that this is probably the city's most inspiriting hour, the transition from work to home, the streets thronged with men and women rushing back to their families, to their friends, to their solitary lives, and he enjoys being outside among them, encircled by the vast collective exhale filling the air. He has just written a brief letter to his parents and a longer letter to Gwyn, and now he is trying to write something cogent about the work of George Oppen, a contemporary American poet whom he greatly

admires. He copies out these lines from Oppen's most recent book, *This In Which*:

> Impossible to doubt the world: it can be seen
> And because it is irrevocable
>
> It cannot be understood, and I believe that fact is lethal.

He is about to jot down some comments on this passage, but before he can proceed a shadow falls across the page of the notebook. He glances up, and there, standing directly in front of him, is Rudolf Born. Before Walker can say or do anything, the future husband of Hélène Juin sits down in the empty chair beside him. Walker's pulse begins to race. He is breathless, speechless. It wasn't supposed to happen this way, he tells himself. If and when they crossed paths, he was the one who was going to spot Born, not the other way around. He was going to be walking down a crowded street, in a position to avert his eyes and escape unnoticed. That was how he always saw it in his head, and now here he is out in the open, defenseless, sitting on his dumb, sorry ass, unable to pretend Born isn't there, trapped.

The white suit is gone, replaced by a cream-colored jacket, and a silk foulard is hanging around his neck, a blue-and-green patterned affair no doubt worn to bounce off the light blue of his shirt – still and ever the rumpled dandy, Walker thinks, wearing the same sardonic smile as of old.

Well, well, Born says, with false good humor, pronouncing the words in such a way as to emphasize their falseness. We meet again, Walker. What a pleasant surprise.

Walker knows that he is going to have to talk to him, but for the time being he can't get any words out of his mouth.

I was hoping I'd run into you, Born continues. Paris is such a small city, it was bound to happen sooner or later.

Who told you I was here? Walker finally asks. Margot?

Margot? I haven't talked to Margot in months. I didn't even know she was in town.

Who was it, then?

You forget that I taught at Columbia. I have Columbia connections, and the head of your program just happens to be a friend of mine. I had dinner with him the other night, and he was the one who told me. He

said you were living in some fleabag on the rue Mazarine. Why didn't you go to Reid Hall? The rooms might not be as big there, but at least they aren't crawling with bugs.

Walker has no desire to discuss his living arrangements with Born, no interest in wasting his breath on small talk. Ignoring the question, he says: I haven't forgotten, you know. I still think about it all the time.

Think about what?

What you did to that boy.

I didn't do anything to him.

Please . . .

One thrust, that was all. You were there. You saw what happened. He was going to shoot us. If I hadn't attacked first, we both would have been killed.

But the gun wasn't loaded.

We didn't know that, did we? He said he was going to shoot, and when someone points a gun at me and says he's going to shoot, I take him at his word.

What about the park? Over twelve more stab wounds after the first one. Why on earth did you do that?

I didn't. I know you don't believe me, but I had nothing to do with that. Yes, I carried him into the park after you left, but by the time I got there he was already dead. Why would I go on stabbing someone after he was dead? All I wanted was to get out of there as quickly as I could.

Then who did it?

I have no idea. A sick person. A goblin of the night. New York is a sinister place, after all. It could have been anyone.

I talked to the police, you know. In spite of your not so subtle warning.

I figured you would. That's why I left in such a hurry.

If you were innocent, why not stay and fight it out in court?

For what? They would have acquitted me in the end, and I couldn't afford to lose all the time it would have taken to defend myself. The kid deserved to die. The kid died. That's all there is to it.

No remorse, then.

No remorse. None whatsoever. I don't even blame you for turning against me and going to the police. You did what you thought was right. Mistakenly, of course, but that's your problem, not mine. I saved your life, Adam. Remember that. If the gun had been loaded, you'd still be thanking me for what I did. The fact that it wasn't loaded doesn't really change anything, does it? As long as we thought it was loaded, it was loaded.

Walker is willing to concede the point, but there is still the question of the park, the question of how and when the boy died, and he has no doubt that Born's version of events is untrue – for the simple reason that it could not have happened so quickly. A single stab wound to the stomach can lead to death, but inevitably it is a slow and protracted death, which means that Williams must have been alive when Born reached the park, and therefore the additional wounds that ended up killing the boy were inflicted by Born himself. Nothing else makes sense. Why would another person go to the trouble of stabbing a dead teenager more than a dozen times? If Williams was still breathing when Born left the park, it might be possible to build an argument for a second attacker – far-fetched but possible – but only if the object was to steal the boy's money, and the police told Walker back in the spring that no robbery had taken place. The kid's wallet was found in his pocket, and sixteen untouched dollars were inside the wallet, which eliminates theft as a motive for the crime. *Why would I go on stabbing someone after he was dead?* Because he wasn't dead, and you kept on plunging your knife into him until you made sure he was, and then, even after you finished the job, you continued stabbing him because you were engulfed by rage, because you were out of your mind and enjoyed what you were doing.

I don't want to talk about it anymore, Walker says, reaching into his pocket and pulling out some coins to pay for his beer. I have to go.

Suit yourself, Born replies. I was hoping we could bury the hatchet and become friends again. It even occurred to me that you might enjoy meeting the daughter of my future wife. Cécile is a delightful, intelligent girl of eighteen – a literature student, an excellent pianist, just the kind of person who would interest you.

No thanks, Walker says, standing up from the table. I don't need you to play matchmaker for me. You already did that once, remember?

Well, if you ever change your mind, give me a call. I'd be happy to introduce her to you.

At that point, just as Walker is turning to go, Born reaches into the breast pocket of his cream-colored blazer and withdraws a business card with his address and telephone number on it. Here, he says, handing the card to Walker. All my coordinates. Just in case.

For a brief moment, Walker is tempted to tear up the card and throw the pieces onto the ground – the same way he tore up the check in New York last spring – but then he decides against it, not wanting to disgrace himself with such a cheap and petty insult. He slips the card into his

pocket and says good-bye. Born nods but says nothing. As Walker leaves, the sun shoots across the sky and explodes into a hundred thousand splinters of molten light. The Eiffel Tower falls down. Every building in Paris bursts into flame. End of Act I. Curtain.

He has put himself in an untenable position. As long as he was ignorant of Born's whereabouts, he could live with the uncertainty of a potential encounter, all the while deluding himself into believing that luck would be with him and the dreaded moment would never come, or come late, so late that his time in Paris would not be destroyed by fears of another encounter, other encounters. Now that it has happened, and happened early, much earlier than he would have thought possible, he finds it unbearable to have Born's address in his pocket and not be able to go to the police to demand that he be arrested. Nothing would make him happier than to see the murderer of Cedric Williams brought to justice. Even if they let him off, he would have to suffer through the expense and humiliation of a trial, and even if the case never went to court, he would have to endure the unpleasantness of being grilled by the police, the rigors of a drawn-out investigation. But short of abducting Born and hauling him back to New York, what can Walker do? He ponders the situation for the rest of the day and deep into the night, and then an idea occurs to him, a diabolical idea, an idea so cruel and underhanded that he is stunned by the mere fact that he is capable of imagining such a thing. It won't put Born in prison, alas, but it will make his life extremely uncomfortable, and if Walker can pull off his plan successfully, it will deprive Hélène Juin's future husband of the one object he covets most in the world. Walker is both thrilled and disgusted with himself. He has never been a vengeful person, has never actively sought to hurt anyone, but Born is in a different category, Born is a killer, Born deserves to be punished, and for the first time in his life Walker is out for blood.

The plan calls for a practiced liar, a social acrobat skilled in the fine art of duplicity, and since Walker is neither one of those things, he knows that he is the worst man for the job he has given himself. Right from the start, he will be forced to act against his own nature, again and again he will slip and fall as he struggles to gain a secure footing on the battleground he has mapped out in his mind, and yet in spite of his misgivings, he marches off to the Café Conti the next morning to drop another *jeton* into the pay telephone and put his scheme into operation.

He is dumbfounded by his boldness, his resolve. When Born answers on the third ring, the surprise in the man's voice is palpable.

Adam Walker, he says, doing his best to mask his astonishment. The last person on earth I was expecting to hear from.

Forgive the intrusion, Walker says. I just wanted you to know that I've done some serious thinking since we talked yesterday.

Interesting. And where have your thoughts led you?

I've decided I want to bury the hatchet.

Doubly interesting. Yesterday, you accuse me of murder, and today you're willing to forgive and forget. Why the sudden turnaround?

Because you convinced me you were telling the truth.

Am I to take this as a sincere apology – or are you angling for some new favor from me? You wouldn't be thinking of trying to resurrect your dead magazine, for example?

Of course not. That's all in the past.

It was a hurtful thing you did, Walker. Tearing up the check into little pieces and sending it back to me without a word. I was deeply insulted.

If I offended you in any way, I'm truly sorry. I was more or less in shock after what happened. I didn't know what I was doing.

And you know what you're doing now?

I think so.

You think so. And tell me young man, what exactly do you want?

Nothing. I called because you asked me to call. In case I changed my mind.

You want to get together, then. Is that it? You're telling me you'd like to resume our friendship.

That was the idea. You mentioned meeting your fiancée and her daughter. I thought that would be a nice way to begin.

*Nice*. Such an insipid word. You Americans have a real gift for banalities, don't you?

No doubt. We're also good at apologizing when we feel we're in the wrong. If you don't want to see me, just say so. I'll understand.

Forgive me, Walker. I was being nasty again. I'm afraid it comes with the territory.

We all have our moments.

Indeed. And now you want to break bread with Hélène and Cécile. As per my invitation of yesterday. Consider it done. I'll leave word at your hotel as soon as I've made the arrangements.

*

The dinner is set for the following night at Vagenende, a turn-of-the-century brasserie on the Boulevard Saint-Germain. Walker arrives promptly at eight, the first member of the party to show up, and as he is led to Monsieur Born's table, he is too nervous and distracted to pay much attention to his surroundings: the dark, oak-paneled walls, the brass fixtures, the stiff white tablecloths and napkins, the hushed conversations in other parts of the room, the sound of silver utensils clanking against china. Thirty-four hours after his demented, groveling conversation with Born, this is what his lies have earned him: unending fear, unmitigated self-contempt, and the priceless opportunity to meet Born's future wife and stepdaughter. Everything hinges on what happens with Hélène and Cécile Juin. If he can manage to form a connection with them, with either one of them, a relation independent of any connection with Born, then sooner or later it will become possible for him to reveal the truth about Riverside Drive, and if Walker can persuade them to accept his story about the killing of Cedric Williams, then there is a chance, a better than even chance, that the wedding will be called off and Born will be forsaken by his bride-to-be. That is all Walker has set out to accomplish: to break up the marriage before it becomes a legal fact. Not such an onerous punishment for the crime of murder, perhaps, but, given the available options, harsh enough. Born rejected. Born humiliated. Born crumpled up in misery. Hateful as Walker finds it to be pandering to him with false apologies and insincere avowals of friendship, he understands that he has no other choice. If Hélène and Cécile prove to be intractable, then he will abandon the effort and quietly declare defeat. But only if, and only when, and until that moment comes, he is determined to go on playing cards with the devil.

His initial findings are inconclusive. By temperament or circumstance, both mother and daughter come across as modest and reserved, not easily approachable or given to lighthearted talk, and since Born dominates the early going with introductions, explanations, and various other comments, little is said by either one of them. When Walker gives a brief account of his first days in Paris, Hélène compliments him on his French; at another point, Cécile blandly inquires if he enjoys living in a hotel. The mother is tall, blonde, and well dressed, by no means a beauty (her face is too long, Walker thinks, a bit on the horsey side), but like many middle-class Frenchwomen of a certain age, she carries herself with considerable poise and assurance – a question of style, perhaps, or else the product of some arcane Gallic wisdom concerning the

nature of femininity. The daughter, who has just turned eighteen, is a student at the Lycée Fénelon on the rue de l'Éperon, which is less than a five-minute walk from the Hôtel du Sud. She is a smaller, less-imposing creature than her mother, with short brown hair, thin wrists and narrow shoulders, and alert, darting eyes. Walker notices that those eyes have a tendency to squint, and it occurs to him (correctly, as it turns out) that Cécile normally wears glasses and has decided to live without them for the duration of the dinner. No, not a pretty girl, almost mousy in fact, but nevertheless an interesting face to look at: tiny chin, long nose, round cheeks, an expressive mouth. Every now and then, that mouth tugs downward with a clandestine sort of amusement, not quite blossoming into a smile, but for all that showing a sharply developed sense of humor, someone awake to the comic possibilities of any given moment. There is no question that she is extremely intelligent (for the past four minutes Born has been bragging to Walker about her outstanding grades in literature and philosophy, her passion for the piano, her mastery of ancient Greek), but much as Cécile has working in her favor, Walker sadly acknowledges that he is not attracted to her, at least not in the way he would have hoped. She is not his type, he says to himself, falling back on that vague, overused term, which stands in for the infinite complexities of physical desire. But what is his type? he wonders. His own sister? The sex-hungry Margot, who is ten years older than he is? Whatever it is he wants, it is not Cécile Juin. He looks at her and sees a child, a work in progress, a not yet fully formed person, and at this point in her life she is too withdrawn and self-conscious to give off any of the erotic signals that would inspire a man to run after her. That isn't to say he won't do his best to cultivate a friendship with her, but there will be no kissing or touching, no romantic entanglements, no attempt to lure her into bed.

He despises himself for thinking such thoughts, for looking upon the innocent Cécile as if she were nothing more than a sex object, a potential victim of his seductive powers (assuming he has any), but at the same time he knows that he is fighting a war, an underground guerrilla war, and this dinner is the first battle of that war, and if he could win the battle by seducing his adversary's future stepdaughter, he would not hesitate to do it. But the young Cécile is not a candidate for seduction, and therefore he will have to devise more subtle tactics to advance his purpose, shifting from an all-out assault on the daughter to a two-pronged offensive against mother and daughter both – in an attempt to ingratiate himself with them and eventually lure them over to his side. All this must be

accomplished under Born's watchful gaze, the intolerable, suffocating presence of a man he can barely bring himself to look at. The wily, skeptical Born is no doubt deeply suspicious of the two-faced Walker, and who knows if he hasn't merely pretended to accept the latter's pretend apology in order to find out what mischief the boy is up to? There is an edge to Born's voice buried under the pleasant chatter and false bonhomie, an anxious, straining tone that seems to suggest he is on his guard. It will not be wise to see him again, Walker tells himself, which makes it all the more imperative to establish his separate peace with the Juins tonight, before the dinner comes to an end.

The women are on the other side of the table. He is opposite Cécile, and Born is sitting to his left, face to face with Hélène. Walker studies Hélène's eyes as she looks at her betrothed, and he becomes just as baffled as Margot was when he detects no spark emanating from them. Other feelings lurk in those eyes, perhaps – wistfulness, kindness, sadness – but love is not among them, much less happiness or a single trace of joy. But how can there be happiness for a woman in Hélène's position, for someone who has spent the past six or seven years living in a state of grief and suspended animation as her half-dead husband languishes in a hospital? He imagines the comatose Juin stretched out in bed, his body hooked up to countless machines and a tangle of respiration tubes, the only patient in a large, deserted ward, living but not living, dying but not dying, and suddenly he remembers the film he saw with Gwyn two months ago, *Ordet*, the film by Carl Dreyer, sitting next to his sister in the balcony of the New Yorker Theatre, and the dead farmer's wife laid out in her coffin, and his tears when she sat up and came to life again, but no, he says to himself, that was just a story, a make-believe story in a make-believe world, and this is not that world, and there will be no miraculous resurrections for Juin, Hélène's husband will never sit up and come back to life. From Juin's bed in the hospital Walker's mind jumps to another bed, and before he can put a stop to it, he is revisiting the repugnant scene Margot described to him a few days ago: Margot in bed with the two men, Born and the other one, what was his name, François, Margot in bed with Born and François, the three of them naked, fucking, and now he sees Born watching François push his hardened cock into Margot, and there is Born, naked in his chunky, odious flesh, swept up in the throes of arousal, jerking off as he watches his girlfriend do it with another man . . .

Walker smiles at Cécile in an attempt to dissolve the image, and as

she smiles back at him – a bit puzzled, but apparently pleased by the attention – he wonders if this kind of debauchery doesn't explain why Born is so keen on marrying Hélène. He is struggling to turn his back on himself, to resist his sordid, malevolent urges, and she represents respectability to him, a wall against his own madness. Walker notes how decorously he behaves with Hélène, addressing her by the formal *vous* instead of the more intimate, familiar *tu*. It is the language of counts and countesses, the language of marriage in the highest reaches of the upper class, and it creates a distance from both self and world that serves as a form of protection. It is not love that Born is looking for but safety. The libidinous Margot brought out the worst in him. Will the calm and repressed Hélène turn him into a new man? Dream on, Walker says to himself. A person of your intelligence should know better than to think that.

By the time they place their orders, Walker has been told that Hélène works as a speech pathologist at a clinic in the fourteenth arrondissement. She has been in the profession since the early fifties – in other words, long before her husband's accident – and although she now depends on this job to generate the income needed to support her small household, Walker quickly understands that she is a dedicated practitioner, that her career gives her immense satisfaction and is probably the single most important element of her life. Find yourself drowning in a sea of trouble, and hard work can become the raft that ends up keeping you afloat. Walker reads it in her eyes, is impressed by how noticeably they have brightened now that Born has mentioned the subject, and suddenly there is a possible opening, a chance to engage her in pertinent dialogue. The truth is that Walker is genuinely interested in what she does. He has read Jakobson and Merleau-Ponty on aphasia and language acquisition, has given serious thought to these matters because of his engagement with words, and therefore he does not feel like a fraud or a conniver when he starts pelting her with questions. At first, Hélène is taken aback by his enthusiasm, but once she realizes that he is in earnest, she begins to talk about articulation disorders in children, her methods of treating the lisping, garble-mouthed, stuttering youngsters who come to her clinic, but no, she doesn't only work with children, there are the adults as well, the old people, the victims of stroke and various brain injuries, the aphasics, the ones who have lost the power of speech or can't remember words or jumble words to such an extent that *pen* becomes *paper* and *tree* becomes *house*. There are

several different forms of aphasia, Walker learns, depending on which part of the brain is affected – Broca's aphasia, Wernicke's aphasia, conduction aphasia, transcortical sensory aphasia, anomic aphasia, and so on – and isn't it intriguing, Hélène says, smiling for the first time since she entered the restaurant, truly smiling at last, isn't it intriguing that thought cannot exist without language, and since language is a function of the brain, we would have to say that language – the ability to experience the world through symbols – is in some sense a physical property of human beings, which proves that the old mind–body duality is so much nonsense, doesn't it? Adieu, Descartes. The mind and the body are one.

He is discovering that the best way to get to know them is to leave himself out of it, to ask questions rather than give answers, to make them talk about themselves. But Walker is not adept at this kind of interpersonal manipulation, and he falls into an uncomfortable silence when Born barges in with some pointedly negative comments about the Israeli army's refusal to withdraw from Sinai and the West Bank. Walker senses that he is trying to goad him into an argument, but the fact is that he agrees with Born's stance on this issue, and rather than let him know that, he says nothing, waiting for the harangue to run its course by looking at Cécile's mouth, which is again tugging downward in response to some secret inner mirth. He could be wrong, but it appears that she finds the intensity of Born's opinions rather funny. A couple of minutes later, the rant is interrupted when the appetizers are set before them. Seizing his opportunity, Walker breaks the sudden silence by asking Cécile about her study of ancient Greek. Greek wasn't offered at the high school he went to, he says, and he envies her for having the chance to learn it. He has only two years of college left, and by now it's probably too late for him to start.

Not really, she says. Once you learn the alphabet, it's not as hard as it looks.

They talk about Greek literature for a while, and before long Cécile is telling him about her summer project – a crazy, overly ambitious plan that has led to three months of constant frustration and regret. God knows what possessed her to try in the first place, she says, but she got it into her head to take on a book-length poem by the most difficult writer imaginable and translate it into French. When Walker asks who the writer is, she shrugs and says that he hasn't heard of him, that no one has heard of him, and indeed, when she mentions the poet's name, Lycophron, who lived around 300 B.C., Walker admits that she is right. The poem is about Cassandra, she goes on, the daughter of Priam, the

last king of Troy – poor Cassandra, who had the misfortune to be loved by Apollo. He offered her the gift of prophecy, but only if she agreed to sacrifice her virginity to him in exchange. At first she said yes, then she said no, and the jilted Apollo took his revenge on her by poisoning his gift, making sure that none of Cassandra's prophecies would ever be believed. Lycophron's poem is set during the Trojan War, and Cassandra is in prison, already mad, about to be murdered with Agamemnon, spewing forth endless ravings and visions of the future in a language so complex, so crammed with metaphors and allusions, that it is almost unintelligible. It is a poem of shrieks and howls, Cécile tells him, a great poem in her opinion, a wild and utterly modern poem, but so daunting and elusive, so far beyond her powers of comprehension, that after hours and hours of work she has managed to translate only a hundred and fifty lines. If she keeps it up, she says, mouth tugging downward once again, it will take her only ten or twelve years to finish.

In spite of her self-deprecating manner, Walker can't help admiring the girl's courage for tackling such a formidable poem, a poem he himself would now like to read, and consequently he asks her if any translations exist in English. She doesn't know, she says, but she would be happy to find out for him. Walker thanks her and then adds (out of simple curiosity, with no ulterior motive) that he would like to read her version of the opening lines in French. But Cécile demurs. It couldn't possibly interest you, she says. It's pure rubbish. At which point Hélène pats her daughter's hand and tells her not to be so hard on herself. Born then pipes in and addresses Cécile as well: Adam is a translator, too, you know. A poet first, but also a translator of poems. From Provençal, no less. He once gave me a work by my would-be namesake, Bertran de Born. An impressive fellow, old Bertran. He tended to lose his head at times, but a good poet, and Adam did an excellent translation.

Oh? Cécile says, looking at Walker. I wasn't aware of that.

I don't know about excellent, he says, but I have done a little translating.

Well, she replies, in that case . . .

And just like that, with no forewarning, with no devious maneuvers on his part, Walker finds himself arranging to get together with Cécile tomorrow afternoon at four o'clock to have a look at her manuscript. A small victory, perhaps, but quite suddenly he has accomplished everything he set out to do this evening. There will be further contact with the Juins, and Born will be nowhere in sight.

*

The following morning, he is sitting at his wobbly desk with a pen in his hand, looking over a recent poem and becoming more and more disenchanted with it, wondering if he should forge on with his efforts, put the manuscript aside for later reflection, or simply chuck it into the wastebasket. He lifts his head for a peek out the windows: gray and overcast, a mountain of clouds bulking up to the west, yet another shift in the ever-shifting Paris sky. He finds the gloom indoors rather pleasant – a soothing gloom, as it were, a companionable gloom, a gloom one could converse with for hours. He puts down his pen, scratches his head, exhales. Unbidden, a forgotten verse from Ecclesiastes comes roaring into his consciousness. *And I gave my heart to know wisdom, and to know madness and folly* . . . As he jots down the words in the right-hand margin of his poem, he wonders if this isn't the truest thing he has written about himself in months. The words might not be his own, but he feels that they belong to him.

Ten-thirty, eleven o'clock. The yellowish glow of the electric bulb radiating from the wine-bottle lamp on the desk. The dripping faucet, the peeling wallpaper, the scratching of his pen. He hears the sound of footsteps on the stairs. Someone is approaching, slowly mounting the circular staircase toward his floor, the top floor, and at first he assumes it is Maurice, the semi-inebriated hotel manager, coming to deliver a telegram or the morning mail, affable Maurice Petillon, man of a thousand stories about nothing at all, but no, it can't be Maurice, for now Walker detects the clicking sound of high heels, and therefore it must be a woman, and if it's a woman, who else can it be but Margot? Walker is glad, inordinately glad, positively stupid with happiness at the prospect of seeing her again. He jumps out of his chair and rushes to open the door before she has time to knock.

She is holding a small, wax-coated patisserie bag filled with freshly baked croissants. Under normal circumstances, a person who shows up bearing gifts is a person in a happy frame of mind, but Margot looks peeved and out of sorts today, and she barely manages a smile as she plants a frosty, perfunctory kiss on Walker's mouth. When Walker puts his arms around her, she wriggles out of his grasp and strides into the room, tossing the bag onto the desk and then sitting down on the unmade bed. Walker closes the door behind him, advances as far as the desk, and stops.

What's wrong? he says.

There's nothing wrong with me, Margot replies. I want to know what's wrong with you.

With me? Why should anything be wrong with me? What are you talking about?

Last night, I happened to be walking with a friend down the Boulevard Saint-Germain. It was about eight-thirty or nine o'clock. We passed that restaurant, you know the one I'm talking about, the old brasserie, Vagenende, and for no particular reason, giant idiot that I am, or maybe because I used to go there with my parents when I was a little girl, I looked through the window. And who do you think I saw?

Ah, Walker says, feeling as if he has just been slapped across the face. You don't have to tell me. I already know the answer.

What are you up to, Adam? What kind of warped game are you involved in now?

Walker lowers himself onto the chair behind the desk. There is no air left in his lungs; his head is about to detach itself from his body. He looks away from Margot, whose eyes never leave him, and begins fiddling with the bag of croissants.

Well? she says. Aren't you going to talk?

I want to, he says at last. I want to tell you everything.

Then why don't you?

Because I don't know if I can trust you. You can't breathe a word about this to anyone, do you understand? You have to promise me that.

Who do you think I am?

I don't know. Someone who disappointed me. Someone I like very much. Someone I want to be friends with.

But you don't think I can keep a secret.

Can you?

No one ever asked me before. How can I know unless I try?

Well, at least that's honest.

You decide. I'm not going to force you to talk when you don't want to talk. But if you don't talk, Adam, I'm going to stand up and leave this room, and you'll never see me again.

That's blackmail.

No it's not. It's the simple truth, that's all.

Walker lets out a prolonged sigh of defeat, then stands up from the chair and begins pacing back and forth in front of Margot, who watches him in silence from the bed. Ten minutes go by, and in those minutes he tells her the story of the past several days: the accidental meeting with Born, which he now suspects was not an accident, Born's spurious denials about the murder of Cedric Williams, the invitation to meet Hélène and Cécile, the

business card he almost tore up, hatching the plan to block Born's marriage to Hélène, the contrite telephone call to set the plan in motion, the dinner at Vagenende, his upcoming date with Cécile at four o'clock this afternoon. When Margot has heard him out, she pats the bed with her left hand and asks Walker to sit down beside her. Walker sits, and the moment his body touches the mattress, Margot grabs hold of his two shoulders with her two hands, turns him toward her, brings her face to within inches of his, and says in a low voice filled with determination: Give it up, Adam. You don't have a chance. He'll slice you into little pieces.

It's too late, Walker says. I've already started now, and I'm not going to stop until I've seen it through to the end.

You talk about trust. What makes you think you can trust Hélène Juin? You've only just met her.

I know. It's going to take a while before I'm sure. But my first impression of her is a good one. She strikes me as a solid, honest person, and I don't think she really cares that much about Born. She's grateful to him, he's been kind to her, but she's not in love with him.

The minute you tell her about what happened in New York, she'll turn around and go straight to Rudolf. I promise you.

Maybe. But even if she does, what can happen to me?

All kinds of things.

Born might try to punch me in the face, but he's not going to come after me with his knife.

I'm not talking about the knife. Rudolf has connections, a hundred powerful connections, and before you start to mess with him, you should know who you're dealing with. He's not just anyone.

Connections?

With the police, with the military, with the government. I can't prove anything, but I've always felt he's something more than just a university professor.

Such as?

I don't know. Secret intelligence, espionage, dirty work of some kind or another.

And why on earth do you suspect that?

Telephone calls in the middle of the night . . . mysterious, unexplained absences . . . the people he knows. Cabinet ministers, army generals. How many young professors go out to dinner with top government officials? Rudolf is on the inside, and that makes him a dangerous person for you to know. Especially here in Paris.

It sounds rather flimsy to me.

Do you remember the dinner at our apartment in New York last spring?

Vividly. How could I forget it?

He was on the phone when I let you into the apartment. Then he came out – furious, breathing fire, hysterical. *How many years have I given them?* What did he mean by that? Principles! Battles! The ship is going down! There was a problem in Paris, and I can tell you now that it had nothing to do with academic business or his father's estate. It was connected to the government, to his secret life in whatever agency he works for. That's why he got so worked up when you started talking about the CIA. Don't you remember? He told you all those things about your family, and you were shocked, you couldn't believe how much information he'd managed to dig up about you. You said he must be an agent of some kind. You were right, Adam. You sniffed out something about him, and he started laughing at you, he tried to turn it into a joke. That's when I knew I was right.

Maybe. But it's still just a guess.

Then why wouldn't he tell me what the problem was? He didn't even bother to make up an excuse. It doesn't concern you, he said, don't ask so many questions. So off he flies to Paris, and when he comes back, he's engaged to Hélène Juin and I'm thrown out the door.

They go on talking for another fifteen or twenty minutes, and the more vehement Margot becomes about her suspicions concerning undercover operations, government conspiracies, and the psychological pressures of leading a double life, the less Walker seems to care. Margot is puzzled by his indifference. She calls it curious, unhealthy, irrational, but Walker explains that Born's activities are of no interest to him. The only thing that counts is the murder of Cedric Williams, and even if Born turned out to be the head of the entire French intelligence system, it wouldn't matter to him. There is just one moment when his attention seems fully engaged, and that follows a tossed-off comment from Margot about Born's past – something to do with spending his childhood in a large house outside Paris, which was where she first met him when she was three years old. What about Guatemala? Walker asks, remembering that Born said to him that he had grown up in Guatemala.

He was pulling your leg, Margot replies. Rudolf has never been anywhere near the place.

I thought as much. But why Guatemala?

Why not Guatemala? He enjoys making up stories about himself. Fooling people, telling little lies – they're grand entertainment for Rudolf.

Although little of concrete value emerges from this conversation (too many assumptions, not enough facts), it nevertheless seems to mark a turning point in his relations with Margot. She is worried about him, worried for him, and the anxiety and concern he sees in her eyes is both comforting (the issue of trust is no longer in doubt) and somewhat troubling. She is drawing closer to him, her affection has become more manifest, more sincere, and yet there is something maternal about that anxiety, a sense of wisdom frowning down on the errors of youth, and for the first time in the months he has known her, he can feel the difference in their ages, the gap of ten years that stands between them. He hopes this will not become a problem. He needs Margot now. She is his only ally in Paris, and being with her is the only medicine that can prevent him from brooding about Gwyn, from longing for Gwyn. No, he is not unhappy that she spotted him in the restaurant last night with Born and the Juins. Nor is he unhappy that he has just bared his soul to her. Her reaction has proved that he means something to her, that he represents more than just another body to climb into bed with, but he knows that he mustn't abuse her friendship, for Margot is not entirely there, and she has only just so much of herself to give. Ask for too much, and she is liable to resent it, perhaps even abscond.

Leaving the untouched croissants on the desk, they go out into the dank, sunless weather to look for a place to eat. Margot holds his hand as they walk along in silence, and ten minutes later they are sitting across from each other at a corner table in the Restaurant des Beaux-Arts. Margot buys him a copious three-course lunch (refusing to let him pay, insisting that he order dessert and a second cup of coffee), and then they move on to the rue de l'Université. The Jouffroy apartment is on the fifth floor of a six-story building, and as they squeeze into the cramped birdcage of an elevator to begin their ascent, Walker puts his arms around Margot and covers her face with a barrage of short, intense kisses. Margot bursts out laughing, and she is still laughing as she extracts a key from her purse and unlocks the door of the apartment. It turns out to be a sumptuous place, far more lavish than anything Walker could have imagined, an immense palace of comfort expressing wealth on a scale he has not encountered before. Margot once told him that her father worked in banking, but she neglected to add that he was the president of the bank, and now that she is giving Walker a brief tour of the rooms, with their thick Persian rugs

and gilt-edged mirrors, with their crystal chandeliers and antique furnishings, he feels he is gaining new insight into the disaffected, elusive Margot. She is a person at odds with the environment she was born into, at odds with it but not in outright rebellion (for here she is, temporarily back with her parents as she searches for a place of her own), yet what a disappointment it must be to them that she is still unmarried at thirty, nor can her halfhearted attempts to become a painter sit terribly well in this dominion of bourgeois respectability. Ambiguous Margot, with her love of cooking and her love of sex, still struggling to find a place for herself, still not entirely free.

Or so Walker muses as he follows her into the kitchen, but a minute later he learns that the portrait is somewhat more complex than the one he has been fashioning in his mind. Margot does not live in the apartment with her parents. She has a room upstairs, a tiny maid's room that her grandmother bought for her as a twenty-first-birthday present, and the only reason she entered the apartment this afternoon was to look for a pack of cigarettes (which she now finds in a drawer next to the sink). The tour was a little bonus, she adds, so Walker would have an idea of how and where she grew up. When he asks her why she prefers camping out in a minute *chambre de bonne* to sleeping in comfort down here, Margot smiles and says: Figure it out for yourself.

It is a spartan room, less than a third the size of his room at the hotel. Space for a small desk and chair, a small sink, and a small bed with storage drawers under the mattress. Pristine in its cleanliness, no adornments anywhere – as if they have stepped into the cell of a novitiate nun. Just one book in sight, lying on the floor beside the bed: a collection of poems by Paul Éluard, *Capitale de la douleur*. A few sketchbooks piled up on the desk along with a drinking glass filled with pencils and pens; some canvases on the floor, leaning against the wall with their backs facing out. Walker would love to turn them around, would love to open the sketchbooks, but Margot doesn't offer to show them to him, and he doesn't dare touch anything without her permission. He is awed by the simplicity of the room, awed by this unearthly glimpse into Margot's inner world. How many people has she allowed to come in here? he wonders.

He would like to think he is the first.

They spend two hours together in Margot's narrow bed, and when Walker finally leaves, he is running late for his appointment with Cécile Juin. It is entirely his fault, but the truth is that he forgot all about the

meeting. From the moment he started kissing Margot, the four o'clock rendezvous vanished from his mind, and if not for Margot herself, who glanced over at the alarm clock and said to him: *Aren't you supposed to be somewhere in fifteen minutes?*, he would still be lying next to her – rather than bounding from the bed, jumping into his clothes, and scrambling to get out of there.

He is mystified by this gesture of help. Just hours earlier, she was adamantly opposed to his plan, and now she seems to be acting as his accomplice. Has she rethought her position, he asks himself, or is she subtly mocking him in some way, testing him to find out if he is actually stupid enough to walk into the trap she feels he has set for himself? He suspects the latter interpretation is the correct one, but even so, he thanks her for reminding him of the date, and then, just as he is about to open the door and leave the tiny room, he rashly tells Margot that he loves her.

No you don't, she says, shaking her head and smiling. But I'm glad you think you do. You're a crazy boy, Adam, and every time I see you, you're crazier than you were the last time. Before long, you'll be just as crazy as I am.

He walks into La Palette at twenty-five past four, almost half an hour late. He would not be surprised if Cécile has already left, storming out in a huff and vowing to rain down a thousand curses on him if he should ever cross her path again. But no, she is still there, sitting calmly at a table in the back room, reading a book, a half-finished bottle of Orangina in front of her, wearing glasses this time, and a fetching little dark blue hat that resembles a beret. Embarrassed, out of breath from running, his clothes disheveled, his body no doubt reeking of sex, and with the word *crazy* still resounding in his head, Walker approaches the table, already stammering a multitude of apologies as Cécile glances up at him and smiles – a wholly undeserved smile of forgiveness.

Still, even as he sits down in the chair across from her, Walker goes on apologizing, inventing some far-fetched excuse about standing in line at the post office for more than an hour to make a long-distance call to New York, but Cécile shrugs it off, telling him not to worry, there's no problem, he doesn't have to explain anything. Then, holding up her left wrist, she taps her watch with her right index finger and says: We have a rule in Paris. Whenever people arrange to get together, the first one to arrive gives the other person an extra half hour to show up – no

questions asked. It's four twenty-five now. By my reckoning, that makes you five minutes early.

Well, Walker says, impressed by the daffiness of this logic, then I'm rattling on for nothing, aren't I?

That's what I've been trying to tell you.

Walker orders a coffee, his sixth or seventh of the day, and then, with a characteristic downward tug of her mouth, Cécile points to the book she was reading when he came in – a small green hardcover volume with no dust jacket, apparently quite old, a frayed and battered object that looks like something rescued from a trash bin.

I found it, she says, unable to control her mouth anymore as it breaks into a full-fledged smile. Lycophron in English. The Loeb Classical Library, published by Harvard University Press. Nineteen twenty-one. With a translation by – (she opens the book to the title page) – A. W. Mair, professor of Greek, Edinburgh University.

That was fast, Walker says. How in the world did you manage to find it?

Sorry. I can't tell you.

Oh? And why not?

It's a secret. Maybe I'll tell you when you give it back to me, but not before then.

You mean I can borrow it?

Of course. You can keep it for as long as you like.

And what about the translation? Have you looked at it?

My English isn't very good, but it strikes me as stuffy and pedantic, rather old-school, I'm afraid. Worse yet, it's a literal prose translation, so all the poetry is missing. But at least it gives you a sense of the thing – and why it's given me so much trouble.

Cécile opens the book to the second page of the poem and points to line thirty-one, where Cassandra's monologue begins. She says to Walker: Why not read some of it out loud to me? Then you can judge for yourself.

Walker takes the book from her and immediately plunges in: Alas! hapless nurse of mine burnt even aforetime by the warlike pineships of the lion that was begotten in three evenings, whom of old Triton's hound of jagged teeth devoured with his jaws. But he, a living carver of the monster's liver, seething in steam of cauldron on a flameless hearth, shed to ground the bristles of his head; he the slayer of his children, the destroyer of my fatherland; who smote his second mother invulnerable with grievous shaft upon the breast; who, too, in the midst of the

racecourse seized in his arms the body of his wrestler sire beside the steep hill of Cronus, where is the horse-affrighting tomb of earth-born Ischenus; who also slew the fierce hound that watched the narrow straits of the Ausonian sea, fishing over her cave, the bull-slaying lioness whom her father restored again to life, burning her flesh with brands; she who feared not Leptynis, the goddess of the underworld . . .

Walker puts down the book and smiles. This is insane, he says. I'm absolutely lost.

Yes, it's a terrible translation, Cécile says. Even I can hear that.

It's not just the translation. I have no idea what's going on.

That's because Lycophron is so indirect. *Lycophron the obscure*. There's a reason why they called him that.

Still . . .

You have to know the references. The nurse is a woman named Ilios, for example, and the lion is Heracles. Laomedon promised to pay Poseidon and Apollo for building the walls of Troy, but after he reneged, a sea monster appeared – Triton's hound – to devour his daughter, Hesione. Heracles climbed into the monster's belly and cut it to bits. Laomedon said he would reward Heracles for killing the monster by giving him the horses of Tros, but again he broke his word, and the angry Heracles punished him by burning down the city of Troy. That's the background of the first few lines. If you don't know the references, you're bound to be lost.

It's like trying to translate *Finnegans Wake* into Mandarin.

I know. That's why I'm so sick of it. Summer vacation ends next week, but my summer project is already kaput.

You're giving up?

When I came home from dinner last night, I read over my translation again and dumped it in the garbage. It was dreadful, positively dreadful.

You shouldn't have done that. I was looking forward to reading it.

Too embarrassing.

But you promised. That's why we're sitting here now – because you were going to show me your translation.

That was the original idea, but then I changed the plan.

Changed it to what?

To giving you this book. At least I've accomplished something today.

I don't think I want it anymore. The book belongs to you. You should hold on to it, as a keepsake from your summer of struggle.

But I don't want it either. Just looking at it makes me ill.

What should we do with it, then?

I don't know. Give it to someone else.

We're in France, remember? What French person in his right mind would be interested in a bad English translation of an impenetrable Greek poem?

Good point. Why don't we just throw it away?

Too harsh. Books should be treated with respect, even the ones that make us ill.

Then we'll leave it behind. Right here on this bench. An anonymous gift to an unknown stranger.

Perfect. And once we pay the bill and walk out of this café, we'll never talk about Lycophron again.

So begins Walker's friendship with Cécile Juin. In many ways, he finds her a thoroughly impossible creature. She fidgets and trembles, she bites her nails, she doesn't smoke or drink, she is a militant vegetarian, she puts too many demands on herself (e.g., the destroyed translation), and at times she is shockingly immature (e.g., the silly business about not telling him where she found the book, her girlish fixation on *secrets*). On the other hand, she is without question one of the most brilliant people he has ever met. Her mind is a wondrous instrument, and she can think circles around him on any topic imaginable, dazzling him with her knowledge of literature and art, music and history, politics and science. Nor is she simply a memory machine, one of those prototypical top students with a capacity for ingesting vast amounts of unfiltered information. She is sensitive and acute, her opinions are unfailingly original, and, shy and nervous as she is, she stubbornly holds her ground in any argument. For six straight days, Walker meets her for lunch at the student cafeteria on the rue Mazet. They spend the afternoons together wandering in and out of bookstores, going to movies, visiting art galleries, sitting on benches along the Seine. He is relieved that he is not physically attracted to her, that he can confine his thoughts about sex to Margot (who spends one night with him in his hotel during this period) and to the absent Gwyn, who is never far from him. In a word, despite Cécile's maddening idiosyncrasies, he enjoys the company of her mind more than enough to forgo any thoughts about her body, and he gladly keeps his hands to himself.

Proceeding cautiously, he does not ask her any direct questions about Born. He wants to know what she thinks of him, wants to know how she feels about her mother's impending marriage to this *old family friend*, but

there is ample time in front of him, the divorce will not go through until the spring, and he prefers to wait until their friendship has firmly taken root before delving into such private matters. Nevertheless, her silence is instructive, he believes, for if she were especially fond of Born, or if she were enthusiastic about the marriage, she would inevitably talk about those things every now and then, but Cécile says nothing, and therefore he concludes that she has misgivings about her mother's decision. Perhaps she looks on it as a betrayal of her father, he thinks, but that is far too delicate a subject for him to bring up with her, and until Cécile mentions it herself, he will continue to pretend he knows nothing about the man in the hospital, the all but dead father who will never wake again.

On the fifth day of their daily rambles, Cécile tells him that her mother would like to know if he is free to come to their apartment for dinner the following night, the last night before the new term at the lycée begins. Walker's first impulse is to decline the invitation, since he fears Born will be included in the company, but it turns out that Born is in London on family business (family business?) and that it will just be the three of them, Hélène, Cécile, and himself. Of course, he says, he will be happy to go to such a small dinner. Large gatherings make him uncomfortable, but a quiet evening with mother and daughter Juin sounds terrific. When he says the word *terrific* (*formidable*), Cécile's face lights up with an expression of blazing, untempered joy. In that instant, Walker suddenly understands that the invitation has not come from Hélène but from Cécile, that she has put her mother up to asking him to their apartment and in all likelihood has been badgering her about it for days. Until now, Cécile has been rather guarded in his presence, holding back from any spontaneous outbursts of emotion, and this look of joy spreading across her face is a deeply worrying sign. The last thing he wants is for her to start developing a crush on him.

They live on the rue de Verneuil in the seventh arrondissement, a street that runs parallel to the rue de l'Université, but unlike the palatial residence of Margot's family, the Juins' apartment is small and simply furnished, no doubt a reflection of Hélène's reduced financial circumstances following her husband's accident. But the place is extremely well cared for, Walker notices, everything is where it should be, immaculate, tidy, trim, from the spotless glass coffee table to the waxed and gleaming parquet floors, as if this will for order is an attempt to keep the chaos and unpredictability of the world at arm's length. Who can blame Hélène for such fanatical diligence? Walker thinks. She is trying to hold herself

together. She is trying to hold both herself and Cécile together, and with the heavy burden she has to bear, who knows if this isn't why she is planning to divorce her husband and marry Born: to get out from under, to be able to breathe again?

With Born missing from the equation, Walker finds Hélène to be somewhat softer and more congenial than the woman he met at the restaurant several days ago. She is still reserved, still enveloped in an air of rectitude and propriety, but when she greets him at the door and shakes his hand, he is startled by how warmly she looks into his eyes, as if she is genuinely glad that he has turned up. Maybe he was wrong about Cécile having to twist her arm to get him invited to the house. When all is said and done, maybe it was Hélène who proposed the idea herself: What about this odd American boy you've been palling around with, Cécile? Why don't you ask him to dinner so I can learn something more about him?

Again, Cécile has chosen to dispense with her glasses for the evening, but contrary to what happened at the dinner in the restaurant, she is not squinting. Walker assumes that she has started wearing contact lenses, but he refrains from asking her about it on the off chance that such a question will embarrass her. She seems more quiet than usual, he thinks, more poised and in control of herself, but he can't tell if it's because she is making a conscious effort to act in a certain way or because she feels more inhibited with him in front of her mother. Course by course, the food is brought to the table: pâté with cornichons to start with, a pot-au-feu, an endive salad, three different cheeses, and crème caramel for dessert. Walker compliments Hélène on each dish, and while he honestly enjoys every morsel that enters his mouth, he knows that her cooking is not in the same league as Margot's. Innumerable matters of no importance are discussed. School and work, the weather, the differences between the subway systems in Paris and New York. The conversation brightens considerably when he and Cécile begin to talk about music, and when the meal is over he finally persuades her (after how many truculent refusals?) to play something for him, something for him and her mother. There is a small upright piano in the room – which serves as a combination living room–dining room – and as Cécile stands up from the table and begins walking toward the instrument, she asks: Anything in particular? Bach, he says, without hesitation. A two-part invention by Bach.

She plays well, she hits all the notes of the piece with dogged precision, her dynamics are steady, and if her phrasing is a bit mechanical,

if she doesn't quite attain the fluency of a seasoned professional, who can fault her for being anything other than what she is? She is not a professional. She is an eighteen-year-old high school student who plays the piano for her own pleasure, and she renders the Bach efficiently, dexterously, and with much feeling. Walker remembers his own fumbling attempts to learn the piano when he was a boy and how disappointed he was to discover that he had no aptitude for it whatsoever. He therefore applauds Cécile's performance with great enthusiasm, praising her efforts and telling her how good he thinks she is. Not really good, she says, with that annoying modesty of hers. So-so. But even as she denigrates herself, Walker can see her mouth tugging downward, see her struggling to suppress a smile, and he understands how much his compliments have meant to her.

A moment later, she excuses herself and marches off down the hall (no doubt to visit the bathroom), and for the first time all evening, Walker is alone with her mother. Since Hélène knows it will not be long before Cécile returns, she gets right to the point, not wanting to waste a second.

Be careful with her, Mr. Walker, she says. She's a complex, fragile person, and she has no experience with men.

I like Cécile very much, he says, but not in the way you seem to be suggesting. I enjoy being with her, that's all. As a friend.

Yes, I'm sure you like her. But you don't love her, and the problem is that she's fallen in love with you.

Has she told you that?

She doesn't have to tell me. All I have to do is look.

She can't be in love with me. I've only known her for a week.

A year, a week, what difference does it make? These things happen, and I don't want her to get hurt. Please be careful. I beg of you.

Dread has become fact. Innocence has turned into guilt, and hope is a word that rhymes with despair. In every part of Paris, people are jumping out of windows. The metro is flooded with human excrement. The dead are crawling from their graves. End of Act II. Curtain.

Act III. As Walker leaves the Juin apartment and staggers out into the chilly September night, there is no doubt in his mind that Hélène has told him the truth. He already suspected it himself, and now that these suspicions have been confirmed, he understands that he will have to come up with a new strategy. To begin with, there will be no more daily jaunts with Cécile. Fond as he has become of her, he must be careful (yes, Hélène

was right), he must be very careful not to do anything that will hurt her. But what does careful mean? Cutting off relations with her strikes him as unnecessarily cruel, and yet if he goes on seeing her, would she not then interpret his continued interest in her as a sign of encouragement? There is no simple solution to this dilemma. For the fact is that he must see her, perhaps not as often as before, perhaps not for so many hours at a stretch, but he must see her because she is the person he has decided to unburden himself to, the one who is going to be told about the killing of Cedric Williams. Cécile will believe the story. If he goes to her mother instead, there is a good chance that Hélène will not. But if Cécile believes the story, then his chances with Hélène will improve, since it is more than likely that she will believe what her daughter tells her.

He calls Margot the next morning, hoping to distract himself from this muddle of uncertainties by spending some time with her – depending on her mood, of course, and depending on whether she is free.

That's funny, Margot says. I was just about to pick up the phone and call your hotel.

I'm glad, Walker replies. That means we were thinking about each other at the same moment. Mental telepathy is the best indication of a strong bond between people.

You say the strangest things . . .

Do you want to tell me why you were going to call, or should I tell you why I called?

You first.

Very simple. I'm dying to see you.

I would love to get together, but I can't. That's why I wanted to talk to you.

Is something wrong?

No, not at all. I'm going away for a week and I wanted to let you know.

Away?

Yes, to London.

London?

Why do you keep repeating what I say?

I'm sorry. But someone else is in London, too.

Along with about ten million other people. Are you thinking of anyone in particular?

I thought maybe you knew.

What are you talking about?

Born. He went to London three days ago.

And why should I care about that?

You're not going to see him, are you?

Don't be ridiculous.

Because if you *are* going to see him, I don't think I could take it.

What's gotten into you? Of course I'm not going to see him.

Then why are you going?

Don't do this, Adam. You have no right to ask that question.

I thought I did.

I don't have to account for myself to anyone – least of all to you.

Sorry. I'm acting like an idiot, aren't I? The question is withdrawn.

If you must know, I'm going to see my sister. She's married to an Englishman and lives in Hampstead. Her little boy is turning three, and I'm invited to the birthday party. Also – just to complete the picture – my mother is traveling with me.

Can I see you before you go?

We're leaving for the airport in an hour.

Too bad. I'm going to miss you. Really, really miss you.

It's only eight days. Get a grip on yourself, little man. I'll be back before you know it.

After this dispiriting talk with Margot, he returns to his room at the hotel and mopes around for a few hours, unable to summon the energy to begin working at his desk, unable to concentrate on the book he is trying to read (Georges Perec's *Les Choses: Une Histoire des années soixante*), and before long he is thinking about Cécile again, remembering that today is her first day of school and that not far from where he is sitting she is in a classroom at the Lycée Fénelon, listening to one of her teachers expound on Molière's prosody as she fiddles with her bag of newly sharpened pencils. He will avoid her for the time being, he says to himself, and when his own classes begin in eight days (the exact day of Margot's return), he will have a legitimate excuse for seeing her less often, and as the time they spend together diminishes, perhaps her infatuation with him will diminish as well.

For the next three days, he steadfastly adheres to this regimen of silence. He sees no one, talks to no one, and bit by bit he begins to feel somewhat stronger in his loneliness, as if the stringencies he has forced upon himself have ennobled him in some way, reacquainting him with the person he once imagined himself to be. He writes two short poems that might actually have something to them (*never nothing but the dream of nothing / never anything but the dream of all*), spends an entire afternoon

setting down his thoughts about the resurrection scene in Dreyer's film, and composes a long, lushly rhapsodic letter to Gwyn about the vagaries of the Paris sky as seen through the windows of his room: *To live here is to become a connoisseur of clouds, a meteorologist of whims.* Then, early on the fourth day, just after he has woken up, as he is taking his first sips of the bitter instant coffee he prepares each morning with water boiled on the electric hot plate beside his bed, there is a knock on the door.

Still blurred, still dopey from the warmth of the bed, the tousled, undressed Walker slips into a pair of pants and heads for the door, tiptoeing gingerly on his bare feet, not wanting to pick up any splinters from the crumbling planks. Again he assumes it is Maurice, and again his assumption is wrong, but thinking that it must be Maurice, he doesn't bother to ask who is there.

Cécile is standing in front of him. She is tense, she is biting her lower lip, and she is trembling, as if small electric currents were passing through her body, as if she were about to rise up into the air and levitate.

Walker says: Aren't you supposed to be in school?

Don't worry about school, she answers, stepping across the threshold before he can invite her in. This is more important than school.

All right, it's more important than school. In what way?

You haven't called me since the night of the dinner. What's happened to you?

Nothing. I've been busy, that's all. And I figured you were busy, too. You just started your classes this week, and you must be drowning in homework. I wanted to give you a few days to settle in.

That's not it. That's not it at all. My mother talked to you, that's what happened. My stupid mother talked to you and scared you off. Well, just for your information, my mother doesn't know anything about me. I can take care of myself just fine, thank you.

Slow down, Cécile, Walker says, raising his right arm and thrusting it toward her with an open palm – the pose of a cop directing traffic. I woke up about three minutes ago, he continues, and I'm still trying to shake the cobwebs out of my head. Coffee. That's what I was doing. I was drinking coffee. You wouldn't want some, would you?

I don't like coffee. You know that.

Tea?

No thank you.

All right. No coffee, no tea. But please sit down. You're making me nervous.

He gestures to the chair behind the desk, then approaches the desk to pull out the chair for her, and as Cécile walks toward it, he retrieves his bowl of coffee and carries it over to the bed. He sits down on the sagging, U-shaped mattress at the same instant she sits down on the creaking chair. For some reason, he finds the effect comical. He takes a sip of the no longer hot coffee and smiles at her, hoping their simultaneous touch-down was as funny to her as it was to him, but nothing is funny to Cécile just now, and she does not smile back.

Your mother, he says. Yes, she talked to me. It happened when you left the room after playing the piano, and the conversation lasted for all of fifteen or twenty seconds. She talked and I listened, but she didn't scare me off.

No?

Of course not.

Are you sure?

Positively.

Then why have you disappeared?

I haven't disappeared. I was planning to call you on Saturday or Sunday.

For real?

Yes, for real. Stop it now. No more questions, all right? No more doubts. I'm your friend, and I want to stay your friend.

It's just –

Enough. I want to stay your friend, Cécile, but I can't do that unless you begin to trust me.

Trust you? What are you talking about? Of course I trust you.

Not really. We've spent a lot of time together lately, and in that time we've talked about all sorts of things – books and philosophers, art and music, films, politics, even shoes and hats – but you've never once opened up to me about yourself. You don't have to hide. I know what trouble is. I know what happens to families when things go wrong. The other day, when I told you about what happened to my brother, Andy, I thought that might get you talking, but you never said a word. I know about your father's accident, Cécile, I know about the hell you and your mother have been living in, I know about the divorce, I know about your mother's marriage plans. Why don't you ever mention these things to me? That's what friends are for. To share each other's pains, to help each other out.

It's too hard, she says, lowering her eyes and looking at her hands as she speaks. That's why I'm so happy when I'm with you. Because I don't

have to think about those things, because I can forget how rotten and terrible the world is . . .

She is still talking, but he is no longer listening to her, no longer paying close attention because a sudden thought has taken hold of him, and he is wondering if this might not be the moment to tell her the story, the story of Born and Cedric Williams, the killing of Cedric Williams, the right moment because of the reassurances he has just given her, his declarations of friendship, which might make her receptive enough to listen to him in a state of relative calm, to absorb the brutal account of what Born did to that boy without causing irreparable damage to her, this *fragile person,* as her mother put it, this trembling, nail-biting person, the vulnerable Cécile who nevertheless spent the summer translating a poem of such excessive violence, such nightmarish horror, that he himself was shocked by Cassandra's howling monologue about ripping apart she-dog monsters and burning down cities and slaughtering one's own children, and yet all that is in the realm of myth, imaginary violence from long ago, whereas Born is a real person, a living, breathing person whom she has known all her life, the man who intends to marry her mother, and whether she is for or against that marriage, what will it do to her when she learns what this man is capable of, when he tells her about the murderous attack he witnessed with his own eyes, and even as he thinks that now is the time to talk to her about that night in New York last spring, he hesitates, he cannot bring himself to do it, he mustn't do it, he will not do it, and come what may he will not enlist Cécile as an intermediary to carry the news to her mother, he will go directly to Hélène himself, that is the proper solution, the only decent solution, and even if he fails to win her over, he must not and will not involve Cécile in this ugly business.

*Is everything all right, Adam?*

The spell is finally broken. Walker looks up, nods his head, and gives her a brief, apologetic smile. I'm sorry, he says. I was thinking about something.

Something important?

No, not at all. I was remembering the dream I had last night. You know how it is when you wake up. Your body springs into action, but your mind is still in bed.

You're not angry with me for coming here, are you?

Not in the least. I'm glad you came.

You do like me a little bit, don't you?

What kind of question is that?

Do you think I'm ugly or repulsive?

Don't be absurd.

I know I'm not pretty, but I'm not too disgusting to look at, am I?

You have a lovely face, Cécile. A delicate face with beautiful, intelligent eyes.

Then why don't you ever touch me or try to kiss me?

What?

You heard what I said.

Why? I don't know. Because I haven't wanted to take advantage of you, I suppose.

You think I'm a virgin, don't you?

To tell you the truth, I haven't thought about it one way or the other.

Well, I'm not. Just so you know. I'm not a virgin anymore, and I never will be again.

Congratulations.

It happened last month in Brittany. The boy's name was Jean-Marc, and we did it three times. He's a good person, Jean-Marc, but I'm not in love with him. Do you understand what I'm saying?

I think so.

And?

You have to give me time.

What does that mean?

It means that I'm deeply in love with someone in New York. She broke up with me just before I left for Paris, and I'm still suffering, still trying to regain my balance. I'm not ready for anything new right now.

I understand.

Good. That makes things a lot simpler.

Not simpler – more complicated. But that won't change anything in the end.

Oh?

Once you get to know me better, you'll see that I have one very special quality, something that sets me apart from everyone else.

And what quality is that?

Patience, Adam. I'm the most patient person in the world.

It has to be a Saturday, he decides. Hélène is off from work, Cécile has a half day of school, and therefore Saturday is the only day of the week

when he can go to the Juin apartment with the certainty that he will be alone with Hélène. And he wants to act now, to talk to her while Born is still in London, since that is the only way he can eliminate the risk of having Born walk in on them in the middle of their conversation. He calls Hélène at the clinic. He says he has something important to discuss with her about Cécile. No, nothing catastrophic, he replies, in fact quite the opposite, but he needs to talk to her, and it would be best for all concerned if they can meet at a time when Cécile will not be present. It is Hélène herself who suggests that he come to the apartment on Saturday morning. Cécile will be at the lycée then, and if he shows up at around nine o'clock, they will be able to finish their talk before Cécile comes home. What does he prefer? she asks. Coffee or tea? Croissants, brioches, or tartines beurrées? Coffee and tartines, he says. Yogurt? Yes, yogurt would be very nice. It's settled, then. He will come for breakfast on Saturday morning. Hélène's voice on the phone is so accommodating, so full of kindness and playful complicity that Walker has no choice but to revise his opinion of her after they hang up. She is awkward with strangers, perhaps, but once she gets to know someone a little bit, she relaxes her guard and begins to show her true colors. Those colors have become more and more attractive to him. Hélène clearly likes him, and the fact of the matter is, he likes her too. All the more motivation to remove Born from the premises as quickly as possible. If it can be done. If he has the wherewithal to make her believe him.

The rue de Verneuil, Saturday morning. For the first half hour, Walker concentrates on Cécile, doing what he can to put Hélène's mind at rest about her daughter's feelings for him and prove that the situation is not as dire as she thought it was. He tells her about his conversation with Cécile on Thursday (neglecting to mention that it took place in the morning, when she was supposed to have been at school) and says that everything is out in the open now. Cécile knows that he is unavailable to her, that he has just been through a shattering breakup with someone in New York and is in no condition to begin a romance with her or anyone else.

Is that true, Hélène asks, or were you just making it up to protect her?

I wasn't making it up, Walker says.

Poor boy. You must be having a hard time of it.

I am. But that doesn't mean I don't deserve to.

Ignoring this cryptic remark, Hélène pushes on: And what did she say when you told her about your . . . situation?

She said she understood.

That's all? She didn't make a scene?

No scene. She was very calm.

I'm surprised. That isn't like her.

I know she's high-strung, Madame Juin, I know she isn't terribly stable, but she's also a remarkable person, and my feeling is that she's a lot stronger than you think she is.

That's a matter of opinion, of course, but let's hope you're right.

Also, and this will interest you, you were wrong when you told me she has no experience with men.

Well, well. And where did she acquire this experience?

I've already said enough. If you want to know, you'll have to ask Cécile herself. I'm not a spy, after all.

How tactless of me. You're absolutely right. Forgive me for asking the question.

My only point is that Cécile is growing up, and maybe it's time to let her go. You don't have to worry about her so much anymore.

It's impossible not to worry about that girl. That's my job, Adam. I worry about Cécile. I've been worrying about her all her life.

[After the word *life*, there is a break in Walker's manuscript, and the conversation abruptly comes to an end. Until this point, the notes have been continuous, an uninterrupted march of densely packed, single-spaced paragraphs, but now there is a blank that covers approximately a quarter of a page, and when the text resumes below this white rectangle, the tone of the writing is different. There isn't much left to tell (we are on page 28 by now, which means there are just three pages to go), but Walker abandons the meticulous, step-by-step approach he has taken so far and rapidly summarizes the final events of the narrative. I can only assume that he was in the middle of the conversation with Hélène when he stopped writing for the day, and when he woke up the next morning (if he slept at all), his condition had taken a turn for the worse. These were the last days of his life, remember, and he must have felt too ravaged, too depleted, too frail to go on as before. Even earlier, over the course of the first twenty-eight pages, I had noticed a slow but ineluctable dwindling of strength, a loss of attention to detail, but now he is too incapacitated to put in anything but the bedrock essentials. He begins *Fall* with a fairly elaborate description of the Hôtel du Sud, he mentions what Born is wearing during their first encounter at the café, but little by little his descriptions

begin to have less to do with the physical world than with inner states. He stops talking about clothes (Margot, Cécile, Hélène – not one word about how they are dressed), and only when it seems crucial to his purpose does he bother to depict his surroundings (a few sentences about the atmosphere in Vagenende, a few sentences about the Juin apartment), but mostly the story consists of thought and dialogue, what people are thinking and what people are saying. By the last three pages, the collapse is nearly total. Walker is vanishing from the world, he can feel the life ebbing out of his body, and yet he forges on as best he can, sitting down at his computer one last time to bring the story to an end.]

H. and W. at the kitchen table. Coffee, bread and butter, a pot of yogurt. There is little left to talk about concerning C. Before it is too late, he must push H. in a new direction, get her to start talking about her husband, about Born. Must confirm that facts are correct before diving in. Born mentioned the marriage to him last spring, M. has echoed this with added information about the divorce, C. has not contradicted this, but H. has yet to broach the subject with him. How to proceed? He begins by mentioning *Rudolf,* describes their meeting in New York back in April, never hints they are anything to each other but warm friends, then tells about Born's return from Paris in May and how excited he was when he announced that he was *marrying her.* Is it true? H. nods. Yes, it's true. Then she says it is the most wrenching decision she has ever made. In a flood, she begins to talk about her husband, to tell him about the car accident in the Pyrenees, the hairpin turn and the crash down the side of the mountain, the hospital, the anguish of the past six and a half years, the devastation wrought on C. – a flood of words, and then a flood of tears. W. barely has the heart to go on. The tears abate. She is embarrassed, apologetic. How strange that she should be confiding in him, she says, a young boy from New York scarcely older than her daughter, a person she scarcely knows. But Rudolf thinks the world of you, and you've been so kind to C. – maybe that's the reason.

He is ready to abandon the whole business. Keep your mouth shut, he says to himself, leave the poor woman alone. But he can't. His anger is simply too great, and so he jumps off the cliff and begins talking about Cedric Williams and Riverside Drive – regretting it, hating himself with every word he speaks, but unable to stop. H. listens in stunned silence. His words are a sharpened axe, and he is chopping off her head, he is killing her.

There is no question that she believes him. He can see from the way she looks at him that she knows he is telling the truth. But it makes no difference. He is demolishing her life, and she has no alternative but to defend herself. How dare you make these hideous accusations – with no proof, with nothing to support what you're saying?

I was there, he says. The proof is in my eyes, in what I saw.

But she will not accept this. Rudolf is a distinguished professor, an intellectual, a man from one of the finest families, etc. He is her friend, he has rescued her from years of misery, he is like no other man in the world.

Hard face. No more tears, no more self-pity. Furious in her self-righteousness.

W. stands up to go. There is nothing more to say to her. Only this, which he delivers just before he walks out of the apartment: I thought it was my duty to tell you. Step back from it for a moment, and you'll understand that I have no possible reason to lie to you. I want you and Cécile to be happy – that's all – and I think you're about to make a terrible mistake. If you don't believe me, then do yourself a favor and ask Rudolf why he carries around a switchblade in his pocket.

Sunday morning. A knock on the door. The bleary-eyed, unshaven Maurice, still recovering from his Saturday night binge. A telephone call for you, *jeune homme.*

W. walks downstairs to the reception desk and picks up the phone. Born's voice says to him: I hear you've been saying bad things about me, Walker. I thought we had an understanding, and now you turn around and stab me in the back. Just like a Jew. Just like the stinking Jew you are, with your bogus Anglo-Saxon name and your filthy little mouth. There are laws against this kind of thing, you know. Slander, defamation of character, spreading lies about people. Why don't you go home? Pack up and leave Paris. Quit the program and get out of here. If you stay around, you'll regret it, Walker, I promise you. Your ass will be so cooked, you won't be able to sit down again for the rest of your life.

Monday afternoon. He parks himself in front of the Lycée Fénelon, waiting for Cécile to emerge from the building. When she finally comes out, encircled by a throng of other students, she looks him in the eye and turns her head away. She begins walking toward the rue Saint-André des Arts. W. runs to catch up with her. He grabs her by the elbow, but she

shrugs him off. He grabs her again, forcing her to stop. What's wrong? he says. Why won't you talk to me?

How could you? she answers, barking at him in a loud, strident voice. Saying all those *monstrous things* to my mother. You're sick, Adam. You're no good. Your tongue should be ripped out of your mouth.

He tries to calm her down, to make her listen to him.

*I never want to see you again.*

He makes one last effort to reason with her.

She begins to cry. Then she spits in his face and walks off.

Monday night. The voluminous, gum-chewing whore on the rue Saint-Denis. It is his first experience with a prostitute. The room smells of insecticide, sweat, and traces of vomit.

Tuesday. He spends the entire day walking through Paris. He sees a priest playing cricket with a gang of schoolboys in the Luxembourg Gardens. He gives ten francs to a clochard on the rue Monge. The late-September sky darkens around him, turning from metallic blue to the deepest shade of indigo. He has run out of ideas.

Tuesday night. At 3 a.m., a loud noise just outside his room. He is fast asleep, exhausted from his marathon trek through the city. Someone is knocking. No, not someone, several someones. An army of fists is pounding on his door.

Two policemen in uniform, young French gendarmes with guns in their holsters and sticks in their hands. An older man in a business suit. Befuddled Maurice lurking at the door. They ask if his name is Adam Walker – *Valk-air*. They ask for his papers, meaning his American passport, and when he gives it to one of the gendarmes, it is not returned to him. Then the older man instructs the other gendarme to search the armoire. The bottom drawer is opened, and out comes a large brick wrapped in aluminum foil. The younger man gives it to the older man, who begins peeling back the foil. Hashish, he says. A good two and a half kilos, maybe three.

The exquisite irony of Born's retaliation. The boy who never took drugs is charged with possession of drugs.

They take him away. In the backseat of the car, W. tells the older man that he is innocent, that someone planted the drugs in his room while he was out walking. The man tells him to shut up.

They lead him into a building, put him in a room, and lock the door. He has no idea where he is. All he knows is that he is sitting in a small, empty room somewhere in Paris and that handcuffs have been placed around his wrists. Has he been arrested? He isn't sure. No one said a word to him, but he finds it odd that he hasn't been photographed and fingerprinted, that he is sitting in this small, empty room and not in the lockup cell of some prison.

He sits there for close to seven hours. At ten-thirty, he is taken from the building and driven to the Palais de Justice. The handcuffs are removed from his wrists. He goes into an office and talks to a man who claims to be the *juge d'instruction*. It could be that the man is who he says he is, but W. suspects not. He is growing more and more convinced that he is in a farce directed by Rudolf Born, and *all the men and women are merely players*.

The examining magistrate, assuming he is the examining magistrate, tells W. that he is a lucky young man. Possession of such a large quantity of illicit drugs is a serious crime in France, punishable by X many years in prison. Fortunately for W., a man with considerable influence in government circles has interceded on his behalf, arguing for clemency in light of the accused's heretofore unblemished record. The Ministry of Justice is therefore prepared to strike a bargain with W. They will drop the charges if he agrees to deportation. He will never be allowed to enter France again, but he will be a free man in his own country.

The *juge d'instruction* opens the top drawer of his desk and takes out W.'s passport (which he holds up in his right hand) and an airline ticket (which he holds up in his left). This is a one-time offer, he says. Take it or leave it.

W. will take it.

Good, the man says. A wise decision. The plane leaves this afternoon at three. That will give you just enough time to return to your hotel and pack. An officer will accompany you, of course, but once the plane takes off and leaves French soil, the affair will be closed. We earnestly hope that this is the last we'll ever see of you. Have a pleasant journey, Mr. Walker.

And so ends W.'s brief sojourn in the land of Gaul – expelled, humiliated, banned for life.

He will never go back there, and he will never see any of them again.

Good-bye, Margot. Good-bye, Cécile. Good-bye, Hélène.

Forty years later, they are no more substantial than ghosts.

They are all ghosts now, and W. will soon be walking among them.

# IV

Riding back on the plane from San Francisco to New York, I searched my memory for the exact moment when I had first spotted Walker in the fall of 1967. I hadn't known that he had gone off to study in Paris for the year, but a few days into the semester, when we held our first editorial meeting of the *Columbia Review* (Adam and I were both on the board), I noticed that he wasn't there. What happened to Walker? I asked someone, and that was when I learned he was in Europe, enrolled in the Junior Year Abroad Program. Not long after that (a week? ten days?), he suddenly appeared again. I was taking Edward Tayler's seminar on sixteenth-and seventeenth-century poetry (Wyatt, Surrey, Raleigh, Greville, Herbert, Donne), the same Edward Tayler who had taught Milton back in the spring. Walker and I had been in that class together, and we were both of the opinion that Tayler was hands down the best professor in the English Department. Since the seminar was primarily for graduate students, I felt lucky to have been admitted as a third-year undergraduate, and I worked my head off for the sly, ironical, tight-lipped, ever-brilliant Tayler, wanting to earn the respect of this demanding, much-admired person. The seminar met twice a week for an hour and a half, and at the third or fourth session, with no explanation from anyone, there was Walker again, unexpectedly among us, the thirteenth member of a class officially limited to twelve.

We talked in the hall afterward, but Adam seemed distracted, unwilling to say much about his precipitous return to New York (I now know why). He mentioned that the program in Paris had been a disappointment to him, that the courses he was allowed to take had not been interesting enough (all grammar, no literature), and rather than waste a year in the sub-basement of the French educational bureaucracy, he had opted to come back. Quitting the program on such short notice had caused some upheavals, but Columbia had acted with unusual kindness, he felt, and even though classes had already begun when he bolted from Paris, a long talk with one of the deans had settled the matter, and he had been reinstated as a full-time student in good standing – which meant that he didn't have to worry about the draft, at least not for another four

semesters. The only problem was that he had no permanent place to live. He had shared his old apartment with his sister in July and August, but after he left for what he had thought would be a full year, she had found another roommate, and now he was out in the cold. For the time being, he was crashing with different friends in the neighborhood while he hunted for a new apartment of his own. In fact, he said, glancing down at his watch, he had an appointment in twenty minutes to look at a small studio that had just opened up on 109th Street, and he had to be off. See you later, he said, and then he began running toward the stairs.

I knew that Adam had a sister, but this was the first I'd heard about her being in New York – a resident of Morningside Heights, no less, and doing graduate work in English at Columbia. Two weeks later, I caught my first sight of her on campus. She was walking past Rodin's statue of the thinker on her way into Philosophy Hall, and because of the strong, almost eerie resemblance to her brother, I felt certain that the young woman flitting past me was Walker's sister. I have already mentioned how beautiful she was, but saying that doesn't do justice to the overwhelming impact she had on me. Gwyn was ablaze with beauty, an incandescent being, a storm in the heart of every man who laid eyes on her, and seeing her for the first time ranks as one of the most astonishing moments of my life. I wanted her – from the first second I wanted her – and, with the passionate obstinacy of a daydreaming fool, I went after her.

Nothing ever happened. I got to know her a little bit, we met for coffee a couple of times, I asked her out to the movies (she turned me down), I invited her to a concert (she turned me down), and then, accidentally, we both wound up at a large Chinese dinner one night and discussed the poems of Emily Dickinson for half an hour. A short time after that, I persuaded her to go for a walk with me in Riverside Park, tried to kiss her, and was pushed away. Don't, Jim, she said. I'm involved with someone else. I can't do this.

That was the end of it. Several swings of the bat, failure to make contact on any pitch, and the game was over. The world fell apart, the world put itself together again, and I muddled on. To my great good fortune, I have been with the same woman for close to thirty years now. I can't imagine my life without her, and yet every time Gwyn enters my thoughts, I confess that I still feel a little pang. She was the impossible one, the unattainable one, the one who was never there – a specter from the Land of If.

An invisible America lay silent in the darkness beneath me. As I sat on the jet from San Francisco to New York, revisiting the bad old days of 1967, I realized that I would have to write her a condolence letter first thing the next morning.

It turned out that Gwyn had already been in touch. When I walked through the door of my house in Brooklyn, my wife gave me a warm, fervent hug (I had called from San Francisco, she knew Adam was dead), and then she told me that earlier in the day a message had been left for me on the answering machine by someone named Gwyn Tedesco.

Is that the Gwyn I think it is? she asked.

I called her at ten o'clock the next morning. I had wanted to write a letter, to express my feelings on paper, to give her something more than the empty platitudes we sputter forth at such times, but her message had sounded urgent, there was an important matter she needed to discuss with me, and so I called her back and never wrote the letter.

Her voice was the same, remarkably the same as the one that had mesmerized me forty years ago. A lilting gravity, crystal enunciation, the barest residue of the mid-Atlantic accent of her childhood. The voice was the same, but Gwyn herself was no longer the same, and as the conversation continued, I began projecting various pictures of her in my head, wondering how well or badly her beautiful face had fared over the course of time. She was sixty-one years old now, and it suddenly occurred to me that I had no desire to see her again. It could only lead to disappointment, and I didn't want my hazy memories of the past to be blown apart by the hard facts of the present.

We exchanged the customary platitudes, rambling on for several minutes about Adam and his death, about how difficult it was for her to accept what had happened, about the rough blows life deals us. Then we caught up on the past for a little while, talking about our marriages, our children, and our work – a comfortable back-and-forth, very friendly on both sides, so much so that I even found the nerve to ask her if she remembered the day in Riverside Park when I tried to kiss her. Of course she remembered, she said, laughing for the first time, but how was she to know that scrawny Jim the college boy would grow up to become James Freeman? I never grew up, I said. And I'm still just Jim. Not so scrawny anymore, but still just Jim.

Yes, it was all quite amiable, and even though we had vanished from each other's lives decades earlier, Gwyn talked as if little or no time had

elapsed, as if those decades amounted to nothing more than a month or two. The familiarity of her tone lulled me into a kind of drowsy openness, and because my defenses were down, when she finally got to the business at hand, that is, when she finally explained why she had called me, I made a terrible blunder. I told her the truth when I should have lied.

Adam sent me an e-mail, she said, a long e-mail written a few days before he . . . just a few days before the end. It was a beautiful letter, a farewell letter I now realize, and in one of the paragraphs toward the bottom he mentioned that he was writing something, a book of some kind, and if I wanted to read it, I should contact you. But only after he was dead. He was very insistent about that. Only after he was dead. He also warned me that I might find the manuscript extremely upsetting. He apologized for that in advance, asking me to forgive him if the book hurt me in any way, and then he said no, I shouldn't bother to read it, I should forget the whole thing. It was terribly confusing. In the very next sentence, he changed his mind again and told me to go ahead if I wanted to, that I had a right to see it, and if I did want to see it, I should contact you, since you had the only copy. I didn't understand that part. If he wrote the book on a computer, wouldn't he have saved it on his hard drive?

He told Rebecca to delete it, I said. It's gone from the computer now, and the only copy is the one he printed out and sent to me.

So the book really exists.

Sort of. He meant to write it in three chapters. The first two are in fairly good shape, but he didn't manage to finish the third. Just some notes for it, a hastily written outline.

Did he want you to help him get it published?

He never talked about publishing, not directly in any case. All he wanted was for me to read the manuscript, and then it would be up to me to decide what to do with it.

Have you decided?

No. To tell you the truth, I haven't even thought about it. Until you mentioned publishing just now, the idea had never crossed my mind.

I think I should have a look at it, don't you?

I'm not sure. It's your call, Gwyn. If you want to see it, I'll make a copy and FedEx it to you today.

Will I be upset?

Probably.

Probably?

Not by all of it, but one or two things might upset you, yes.

One or two things. Oh dear.

Don't worry. As of this moment, I'm putting the decision in your hands. Not a word of Adam's book will ever be published without your approval.

Send it, Jim. Send it today. I'm a big girl now, and I know how to swallow my medicine.

How simple it would have been to cover my tracks and deny the existence of the book, or tell her that I had lost it somewhere, or claim that Adam had promised to send it to me but never did. The subject had caught me by surprise, and I couldn't think fast enough to start spinning out a fake story. Even worse, I had told Gwyn there were three chapters. Only the second one had the potential to wound her (along with a couple of remarks in the third, which I easily could have crossed out), and if I had said that Adam had written only two chapters, *Spring* and *Fall,* she would have been spared from having to go back to the apartment on West 107th Street and relive the events of that summer. But she was expecting three chapters now, and if I sent her only two, she would call right back and ask for the missing pages. So I photocopied everything I had – *Spring, Summer,* and the notes for *Fall* – and shipped them off to her address in Boston that afternoon. It was a rotten thing to do to her, but by then I no longer had a choice. She wanted to read her brother's book, and the only copy in the world belonged to me.

She called two days later. I don't know what I was expecting from her, but I had taken it for granted somehow that intense emotions would be involved – angry tears, threats, shame that her secret had been exposed – but Gwyn was unnaturally subdued, more numb than insulted, I think, as if the book had clobbered her into a state of puzzled disbelief.

I don't understand, she said. Most of it is so accurate, so exactly right, and then there are all those things he made up. It doesn't make any sense.

What things? I asked, knowing full well what she was referring to.

I loved my brother, Jim. When I was young, he was closer to me than anyone else. But I never slept with him. There was no grand experiment when we were kids. There was no incestuous affair in the summer of 1967. Yes, we lived together in that apartment for two months, but we had separate bedrooms, and there was never any sex. What Adam wrote was pure make-believe.

It's probably not my place to ask, but why would he do such a thing? Especially if the other parts of the story are true.

I don't know that they're true. At least I can't verify that they're true. But all those other things tally with what Adam told me back then, forty years ago. I never met Born or Margot or Cécile or Hélène. I wasn't with Adam in New York that spring. I wasn't with him in Paris that fall. But he did talk to me about those people, and everything he said about them in 1967 matches up with what he says about them in the book.

All the odder, then, that he should make up those things about you.

I know you don't believe me. I know you think I'm trying to protect myself, that I don't want to admit those things could have happened between us. But it wasn't like that, I promise. I've been thinking about it for the past twenty-four hours, and the only answer I've come up with is that those pages are a dying man's fantasy, a dream of what he wished had happened but never did.

Wished?

Yes, wished. I'm not denying those feelings were in the air, but I had no interest in acting on them. Adam was too attached to me, Jim. It was an unhealthy attachment, and after we'd been living together for a while that summer, he started telling me that I'd spoiled him for other women, that I was the only woman he could ever love, and that if we weren't brother and sister, he would marry me in a second. Sort of joking, of course, but I didn't like it. To be perfectly honest, I was relieved when he went to Paris.

Interesting.

And then, as we both know, less than a month later he was back – booted out in disgrace, as he put it to me at the time. But I had another roommate by then, and Adam had to look for a new apartment of his own. We were still friends, still the best of friends, but I started to put a little distance between us, to back away from him for his own good. You saw a fair amount of him during your last two years of college, but how often did you see him with me?

I'm trying to remember . . . Not a lot. No more than a couple of times.

I rest my case.

So what happens to his book now? Do we put it in a drawer and forget about it?

Not necessarily. In its present form, the book is unpublishable. Not only is it untrue – at least partly untrue – but if those untrue pages ever found their way into the world, they would create misery and disaster

for untold numbers of people. I'm a married woman, Jim. I have two daughters and three grandchildren, dozens of relatives, hundreds of friends, a stepniece I'm very fond of, and it would be a crime to publish the book as it stands now. Agreed?

Yes, yes. You won't get an argument from me.

On the other hand, I was deeply moved by the book. It brought my brother back to me in ways I hadn't expected, in ways that utterly surprised me, and if we can transform it into something publishable, I would give the project my blessing.

I'm a little lost. How do you make an unpublishable book publishable?

That's where you come into it. If you're not interested in helping, we'll drop the matter now and never talk about it again. But if you do want to help, then this is what I propose. You take the notes for the third part and put them into decent shape. That shouldn't be too hard for you. I could never do it myself, but you're the writer, you'll know how to handle it. Then, most important, you go through the manuscript and change all the names. Remember that old TV show from the fifties? *The names have been changed to protect the innocent*. You change the names of the people and the places, you add or subtract any material you see fit, and then you publish the book under your own name.

But then it wouldn't be Adam's book anymore. It feels dishonest somehow. Like stealing . . . like some weird form of plagiarism.

Not if you frame it correctly. If you give credit to Adam for the passages he wrote – to the real Adam under the false name you'll invent for him – then you won't be stealing from him, you'll be honoring him.

But no one will know it's Adam.

Does it matter? You and I will know, and as far as I'm concerned, we're the only ones who count.

You're forgetting my wife.

You trust her, don't you?

Of course I trust her.

Then the three of us will know.

I'm not sure, Gwyn. I need to think about it. Give me a little time, okay?

Take all the time you need. There's no rush.

Her story was convincingly told, more than plausible, I felt, and for her sake I wanted to believe it. But I couldn't, at least not entirely, at least not with a strong doubt that the text of *Summer* was a story of lived

experience and not some salacious dream of a sick and dying man. To satisfy my curiosity, I took a day off from the novel I was writing and went up to the Columbia campus, where I learned from an administrator at the School of International Affairs that Rudolf Born had been employed as a visiting professor during the 1966–67 academic year, and then, after a session in the microfilm room of Butler Library, the same Castle of Yawns where Walker had worked over the summer, that the corpse of eighteen-year-old Cedric Williams had been discovered one May morning in Riverside Park with more than a dozen knife wounds in his chest and upper body. These *other things,* as Gwyn had called them, had been accurately reported in Walker's manuscript, and if these other things were true, why would he have gone to the trouble of fabricating something that wasn't true, damning himself with a highly detailed, self-incriminating account of incestuous love? It's possible that Gwyn's version of those two summer months was correct, but it's also possible that she lied to me. And if she lied, who can blame her for not wanting the facts to be dragged out into the open? Anyone would lie in her situation, everyone would lie, lying would be the only alternative. As I rode back to Brooklyn on the subway, I decided that it didn't matter to me. It mattered to her, but not to me.

Several months went by, and in that time I scarcely thought about Gwyn's proposal. I was hard at work on my book, entering the last stages of a novel that had already consumed several years of my life, and Walker and his sister began to recede, to melt away, turning into two dim figures on the far horizon of consciousness. Whenever Adam's book happened to make an appearance in my mind, I was fairly certain that I didn't want to get involved with it, that the episode was finished. Then, two things happened that led me to reverse my thinking. I came to the end of my own book, which meant that I was free to turn my attention to other things, and I stumbled upon some new information connected to Walker's story, a coda, as it were, a last little chapter that gave the project new meaning for me – and with that meaning an impetus to begin.

I have already described how I revamped Walker's notes for *Fall*. As for the names, they have been invented according to Gwyn's instructions, and the reader can therefore be assured that Adam Walker is not Adam Walker. Gwyn Walker Tedesco is not Gwyn Walker Tedesco. Margot Jouffroy is not Margot Jouffroy. Hélène and Cécile Juin are not Hélène and Cécile Juin. Cedric Williams is not Cedric Williams. Sandra Williams is not Sandra Williams, and her daughter, Rebecca, is not Rebecca. Not

even Born is Born. His real name was close to that of another Provençal poet, and I took the liberty to substitute the translation of that other poet by not-Walker with a translation of my own, which means that the remarks about Dante's *Inferno* on the first page of this book were not in not-Walker's original manuscript. Last of all, I don't suppose it is necessary for me to add that my name is not Jim.

Westfield, New Jersey, is not Westfield, New Jersey. Echo Lake is not Echo Lake. Oakland, California, is not Oakland, California. Boston is not Boston, and although not-Gwyn works in publishing, she is not the director of a university press. New York is not New York, Columbia University is not Columbia University, but Paris is Paris. Paris alone is real. I managed to keep it in because the Hôtel du Sud vanished long ago, and all recorded evidence of not-Walker's stay there in 1967 has long since vanished as well.

I finished my novel late last summer (2007). Soon after that, my wife and I began organizing a trip to Paris (her sister's daughter was marrying a Frenchman in October), and the talk about Paris got me thinking about Walker again. I wondered if I could track down some of the players from the unsuccessful revenge drama he mounted there forty years ago, and if I could, whether any of them would be willing to talk to me. Born was of particular interest, but I would have been glad to sit down with any of the others I managed to find – Margot, Hélène, or Cécile. I had no luck with the first three, but when I googled Cécile Juin on the Internet, abundant amounts of information came flying up onto the screen. After my encounter with the eighteen-year-old girl in Walker's manuscript, I wasn't surprised to learn that she had grown up to be a literary scholar. She had taught at universities in Lyon and Paris, and for the past ten years she had been attached to the CNRS (the National Center for Scientific Research) as part of a small team investigating the manuscripts of eighteenth- and nineteenth-century French writers. Her specialty was Balzac, about whom she had published two books, but numerous other papers and articles were mentioned as well, a whole catalogue of work spanning three decades. Good for her, I thought. And good for me, too, since I was now in a position to write to her.

We exchanged two short letters. In mine, I introduced myself as a friend of Walker's, told her the news of Adam's recent death, and asked if it would be possible for us to get together during my upcoming visit to Paris. It was short and to the point, with no questions about her mother's

marriage to Born, nothing about Walker's notes for *Fall*, simply a request to meet her in October. She wrote back promptly. In my translation from the French, her letter read as follows:

> I am devastated to learn of Adam's death. I knew him briefly when I was a young girl in Paris many years ago, but I have never forgotten him. He was the first love of my life, and then I did him an ugly turn, a thing so cruel and unforgivable that it has been weighing on my conscience ever since. I sent him a letter of apology after he returned to New York, but the letter came back to me, marked *Addressee Unknown*.
>
> Yes, I will be happy to see you when you come to Paris next month. Please be warned, however. I am a silly old woman, and my emotions tend to run away from me. If we talk about Adam (which I assume we will), there's a good chance that I will break down and start crying. You mustn't take it personally.

Fifty-eight wasn't old, of course, and I doubted there was anything about Cécile Juin that could be described as silly. The woman's sense of humor was apparently intact, then, and successful as she was in her narrow world of academic research, she must have understood how peculiar a life she had chosen for herself: sequestered in the small rooms of libraries and underground vaults, poring over the manuscripts of the dead, a career spent in a soundless domain of dust. In a P.S. to her letter, she revealed how sardonically she looked upon her work. She recognized my name, she said, and if I was the James Freeman she thought I was, she wondered if I would be willing to participate in a survey she and her staff were conducting on the composition methods of contemporary writers. Computer or typewriter, pencil or pen, notebook or loose sheets of paper, how many drafts to finish a book. Yes, I know, she added, very dull stuff. But that's our job at the CNRS: to make the world as dull as possible.

There was self-mockery in her letter, but there was also anguish, and I was somewhat startled by how vividly she remembered Walker. She had known him for only a couple of weeks in the distant days of her girlhood, and yet their friendship must have opened up something in her that altered her perception of herself, that thrust her for the first time into a direct confrontation with the depths of her own heart. *I have never forgotten him. He was the first love of my life.* I hadn't been prepared for

such a forthright confession. Walker's notes had dealt with the problem of her growing crush on him, but her feelings turned out to have been even more intense than he had imagined. And then she spat in his face. At the time, she must have felt her anger was justified. He had slandered Born, he had upset her mother, and Cécile had felt betrayed. But then, not long after that, she had written him a letter of apology. Did that mean she had rethought her position? Had something happened to make her believe Walker's accusations were true? It was the first question I was intending to ask her.

My wife and I booked a room at the Hôtel d'Aubusson on the rue Dauphine. We had stayed there before, had stayed in several Paris hotels over the years, but I wanted to go back to the rue Dauphine this time because it happened to be smack in the middle of the neighborhood where Walker had lived in 1967. The Hôtel du Sud might have been gone, but many of the other places he had frequented were not. Vagenende was still there. La Palette and the Café Conti were still open for business, and even the cafeteria on the rue Mazet was still dishing out inedible food to hungry students. So much had changed in the past forty years, and the once down-at-the-heels neighborhood had evolved into one of the most fashionable areas of Paris, but most of the landmarks from Walker's story had survived. After checking into the hotel on the first morning, my wife and I went outside and wandered through the streets for a couple of hours. Every time I pointed out one of those places to her, she would squeeze my hand and emit a small, sarcastic grunt. You're incorrigible, she finally said. Not at all, I replied. Just soaking up the atmosphere . . . preparing myself for tomorrow.

Cécile Juin showed up at four o'clock the following afternoon, striding into the hotel bar with a small leather briefcase tucked under her left arm. Judging from Walker's descriptions of her in the notes for *Fall*, her body had expanded dramatically since 1967. The thin, narrow-shouldered girl of eighteen was now a round, plumpish woman of fifty-eight with short brown hair (dyed, some gray roots visible when she shook my hand and sat down across from me), a slightly wrinkled face, a slightly sagging chin, and the same alert and darting eyes Walker had noticed when they first met. Her manner was a bit skittish, perhaps, but she was no longer the trembling, nail-biting bundle of nerves who had caused her mother so much worry in the past. She was a woman in full possession of herself, a woman who had traveled great distances in the years since Walker had known her. A few seconds after she sat down, I was a little

surprised to see her pull out a pack of cigarettes, and then, as the minutes rolled on, doubly surprised to learn that she was a heavy smoker, with a deep, rumbling cough and the rough-edged contralto voice of a tobacco veteran. When the barman arrived at our table and asked us what we wanted, she ordered a whiskey. Neat. I told him to make it two.

I had prepared myself for a prissy, schoolmarmish eccentric. Cécile might have had her eccentricities, but the woman I met that day was down-to-earth, funny, enjoyable to be with. She was simply but elegantly dressed (a sign of confidence, I felt, a sign of self-respect), and although she wasn't someone who bothered with lipstick or nail polish, she looked thoroughly feminine in her gray woolen suit – with silver bracelets around each wrist and a bright, multicolored scarf wrapped around her neck. During the course of our long, two-hour conversation, I found out that she had spent fifteen years in psychoanalysis (from age twenty to thirty-five), had been married and divorced, had married again to a man twenty years older than she was (he died in 1999), and that she had no children. On this last point she commented: A few regrets, yes, but the truth is I probably would have been a terrible mother. No aptitude, you understand.

For the first twenty or thirty minutes, we mostly talked about Adam. Cécile wanted to know everything I could tell her about what had happened in his life from the moment she lost touch with him. I explained that I had lost touch with him as well, and since we hadn't resumed contact until just before his death, my only source of information was the letter he had written to me last spring. One by one, I took her through the salient points Walker had mentioned – falling down the stairs and breaking his leg on the night of his graduation from college, the luck of drawing a high number in the draft lottery, his move to London and the years of writing and translating, the publication of his first and only book, the decision to abandon poetry and study law, his work as a community activist in northern California, his marriage to Sandra Williams, the difficulties of being an interracial couple in America, his stepdaughter, Rebecca, and her two children – and then I added that if she wanted to learn more, she should probably arrange to meet with his sister, who would no doubt be glad to fill her in on the smallest details. As promised, Cécile broke down and cried. It touched me that she understood herself well enough to have been able to predict those tears, but even though she knew they were coming, there was nothing forced or willed about them. They were genuine, spontaneous tears, and although I had

been expecting them myself, I genuinely felt sorry for her.

She said: He lived around here, you know. Just thirty seconds away, on the rue Mazarine. I walked past the building on my way to see you just now – the first time I've been on that street in years. Odd, isn't it? Odd that the hotel should be gone, that terrible, broken-down place where Adam lived. It's so alive in my memory, how can it possibly be gone? I was there only once, one time for an hour or two, but I can't forget it, it's still burning inside me. I went there because I was angry at him. One day early in the morning, I cut school and walked over to the hotel. I climbed the rickety stairs, I knocked on his door. I wanted to strangle him because I was so angry, because I loved him so much. I was an idiot girl, you understand, an impossible, unlikable girl, a gawky imbecile girl with glasses on my nose and a sick, quivering heart, and I had the temerity to fall in love with a boy like Adam, perfect Adam, why in God's name did he even talk to me? He let me in. He calmed me down. He was kind to me, so kind to me, my life was in his hands, and he was kind to me. I should have known then what a good person he was. I never should have doubted a word he said. Adam. I dreamed of kissing him. That was all I ever wanted – to be kissed by Adam, to give myself to Adam – but time ran out on me, and we never kissed, we never touched, and before I knew it he was gone.

That was when Cécile broke down and started to cry. It took two or three minutes before she was able to talk again, and when the conversation continued, the first thing she said opened the door onto the next phase of our encounter. I'm sorry, she mumbled. I'm blathering on like a madwoman. You have no idea what I'm talking about.

But I do, I said. I know exactly what you're talking about.

You can't possibly know.

Believe me, I do. You were angry at Adam because he hadn't called you for several days. The night before you went back to school, he had dinner with you and your mother at your apartment on the rue de Verneuil. After dessert, you played the piano for him – a two-part invention by Bach – and then, because you left the room for a while, your mother had a chance to speak to Adam one-on-one, and what she said to him, in your words, *scared him off*.

Did he tell you this?

No, he didn't tell me. But he wrote about it, and I've read the pages he wrote.

He sent you a letter?

It was a short book, actually. Or an attempt to write a book. He spent the last months of his life working on a memoir about nineteen sixty-seven. It was an important year for him.

Yes, a very important year. I think I'm beginning to understand.

If not for Adam's manuscript, I never would have heard of you.

And now you want to find out what happened, is that it?

I can see why Adam thought you were so intelligent. You catch on fast, don't you?

Cécile smiled and lit another cigarette. I seem to be at a disadvantage, she said.

In what way?

You know a lot more about me than I know about you.

Only the eighteen-year-old you. Everything else is a blank. I looked for Born, I looked for Margot Jouffroy, I looked for your mother, but you were the only one I could find.

That's because all the others are dead.

Oh. How awful. I'm so sorry . . . especially about your mother.

She died six years ago. In October – exactly six years ago tomorrow. About a month after the attacks on New York and Washington. She'd had heart trouble for some time, and one day her heart simply gave out on her. She was seventy-six. I wanted her to live to a hundred, but as you know, what we want and what we get are rarely the same thing.

And Margot?

I barely knew her. I was told she killed herself. A long time ago now – all the way back in the seventies.

And Born?

Last year. I think. But I'm not absolutely sure. There's a slim chance he's still alive somewhere.

Did he and your mother stay married until her death?

Married? They were never married.

Never married? But I thought –

They talked about it for a while, but it never happened.

Was Adam responsible for stopping it?

Partly, I suppose, but not entirely. When he talked to my mother and made those wild accusations about Rudolf, she didn't believe him. Nor did I, for that matter.

You were so incensed, you spat in his face, didn't you?

Yes, I spat in his face. It was the single worst thing I've done in my life, and I still can't forgive myself for it.

You wrote to Adam to apologize. Does that mean you changed your mind about his story?

No, not then. I wrote because I was ashamed of what I did, and I wanted him to know how bad I felt about it. I tried to talk to him in person, but when I finally found the courage to call his hotel, he wasn't there anymore. They told me he'd gone back to America. I couldn't understand it. Why would he leave so suddenly? The only explanation I could think of was that he was so upset by what I'd done to him that he couldn't bear the thought of staying in Paris. How's that for a selfish reading of events? When I asked Rudolf to talk to the head of the Columbia program and find out what had happened, he reported that Adam had left because he wasn't satisfied with the courses he was taking. That seemed utterly feeble to me, and I didn't buy it for a second. I was convinced he'd left because of me.

You know better now, don't you?

Yes, I know better. But it took years before I learned the truth.

Years. Which means that Adam's story had no effect on your mother's decision.

I wouldn't say that. After Adam left, Rudolf couldn't stop talking about him. He had been accused of murder, after all, and he was outraged, quite bonkers really, and he fumed and railed against Adam for weeks. He should be put in jail for twenty years, he said. He should be strung up and hanged from the nearest lamppost. He should be carted off to Devil's Island. It was all so excessive, so over the top, that my mother began to feel a little annoyed with him. She had known Rudolf for a long time, many years, almost as long as she'd known my father, and for the most part he had been extremely gentle with her – considerate, thoughtful, gracious. There were a few hotheaded moments, of course, especially when he started talking about politics, but that was politics, not personal business. Now he was on a rampage, and I think she was beginning to have some doubts about him. Was she honestly prepared to spend the rest of her life with a man who had such a violent temper? After a month or two, Rudolf began to calm down, and by Christmastime the fits and crazy outbursts had stopped. The winter was tranquil, I recall, but then it was spring, May sixty-eight, and the whole country exploded. For me, it was one of the greatest periods of my life. I marched, I demonstrated, I helped shut down my school, and suddenly I had turned into an activist, a bright-eyed revolutionary agitating to bring down the government. My mother was sympathetic to

the students, but right-wing Rudolf had nothing but contempt for them. He and I got into some dreadful arguments that spring, fierce shouting matches about law and justice, Marx and Mao, anarchy and rebellion, and for the first time politics was no longer just politics, it was personal business. My mother was caught in the middle, and it made her more and more unhappy, more and more silent and withdrawn. The divorce from my father was supposed to become final at the beginning of June. In France, divorcing couples have to talk to a judge one last time before he can sign the papers. They're asked to reconsider, to rethink their decision and make sure they want to go ahead with it. My father was in the hospital – I imagine you know all about that – and my mother went to see the judge on her own. When he asked her if she had any second thoughts about her decision, she said yes, she had changed her mind and didn't want a divorce. She was protecting herself against Rudolf, you understand. She didn't want to marry him anymore, and by staying married to my father, she *couldn't* marry him anymore.

How did Born react?

With tremendous kindness. He said that he understood why she couldn't go through with it, that he admired her for her steadfastness and courage, that he thought she was an extraordinary and noble woman. Not what you would expect, but there you have it. He behaved beautifully.

How much longer did your father go on living?

A year and a half. He died in January nineteen seventy.

Did Born come back and propose again?

No. He left Paris after sixty-eight and started teaching in London. We saw him at my father's funeral, and a couple of weeks after that he wrote my mother a long, heartfelt letter about the past, but that was the end of it. The subject of marriage never came up again.

And what about your mother? Did she find someone else?

She had some male friends over the years, but she never remarried.

And Born moved to London. Did you ever see him again?

Once, about eight months after my mother died.

And?

I'm sorry. I don't think I can talk about it.

Why not?

Because if I tried to tell you what happened, I couldn't begin to convey what a strange and disturbing experience it was for me.

You're pulling my leg, right?

Just a little bit. To use your terms, I can't *tell* you anything, but you can *read* about it if you want to.

Ah, I see. And where is this mysterious text of yours?

In my apartment. I've been keeping a diary since I was twelve years old, and I wrote a number of pages about what happened during my visit to Rudolf's house. An on-the-spot, eyewitness account, if you will. I think it might interest you. If you like, I can photocopy the pages and bring them here tomorrow. If you're not in, I'll drop them off at the desk.

Thank you. That's very generous of you. I can't wait to read them.

And now, Cécile said, grinning broadly as she reached into her leather bag and pulled out a large red notebook, shall we get on with the survey for the CNRS?

The next afternoon, when my wife and I returned to the hotel after a long lunch with her sister, the package was waiting for me. In addition to the photocopied pages from her diary, Cécile included a short cover letter. She thanked me for the whiskeys, for tolerating her *grotesque and unpardonable* tears, and for giving up so much of my time to talk to her about Adam. Then she apologized for her illegible handwriting and offered to help me if I had any trouble deciphering it. I found it perfectly legible. Every word was clear, not one letter or punctuation mark confused me. The diary was written in French, of course, and what follows is my translation of that French into English, which I am including with the author's full permission.

I have nothing more to say. Cécile Juin is the last person from Walker's story who is still alive, and because she is the last, it seems fitting that she should have the last word.

## CÉCILE JUIN'S DIARY

4/27. A letter today from Rudolf Born. Six months after the fact, he has only just now learned of Mother's death. How long has it been since I last saw him, last heard from him? Twenty years, I think, perhaps twenty-five.

He sounds distraught, shattered by the news. Why would it mean so much to him now, after all these years of silence? He writes eloquently about the strength of her character, her dignified bearing and inner warmth, her attunement to the minds of others. He never stopped loving

her, he says, and now that she has left this world, he feels that a part of him has left it with her.

He is retired. 71, unmarried, in good health. For the past six years, he has been living in a place called Quillia, a small island between Trinidad and the Grenadines at the juncture of the Atlantic and the Caribbean, just north of the equator. I have never heard of it. I must remember to look it up.

In the last sentence of the letter, he asks for news of me.

4/29. I have written back to R.B. Much more openly than I intended to, but once I started to talk about myself, I found it difficult to stop. When the letter reaches him, he will know about my work, about my marriage to Stéphane, about Stéphane's death three years ago, and how lonely and burnt out I feel most of the time. I wonder if I haven't gone a bit too far.

What are my feelings toward this man? Complicated ones, ambiguous ones, combining compassion and indifference, friendship and wariness, admiration and bemusement. R.B. has many excellent qualities. High intelligence, good manners, a ready laugh, generosity. After Father's accident, he stepped in and became our moral support, the rock on which we stood for many years. He was saintly with Mother, a chivalrous companion, helpful and doting, always there in time of trouble. As for me, who was not even twelve when our world caved in, how many times did he lift me out of the doldrums with his encouragement and praise, his pride in my meager accomplishments, his indulgent attitude toward my adolescent sufferings? So many positive attributes, so much to feel grateful for, and yet I continue to resist him. Does it have something to do with our bitter clashes in May '68, those frantic weeks in May when we were at perpetual war with each other, causing a rift between us that was never fully repaired? Perhaps. But I like to think of myself as a person who doesn't bear grudges, who is capable of forgiving others – and deep down I believe he was forgiven long ago. Forgiven because I laugh when I think about that time now and feel no anger. Instead, what I feel is doubt, and that was something which began to take hold in me several months earlier – back in the fall, when I fell in love with Adam Walker. Dear Adam, who came to Mother with those horrible accusations about R.B. Impossible to believe him, but now that so many years have passed, now that one has pondered and dissected and endlessly reexamined Adam's motive for saying such things, it becomes difficult to know what to think. Surely there was bad blood between Adam and

R.B., surely Adam felt it would be in Mother's best interest to call off the marriage, and so he made up a story to frighten her into changing her mind. A terrifying story, too terrifying to be true, and therefore a miscalculation on his part, but Adam was essentially a good person, and if he thought there was something tainted about R.B.'s past, then perhaps there was. Hence my doubt, which has been festering in me for years. But I can't condemn a man on the strength of doubt alone. There must be proof, and since there is no proof, I must take R.B. at his word.

*5/11.* A response from R.B. He writes that he is living in seclusion in a large stone house overlooking the ocean. The house is called Moon Hill, and conditions there are quite primitive. The windows are broad apertures cut out of the rock with no glass covering them. The air blows in, the rain blows in, the insects and birds blow in, and there is little distinction between indoors and outdoors. He has a private generator for producing electricity, but the machine breaks down often, and half the time they light the rooms with kerosene lamps. There are four people in the household: a handyman-caretaker named Samuel, an old cook, Nancy, and a young cleaning woman, Melinda. There is a telephone and a radio, but no television, no mail delivery, and no running water. Samuel goes to the post office in town to pick up his letters (twelve miles away), and water is stored in wooden tanks above the sinks and toilets. Shower water comes out of a disposable plastic bag that hangs from a hook above your head. The landscape is both lush and barren. Profuse vegetation everywhere (palm trees, rubber plants, a hundred varieties of wildflowers), but the volcanic earth is strewn with rocks and boulders. Land crabs plod through his garden (he describes them as small armored tanks, prehistoric creatures who look as if they belong on the moon), and because of the frequent infestations of mosquitoes, not to mention the constant threat of tarantulas, everyone sleeps in beds covered with protective white netting. He spends his days reading (for the past two months he has been diligently plowing through Montaigne again) and taking notes for a memoir he hopes to begin in the near future. Every evening, he settles into his hammock by the window in the living room and videotapes the sunset. He calls it the most astonishing spectacle on earth.

My letter has overwhelmed him with nostalgia, he says, and he regrets now that he allowed himself to disappear from my life. We were once so close, such good friends, but after he and my mother parted ways, he didn't feel he had the right to remain in touch. Now that the ice has been

broken again, he has every intention of keeping up a correspondence with me – assuming that is something I would want as well.

He is saddened to learn of my husband's death, saddened to learn of the difficulties I have been having of late. But you're still young, he adds, still in your early fifties, with much to look forward to, and you mustn't give up hope.

These are trite and conventional remarks, perhaps, but I sense that he means well, and who am I to scorn well-meant gestures of earnest sympathy? The truth is that I am touched.

Then, a sudden inspiration. Why not pay him a visit? The holidays are approaching, he says, and perhaps a little jaunt to the West Indies would do me some good. There are several spare bedrooms in his house, and putting me up would pose no problem. How happy it would make him to see me again, to spend some time together after so many years. He writes down his telephone number in case I'm interested.

Am I interested? It is difficult to say.

5/12. Information about Quillia is scant. I have already combed the Internet, which has yielded a couple of short, superficial histories and various bits of tourist data. With the latter entries, the writing is atrocious, banal to the point of absurdity: *the resplendent sun . . . the glorious beaches . . . the bluest blue water this side of heaven.*

I am sitting in the library now, but it turns out that there are no books devoted exclusively to Quillia – only a smattering of references buried in the larger volumes about the region. During pre-Columbian times, the inhabitants were the Ciboney Indians, who subsequently left and were supplanted by the Arawaks, who in their turn were followed by the Caribs. When colonization began in the 16th century, the Dutch, the French, and the English all took an interest in the place. There were skirmishes with the Indians, skirmishes among the Europeans, and when black slaves started arriving from Africa, much slaughter ensued. By the 18th century, the island was declared a neutral zone, exploited equally by the French and the English, but after the Seven Years' War and the Treaty of Paris, the French decamped and Quillia fell under the control of the British Empire. In 1979, the island became independent.

It is five miles across. Subsistence farming, fishing, boatbuilding, and an annual hunt for a single whale. The population is three and a half thousand – mostly of African descent, but also Carib, English, Irish, Scottish, Asian, and Portuguese. One book reports that a large

contingent of Scottish sailors was stranded on Quillia in the 18th century. With no possibility of returning home, they settled there and mingled with the blacks. Two centuries later, the result of this interbreeding is a curious mixed race of redheaded Africans, blue-eyed Africans, and albino Africans. As the author notes: *The island is a laboratory of human possibilities. It explodes our rigid, preconceived ideas about race – and perhaps even destroys the concept of race itself.*

A nice phrase, that. *A laboratory of human possibilities.*

5/14. A hard day. This afternoon, I realized that it has been exactly four months since my last period. Does this mean it's finally happened? I keep hoping for the old, familiar cramps, the bloat and irritation, the blood flowing out of me. It isn't a question of no longer being able to bear children. I never particularly wanted them. Alexandre more or less talked me into it, but we split up before anything ever happened. With Stéphane, children were out of the question.

No, it isn't about children anymore. I'm too old for that now, even if I wanted to become pregnant. It's more about losing my place as a woman, of being expelled from the ranks of femininity. For forty years, I was proud to bleed. I bore up under *the curse* with the happy knowledge that I was sharing an experience with every other woman on the planet. Now I have been cut adrift, neutered. It feels like the beginning of the end. A postmenopausal woman today, an old crone tomorrow, and then the grave. I'm too worn out even to cry.

Perhaps I should go to Quillia, after all, in spite of my reservations. I need to shake things up for myself, to breathe new air.

5/17. I have just spoken to R.B. Odd to hear that voice again after all this time, but he sounded vigorous, in top form. When I told him I'd decided to accept his invitation, he began shouting into the phone. Splendid! Splendid! What excellent news!

One month from now (in R.B.'s words), we will be drinking Samuel's rum punches, taking turns filming the sunset, and having the time of our lives.

I will book the tickets tomorrow. Five days in late June. Subtract the two days of travel, and that leaves three full days on Quillia. If I'm having the time of my life, I can always extend the visit. If I find it unbearable, I don't suppose three days will be too much to bear.

*6/23.* After a long flight across the Atlantic, I am sitting in a transit lounge at the Barbados airport, waiting for the small, one-propeller plane that will take me to Quillia two and a half hours from now (if it leaves on time).

Insufferable heat, everywhere a dense circle of heat closing around my body, the heat of the tropics, a heat that melts the thoughts in your head.

In the main terminal, a dozen soldiers patrolling the floor with machine guns. An air of menace and mistrust, hostility in every glance. What is going on? A dozen black soldiers with machine guns in their hands, and the crowds of grim, sweating travelers with their overstuffed bags and cranky children.

In the transit lounge, nearly everyone is white. Long-haired American surfers, Australians drinking beer and talking in loud voices, Europeans of various unknown nationalities, a couple of Asian faces. Boredom. Fans circling overhead. Piped-in music that is not music. A place that is not a place.

*Nine hours later.* The one-propeller plane was the smallest flying machine I have ever been in. I sat up front with the pilot, the other two passengers sat directly behind us, and the instant we took off, I understood that we were at the mercy of every puff of wind that might blow our way, that even the smallest disturbance in the surrounding air could throw us off course. We lurched and wobbled and dipped, my stomach was in my mouth, and yet I enjoyed myself, enjoyed the feathery weightlessness of the ride, the sense of being in such close contact with that unstable air.

Seen from above, the island is no more than a small dot, a gray-green speck of cooled lava jutting out of the ocean. But the water around it is blue – yes, the bluest blue water this side of heaven.

It would be an exaggeration to call the Quillia airport an airport. It is a landing strip, a ribbon of tarmac unspooled at the base of a tall, hulking mountain, and it can accommodate nothing bigger than planes the size of toys. We retrieved our bags in the terminal – a tiny cinder-block hut – and then went through the ordeal of customs and passport control. Not even in post–9/11 Europe have I been subjected to such a thorough examination of my belongings. My suitcase was opened, and every article of clothing was lifted out and inspected, every book was shaken by the spine, every shoe was turned upside down, peered into, searched – slowly and methodically, as if this were a procedure that could not, under any circumstances, be conducted in haste. The man in charge of passport

control was dressed in a snappy, neatly pressed uniform, a symbol of authority and officialdom, and he too took his sweet time before letting me go. He asked the purpose of my visit, and in my mediocre, heavily accented English, I told him that I'd come to spend a few days with a friend. Which friend? Rudolf Born, I said. The name seemed to ring a bell with him, and then he asked (inappropriately, I believe) how long I had known Mr. Born. All my life, I said. All your life? My answer seemed to have thrown him. Yes, all my life, I repeated. He was a close friend of my parents'. Ah, your parents, he said, nodding in contemplation, apparently satisfied by my answer. I thought we had come to the end of our business, but then he opened my passport, and for the next three minutes he scrutinized it with the zealous, patient eye of a forensics expert, carefully studying each page, pausing over each marking, as if my past travels were the key to solving the mystery of my life. At last, he took out a form printed on a narrow slip of paper, positioned it at right angles with the edge of his desk, and filled in the blanks with a small, meticulous hand. After stapling the form into my passport, he inked his rubber stamp, pressed the rubber onto a spot beside the form, and delicately added the name of Quillia to the roster of countries I have been allowed to enter. French bureaucrats are notorious for their maniacal exactitude and cold efficiency. Next to this man, they are all amateurs.

I stepped out into the broiling four o'clock heat, expecting to find R.B. waiting for me, but he wasn't there. My escort to the house was Samuel, the handyman-caretaker, a strong, well-built, exceedingly handsome young man of around thirty – with exceedingly black skin, which would suggest he is not descended from that band of Scottish sailors marooned here in the 18th century. After my encounter with the remote and taciturn men at the airport terminal, I found it a relief to be smiled at again.

It didn't take long to understand why the job of accompanying me to Moon Hill had been given to Samuel. We rode in a car for the first ten minutes, which led me to assume we would drive all the way to the house, but then Samuel stopped the car, and the rest of the journey – that is to say, the bulk of the journey, the more than one-hour journey still in front of us – was made on foot. It was an arduous trek, an excruciating climb up a steep, root-entangled path that sapped my strength and left me gasping for breath after five minutes. I am a person who sits in libraries, a fifty-three-year-old woman who smokes too many cigarettes and weighs twenty pounds more than she should, and my body is not cut out for exertions of this sort. I was thoroughly humiliated by my ineptitude,

by the sweat that poured out of me and drenched my clothes, by the swarms of mosquitoes dancing around my head, by my frequent calls to stop and rest, by the slippery soles of my sandals, which made me fall, not once, not twice, but again and again. But even worse, far worse than my petty physical woes, there was the shame of watching Samuel in front of me, the shame of seeing Samuel *carry my suitcase on his head,* my too heavy suitcase, loaded down with the weight of too many unnecessary books, and how not to see in that image of a black man carrying a white woman's possessions *on his head* the horrors of the colonial past, the atrocities of the Congo and French Africa, the centuries of affliction –

I mustn't go on like this. I'm working myself into a lather, and if I mean to get through these days with my mind intact, I must maintain my composure. The reality is that Samuel wasn't the least bit distressed about what he was doing. He has been up and down this mountain thousands of times, he carries provisions on his head as a matter of course, and for someone born on an island as poor as this one, working in the house of a man like R.B. is considered a good job. Whenever I asked him to stop, he did so without complaint. No trouble, ma'am. Just take it nice and easy. We'll get there when we get there.

R.B. was napping in his room when we reached the top of the mountain. Incomprehensible as that might have been, it gave me a chance to settle into my own room (high, high up, overlooking the ocean) and pull myself together. I showered, put on a fresh set of clothes, and did my hair. Minor improvements, perhaps, but at least I didn't have to live through the embarrassment of being seen in such a sorry state. The walk up the mountain had nearly destroyed me.

In spite of my efforts, I could see the disappointment in his eyes when I entered the living room an hour later – the first look after so many years, and the sad acknowledgment that the young girl of long ago had turned into a frowsy, none-too-attractive, postmenopausal woman in late middle age.

Unfortunately – no, I think I mean fortunately – the disappointment was mutual. In the past, I had found him to be a seductive figure, good-looking in a rough sort of way, something close to an ideal embodiment of male confidence and power. R.B. was never a thin man, but in the years since I last saw him, he has put on considerable amounts of weight, a truckload of excess poundage, and as he stood up to greet me (dressed in shorts, with no shirt, no shoes or socks), I was astonished to see how large his stomach had grown. It is a great medicine ball of a stomach

now, and with most of the hair gone from his head, his skull reminded me of a volleyball. A ridiculous image, I know, but the mind is always churning forth its quirky nonsense, and that was what I saw when he stood up and approached me: a man composed of two spheres, a medicine ball and a volleyball. He is much bigger, then, but not whalelike, not blubbery or drooping with flab – just large. The skin around his stomach is quite taut, actually, and except for the fleshy creases around his knees and neck, he looks fit for a man his age.

An instant after I saw it, the crestfallen look vanished from his eyes. With all the aplomb of a practiced diplomat, R.B. broke into a smile, opened his arms, and hugged me. It's a miracle, he said.

That hug proved to be the high point of the evening. We drank the rum punches Samuel prepared for us (very good), I watched R.B. film the sunset (I found it inane), and then we sat down to dinner (heavy food, beef drowned in a thick sauce, inappropriate fare for this climate – better suited to Alsace in midwinter). The old cook, Nancy, is not old at all – forty, forty-five at most – and I wonder if she doesn't have two jobs in this household: cook by day, R.B.'s bed partner at night. Melinda is in her early twenties, and therefore is probably too young to fill the latter role. She is a beautiful girl, by the way, as beautiful as Samuel is handsome, a tall, lanky thing with an exquisite gliding walk, and from the little looks they give each other, I would guess that she and Samuel are an item. Nancy and Melinda served us the food, Samuel cleared the table and washed the dishes, and as the meal wore on I found myself growing increasingly uncomfortable. I don't like being waited on by servants. It offends me somehow, especially in a situation like this one, with three people working for just two others, three black people working for two white people. Again: unpleasant echoes of the colonial past. How to get rid of this feeling of shame? Nancy, Melinda, and Samuel went about their tasks with stolid equanimity, and though I received a number of courteous smiles, they seemed guarded and aloof, indifferent. What must they think of us? They probably laugh at us behind our backs – with good reason.

The servants got me down, yes, but not as much as R.B. himself did. After his warm welcome, I felt as if he no longer knew what to do with me. He kept saying that I must be tired, that the trip must have worn me out, that jet lag is a modern invention designed to ruin the human body. I won't deny that I was exhausted and jet-lagged, that my muscles ached from my battle with the mountain, but I wanted to stay up and talk, to

*reminisce about old times* as he put it in one of his letters, and he seemed reluctant to go there with me. Our conversation over dinner was brutally dull. He told me about his discovery of Quillia and how he had managed to buy this house, discussed some of the particulars of local life, and then lectured me on the flora and fauna of the island. Mystifying.

I am in bed now, encased in a dome of white mosquito netting. My body is smeared with an odious product called OFF, a mosquito repellent that smells of toxic, life-threatening chemicals, and the green anti-mosquito coils on either side of the bed are slowly burning down, emitting curious little trails of smoke.

I wonder what I am doing here.

*6/26*. Nothing for two days. It has been impossible to write, impossible to find a moment's peace, but now that I have left Moon Hill and am on my way back to Paris, I can pick up the story and push on to the bitter end. Bitter is precisely the word I want to use here. I feel bitter about what happened, and I know I will be tasting that bitterness for a long time to come.

It started the next morning, the morning after my arrival at the house, the 24th. Sitting over breakfast in the dining room, R.B. calmly put down his cup of coffee, looked me in the eye, and asked me to marry him. It was so far-fetched, so utterly unexpected, I burst out laughing.

—You can't be serious, I said.

—Why not? he answered. I'm all alone here. You have no one in Paris, and if you came to Quillia and lived with me, I would make you the happiest woman in the world. We're perfect for each other, Cécile.

—You're too old for me, old friend.

—You've already been married to a man older than I am.

—That's just it. Stéphane is dead, isn't he? I have no desire to become a widow again.

—Ah, but I'm not Stéphane, am I? I'm strong. I'm in perfect health. I have years and years ahead of me.

—Please, Rudolf. It's out of the question.

—You're forgetting how much we adored each other.

—I liked you. I always liked you, but I never adored you.

—Years ago, I wanted to marry your mother. But that was only an excuse. I wanted to live with her so I could be near you.

—That's ridiculous. I was a child back then – an awkward, undeveloped child. You weren't interested in me.

—It was all working so well. It was about to happen, it would have happened, the three of us wanted it to happen, and then that American boy came to Paris and ruined everything.

—It wasn't because of him. You know that. My mother didn't believe his story, and neither did I.

—You were right not to believe him. He was a liar, a twisted, angry boy who turned against me and tried to wreck my life. Yes, I've made terrible mistakes over the years, but killing that kid in New York wasn't one of them. I never put a hand on him. Your boyfriend made it all up.

—My boyfriend? That's a good one. Adam Walker had better things to do than fall for someone like me.

—And to think . . . I was the one who introduced him to you. I thought I was doing you a favor. What a miserable joke.

—You did do me a favor. And then I turned around and insulted him. I called him a crazy person. I said his tongue should be torn out of his mouth.

—You never told me that. Good work, Cécile. I'm proud of you for showing such spirit. The boy got what he deserved.

—Deserved? What does that mean?

—I'm alluding to his hasty departure from France. You know why he left, don't you?

—He left because of me. Because I spat in his face.

—No, no, nothing as simple as that.

—What are you talking about?

—He was deported. The police caught him with three kilos of drugs – marijuana, hashish, cocaine, I can't remember the substance now. They were tipped off by the manager of that putrid hotel he lived in. The cops searched his room, and that was the end of Adam Walker. He had two choices: stand trial in France or leave the country.

—Adam with drugs? It isn't possible. He was against drugs, he hated them.

—Not according to the police.

—And how do you know that?

—The examining magistrate was a friend of mine. He told me about the case.

—How convenient. And why would he bother to talk to you about a thing like that?

—Because he knew I was acquainted with Walker.

—You were involved in it, weren't you?

—Of course not. Don't be silly.

—You were. Admit it, Rudolf. You were the one who got Adam kicked out of the country.

—You're wrong, my darling. I can't say that I was sorry to see him go, but I wasn't responsible.

—It's so far in the past. Why tell lies about it now?

—I swear on your mother's grave, Cécile. I had nothing to do with it.

I didn't know what to think. Perhaps he was telling the truth, perhaps he wasn't, but the moment he started talking about my mother's grave, I realized that I didn't want to be in the room with him anymore. I was too upset, too close to tears, too distracted to go on talking. First his insane proposal of marriage, and then the ghastly news about Adam, and suddenly I couldn't sit at that table a second longer. I stood up from my chair, told him I wasn't feeling well, and quickly retreated to my room.

Half an hour later, R.B. knocked and asked if he could come in. I hesitated for a few moments, wondering if I had the strength to confront him again. Before I could decide, there was another knock, louder and more insistent than the first one, and then he opened the door himself.

—I'm sorry, he said, as his large, half-naked body lumbered toward a chair in the far corner of the room. I didn't mean to unnerve you. I'm afraid I took the wrong approach.

—Approach? Approach to what?

As R.B. lowered himself into the chair, I sat down on a small wooden bench just below the window. We were no more than three feet apart. I wished he hadn't walked in on me so soon after my abrupt exit from the dining room, but he looked sufficiently contrite for me to think that further conversation might be possible.

—Approach to what? I repeated.

—To certain . . . how shall I put it? . . . to certain future . . . to certain possible domestic arrangements in the future.

—I'm sorry to disappoint you, Rudolf, but I'm not interested in marriage. Not with you or anyone else.

—Yes, I know. That's your position today, but tomorrow you might have a different view of the matter.

—I doubt it.

—It was a mistake not to share my thoughts with you. I've been living with this idea ever since I received your letter last month, and after turning it around in my mind for so long, it felt real to me, as if all I had to

do was say the word and it would happen. I've probably been alone too much these past six years. I sometimes confuse my thoughts about the world with the world itself. I'm sorry if I offended you.

—I wasn't offended. Surprised would be the appropriate word, I think.

—Given your position – the position you hold now, in any case – I would like to suggest an experiment. An experiment in the form of a business proposal. Do you remember the book I told you about in one of my letters?

—You mentioned that you were taking notes for a memoir you wanted to write.

—Exactly. I'm nearly ready to begin, and I want you to help me with it. I want us to write the book together.

—You're forgetting that I already have a job in Paris. A job that means quite a lot to me.

—Whatever salary they give you at the CNRS, I'll double it.

—It isn't a question of money.

—I'm not asking you to quit your job. All you have to do is apply for a leave of absence. The book should take us about a year to write, and if you don't want to stay with me here after we're finished, go back to Paris. In the meantime, you'll be earning twice what you earn now – with free room and board, by the way – and in the process you might discover that you want to marry me. An experiment in the form of a business proposal. Do you see what I'm talking about?

—Yes, I see. But why would I be interested in working on someone else's book? I have my own work to do.

—Once you know what the book is about, you'll be interested.

—It's a book about your life.

—Yes, but do you know anything about my life, Cécile?

—You're a retired professor of government and international affairs.

—Among other things, yes. But I didn't only teach government, I worked for it as well.

—The French government?

—Of course. I'm French, aren't I?

—And what kind of work did you do?

—Secret work.

—Secret work . . . Are you talking about espionage?

—Skullduggery in all its many forms, my dear.

—Well, well. I had no idea.

—It goes all the way back to Algeria for me. I started young, and I

went on working for them straight through to the end of the Cold War.

—In other words, you have some gripping stories to tell.

—More than gripping. Stories to curdle your blood.

—Are you allowed to publish these stories? I thought there were laws that prevented government workers from exposing state secrets.

—If we run into any difficulties, we'll redo the manuscript and publish it as a novel – under your name.

—My name?

—Yes, your name. I'll keep myself out of it, and you can have all the glory.

I no longer believed a word he was saying. By the time R.B. left the room, I was convinced he was mad, that he had lost his mind and gone stark raving mad. He'd spent too many years on Quillia, and the tropical sun had cooked the wires in his brain and pushed him over the edge of sanity. Espionage. Marriage. Memoirs that transformed themselves into novels. He was like a child, a desperate child who made up things as he went along, saying whatever popped into his head and then spinning it out into a fiction that would serve his purpose at any given moment – in this case, the bizarre, wholly preposterous idea that he wanted to marry me. He didn't want to marry me. He couldn't want to marry me. But if he did, and if he thought he could, then it only proved that he was no longer in his right mind.

I pretended to play along with him, acting as if I took his *experiment in the form of a business proposal* seriously. Was I too afraid to challenge him, or was I simply trying to avoid an unpleasant scene? A little of both, I think. I didn't want to say anything that would provoke his anger, but at the same time I found the conversation unbearably tedious, and I wanted to get rid of him as quickly as I could. So you'll think it over? he asked. Yes, I said, I promise to think it over. But you'll have to tell me more about the book before I make my decision. Of course, he answered, that goes without saying. I have some chores to do with Samuel now, but we can talk about it over lunch. Then he patted me on the cheek and said: I'm so glad you've come. The world has never looked more beautiful to me.

I didn't go to lunch. I said that I wasn't feeling well, which was partly true and partly not true. I could have gone if I had pushed myself, if I had actively wanted to go, but I wasn't in the mood to push myself, and I didn't want to go. I needed a break from R.B., and the fact was that the

trip had taken its toll on me. I felt exhausted, jet-lagged, spent. Without bothering to take off my clothes, I lay down on the bed and napped for three solid hours. I woke up in a sweat, perspiration gushing from every pore of my body, my mouth dry, my head pounding. Stripping off my clothes, I went into the bathroom, hung one of the water-filled plastic bags on the shower hook, opened the nozzle, and let the water rush down onto my head. A lukewarm shower in the midday heat. The bathroom was out in the open, a small, nichelike space carved into the stone and perched on top of the cliff, with nothing below me but the immense, glittering ocean. *The world has never looked more beautiful.* Yes, I said to myself, this is beyond doubt a beautiful place, but it is a harsh beauty, an inhospitable beauty, and I am already looking forward to leaving it.

I thought about writing in my diary, but I was too agitated to sit still. Then it occurred to me that I should suspend all writing for the duration of my visit. What if R.B. sneaked into my room and found the diary, I wondered, what if he saw the things I was saying about him? All hell would break loose. I might even be in danger.

I tried to read, but reading was beyond my powers of concentration just then. All the useless books I had packed for my holiday in the sun. Novels by Bernhard and Vila-Matas, poems by Dupin and du Bouchet, essays by Sacks and Diderot – all worthy books, but useless to me now that I had reached my destination.

I sat in the chair by the window. I paced around the room. I sat down in the chair again.

And what if R.B. hadn't gone mad? I asked myself. What if he was playing with me, proposing marriage in order to tease me and make fun of me, having a good laugh at my expense? That too was possible. Anything was possible.

He drank heavily at dinner that night. A couple of tall rum punches before we sat down at the table, then ample doses of wine throughout the meal. At first, it seemed to have no effect on him. He solicitously asked if I was feeling better, and I said yes, the nap had done me a world of good, and after that we talked about small, inconsequential things, with no mention of marriage, no mention of Adam Walker, no mention of books about undercover intelligence work that can be turned into novels. Although we were speaking French, I wondered if he preferred not to talk about these matters in front of the servants. I also wondered if he wasn't going senile, in the early stages of Alzheimer's or dementia, and had simply forgotten the things we had talked about earlier in the day.

Perhaps thoughts flitted through his head like butterflies or mosquitoes – ephemeral notions that came and went so fast that he couldn't keep track of them anymore.

About ten or fifteen minutes into the meal, however, he began talking about politics. Not in any personal way, not with any stories about his own experiences, but abstractly, theoretically, sounding very much like the professor he had been for most of his adult life. He began with the Berlin Wall. Everyone in the West was so happy when the wall came down, he said, everyone thought a new era of peace and brotherly love had dawned on earth, but in fact it was the most alarming event of recent times. Distasteful as it might have been, the Cold War had held the world together for forty-four years, and now that the simple, black-and-white binary world of us versus them was gone, we had entered a period of instability and chaos similar to the years prior to World War I. Mutual Assured Destruction, MAD. It was a frightening concept, yes, but when one half of humanity is in a position to blow up the other half, and when the other half is in a position to blow up the first half, neither side will pull the trigger. Permanent stalemate. The most elegant answer to military aggression in the history of mankind.

I didn't interrupt. R.B. was talking rationally for once, even if his argument was rather crude. What about Algeria and Indochina, I wanted to ask him, what about Korea and Vietnam, what about U.S. interference in Latin America, the assassinations of Lumumba and Allende, the Soviets rolling their tanks into Budapest and Prague, the long war in Afghanistan? There was little point in asking these questions. I had sat through enough lectures of this sort as a girl to know that tangling with R.B. wasn't worth the trouble. Let him rant, I said to myself, let him spout forth his simplistic opinions, and before long he'll talk himself out and the evening will be over. This was the R.B. of old, and for the first time since I'd set foot in his house, I felt I was on familiar ground.

But he didn't talk himself out, and the evening dragged on much longer than I thought it would. He was only warming up with those comments about the Cold War, clearing his throat, as it were, and for the next two hours he subjected me to the most blistering harangue I had ever heard from him. Arab terrorism, September 11th, the encroaching war in Iraq, the price of oil, global warming, food shortages, mass starvation, a world depression, dirty bombs, anthrax attacks, the annihilation of Israel – what didn't he talk about, what dire, death-rattling prophecy did he not conjure up and spew in my face? Some of the things he said

were so mean and ugly, so vicious in their hatred of anyone who was not a European with white skin, of anyone who was not, finally, Rudolf Born himself, that a moment came when I couldn't bear to listen to him anymore. Stop it, I said. I don't want to hear another word. I'm going to bed.

As I stood up from my chair and left the room, he was still talking, still preaching to me in his drunken, rasping voice, not even aware that I was no longer sitting at the table. The polar ice caps are melting, he said. Fifteen years from now, twenty years from now, the floods will come. Drowned cities, obliterated continents, the end of everything. You'll still be alive, Cécile. You'll get to see it happen, and then you'll drown. You'll drown with all the others, all the billions of others, and that will be the end. How I envy you, Cécile. You'll be there to see the end of everything.

He didn't show up for breakfast the next morning (yesterday). When I asked Nancy if he was all right, she made a small sound in the back of her throat, something akin to a muted, inward laugh, and said that Mr. Born was still in dreamland. I wondered how long he had gone on drinking after I left the dining room.

Four hours later, he emerged for lunch, apparently in good cheer, his eyes bright and focused, ready for action. For the first time since I'd been there, he had taken the trouble to put on a shirt.

—Excuse my intemperate remarks last night, he began. I didn't mean half the things I said – less than half of them, actually, almost nothing.

—Why would you say something you didn't mean? I asked, somewhat thrown by this odd retraction. It wasn't like him to examine his own behavior, to back down from anything he said or did – intemperate or not.

—I was testing out certain ideas, trying to get myself into the proper frame of mind for the work ahead.

—And what work is that?

—The book. The book we're going to make together. After our discussion yesterday morning, I'm convinced you're right, Cécile. The true story can never be published. There are too many secrets, too many bits of dirty business to expose, too many deaths to account for. The French would arrest me if I tried to talk about them.

—Are you saying you want to give up the project?

—No, not at all. But in order to tell the truth, we'll have to fictionalize it.

—That's what you said yesterday.

—I know. It popped into my head while we were talking, but now that

I've had time to think it over, I believe it's the only solution.

—A novel, then.

—Yes, a novel. And now that I'm thinking novel, I understand that limitless possibilities have suddenly opened up to us. We can tell the truth, yes, but we'll also have the freedom to make things up.

—Why would you want to do that?

—To make the story more interesting. We'll be basing the action on my life, of course, but the character who plays me in the book will have to be given a different name. We can't call him Rudolf Born, can we? He'll have to be someone else – Mr. X, for example. Once I become Mr. X, I won't be myself anymore, and once I'm not myself, we can add as many new details as we like.

—Such as?

—Such as . . . maybe Mr. X isn't the person he appears to be. We present him as a man who leads a double life. The world knows him as a dull professor, a man who teaches government and international affairs at some dull institute or university, but in fact he's also a special undercover agent, fighting the good fight against the Soviet Communists.

—We already know that. That's the premise of the book.

—Yes, yes – but wait. What if his double life isn't a double life but a triple life?

—I don't follow.

—He seems to be working for the French, but he's actually working for the Russians. Mr. X is a mole.

—It's beginning to sound like a thriller –

—Thriller. Don't you just love that word? *Thriller*.

—But why would Mr. X betray his country?

—Any number of reasons. After years of work in the field, he becomes disillusioned with the West and converts to the Communist cause. Or else he's a cynic who doesn't believe in anything, and the Russians are paying him good money, more money than the French are paying him, which means that he's earning more than twice as much as he would if he worked for just one side.

—He doesn't seem to be a very sympathetic character.

—He doesn't have to be sympathetic. Just interesting and complex. Think back to May sixty-eight, Cécile. Do you remember all those terrible arguments we had?

—I'll never forget them.

—What if Mr. X, the double agent in league with the enemy, is in perfect

accord with the young Cécile Juin character? What if he's delighted to see France erupt in anarchy, bursting with joy over the disintegration of France and the imminent fall of the government? But he has to protect his cover, and to do that he espouses views directly opposed to the ones he believes in. It adds a nice little twist, don't you think?

—Not bad.

—I've thought of another scene. It might be difficult to pull off, but if we stick with the idea of turning Mr. X into a mole, it would be crucial – one of the darkest, most lacerating moments in the book. Mr. X has a French colleague, Mr. Y. They've been close friends for many years, they've lived through some harrowing adventures together, but now Mr. Y suspects that Mr. X is working for the Soviets. He confronts Mr. X and tells him that if he doesn't quit the service immediately, he will have him arrested. These are the early sixties, remember. Capital punishment was still in force, and arrest means the guillotine for Mr. X. What can he do? He has no choice but to kill Mr. Y. Not with a bullet, of course. Not with a blow to the head or a knife in the belly, but by more subtle means that will allow him to escape detection. It's summer. Mr. Y and his family are vacationing in the mountains somewhere in the south of France. Mr. X goes down there, sneaks onto the property in the middle of the night, and disconnects the brakes of Mr. Y's car. The next morning, on his way into town to buy bread at the local bakery, Mr. Y loses control of the car and crashes down the side of a mountain. Mission accomplished.

—What are you saying, Rudolf?

—Nothing. I'm telling you a story, that's all. I'm describing how Mr. X kills Mr. Y.

—You're talking about my father, aren't you?

—Of course not. Why would you think that?

—You're telling me how you tried to kill my father.

—Nonsense. Your father was never in the service. You know that. He worked for the Ministry of Culture.

—So you say. Who knows what he really did?

—Stop it, Cécile. We're just having a little fun.

—It's not funny. It's not the least bit funny. You're making me sick to my stomach.

—My dear girl. Calm down. You're acting like a simpleton.

—I'm walking out of here, Rudolf. I can't stand to be with you for another minute.

—Right now, in the middle of lunch? Just like that?

—Yes, just like that.

—And I thought –

—I don't care what you thought.

—All right, go if you want to. I won't try to stop you. I've done nothing but shower you with kindness and affection since you came here, and now you turn on me like this. You're a ridiculous, hysterical woman, Cécile. I'm sorry I invited you to my house.

—I'm sorry I came.

I was already standing by then, already making my way across the room, already in tears. Just before I reached the hall, I turned around for a last look at the man my mother almost married, the man who had asked me to be his wife, and there he was, sitting with his back to me, hunched over his plate, shoveling food into his mouth. Total indifference. I hadn't even left the house, and already I had been expunged from his mind.

I went into my bedroom to gather up my things. There would be no Samuel to accompany me this time, and since I wouldn't be able to get down the mountain with the suitcase in my hand, the bag would have to stay. I transferred some clean underwear into my purse, kicked off my sandals and put on a pair of sneakers, then checked to make sure that my passport and money were where they should have been. The thought of leaving my clothes and books behind caused a small twinge of regret, but the feeling evaporated after a couple of seconds. My plan was to walk to the town of Saint Margaret and buy a ticket for the next available flight to Barbados. It was twelve miles from the house. I could do that. As long as I was on flat ground, I could walk forever.

Climbing down the mountain was less of a challenge than climbing up had been. I broke into a sweat, of course, I was bedeviled by the same aerial attacks of gnats and mosquitoes, but I didn't fall this time, not even once. I moved at a moderate pace, neither too plodding nor too rushed, pausing every now and then to examine wildflowers by the side of the road – bright, beautiful things whose names were unknown to me. Burning red. Burning yellow. Burning blue.

As I approached the bottom of the mountain, I began to hear something, a sound or collection of sounds that I was unable to identify. At first, I thought it resembled the chirping of crickets or cicadas, the persistent metallic cries of insects in the afternoon heat. But it was too hot for insects to be calling to one another just then, and as I drew closer, I understood that the sounds were too loud, that the rhythms of the

sounds were too complex, too pulsing and intricate to be coming from any living thing. A barrier of trees blocked my view. I kept on walking, but the barrier didn't end until I reached the very bottom. Once I got there, I stopped, turned to my right, and finally saw where the sounds were coming from, finally saw what my ears had been telling me.

A barren field stretched out before me, a barren, dusty field cluttered with gray stones of various shapes and sizes, and scattered among the stones in that field were fifty or sixty men and women, each holding a hammer in one hand and a chisel in the other, pounding on the stones until they broke in two, then pounding on the smaller stones until they broke in two, and then pounding on the smallest stones until they were reduced to gravel. Fifty or sixty black men and women crouching in that field with hammers and chisels in their hands, pounding on the stones as the sun pounded on their bodies, with no shade anywhere and sweat glistening on every face. I stood there watching them for a long time. I watched and listened and wondered if I had ever seen anything like it. This was the kind of work one usually associated with prisoners, with people in chains, but these people weren't in chains. They were working, they were making money, they were keeping themselves alive. The music of the stones was ornate and impossible, a music of fifty or sixty clinking hammers, each one moving at its own speed, each one locked in its own cadence, and together they formed a fractious, stately harmony, a sound that worked itself into my body and stayed there long after I had left, and even now, sitting on the plane as it flies across the ocean, I can still hear the clinking of those hammers in my head. That sound will always be with me. For the rest of my life, no matter where I am, no matter what I am doing, it will always be with me.

[2007–2008]

SUNSET PARK

*Miles Heller*

# I

For almost a year now, he has been taking photographs of abandoned things. There are at least two jobs every day, sometimes as many as six or seven, and each time he and his cohorts enter another house, they are confronted by the things, the innumerable cast-off things left behind by the departed families. The absent people have all fled in haste, in shame, in confusion, and it is certain that wherever they are living now (if they have found a place to live and are not camped out in the streets) their new dwellings are smaller than the houses they have lost. Each house is a story of failure – of bankruptcy and default, of debt and foreclosure – and he has taken it upon himself to document the last, lingering traces of those scattered lives in order to prove that the vanished families were once here, that the ghosts of people he will never see and never know are still present in the discarded things strewn about their empty houses.

The work is called trashing out, and he belongs to a four-man crew employed by the Dunbar Realty Corporation, which subcontracts its "home preservation" services to the local banks that now own the properties in question. The sprawling flatlands of south Florida are filled with these orphaned structures, and because it is in the interest of the banks to resell them as quickly as possible, the vacated houses must be cleaned, repaired, and made ready to be shown to prospective buyers. In a collapsing world of economic ruin and relentless, ever-expanding hardship, trashing out is one of the few thriving businesses in the area. No doubt he is lucky to have found this job. He doesn't know how much longer he can bear it, but the pay is decent, and in a land of fewer and fewer jobs, it is nothing if not a good job.

In the beginning, he was stunned by the disarray and the filth, the neglect. Rare is the house he enters that has been left in pristine condition by its former owners. More often there will have been an eruption of violence and anger, a parting rampage of capricious vandalism – from the open taps of sinks and bathtubs overflowing with water to sledgehammered, smashed-in walls or walls covered with obscene graffiti or walls pocked with bullet holes, not to mention the ripped-out copper

pipes, the bleach-stained carpets, the piles of shit deposited on the living room floor. Those are extreme examples, perhaps, impulsive acts triggered by the rage of the dispossessed, disgusting but understandable statements of despair, but even if he is not always gripped by revulsion when he enters a house, he never opens a door without a feeling of dread. Inevitably, the first thing to contend with is the smell, the onslaught of sour air rushing into his nostrils, the ubiquitous, commingled aromas of mildew, rancid milk, cat litter, crud-caked toilet bowls, and food rotting on the kitchen counter. Not even fresh air pouring in through open windows can wipe out the smells; not even the tidiest, most circumspect removal can erase the stench of defeat.

Then, always, there are the objects, the forgotten possessions, *the abandoned things*. By now, his photographs number in the thousands, and among his burgeoning archive can be found pictures of books, shoes, and oil paintings, pianos and toasters, dolls, tea sets, and dirty socks, televisions and board games, party dresses and tennis racquets, sofas, silk lingerie, caulking guns, thumbtacks, plastic action figures, tubes of lipstick, rifles, discolored mattresses, knives and forks, poker chips, a stamp collection, and a dead canary lying at the bottom of its cage. He has no idea why he feels compelled to take these pictures. He understands that it is an empty pursuit, of no possible benefit to anyone, and yet each time he walks into a house, he senses that the things are calling out to him, speaking to him in the voices of the people who are no longer there, asking him to be looked at one last time before they are carted away. The other members of the crew make fun of him for this obsessive picture taking, but he pays them no heed. They are of little account in his opinion, and he despises them all. Brain-dead Victor, the crew boss; stuttering, chatterbox Paco; and fat, wheezing Freddy – the three musketeers of doom. The law says that all salvageable objects above a certain value must be handed over to the bank, which is obliged to return them to their owners, but his co-workers grab whatever they please and never give it a second thought. They consider him a fool for turning his back on these spoils – the bottles of whiskey, the radios, the CD players, the archery equipment, the dirty magazines – but all he wants are his pictures – not things, but the pictures of things. For some time now, he has made it his business to say as little as possible when he is on the job. Paco and Freddy have taken to calling him El Mudo.

He is twenty-eight years old, and to the best of his knowledge he has no ambitions. No burning ambitions, in any case, no clear idea of what

building a plausible future might entail for him. He knows that he will not stay in Florida much longer, that the moment is coming when he will feel the need to move on again, but until that need ripens into a necessity to act, he is content to remain in the present and not look ahead. If he has accomplished anything in the seven and a half years since he quit college and struck out on his own, it is this ability to live in the present, to confine himself to the here and now, and although it might not be the most laudable accomplishment one can think of, it has required considerable discipline and self-control for him to achieve it. To have no plans, which is to say, to have no longings or hopes, to be satisfied with your lot, to accept what the world doles out to you from one sunrise to the next – in order to live like that you must want very little, as little as humanly possible.

Bit by bit, he has pared down his desires to what is now approaching a bare minimum. He has cut out smoking and drinking, he no longer eats in restaurants, he does not own a television, a radio, or a computer. He would like to trade in his car for a bicycle, but he can't get rid of the car, since the distances he must travel for work are too great. The same applies to the cell phone he carries around in his pocket, which he would dearly love to toss in the garbage, but he needs it for work as well and therefore can't do without it. The digital camera was an indulgence, perhaps, but given the drear and slog of the endless trash-out rut, he feels it is saving his life. His rent is low, since he lives in a small apartment in a poor neighborhood, and beyond spending money on bedrock necessities, the only luxury he allows himself is buying books, paperback books, mostly novels, American novels, British novels, foreign novels in translation, but in the end books are not luxuries so much as necessities, and reading is an addiction he has no wish to be cured of.

If not for the girl, he would probably leave before the month was out. He has saved up enough money to go anywhere he wants, and there is no question that he has had his fill of the Florida sun – which, after much study, he now believes does the soul more harm than good. It is a Machiavellian sun in his opinion, a hypocritical sun, and the light it generates does not illuminate things but obscures them – blinding you with its constant, overbright effulgences, pounding on you with its blasts of vaporous humidity, destabilizing you with its miragelike reflections and shimmering waves of nothingness. It is all glitter and dazzle, but it offers no substance, no tranquillity, no respite. Still, it was under this sun that he first saw the girl, and because he can't talk himself into giving her up,

he continues to live with the sun and try to make his peace with it.

Her name is Pilar Sanchez, and he met her six months ago in a public park, a purely accidental meeting late one Saturday afternoon in the middle of May, the unlikeliest of unlikely encounters. She was sitting on the grass reading a book, and not ten feet away from her he too was sitting on the grass reading a book, which happened to be the same book as hers, the same book in an identical soft-cover edition, *The Great Gatsby*, which he was reading for the third time since his father gave it to him as a present on his sixteenth birthday. He had been sitting there for twenty or thirty minutes, inside the book and therefore walled off from his surroundings, when he heard someone laugh. He turned, and in that first, fatal glimpse of her, as she sat there smiling at him and pointing to the title of her book, he guessed that she was even younger than sixteen, just a girl, really, and a little girl at that, a small adolescent girl wearing tight, cut-off shorts, sandals, and a skimpy halter top, the same clothes worn by every half-attractive girl throughout the lower regions of hot, sun-spangled Florida. No more than a baby, he said to himself, and yet there she was with her smooth, uncovered limbs and alert, smiling face, and he who rarely smiles at anyone or anything looked into her dark, animated eyes and smiled back at her.

Six months later, she is still underage. Her driver's license says she is seventeen, that she won't be turning eighteen until May, and therefore he must act cautiously with her in public, avoid at all costs doing anything that might arouse the suspicions of the prurient, for a single telephone call to the police from some riled-up busybody could easily land him in jail. Every morning that is not a weekend morning or a holiday morning, he drives her to John F. Kennedy High School, where she is in her senior year and doing well, with aspirations for college and a future life as a registered nurse, but he does not drop her off in front of the building. That would be too dangerous. Some teacher or school official could catch sight of them in the car together and raise the alarm, and so he glides to a halt some three or four blocks before they reach Kennedy and lets her off there. He does not kiss her good-bye. He does not touch her. She is saddened by his restraint, since in her own mind she is already a full-grown woman, but she accepts this sham indifference because he has told her she must accept it.

Pilar's parents were killed in a car wreck two years ago, and until she moved into his apartment after the school year ended last June, she lived with her three older sisters in the family house. Twenty-year-old Maria,

twenty-three-year-old Teresa, and twenty-five-year-old Angela. Maria is enrolled in a community college, studying to become a beautician. Teresa works as a teller at a local bank. Angela, the prettiest of the bunch, is a hostess in a cocktail lounge. According to Pilar, she sometimes sleeps with the customers for money. Pilar hastens to add that she loves Angela, that she loves all her sisters, but she's glad to have left the house now, which is filled with too many memories of her mother and father, and besides, she can't stop herself, but she's angry at Angela for doing what she does, she considers it a sin for a woman to sell her body, and it's a relief not to be arguing with her about it anymore. Yes, she says to him, his apartment is a shabby little nothing of a place, the house is much bigger and more comfortable, but the apartment doesn't have eighteen-month-old Carlos Junior in it, and that too is an immense relief. Teresa's son isn't a bad child as far as children go, of course, and what can Teresa do with her husband stationed in Iraq and her long hours at the bank, but that doesn't give her the right to pawn off babysitting duties on her kid sister every other day of the week. Pilar wanted to be a good sport, but she couldn't help resenting it. She needs time to be alone and to study, she wants to make something of herself, and how can she do that if she's busy changing dirty diapers? Babies are fine for other people, but she wants no part of them. Thanks, she says, but no thanks.

He marvels at her spirit and intelligence. Even on the first day, when they sat in the park talking about *The Great Gatsby*, he was impressed that she was reading the book for herself and not because a teacher had assigned it at school, and then, as the conversation continued, doubly impressed when she began to argue that the most important character in the book was not Daisy or Tom or even Gatsby himself but Nick Carraway. He asked her to explain. Because he's the one who tells the story, she said. He's the only character with his feet on the ground, the only one who can look outside of himself. The others are all lost and shallow people, and without Nick's compassion and understanding, we wouldn't be able to feel anything for them. The book depends on Nick. If the story had been told by an omniscient narrator, it wouldn't work half as well as it does.

*Omniscient narrator*. She knows what the term means, just as she understands what it is to talk about *suspension of disbelief, biogenesis, antilogarithms,* and *Brown v. Board of Education*. How is it possible, he wonders, for a young girl like Pilar Sanchez, whose Cuban-born father worked as a letter carrier all his life, whose three older sisters dwell contentedly in

a bog of humdrum daily routines, to have turned out so differently from the rest of her family? Pilar wants to know things, she has plans, she works hard, and he is more than happy to encourage her, to do whatever he can to help advance her education. From the day she left home and moved in with him, he has been drilling her on the finer points of how to score well on the SATs, has vetted every one of her homework assignments, has taught her the rudiments of calculus (which is not offered by her high school), and has read dozens of novels, short stories, and poems out loud to her. He, the young man without ambitions, the college dropout who spurned the trappings of his once privileged life, has taken it upon himself to become ambitious for her, to push her as far as she is willing to go. The first priority is college, a good college with a full scholarship, and once she is in, he feels the rest will take care of itself. At the moment, she is dreaming of becoming a registered nurse, but things will eventually change, he is certain of that, and he is fully confident that she has it in her to go on to medical school one day and become a doctor.

She was the one who proposed moving in with him. It never would have occurred to him to suggest such an audacious plan himself, but Pilar was determined, at once driven by a desire to escape and enthralled by the prospect of sleeping with him every night, and after she begged him to go to Angela, the major breadwinner of the clan and therefore the one with the final word on all family decisions, he met with the oldest Sanchez girl and managed to talk her into it. She was reluctant at first, claiming that Pilar was too young and inexperienced to consider such a momentous step. Yes, she knew her sister was in love with him, but she didn't approve of that love because of the difference in their ages, which meant that sooner or later he would grow bored with his adolescent plaything and leave her with a broken heart. He answered that it would probably end up being the reverse, that he would be the one left with a broken heart. Then, brushing aside all further talk of hearts and feelings, he presented his case in purely practical terms. Pilar didn't have a job, he said, she was a drag on the family finances, and he was in a position to support her and take that burden off their hands. It wasn't as if he would be abducting her to China, after all. Their house was only a fifteen-minute walk from his apartment, and they could see her as often as they liked. To clinch the bargain, he offered them presents, any number of things they craved but were too strapped to buy for themselves. Much to the shock and jeering amusement of the three clowns at work, he temporarily reversed his stance on the do's and don'ts of trash-out

etiquette, and over the next week he calmly filched an all-but-brand-new flat-screen TV, a top-of-the-line electric coffeemaker, a red tricycle, thirty-six films (including a boxed collector's set of the *Godfather* movies), a professional-quality makeup mirror, and a set of crystal wineglasses, which he duly presented to Angela and her sisters as an expression of his gratitude. In other words, Pilar now lives with him because he bribed the family. He bought her.

Yes, she is in love with him, and yes, in spite of his qualms and inner hesitations, he loves her back, however improbable that might seem to him. Note here for the record that he is not someone with a special fixation on young girls. Until now, all the women in his life have been more or less his own age. Pilar therefore does not represent an embodiment of some ideal female type for him – she is merely herself, a small piece of luck he stumbled across one afternoon in a public park, an exception to every rule. Nor can he explain to himself why he is attracted to her. He admires her intelligence, yes, but that is finally of scant importance, since he has admired the intelligence of other women before her without feeling the least bit attracted to them. He finds her pretty, but not exceptionally pretty, not beautiful in any objective way (although it could also be argued that every seventeen-year-old girl is beautiful, for the simple reason that all youth is beautiful). But no matter. He has not fallen for her because of her body or because of her mind. What is it, then? What holds him here when everything tells him he should leave? Because of the way she looks at him, perhaps, the ferocity of her gaze, the rapt intensity in her eyes when she listens to him talk, a feeling that she is entirely present when they are together, that he is the only person who exists for her on the face of the earth.

Sometimes, when he takes out his camera and shows her his pictures of the abandoned things, her eyes fill up with tears. There is a soft, sentimental side to her that is almost comic, he feels, and yet he is moved by that softness in her, that vulnerability to the aches of others, and because she can also be so tough, so talkative and full of laughter, he can never predict what part of her will surge forth at any given moment. It can be trying in the short run, but in the long run he feels it is all to the good. He who has denied himself so much for so many years, who has been so stolid in his abnegations, who has taught himself to rein in his temper and drift through the world with cool, stubborn detachment has slowly come back to life in the face of her emotional excesses, her combustibility, her mawkish tears when confronted by the image of an abandoned

teddy bear, a broken bicycle, or a vase of wilted flowers.

The first time they went to bed together, she assured him she was no longer a virgin. He took her at her word, but when the moment came for him to enter her, she pushed him away and told him he mustn't do that. The *mommy hole* was off-limits, she said, absolutely forbidden to male members. Tongues and fingers were acceptable, but not members, under no condition at any time, not ever. He had no idea what she was talking about. He was wearing a condom, wasn't he? They were protected, and there was no need to worry about anything. Ah, she said, but that's where he was wrong. Teresa and her husband always believed in condoms too, and look what happened to them. Nothing was more frightening to Pilar than the thought of becoming pregnant, and she would never risk her fate by trusting in one of those iffy rubbers. She would rather slit her wrists or jump off a bridge than get herself knocked up. Did he understand? Yes, he understood, but what was the alternative? The *funny hole,* she said. Angela had told her about it, and he had to admit that from a strictly biological and medical standpoint it was the one truly safe form of birth control in the world.

For six months now, he has abided by her wishes, restricting all member penetration to her funny hole and putting nothing more than tongue and fingers in her mommy hole. Such are the anomalies and idiosyncrasies of their love life, which is nevertheless a rich love life, a splendid erotic partnership that shows no signs of abating anytime soon. In the end, it is this sexual complicity that binds him fast to her and holds him in the hot nowhere-land of ruined and empty houses. He is bewitched by her skin. He is a prisoner of her ardent young mouth. He is at home in her body, and if he ever finds the courage to leave, he knows he will regret it to the end of his days.

# II

He has told her next to nothing about himself. Even on the first day in the park, when she heard him speak and understood that he came from somewhere else, he didn't tell her that the somewhere else was New York City, the West Village in Manhattan to be precise, but vaguely answered that his life had begun *up north*. A bit later, when he started the SAT drills and introduced her to calculus, Pilar quickly learned that he was more than just an itinerant trash-out worker, that he was in fact a highly educated person with a nimble mind and a love of literature so vast and so informed that it made her English teachers at John F. Kennedy High look like impostors. Where had he gone to school? she asked him one day. He shrugged, not wanting to mention Stuyvesant and the three years he had spent at Brown. When she continued to press him, he looked down at the floor and muttered something about a small state college in New England. The following week, when he gave her a novel written by Renzo Michaelson, who happened to be his godfather, she noticed that it had been published by a company called Heller Books and asked him if there was any connection. No, he said, it's just a coincidence, Heller turns out to be a fairly common name. This prompted her to ask the simple, altogether logical next question about which Heller family he happened to belong to. Who were his parents, and where did they live? They're both gone, he replied. Gone as in dead and gone? I'm afraid so. Just like me, she said, her eyes suddenly filling with tears. Yes, he answered, just like you. Any brothers and sisters? No. I'm an only child.

Lying to her in this way has spared him the discomfort of having to talk about things he has been struggling to avoid for years. He doesn't want her to know that six months after he was born his mother walked out on his father and divorced him to marry another man. He doesn't want her to know that he has not seen or spoken to his father, Morris Heller, founder and publisher of Heller Books, since the summer after his third year at Brown. Least of all does he want her to know anything about his stepmother, Willa Parks, who married his father twenty months after the divorce, and nothing, nothing, nothing about his dead stepbrother, Bobby. These matters do not concern Pilar. They are his own

private business, and until he finds an exit from the limbo that has encircled him for the past seven years, he will not share them with anyone.

Even now, he can't be sure if he did it on purpose or not. There is no question that he pushed Bobby, that the two of them were arguing and he pushed him in anger, but he doesn't know if the push came before or after he heard the oncoming car, which is to say, he doesn't know if Bobby's death was an accident or if he was secretly trying to kill him. The entire story of his life hinges on what happened that day in the Berkshires, and he still has no grasp of the truth, he still can't be certain if he is guilty of a crime or not.

It was the summer of 1996, roughly one month after his father had given him *The Great Gatsby* and five other books for his sixteenth birthday. Bobby was eighteen and a half and had just graduated from high school, having squeaked through by the skin of his teeth in no small part thanks to the efforts of his stepbrother, who had written three final term papers for him at the cut-rate price of two dollars per page, seventy-six dollars in all. Their parents had rented a house outside Great Barrington for the month of August, and the two boys were on their way to spend the weekend with them. He was too young to drive, Bobby was the one with the license, and therefore it was Bobby's responsibility to check the oil and fill the tank before they left – which, needless to say, he failed to do. About fifteen miles from the house, traveling along a twisty, hilly, back-country road, the car ran out of gas. He might not have become so angry if Bobby had shown some remorse, if the dim-witted slacker had taken the trouble to apologize for his mistake, but true to form, Bobby found the situation hilarious, and his first response was to burst out laughing.

Cell phones existed back then, but they didn't have one, which meant they had to get out of the car and walk. It was a hot, oppressively humid day, with squadrons of gnats and mosquitoes swarming around their heads, and he was in a foul temper, irritated by Bobby's moronic nonchalance, by the heat and the bugs, by having to walk down that crummy, narrow little road, and before long he was lashing out at his stepbrother, calling him names, trying to provoke a fight. Bobby kept shrugging him off, however, refusing to respond to his insults. Don't get worked up over nothing, he said, life is full of unexpected turns, maybe something interesting would happen to them because they were on this road, maybe, just maybe, they would discover two beautiful girls around the next bend, two completely naked beautiful girls who would take them

into the woods and make love to them for sixteen straight hours. Under normal circumstances, he would laugh whenever Bobby started talking like that, fall willingly under the spell of his stepbrother's inane prattle, but nothing was normal about what was happening just then, and he was in no mood to laugh. It was all so idiotic, he wanted to punch Bobby in the face.

Whenever he thinks about that day now, he imagines how differently things would have turned out if he had been walking on Bobby's right instead of his left. The shove would have pushed him off the road rather than into the middle of it, and that would have been the end of the story, since there wouldn't have been a story, the whole business would have amounted to less than nothing, a brief outburst that would have been forgotten in no time at all. But there they were, for no special reason arrayed in that particular left–right tandem, he on the inside, Bobby on the outside, walking along the shoulder of the road in the direction of the oncoming traffic, of which there was none, not a single car, truck, or motorcycle for ten minutes, and after he'd been haranguing Bobby nonstop for those ten minutes, his stepbrother's jocular indifference to their plight slowly turned into peevishness, then belligerence, and a couple of miles after they started out, the two of them were shouting at each other at the top of their lungs.

How often had they fought in the past? Countless times, more times than he is able to remember, but there was nothing unusual about that, he feels, since brothers always fight, and if Bobby wasn't his flesh-and-blood brother, he nevertheless had been there for the full span of his conscious life. He was two years old when his father married Bobby's mother and the four of them started living together under the same roof, which necessarily makes it a time beyond recall, a period now wholly expunged from his mind, and therefore it would be legitimate to say that Bobby had always been his brother, even if that wasn't strictly the case. There had been the customary squabbles and conflicts, then, and because he was the younger by two and a half years, his body had received the bulk of the punishment. A dim recollection of his father stepping in to pull a screaming Bobby off him one rainy day somewhere in the country, of his stepmother scolding Bobby for *playing too rough,* of kicking Bobby in the shins when he yanked a toy out of his hands. But it hadn't been all war and combat, there had been lulls and truces and good times as well, and beginning when he was seven or eight, meaning when Bobby was nine or ten or eleven, he can remember actively liking his brother,

perhaps even loving him, and that he was liked and perhaps even loved in return. But they were never close, not close in the way some brothers are, even fighting, antagonistic brothers, and no doubt that had something to do with the fact that they belonged to an artificial family, a constructed family, and each boy's deepest loyalty was reserved for his own parent. It wasn't that Willa had been a bad mother to him or that his father had been a bad father to Bobby. Quite the reverse. The two adults were steadfast allies, their marriage was solid and remarkably free of trouble, and each one bent over backward to give the other's kid every benefit of the doubt. But still, there were invisible fault lines, microscopic fissures to remind them that they were a patched-together entity, something not completely whole. The matter of Bobby's name, for example. Willa was Willa Parks, but her first husband, who had died of cancer at thirty-six, was Nordstrom, and Bobby was Nordstrom as well, and because he had been Nordstrom for the first four and a half years of his life, Willa had been reluctant to change it to Heller. She felt Bobby might be confused, but more to the point, she couldn't bring herself to wipe out the last traces of her first husband, who had loved her and was dead through no fault of his own, and to deprive his son of his name would have made her feel that he was being killed for a second time. The past, then, was part of the present, and the ghost of Karl Nordstrom was the fifth member of the household, an absent spirit who had left his mark on Bobby – who was both a brother and not a brother, both a son and not a son, both a friend and a foe.

They lived under the same roof, but apart from the fact that their parents were husband and wife, they had little in common. By temperament and outlook, by inclination and behavior, by all the measures used to gauge who and what a person is, they were different, deeply and unalterably different. As the years went by, each drifted off into his own separate sphere, and by the time they were bumping along through early adolescence, they rarely intersected anymore except at the dinner table and on family outings. Bobby was bright, quick, and funny, but he was an atrocious student who detested school, and because he was a reckless and defiant mischief maker on top of that, he was labeled *a problem*. By contrast, his younger stepbrother consistently earned the highest grades in his class. Heller was quiet and withdrawn, Nordstrom was extroverted and rambunctious, and each thought the other was going about the business of life in the wrong way. To make matters worse, Bobby's mother was a professor of English at NYU, a woman with a passion for books

and ideas, and how difficult it must have been for her son to listen to her praise Heller for his academic achievements, exult at his acceptance by Stuyvesant, and talk to him over dinner about goddamned bloody *existentialism*. By fifteen, Bobby had turned into a serious pothead, one of those glassy-eyed high school stoners who puke their stomachs out at weekend parties and make small drug deals to keep themselves in extra cash. Stick-in-the-mud Heller, bad-boy Nordstrom, and never the twain could meet. Verbal attacks were occasionally delivered from each side, but the physical fighting had stopped – largely due to the mysteries of genetics. When they found themselves on that road in the Berkshires twelve years ago, the sixteen-year-old Heller stood a couple of centimeters below six feet and weighed one hundred and seventy pounds. Nordstrom, derived from scrawnier stock, was five-eight and weighed one forty-five. The mismatch had canceled all potential bouts. For some time now, they had belonged in different divisions.

What were they arguing about that day? What word or sentence, what series of words or sentences had so enraged him that he lost control of himself and pushed Bobby to the ground? He can't remember clearly. So many things were said during that argument, so many accusations flew back and forth between them, so many buried animosities came roiling to the surface in so many gusts of vehemence and vindictiveness that he has trouble pinpointing the one particular phrase that set him off. At first, it was all quite childish. Irritation on his part over Bobby's negligence, yet one more botch in a long line of botches, how could he be so stupid and careless, look at the mess you've gotten us into now. On Bobby's part, irritation over his brother's tight-assed response to a minor inconvenience, his sanctimonious rectitude, the know-it-all superiority he'd been busting his balls with for years. Boys' stuff, hotheaded adolescent boys' stuff, nothing terribly alarming. But then, as they continued going at each other and Bobby warmed up to the battle, the dispute reached a deeper, more resonant level of bitterness, the nether lode of bad blood. It became the family then and not just the two of them. It was about how Bobby resented being the outcast of the holy four, how he couldn't stand his mother's attachment to Miles, how he'd had it up to here with the punishments and groundings that had been meted out to him by heartless, vengeful adults, how he couldn't bear to listen to another word about academic conferences and publishing deals and why this book was better than that book – he was sick of it all, sick of Miles, sick of his mother and stepfather, sick of everyone in that stinking

household, and he couldn't wait to be gone from there and off at college next month, and even if he flunked out of college, he was through with them and wouldn't be coming back. Adios, assholes. Fuck Morris Heller and his goddamned son. Fuck the whole fucking world.

He can't remember which word or words pushed him over the edge. Perhaps it isn't important to know that, perhaps it will never be possible to remember which insult from that rancorous spew of invective was responsible for the shove, but what is important, what counts above all else, is to know if he heard the car coming toward them or not, the car that was suddenly visible after rounding a sharp curve at fifty miles an hour, visible only when it was already too late to prevent his brother from being hit. What is certain is that Bobby was shouting at him and he was shouting back, telling him to stop, telling him to shut up, and all through that insane shouting match they were continuing to walk down the road, oblivious to everything around them, the woods to their left, the meadow to their right, the hazy sky above them, the birds singing in every pocket of the air, finches, thrushes, warblers, all those things had disappeared by then, and the only thing left was the fury of their voices. It seems certain that Bobby didn't hear the approaching car – or else he wasn't concerned by it, since he was walking on the shoulder of the road and didn't feel he was in danger. But what about you? Miles asks himself. Did you know or didn't you know?

It was a hard, decisive shove. It knocked Bobby off balance and sent him staggering onto the road, where he fell down and cracked his head against the asphalt. He sat up almost immediately, rubbing his head and cursing, and before he could climb to his feet, the car was mowing him down, crushing the life out of him, changing all their lives forever.

That is the first thing he refuses to share with Pilar. The second thing is the letter he wrote to his parents five years after Bobby's death. He had just finished his junior year at Brown and was planning to spend the summer in Providence, working as a part-time researcher for one of his history professors (nights and weekends in the library) and a full-time deliveryman for a local appliance store (installing air conditioners, lugging TVs and refrigerators up narrow flights of stairs). A girl had recently entered the picture, and since she lived in Brooklyn, he played hooky from his research job one weekend in June and drove down to New York to see her. He still had the keys to his parents' apartment on Downing Street, his old bedroom was still intact, and ever since he'd left for college the arrangement was that he could come and go as he

pleased, with no obligation to announce his visits. He started out late on Friday after finishing work at the appliance store and didn't enter the apartment until well past midnight. Both of his parents were asleep. Early the next morning, he was awakened by the sound of their voices coming from the kitchen. He climbed out of bed, opened the door of his room, and then hesitated. They were speaking more loudly and more urgently than usual, there was an anguished undertow in Willa's voice, and if they weren't exactly quarreling (they rarely quarreled), something important was taking place, some crucial business was being settled or hashed about or reexamined, and he didn't want to interrupt them.

The proper response would have been to go back into his room and shut the door. Even as he stood in the hallway listening to them, he knew he had no right to be there, that he must and should withdraw, but he couldn't help himself, he was too curious, too eager to find out what was going on, and so he didn't budge, and for the first time in his life he eavesdropped on a private conversation between his parents, and because the conversation was largely about him, it was the first time he had ever heard them, had ever heard anyone, talk about him behind his back.

He's different, Willa was saying. There's an anger and a coldness in him that frighten me, and I hate him for what he's done to you.

He hasn't done anything to me, his father answered. We might not talk as much as we used to, but that's normal. He's almost twenty-one. He has his own life now.

You used to be so close. That's one of the reasons why I fell in love with you – because of how well you loved that little boy. Remember baseball, Morris? Remember all those hours you spent in the park teaching him how to pitch?

The golden days of yore.

And he was good, too, wasn't he? I mean really good. Starting pitcher on the varsity team his sophomore year. He seemed so happy about it. And then he turned around and quit the team the next spring.

The spring after Bobby died, remember. He was a bit of a mess then. We all were. You can't really blame him for that. If he didn't want to play baseball anymore, that was his business. You talk about it as if you think he was trying to punish me. I never felt that for a second.

That was when the drinking started, wasn't it? We didn't find out until later, but I think it started then. The drinking and the smoking and those crazy kids he used to run around with.

He was trying to imitate Bobby. They might not have gotten along very well, but I think Miles loved him. You watch your brother die, and after that a part of you wants to become him.

Bobby was a happy-go-lucky fuckup. Miles was the grim reaper.

I'll admit there was a certain lugubrious quality to his carryings-on. But he always did well at school. Through thick and thin, he always managed to pull down good grades.

He's a bright boy, I won't dispute that. But cold, Morris. Hollowed out, desperate. I shudder to think about the future . . .

How often have we talked about this? A hundred times? A thousand times? You know his story as well as I do. The kid had no mother. Mary-Lee walked out when Miles was six months old. Until you came on board, he was raised by Edna Smythe, the luminous, legendary Edna Smythe, but still, she was just a nanny, it was just a job, which means that after those first six months he never had the real thing. By the time you entered his life, it was probably too late.

So you understand what I'm talking about?

Of course I do. I've always understood.

He couldn't bear to listen anymore. They were chopping him into pieces, dismembering him with the calm and efficient strokes of pathologists conducting a postmortem, talking about him as if they thought he was already dead. He slipped back into the bedroom and quietly shut the door. They had no idea how much he loved them. For five years he had been walking around with the memory of what he had done to his brother on that road in Massachusetts, and because he had never told his parents about the shove and how deeply he was tormented by it, they misread the guilt that had spread through his system as a form of sickness. Maybe he was sick, maybe he did come across as a shut-down, thoroughly unlikable person, but that didn't mean he had turned against them. Complex, high-strung, infinitely generous Willa; his open-hearted, genial father – he hated himself for having caused them so much sorrow, so much unnecessary grief. They looked on him now as a walking dead man, as someone without a future, and as he sat down on the bed and considered that futureless future hovering dimly before him, he realized that he didn't have the courage to face them again. Perhaps the best thing for all concerned would be to remove himself from their lives, to disappear.

Dear Parents, he wrote the next day, Forgive the abruptness of my decision, but after finishing yet another year of college, I find myself

feeling a little burned out on school and think a pause might do me some good. I've already told the dean that I want to take a leave of absence for the fall semester, and if that turns out to be insufficient, for the spring semester as well. I'm sorry if this disappoints you. The one bright spot is that you won't have to worry about paying my tuition for a while. Needless to say, I don't expect any money from you. I have work and will be able to support myself. Tomorrow, I'm taking off for L.A. to visit my mother for a couple of weeks. After that, as soon as I settle in wherever I happen to wind up living, I will be in touch. Hugs and kisses to you both, Miles.

It's true that he left Providence the following morning, but he didn't go to California to see his mother. He settled in somewhere. Over the past seven-plus years he has settled in at any number of new addresses, but he still hasn't been in touch.

# III

It is 2008, the second Sunday in November, and he is lying in bed with Pilar, flipping through the *Baseball Encyclopedia* in search of odd and amusing names. They have done this once or twice in the past, and it counts heavily for him that she is able to see the humor in this absurd enterprise, to grasp the Dickensian spirit locked inside the two thousand seven hundred pages of the revised, updated, and expanded 1985 edition, which he bought for two dollars at a used bookstore last month. He is roaming among the pitchers this morning, since he always gravitates toward the pitchers first, and before long he stumbles upon his first promising find of the day. Boots Poffenberger. Pili scrunches up her face in an effort not to laugh, then shuts her eyes, then holds her breath, but she can't resist for more than a few seconds. The air comes bursting out of her in a tornado of yelps, screeches, and firecracker guffaws. When the fit subsides, she tears the book from his hands, accusing him of having made it up. He says: I would never do that. Games like this aren't fun unless you take them seriously.

And there it is, sitting in the middle of page 1977: Cletus Elwood "Boots" Poffenberger, born July 1, 1915, in Williamsport, Maryland, a five-foot-ten-inch right-hander who played two years with the Tigers (1937 and 1938) and one year with the Dodgers (1939), compiling a career record of sixteen wins and twelve losses.

He continues on through Whammy Douglas, Cy Slapnicka, Noodles Hahn, Wickey McAvoy, Windy McCall, and Billy McCool. On hearing this last name, Pili groans with pleasure. She is smitten. For the rest of the morning, he is no longer Miles. He is Billy McCool, her sweet and beloved Billy McCool, ace of the staff, ace in the hole, her ace of hearts.

On the eleventh, he reads in the paper that Herb Score has died. He is too young to have seen him pitch, but he remembers the story his father told about the night of May 7, 1957, when a line drive off the bat of Yankee infielder Gil McDougald hit Score in the face and put an end to one of the most promising careers in baseball history. According to his father, who was ten years old at the time, Score was the best left-hander anyone had ever seen, possibly even better than Koufax, who was also

pitching then but didn't come into his own until several years later. The accident occurred exactly one month before Score's twenty-fourth birthday. It was his third season with the Cleveland Indians, following his rookie-of-the-year performance in 1955 (16–10, 2.85 earned run average, 245 strikeouts) and an even more impressive performance the next year (20–9, 2.53 earned run average, 263 strikeouts). Then came the pitch to McDougald on that chilly spring night at Municipal Stadium. The ball knocked Score down *as if he'd been shot by a rifle* (his father's words), and as his motionless body lay crumpled on the field, blood was pouring from his nose, mouth, and right eye. The nose was broken, but more devastating was the injury to the eye, which was hemorrhaging so badly that most people feared he would lose it or be blinded for life. In the locker room after the game, McDougald, utterly distraught, promised to quit baseball *if Herb loses the sight in his eye*. Score spent three weeks in a hospital and missed the rest of the season with blurred vision and depth-perception difficulties, but the eye eventually healed. When he attempted a comeback the next season, however, he was no longer the same pitcher. The sting in his fastball was gone, he was wild, he couldn't strike anyone out. He struggled for five years, won only seventeen games in fifty-seven starts, and then packed it in and went home.

Reading the obituary in the *New York Times*, he is astonished to learn that Score was a cursed man from the beginning, that the 1957 accident was only one of many mishaps that plagued him throughout his life. In the words of obit writer Richard Goldstein: *When he was three, he was struck by a bakery truck, which severely injured his legs. He missed a year of school with rheumatic fever, broke an ankle slipping on a wet locker-room floor and separated his left shoulder slipping on wet outfield grass while in the low minor leagues*. Not to speak of hurting his left arm during the comeback year of 1958, being gravely injured in a car crash in 1998, and suffering a stroke in 2002, from which he never fully recovered. It doesn't seem possible for a man to have encountered so much bad luck in the course of a single lifetime. For once, Miles is tempted to call his father, to chat with him about Herbert Jude Score and the imponderables of fate, the strangeness of life, the what-ifs and might-have-beens, all the things they used to talk about so long ago, but now isn't the time, if there ever is a time it mustn't begin with a long-distance phone call, and consequently he fights off the impulse, holding on to the story until he is with Pilar again that evening.

As he reads the obituary to her, he is alarmed by the sadness that

washes over her face, the depth of misery emanating from her eyes, her downturned mouth, the dejected droop of her shoulders. He can't be certain, but he wonders if she isn't thinking about her parents and their abrupt and terrible deaths, the bad luck that took them from her when she was still so young, still so much in need of them, and he regrets having brought up the subject, feels ashamed of himself for having caused her this hurt. To lift her spirits, he tosses the paper aside and launches into another story, another one of the many stories his father used to tell him, but this one is special, it was folklore around the house for years, and he hopes it will erase the gloom from her eyes. Lucky Lohrke, he says. Has she ever heard of him? No, of course not, she answers, smiling ever so slightly at the sound of the name. Another baseball player? Yes, he replies, but not a very distinguished one. A utility infielder for the Giants and Phillies in the late forties and early fifties, a career .240 hitter, of no particular interest except for the fact that this fellow, Jack Lohrke, a.k.a. Lucky, is the mythic embodiment of a theory of life that contends that not all luck is bad luck. Consider this, he says. While serving in the army during World War II, not only did he survive the D-day invasion and the Battle of the Bulge, but one afternoon, in the thick of combat, he was marching along with four other soldiers, two on either side of him, when a bomb exploded. The four other soldiers were killed instantly, but Lohrke walked through without a scratch. Or this, he continues. The war ends, and Lucky is about to get on a plane that will fly him back home to California. At the last moment, a major or a colonel shows up, pulls rank on him, takes his seat, and Lucky is bumped from the flight. The plane takes off, the plane crashes, and everyone on board is killed.

This is a true story? Pilar asks.

One hundred percent true. If you don't believe me, look it up.

You know the weirdest things, Miles.

Wait. There's still one more to go. It's nineteen forty-six, and Lucky is back on the West Coast, playing baseball in the minor leagues. His team is on the road, traveling by bus. They stop somewhere for lunch, and a call comes for the manager, telling him that Lucky has been promoted to a higher league. Lucky has to report to his new team right away, on the double, and so rather than get back on the bus with his old team, he gathers up his belongings and hitchhikes home. The bus continues, it's a long trip, hours and hours of driving, and in the middle of the night it starts to rain. They're high up in the mountains somewhere, surrounded by darkness, wetness, and the driver loses control of the wheel, the bus

goes tumbling into a ravine, and nine players are killed. Awful. But our little man has been spared again. Think of the odds, Pili. Death comes looking for him three times, and three times he manages to escape.

Lucky Lohrke, she whispers. Is he still alive?

I think so. He'd be well into his eighties by now, but yes, I think he's still with us.

Some days after that, Pilar finds out the scores of her SATs. The news is good, as good or better than he hoped it would be. With her unbroken run of A's in high school and these results from the test, he is convinced she will be accepted by any college she applies to, any college in the country. Ignoring his oath about not eating in restaurants, he takes her to a celebratory dinner the next night and struggles throughout the meal not to touch her in public. He is so proud of her, he says, he wants to kiss every inch of her body, to gobble her up. They discuss the various possibilities in front of her, and he urges her to think about leaving Florida, to take a stab at some of the Ivy League schools up north, but Pilar is reluctant to consider such a step, she can't imagine being so far away from her sisters. You never know, he tells her, things could change between now and then, and it won't do any harm to try – just to see if you can get in. Yes, she answers, but the applications are expensive, and it doesn't make sense to throw away money for no reason. Don't worry about the money, he says to her. He will pay. She mustn't worry about anything.

By the end of the following week, she is up to her neck in forms. Not just from the state universities in Florida, but from Barnard, Vassar, Duke, Princeton, and Brown as well. She fills them out, composes all the required essays (which he reads over but does not alter or correct, since no alterations or corrections are necessary), and then they return to life as they once knew it, before the college madness began. Later that month, he receives a letter from an old friend in New York, one of the boys from the gang of *crazy kids* he used to run around with in high school. Bing Nathan is the only person from the past he still writes to, the only person who has known each one of his many addresses over the years. At first, he was mystified by his willingness to make this exception for Bing, but after he had been gone for six or eight months, he understood that he couldn't cut himself off completely, that he needed at least one link to his old life. It isn't that he and Bing have ever been particularly close. The truth is that he finds Bing somewhat off-putting, at times even obnoxious, but Bing looks up to him, for unknown reasons he has attained the status of exalted figure in Bing's eyes, and that means Bing

can be trusted, relied upon to keep him informed about any changes on the New York front. That is the nub of it. Bing was the one who told him about his grandmother's death, the one who told him about his father's broken leg, the one who told him about Willa's eye operation. His father is sixty-two years old now, Willa is sixty, and they aren't going to live forever. Bing has his ear to the ground. If anything happens to either one of them, he will be on the phone the next minute.

Bing reports that he is now living in an area of Brooklyn called Sunset Park. In mid-August, he and a group of people took over a small abandoned house on a street across from Green-Wood Cemetery and have been camped out there as squatters ever since. For reasons unknown, the electricity and the heat are still functioning. That could change at any second, of course, but for now it appears there is a glitch in the system, and neither Con Ed nor National Grid has come to shut off the service. Life is precarious, yes, and each morning they wake up to the threat of immediate and forcible eviction, but with the city buckling under the pressure of economic hard times, so many government jobs have been lost that the little band from Sunset Park seems to be flying under the municipal radar, and no marshals or bailiffs have shown up to kick them out. Bing doesn't know if Miles is looking for a change, but one of the original members of the group has recently left town, and a room is available for him if he wants it. The previous occupant was named Millie, and to replace Millie with Miles seems alphabetically coherent, he says. *Alphabetically coherent.* Another example of Bing's wit, which has never been his strong point, but the offer seems genuine, and as Bing goes on to describe the other people who are living there (a man and two women, a writer, an artist, and a graduate student, all in their late twenties, all poor and struggling, all with talent and intelligence), it is clear that he is trying to make a move to Sunset Park sound as attractive as possible. Bing concludes that at last word all was well with Miles's father and that Willa left for England in September, where she will be spending the academic year as a visiting professor at Exeter University. In a brief postscript he adds: Think it over.

Does he want to return to New York? Has the moment finally come for the wayward son to crawl home and put his life together again? Six months ago, he probably wouldn't have hesitated. Even one month ago, he might have been tempted to consider it, but now it is out of the question. Pilar has claimed dominion over his heart, and the mere thought of going off without her is unbearable to him. As he folds up Bing's letter

and puts it back in the envelope, he silently thanks his friend for having clarified the issue in such stark terms. Nothing matters anymore except Pilar, and when the time is right, meaning when a little more time has passed and she has reached her next birthday, he will ask her to marry him. It is far from clear that she will accept, but he has every intention of asking her. That is his answer to Bing's letter. Pilar.

The problem is that Pilar is more than just Pilar. She is a member of the Sanchez family, and even if her relations with Angela are somewhat strained at the moment, Maria and Teresa are as close to her as ever. All four girls are still grieving over the loss of their parents, and strong as Pilar's attachment to him might be, her family still comes first. After living with him since June, she has forgotten how determined she was to fly out of the nest. She has become nostalgic for the old days, and not a week goes by now when she doesn't stop by the house to visit with her sisters at least twice. He stays out of it and accompanies her only rarely, as little as possible. Maria and Teresa are polite and innocuous motormouths, unobjectionable but boring company for more than an hour at a stretch, and Angela, who is anything but boring, rubs him the wrong way. He doesn't like how she keeps looking at him, scrutinizing him with that odd combination of contempt and seductiveness in her eyes, as if she can't quite believe her baby sister has snagged him – not that she has any interest in him herself (how could anyone be interested in a grubby trash-out worker?), but it's the principle of the thing, since reason dictates that he should be attracted to her, the beautiful woman, whose job in life is to be a beautiful woman and make men fall for her. That is bad enough, but he still carries around the memory of the bribes he paid her last summer, the countless stolen presents he showered on her every day for a week, and even if it was all to a good purpose, he couldn't help feeling revolted by her avidity, her inexhaustible craving for those ugly, stupid things.

On the twenty-seventh, he allows Pilar to talk him into going to the Sanchez house for Thanksgiving dinner. He does it against his better judgment, but he wants to make her happy, and he knows that if he stays behind he will do nothing but sulk in the apartment until she returns. For the first hour, all goes reasonably well, and he is startled to discover that he is actually enjoying himself. As the four girls prepare the meal in the kitchen, he and Maria's boyfriend, a twenty-three-year-old auto mechanic named Eddie, go into the backyard to keep an eye on little Carlos. Eddie turns out to be a baseball fan, a well-read and

knowledgeable student of the game, and in the aftermath of Herb Score's recent death, they fall into a conversation about the tragic destinies of various pitchers from decades past.

It begins with Denny McLain of the Detroit Tigers, the last man to win thirty games and no doubt the last one who ever will, the top pitcher in America from 1965 to 1969, whose career was destroyed by compulsive gambling binges and a penchant for choosing mobsters as his closest friends. Gone from the scene by the time he was twenty-eight, he later went to prison for drug trafficking, embezzlement, and racketeering, gorged himself up to a titanic three hundred and thirty pounds, and returned to prison for six years in the nineties for stealing two and a half million dollars from the pension fund of the company he worked for.

He did it to himself, Eddie says, so I can't feel no pity for him. But think of a guy like Blass. What the hell happened to him?

He is referring to Steve Blass, who played for the Pittsburgh Pirates from the mid-sixties to the mid-seventies, a consistent double-digit winner, pitching star of the 1971 World Series, who went on to have his best season in 1972 (19–8, 2.49 earned run average), and then, following the end of that season, on the last day of the year, Roberto Clemente, his future Hall of Fame teammate, was killed in a plane crash on his way to deliver emergency relief packages to the survivors of an earthquake in Nicaragua. The next season, Blass could no longer throw strikes. His once excellent control was gone, he walked batter after batter – eighty-four in eighty-eight innings – and his record dropped to 3–9 with a 9.85 earned run average. He tried again the next year, but after one game (five innings pitched, seven batters walked), he quit the game for good. Was Clemente's death responsible for Blass's sudden downfall? No one knows for certain, but according to Eddie, most people in baseball circles tend to believe that Blass was suffering from something called survivor's guilt, that his love for Clemente was so great he simply couldn't go on after his friend was killed.

At least Blass had seven or eight good years, Miles says. Think about poor Mark Fidrych.

Ah, Eddie replies, Mark "the Bird" Fidrych, and then the two of them launch into a eulogy for the brief and flamboyant career of the out-of-nowhere sensation who dazzled the country for the space of a few miraculous months, the twenty-one-year-old boy who was perhaps the most lovable person ever to play the game. No one had seen his like before – a pitcher who talked to the ball, who got down on his knees and

smoothed out the dirt on the mound, whose entire fidgety being seemed to be electrified by constant jolts of hectic, nervous energy – not a man so much as a perpetual motion machine in the shape of a man. For one season he was dominant: 19–9, a 2.34 earned run average, starting pitcher for the American League in the All-Star game, rookie of the year. A few months later, he damaged the cartilage in his knee while horsing around in the outfield during spring training, and then, even worse, tore up his shoulder just after the start of the regular season. His arm went dead, and just like that, the Bird was gone – from pitcher to ex-pitcher in the blink of an eye.

Yes, Eddie says, a sad case, but nothing to compare with what happened to Donnie Moore.

No, nothing to compare, says Miles, nodding in agreement.

He is old enough to have lived through the story himself, and he can still remember the stunned expression in his father's eyes when he looked up from his newspaper at breakfast twenty years ago and announced that Moore was dead. Donnie Moore, a relief pitcher with the California Angels, was brought in to shut down a ninth-inning rally by the Boston Red Sox in the fifth game of the 1986 American League Championship Series. The Angels were ahead by a run, on the verge of winning their first pennant, but with two outs and a runner on first base, Moore delivered one of the most unfortunate pitches ever thrown in the annals of the sport – the one that Boston outfielder Dave Henderson knocked out of the park for a home run, the one that turned the course of the game and led to the Angels' defeat. Moore never recovered from the humiliation. Three years after throwing that life-altering pitch, by then out of baseball, dogged by financial and marital difficulties, perhaps certifiably insane, Moore got into an argument with his wife in the presence of their three children. He pulled out a gun, fired three nonfatal shots into his wife's body, and then turned the gun on himself and blew his brains out.

Eddie looks at Miles and shakes his head in disbelief. I don't get it, he says. What he did wasn't no worse than what Branca did when he threw that pitch to Thomson in fifty-one. But Branca didn't kill himself, did he? He and Thomson are buddies now, they go around the country signing goddamned baseballs together, and whenever you see a picture of them they're smiling at each other, two old coots without a care in the world. Why isn't Donnie Moore out there signing balls with Henderson instead of lying in his grave?

Miles shrugs. It's a question of character, he says. Every man is different from every other man, and when rough things happen, each man reacts in his own way. Moore cracked. Branca didn't.

He finds it soothing to talk about these things with Eduardo Martinez in the late afternoon light of this Thanksgiving Thursday, and even if the subject matter could be considered somewhat grim – stories about failure, disappointment, and death – baseball is a universe as large as life itself, and therefore all things in life, whether good or bad, whether tragic or comic, fall within its domain. Today they are examining instances of despair and blighted hope, but the next time they meet (assuming they meet again), they could fill an afternoon with scores of funny anecdotes that would make their stomachs hurt from laughing so hard. Eddie strikes him as an earnest, well-meaning kid, and he is touched that Maria's new boyfriend has donned a jacket and tie for this holiday visit to the Sanchez household, that he is sporting a fresh haircut, and that the air is filled with the smell of the cologne he has put on for the occasion. The boy is pleasant company, but just as useful as *pleasant* is the simple fact that Eddie is there, that he has been given a male ally in this country of women. When they are called in for dinner, Eddie's presence at the table seems to neutralize Angela's hostility toward him, or at least deflect her attention from him and reduce the number of challenging looks he normally receives from her. There is another person to look at now, another stranger to be sized up and judged, to be deemed worthy or unworthy of yet another younger sister of hers. Eddie seems to be passing the test, but it puzzles Miles that Angela hasn't bothered to arrange a date of her own for the evening, that she is apparently without a boyfriend. Teresa's husband is far away, of course, and he fully expected her to be without a male companion, but why hasn't Angela invited a man to join them? Maybe Miss Beautiful doesn't like men, he thinks. Maybe her work at the Blue Devil cocktail lounge has soured her on the whole business.

Sergeant Lopez has not been home for ten months, and the meal begins with a silent prayer for his continued safety. A few seconds after they begin, everyone looks up as Teresa sniffs back a sudden onrush of tears. Pilar, who is sitting next to her, puts her arm around Teresa's shoulder and kisses her on the cheek. He looks down at the tablecloth again and resists addressing his thoughts to God. God has nothing to do with what is happening in Iraq, he says to himself. God has nothing to do with anything. He imagines George Bush and Dick Cheney being lined up against a wall and shot, and then, for Pilar's sake, for the sake

of everyone there, he hopes that Teresa's husband will be lucky enough to make it back in one piece.

He is beginning to think he will get through this trial without any unpleasantness from Angela. They have polished off several courses by now, everyone is attacking the dessert, and afterward, as a gesture of goodwill, he will offer to do the dishes, do them by himself with no help from anyone, and once he has washed and dried the innumerable plates and glasses and utensils, once he has scrubbed the pots and pans and put everything back in the cupboards, he will go out to the living room and fetch Pilar, telling them that it's late, that he has to work tomorrow, and off they'll go, just the two of them, slipping out of the house and climbing into his car before another word can be spoken. An excellent plan, perhaps, but the moment Angela finishes the last forkful of her pumpkin pie (no Cuban food today, everything strictly American, from the big bird with the stuffing in it to the cranberry sauce and the gravy and the sweet potatoes and the traditional dessert), she puts down her fork, removes the napkin from her lap, and stands up. I need to talk to you, Miles, she says. Let's go out back where we can be alone, okay? It's very important.

It isn't important. It isn't the least bit important. Angela is feeling deprived, that's all it is. Christmas is coming soon, and she wants him to help her out again. What does she mean by that? he asks. Stuff, she says. Like what he did for her this summer. Impossible, he tells her, it's against the law to steal, and he doesn't want to lose his job.

You did it for me once, she says. There's no reason why you can't do it again.

I can't, he repeats. I can't risk getting into trouble.

You're full of shit, Miles. Everybody does it. I hear stories, I know what's been going on. Those trash-out jobs are like walking into a department store. Grand pianos, sailboats, motorcycles, jewelry, all kinds of expensive stuff. The workers pinch everything they can lay their hands on.

Not me.

I'm not asking for a sailboat. And what do I need a piano for when I can't even play? But nice stuff, you know what I mean? Good stuff. Stuff that will make me happy.

You're knocking on the wrong door, Angela.

You're really a stupid guy, aren't you, Miles?

Come to the point. I assume you're trying to tell me something, but all I hear is static.

Have you forgotten how old Pilar is?

You're not serious . . .

No?

You wouldn't dare. She's your own sister, remember?

One call to the cops, and you're toast, my friend.

Cut it out. Pilar would spit in your face. She'd never talk to you again.

Think about the stuff, Miles. Pretty stuff. Big mounds of pretty stuff. It's a lot better than thinking about jail, isn't it?

In the car on the way home, Pilar asks what Angela wanted to talk to him about, but he avoids telling her the truth, not wanting her to know how much contempt he feels for her sister, how profoundly he despises her. He mutters something about Christmas, a secret plan the two of them have been cooking up together that involves the whole family, but he can't breathe a word because Angela has made him promise to keep quiet about it until further notice. This seems to satisfy Pilar, who grins at the prospect of whatever good thing is in store for them, and by the time they are halfway back to their apartment, they are no longer talking about Angela, they are discussing their impressions of Eddie. Pilar finds him *sweet* and not at all bad-looking, but she wonders if he is smart enough for Maria – to which he offers no comment. In his mind, the question is whether Maria is smart enough for Eddie, but he isn't about to offend Pilar by insulting her sister's intelligence. Instead, he reaches out his right hand and begins stroking her hair, asking her what she thinks of the book he gave her this morning, *Dubliners*.

He goes back to work the next day, convinced that Angela's threat is nothing more than a bluff, a nasty little piece of theater designed to break down his resistance and get him to start stealing for her again. He isn't going to fall for such a mindless, transparent trick, and over his dead body will he give her a single thing – not even a toothpick, not even a used paper napkin, not even one of Paco's farts.

On Sunday afternoon, Pilar goes to the Sanchez house to spend a couple of hours with her sisters. Again, he has no wish to join her and remains in the apartment to prepare their dinner while she is gone (he is the one who shops and cooks for them), and when Pilar returns at six o'clock, she tells him that Angela asked her to remind him not to forget about their deal. She says she can't wait forever, Pilar adds, repeating her sister's words with a confused, questioning look in her eyes. What in the world does she mean by that? she asks. Nothing, he says, dismissing this new threat with a curt shake of the head. Absolutely nothing.

Two more days of work, three more days of work, four more days of work, and then, late on Friday, just after wrapping up the final trash-out operation of the week, as he walks away from yet another empty house and heads for his car across the street, he spots two men leaning against the front and back doors of the red Toyota, two large men, one Anglo and the other Latino, two very large men who look like defensive tackles or professional bodybuilders or nightclub bouncers, and if they are bouncers, he thinks, perhaps they are employed by an establishment called the Blue Devil. The wisest course of action would be to turn and run, but it is already too late, the men have already seen him approaching, and if he runs now, he will only make things worse for himself, since it is altogether certain that they will catch up to him in the end. It's not that he is a small person or that he shies away from fights. He stands at six-two now, he weighs one hundred and eighty-seven pounds, and after years of working at jobs that have asked more from his body than his mind, he is in better than passable condition – well built, muscular, strong. But not as strong as either one of the two men waiting for him, and because they are two and he is one, he can only hope the men are here to talk and not to demonstrate their fighting skills.

Miles Heller? the Anglo asks.

What can I do for you? he replies.

We have a message from Angela.

Why doesn't she give it to me herself?

Because you don't listen to her when she talks to you. She thought you might pay more attention if we delivered the message for her.

All right, I'm listening.

Angela is pissed off, and she's beginning to lose her patience. She says you have one more week, and if you don't come through for her by then, she's going to pick up the phone and make that call. You got it?

Yes, I've got it.

Are you sure?

Yes, yes, I'm sure.

Are you sure you're sure?

Yes.

Good. But just to make sure you don't forget you're sure, I'm going to give you a little present. Like one of those strings you tie around your finger when you want to remember something. You know what I'm talking about?

I think so.

Without warning, the man hauls off and punches him in the gut. It is a cannonball of a punch, a punch so colossal in its force and so devastating in its effect that it knocks him to the ground, and as he is knocked to the ground the air is knocked out of his lungs, and along with the air that comes bursting through his windpipe there also comes the entire contents of his stomach, his lunch and his breakfast, remnant particles from last night's dinner, and everything that was inside him a moment ago is now outside him, and as he lies there puking and gasping for breath and clutching his belly in pain, the two large men walk off to their car, leaving him alone in the street, a wounded animal felled by that single blow, a man wishing he were dead.

An hour later, Pilar knows everything. The bluff was not a bluff, and therefore he can no longer hold out on her. They are suddenly in a dangerous spot, and it is essential for her to know the truth. She cries at first, finding it impossible to believe that her sister could act like this, threatening to put him in jail, willing to ruin her happiness for the sake of a few measly things, none of it makes any sense to her. It's not the things, he says. The things are only an excuse. Angela doesn't like him, she's been against him from the start, and Pilar's happiness means nothing to her if that happiness is connected to him. He doesn't understand why she should feel such animosity, but there it is, it's a fact, and they have no choice but to accept it. Pilar wants to jump into the car, drive over to the house, and slap Angela across the face. That's what she deserves, he says, but you can't do it now. You have to wait until after I'm gone.

It is a horrible solution, an unthinkable solution, but the only one left to them under the circumstances. He must leave the state. There is no alternative. He must get out of Florida before Angela picks up the phone and calls the police, and he mustn't come back until the morning of May twenty-third, when Pilar turns eighteen. He is tempted to ask her to marry him right then and there, but too many things are happening at once, they are both miserable and overwrought, and he doesn't want to pressure her or confuse her, to complicate an already complicated business when so little time is left.

He tells her that a friend has a room for him somewhere in Brooklyn. He gives her the address and promises to call every day. Since going back to the family house is out of the question now, she will remain in the apartment. He writes out a check to cover six months' rent in advance, signs over the title of his car to her, and then takes her to the bank, where he shows her how to use the automated teller machine. There are twelve

thousand dollars in his account. He withdraws three thousand for himself and leaves the remaining nine thousand for her. After slipping the bank card into her hand, he puts his arm around her as they walk out into the blaze of the midafternoon sun. It is the first time he has touched her in public, and he does it consciously, as an act of defiance.

He packs a small bag with two changes of clothes, his camera, and three or four books. He leaves everything else where it is – to convince her that he will be coming back.

Early the next morning, he is sitting on a bus headed for New York.

# IV

It is a long, tedious trip, more than thirty hours from start to finish, with close to a dozen stopovers ranging from ten minutes to two hours, and from one leg of the journey to the next the seat adjacent to his is variously occupied by a round, wheezing black woman, a sniffing Indian or Pakistani man, a bony, throat-clearing white woman of eighty, and a coughing German tourist of such indeterminate aspect that he can't tell whether the person sitting next to him is a woman or a man. He says nothing to any of them, keeping his nose in his book or pretending to sleep, and every time there is a break in the journey he scampers out of the bus and calls Pilar.

In Jacksonville, the longest stopover of the trip, he works his way through two fast-food hamburgers and a large bottle of water, chewing and swallowing with care, since his stomach muscles are still exceedingly tender from the punch that knocked him down on Friday. Yes, the pain is just as effective as a string you tie around your finger, and the large man with the stone fist was right to assume he wouldn't forget it. After finishing his snack, he wanders over to the terminal kiosk, where everything from licorice sticks to condoms are for sale. He buys several newspapers and magazines, stocking up on additional reading material in case he wants a pause between books during the hundreds of miles still ahead. Two and a half hours later, as the bus is approaching Savannah, Georgia, he opens the *New York Times,* and on the second page of the arts section, in a column of squibs about upcoming events and the doings of well-known personalities, he sees a small picture of his mother. It is not unusual for him to come across pictures of his mother. It has been happening to him for as long as he can remember, and given that she is a well-known actress, it is only natural that her face should turn up frequently in the press. The short article in the *Times* is of special interest to him, however. Having spent most of her life working in movies and television, his mother is returning to the New York stage after an absence of ten years to appear in a production that will be opening in January. In other words, there is a better than even chance that she is already in New York rehearsing her role, which means that for the first

time in how many years, in how many long, excruciating centuries, both his mother and father will be living in New York at the same moment, which is the selfsame moment when their son will find himself there as well. How odd. How terribly odd and incomprehensible. No doubt it means nothing, nothing whatsoever, and yet why now, he asks himself, why did he choose to go back now? Because he didn't choose. Because the choice was made for him by a large fist that knocked him down and commanded him to run from Florida to a place called Sunset Park. Just another roll of the dice, then, another lottery pick scooped out of the black metal urn, another fluke in a world of flukes and endless mayhem.

Half his life ago, when he was fourteen years old, he was out walking with his father, just the two of them, without Willa or Bobby, who were off somewhere else that day. It was a Sunday afternoon in late spring, and he and his father were walking side by side through the West Village, on no particular errand, he remembers, just walking for the sake of walking, out in the air because the weather was especially fine that day, and after they had been strolling for an hour or an hour and a half, they sat down on a bench in Abingdon Square. For reasons that escape him now, he started asking his father questions about his mother. How and where they met, for example, when they were married, why they hadn't stayed married, and so on. He saw his mother only twice a year, and on his last visit to California he had asked her similar questions about his father, but she hadn't wanted to talk about it, she had brushed him off with a brief sentence or two. The marriage was a mistake from the start. His father was a decent man, but they were wrong for each other, and why bother to go into it now? Perhaps that was what prompted him to interrogate his father that Sunday afternoon in Abingdon Square fourteen years ago. Because his mother's answers had been so unsatisfactory, and he was hoping his father would be more receptive, more willing to talk.

He first saw her onstage, his father said, undaunted by the question, speaking without bitterness, in a neutral tone from the first sentence to the last, no doubt thinking that his son was old enough to know the facts, and now that the boy had asked the question, he deserved a straight and honest answer. Curiously enough, the theater wasn't far from where they were sitting now, his father said, the old Circle Rep on Seventh Avenue. It was October 1978, and she was playing Cordelia in a production of *King Lear,* a twenty-four-year-old actress named Mary-Lee Swann, a glorious name for an actress in his opinion, and she gave a moving performance, he was stirred by the strength and groundedness of her interpretation,

which bore no resemblance to the saintly, simpering Cordelias he had seen in the past. *What shall Cordelia speak? Love, and be silent.* She delivered those words with a self-questioning hesitation that seemed to open up her very insides to the audience. An extraordinary thing to behold, his father said. Utterly heartbreaking.

Yes, his father seemed willing to talk, but the story he told that afternoon was vague, ever so vague and difficult to follow. There were details, of course, the recounting of various incidents, starting with that first night when his father went out for drinks after the play with the director, who was an old friend of his, along with a few members of the cast, Mary-Lee among them. His father was thirty-two at the time, unmarried and unattached, already the publisher of Heller Books, which had been in operation for five years and was just beginning to gain momentum, largely because of the success of Renzo Michaelson's second novel, *House of Words*. He told his son that the attraction was immediate on both sides. An unexpected congruency, perhaps, in that she was a country girl from a backwater in central Maine and he was a lifelong New Yorker, born into a modicum of wealth whereas she came from little or nothing, the daughter of a man who worked as the manager of a hardware store, and yet there they were, making eyes at each other across the table in that little bar off Sheridan Square, he with his two university degrees and she with a high school diploma and a stint at the American Academy of Dramatic Arts, a waitress between roles, a person without interest in books whereas publishing books was his life's work, but who can penetrate the mysteries of desire, his father said, who can account for the unbidden thoughts that rush through a man's mind? He asked his son if he understood. The boy nodded, but in fact he understood nothing.

He was blinded by her talent, his father continued. Anyone who could perform as she had in that demanding, delicate role must have had a greater depth of heart and a wider range of feeling than any of the women he had known in the past. But pretending to be a person and actually being a person were two different things, weren't they? The wedding took place on March 12, 1979, less than five months after their first meeting. Five months after that, the marriage was already in trouble. His father didn't want to bore him by reciting a litany of their disputes and incompatibilities, but what it came down to was this: they loved each other, but they couldn't get along. Did that make any sense to him?

No, it made no sense to him at all. The boy was utterly confused by then, but he was too afraid to admit it to his father, who was making

every effort to treat him as an adult, but he wasn't up to the job that day, the world of adults was unfathomable to him at that point in his life, and he couldn't grasp the paradox of love and discord coexisting in equal measure. It had to be one or the other, love or not-love, but not love and not-love at the same time. He paused for a moment to collect his thoughts, and then he asked the only question that seemed relevant to him, the only question that had any pertinent meaning. If they disliked each other so much, why did they have a baby?

It was going to rescue them, his father said. That was the plan, in any case: make a child together and then hope the love they would inevitably feel for their son or daughter would arrest the disenchantment that was growing between them. She was happy about it at first, his father said, they were both happy about it, but then – . His father abruptly cut himself off in midsentence, looked away for a moment as he shifted mental gears, and finally said: She wasn't prepared to be a mother. She was too young. I shouldn't have pushed her into it.

The boy understood that his father was trying to spare his feelings. He couldn't come out and bluntly declare that his mother hadn't wanted him, could he? That would have been too much, a blow that no person could ever fully absorb, and yet his father's silence and sympathetic evasion of the brute particulars amounted to an admission of that very fact: his mother had wanted no part of him, his birth was a mistake, there was no tenable reason for him to be alive.

When had it started? he wondered. At what point had her early happiness turned into doubt, antipathy, dread? Perhaps when her body began to change, he thought, when his presence inside her began to show itself to the world and it was too late to ignore the bulging extrusion that now defined her, not to speak of the alarm caused by the thickening of her ankles and the spreading of her bottom, all the extra weight that was distorting her once slender, ravishing self. Was that all it was – a fit of vanity? Or was it fear that she would lose ground by having to take time off from work just when she was being offered better, more interesting roles, that she was disrupting her progress at the worst possible moment and might never get back on track? Three months after she gave birth to him (July 2, 1980), she auditioned for the lead in a film to be directed by Douglas Flaherty, *Innocent Dreamer*. She got the part, and three months after that she headed for Vancouver, British Columbia, leaving her infant son in New York with his father and a live-in baby nurse, Edna Smythe, a two-hundred-pound Jamaican woman of forty-six who went on working

as his nanny (and later Bobby's too) for the next seven years. As for his mother, that role launched her career in films. It also brought her a new husband (Flaherty, the director) and a new life in Los Angeles. No, his father said when the boy asked the question, she didn't fight for custody. She was *torn apart,* his father explained, quoting what she had said to him at the time, *giving up Miles was the toughest, most awful decision she had ever made,* but under the circumstances, *there didn't seem to be anything else she could do*. In other words, his father said to him that afternoon in Abingdon Square, she ditched us. You and me both, kid. She gave us the old heave-ho, and that was that.

But no regrets, he quickly added. No second thoughts or morbid exhumations of the past. His marriage to Mary-Lee hadn't worked out, but that didn't mean it could be called a failure. Time had proved that the real purpose of the two years he spent with her was not about building a sustainable marriage, it was about creating a son, and because that son was the single most important creature in the world for him, all the disappointments he'd endured with her had been worth it – no, more than worth it, absolutely necessary. Was that clear? Yes. On that point, the boy did not question what his father was saying to him. His father smiled, then put his arm around his shoulder, drew him in toward his chest, and kissed him on the top of his head. You're the apple of my eye, he said. Never forget that.

It was the only time they talked about his mother in this way. Both before and after that conversation fourteen years ago, it was largely a matter of practical arrangements, scheduling phone calls, buying plane tickets to California, reminding him to send birthday cards, figuring out how to coordinate his school holidays with his mother's acting jobs. She might have disappeared from his father's life, but lapses and inconsistencies notwithstanding, she remained a presence in his. From the very beginning, then, he was the boy with two mothers. His real mother, Willa, who had not given birth to him, and his blood mother, Mary-Lee, who played the role of exotic stranger. The early years do not exist anymore, but going back to when he was five or six years old, he can remember flying across the country to see her, the unaccompanied minor indulged by stewardesses and pilots, sitting in the cockpit before takeoff, drinking the sweet sodas he was rarely allowed to have at home, and the big house up in the hills above Los Angeles with the hummingbirds in the garden, the red and purple flowers, the junipers and mimosas, the cool nights after warm, light-flooded days. His mother was so terribly

pretty back then, the elegant, lovely blonde who was sometimes referred to as the second coming of Carroll Baker or Tuesday Weld, but more gifted than they were, more intelligent in her choice of roles, and now that he was growing up, now that it was evident to her that she would not be having any more children, she called him her little prince, her precious angel, and the same boy who was the apple of his father's eye was anointed the peach of his mother's heart.

She never knew quite what to make of him, however. There were considerable amounts of goodwill, he supposed, but not much knowledge, not the kind of knowledge Willa had, and consequently he seldom felt that he was standing on solid ground with her. From one day to the next, from one hour to the next, she could turn from ebullience to distraction, from joking affability to withdrawn, irritable silence. He learned to be on his guard with her, to prepare himself for these unpredictable shifts, to savor the good moments while they lasted but not to expect them to last very long. She was usually between jobs when he visited, and that might have added to the anxiety that seemed to permeate the household. The telephone would start ringing early in the morning, and then she would be talking to her agent, to a producer, to a director, to a fellow actor, or else accepting or refusing to be interviewed or photographed, to appear on television, to present this or that award, not to mention where to have dinner that night, what party to go to next week, who said what about whom. It was always calmer when Flaherty was around. Her husband helped smooth out the rough patches and keep her nighttime drinking under control (she tended to get a bit slurry when he was off on a job somewhere), and because he had a child of his own from an earlier marriage, his stepfather had a better feel for what he was thinking than his own mother did. His daughter's name was Margie, Maggie, he can't remember now, a girl with freckles and chubby knees, and they sometimes played together in the garden, squirting each other with the hose or staging pretend tea parties as they acted out various bits from the Mad Hatter scene in *Alice in Wonderland*. How old was he then? Six years old? Seven years old? When he was eight or nine, Flaherty, a transplanted Englishman with no interest in baseball, took it upon himself to drive them out to Chavez Ravine one night to watch the Dodgers play against the Mets, his hometown team, the club he pulled for through good years and bad. He was an amiable sort, old Flaherty, a man with much to recommend him, but when Miles returned to California six months later, Flaherty was gone, and his mother was going through her

second divorce. Her new man was Simon Korngold, a producer of low-budget independent films, and against all odds, considering her record with his father and Douglas Flaherty, he is still her man today after seventeen years of marriage.

When he was twelve, she came into his room and asked him to take off his clothes. She wanted to see how he was *developing,* she said, and he reluctantly obliged her by stripping down to his bare skin, sensing that it wasn't within his power to turn down her request. She was his mother, after all, and no matter how frightened or embarrassed he felt to be standing naked in front of her, she had a right to see her son's body. She looked him over quickly, told him to turn around in a circle, and then, fixing her eyes on his genitals, she said: Promising, Miles, but still a long way to go.

When he was thirteen, after a year of tumultuous changes, to both his inner self and his physical self, she made the same request. He was sitting by the pool this time, wearing nothing but a bathing suit, and although he was even more nervous and hesitant than he had been the previous year, he stood up, peeled down the top of his trunks, and gave her a glimpse of what she wanted to see. His mother smiled and said: The little fellow isn't so little anymore, is he? Watch out, ladies. Miles Heller is in town.

When he was fourteen, he flatly said no. She looked somewhat disappointed, he felt, but she didn't insist. It's your call, kid, she said, and then she left the room.

When he was fifteen, she and Korngold threw a party at their house, a large, clamorous party with over a hundred guests, and even though many familiar faces were there, actors and actresses he had seen in films and on television, famous actors, all of them good actors, people who had either moved him or made him laugh many times over the years, he couldn't stand the noise, the sound of all those chattering voices was making him ill, and after doing his best for more than an hour, he stole upstairs to his room and lay down on the bed with a book, his book of the moment, whatever book it happened to be, and he remembers thinking that he much preferred to spend the rest of the evening with the writer of that book than with the thunderous mob downstairs. After fifteen or twenty minutes, his mother burst into the room with a drink in her hand, looking both angry and a little smashed. What did he think he was doing? Didn't he know there was a party going on, and how dare he walk out in the middle of it? So-and-so was here, and so-and-so was

here, and so-and-so was here, and who gave him the right to insult them by going upstairs to read a goddamned *book*? He tried to explain that he wasn't feeling well, that he had a bad headache, and what difference did it make anyway if he wasn't in the mood to stand around yakking with a bunch of grown-ups? You're just like your father, she said, growing more and more exasperated. A bred-in-the-bone sourpuss. You used to be such a fun kid, Miles. Now you've turned into a pill. For some reason, he found the word *pill* deeply funny. Or perhaps it was the sight of his mother standing there with a vodka tonic in her hand that amused him, his flustered, irate mother insulting him with baby words like *sourpuss* and *pill*, and all of a sudden he started to laugh. What's so funny? she asked. I don't know, he answered, I just can't help myself. Yesterday I was your peach, and today I'm a pill. To tell you the truth, I don't think I'm either one. At that moment, which was no doubt his mother's finest moment, her expression changed from one of anger to mirth, changed from one to the other in a single instant, and suddenly she was laughing too. Fuck me, she said. I'm acting like a real bitch, aren't I?

When he was seventeen, she promised to come to New York for his high school graduation, but she never showed up. Curiously, he didn't hold it against her. After Bobby's death, things that had once mattered to him no longer mattered at all. He figured she had forgotten. Forgetting is not a sin – it is simple human error. The next time he saw her, she apologized, bringing up the subject before he had a chance to mention it, which he never would have done in any case.

His visits to California became less frequent. He was in college now, and during the three years he spent at Brown he went out there only twice. There were other meetings, however, lunches and dinners in New York restaurants, several long telephone conversations (always at her initiative), and a weekend together in Providence with Korngold, whose decade of steadfast loyalty to her had made it impossible for him to feel anything but admiration for the man. In some ways, Korngold reminded him of his father. Not in looks or affect or bearing, but in the work he did, which was scrambling to make small, worthwhile films in a world of mega-junk, just as his father was scrambling to publish worthwhile books in a world of fads and weightless ephemera. His mother was well into her forties by then, and she seemed more comfortable with herself than she'd been at the summit of her beauty, less involved in the intrigues of her own life, more open to others. During that weekend in Providence, she asked him if he'd thought about what he wanted to do

after graduation. He wasn't sure, he said. One day he was convinced he would become a doctor, the next day he was tilting toward photography, and the day after that he was planning to go into teaching. Not writing or publishing? she asked. No, he didn't think so, he said. He loved to read books, but he had no interest in making them.

Then he vanished. His mother had nothing to do with the impetuous decision to turn on his heels and run, but once he left Willa and his father, he left her as well. For better or worse, it had to be that way, and it has to be that way now. If he goes to see his mother, she will immediately contact his father and tell him where he is, and then everything he has struggled to accomplish over the past seven and a half years will have been for naught. He has turned himself into a black sheep. That is the role he has willed himself to play, and he will go on playing it even in New York, even as he wanders back to the edge of the flock he left behind. Will he dare to go to the theater and knock on his mother's dressing room door? Will he dare to ring the bell of the apartment on Downing Street? Possibly, but he doesn't think so – or at least he can't think about it now. After all this time, he still doesn't feel quite ready.

Just north of Washington, as the bus enters the final leg of the trip, snow begins to fall. They are moving into winter now, he realizes, the cold days and long nights of his boyhood winters, and suddenly the past has turned into the future. He closes his eyes, thinking about Pilar's face, running his hands over her absent body, and then, in the darkness behind his lids, he sees himself as a black speck in a world made of snow.

*Bing Nathan and Company*

# BING NATHAN

He is the warrior of outrage, the champion of discontent, the militant debunker of contemporary life who dreams of forging a new reality from the ruins of a failed world. Unlike most contrarians of his ilk, he does not believe in political action. He belongs to no movement or party, has never once spoken out in public, and has no desire to lead angry hordes into the streets to burn down buildings and topple governments. It is a purely personal position, but if he lives his life according to the principles he has established for himself, he feels certain that others will follow his example.

When he talks about the world, then, he is referring to his world, to the small, circumscribed sphere of his own life, and not to the world-at-large, which is too large and too broken for him to have any effect on it. He therefore concentrates on the local, the particular, the nearly invisible details of quotidian affairs. The decisions he makes are necessarily small ones, but small does not always mean unimportant, and day after day he struggles to adhere to the fundamental rule of his discontent: to stand in opposition to things-as-they-are, to resist the status quo on all fronts. Since the war in Vietnam, which began nearly twenty years before he was born, he would argue that the concept known as *America* has played itself out, that the country is no longer a workable proposition, but if anything continues to unite the fractured masses of this defunct nation, if American opinion is still unanimous about any one idea, it is a belief in the notion of progress. He contends that they are wrong, that the technological developments of the past decades have in fact only diminished the possibilities of life. In a throwaway culture spawned by the greed of profit-driven corporations, the landscape has grown ever more shabby, ever more alienating, ever more empty of meaning and consolidating purpose. His acts of rebellion are petty ones, perhaps, peevish gestures that accomplish little or nothing even in the short run, but they help to enhance his dignity as a human being, to ennoble him in his own eyes. He takes it for granted that the future is a lost cause, and if the present is all that matters now, then it must be a present imbued with the spirit of the past. That is why he shuns cell phones, computers, and all

things digital – because he refuses to participate in new technologies. That is why he spends his weekends playing drums and percussion in a six-man jazz group – because jazz is dead and only the happy few are interested in it anymore. That is why he started his business three years ago – because he wanted to fight back. The Hospital for Broken Things is located on Fifth Avenue in Park Slope. Flanked by a laundromat on one side and a vintage clothing shop on the other, it is a hole-in-the-wall storefront enterprise devoted to repairing objects from an era that has all but vanished from the face of the earth: manual typewriters, fountain pens, mechanical watches, vacuum-tube radios, record players, wind-up toys, gumball machines, and rotary telephones. Little matter that ninety percent of the money he earns comes from framing pictures. His shop provides a unique and inestimable service, and every time he works on another battered artifact from the antique industries of half a century ago, he goes about it with the willfulness and passion of a general fighting a war.

*Tangibility.* That is the word he uses most often when discussing his ideas with his friends. The world is tangible, he says. Human beings are tangible. They are endowed with bodies, and because those bodies feel pain and suffer from disease and undergo death, human life has not altered by a single jot since the beginning of mankind. Yes, the discovery of fire made man warmer and put an end to the raw-meat diet; the building of bridges enabled him to cross rivers and streams without getting his toes wet; the invention of the airplane allowed him to hop over continents and oceans while creating new phenomena such as jet lag and in-flight movies – but even if man has changed the world around him, man himself has not changed. The facts of life are constant. You live and then you die. You are born out of a woman's body, and if you manage to survive your birth, your mother must feed you and take care of you to ensure that you go on surviving, and everything that happens to you from the moment of your birth to the moment of your death, every emotion that wells up in you, every flash of anger, every surge of lust, every bout of tears, every gust of laughter, everything you will ever feel in the course of your life has also been felt by everyone who came before you, whether you are a caveman or an astronaut, whether you live in the Gobi Desert or the Arctic Circle. It all came to him in a sudden, epiphanic burst when he was sixteen years old. Paging through an illustrated book about the Dead Sea scrolls one afternoon, he stumbled across some photographs of the things that had been unearthed along with the

parchment texts: plates and eating utensils, straw baskets, pots, jugs, all of them perfectly intact. He studied them carefully for several moments, not quite understanding why he found these objects so compelling, and then, after several more moments, it finally came to him. The decorative patterns on the dishes were identical to the patterns on the dishes in the window of the store across the street from his apartment. The straw baskets were identical to the baskets millions of Europeans use to shop with today. The things in the pictures were two thousand years old, and yet they looked utterly new, utterly contemporary. That was the revelation that changed his thinking about human time: if a person from two thousand years ago, living in a far-flung outpost of the Roman Empire, could fashion a household item that looked exactly like a household item from today, how was that person's mind or heart or inner being any different from his own? That is the story he never tires of repeating to his friends, his counterargument to the prevailing belief that new technologies alter human consciousness. Microscopes and telescopes have permitted us to see more things than ever before, he says, but our days are still spent in the realm of normal sight. E-mails are faster than posted letters, he says, but in the end they're just another form of letter writing. He reels off example after example. He knows he drives them crazy with his conjectures and opinions, that he bores them with his long, nattering harangues, but these are important issues to him, and once he gets started, he finds it difficult to stop.

He is a large, hulking presence, a sloppy bear of a man with a full brown beard and a gold stud in his left earlobe, an inch under six feet tall but a wide and waddling two hundred and twenty pounds. His daily uniform consists of a pair of sagging black jeans, yellow work boots, and a plaid lumberjack shirt. He changes his underwear infrequently. He chews his food too loudly. He has been unlucky in love. Of all the things he does in life, playing the drums gives him the most pleasure. He was a boisterous child, a noisemaker of undisciplined exuberance and clumsy, scattershot aggression, and when his parents presented him with a drum set on his twelfth birthday, hoping his destructive urges might take a new form, their hunch proved correct. Seventeen years later, his collection has grown from the standard kit (snare drums, tom-toms, side drum, bass drum, suspended cymbals, hi-hat cymbals) to include more than two dozen drums of various shapes and sizes from around the world, among them a murumba, a batá, a darbuka, an okedo, a kalangu, a rommelpot, a bodhrán, a dhola, an ingungu, a koboro, a ntenga,

and a tabor. Depending on the instrument, he plays with sticks, mallets, or hands. His percussion closet is stocked with standbys such as bells, gongs, bull-roarers, castanets, clappers, chimes, washboards, and kalimbas, but he has also performed with chains, spoons, pebbles, sandpaper, and rattles. The band he belongs to is called Mob Rule, and they average two or three gigs a month, mostly in small bars and clubs in Brooklyn and lower Manhattan. If they earned more money, he would gladly drop everything and spend the rest of his life touring the world with them, but they barely earn enough to cover the costs of their rehearsal space. He loves the harsh, dissonant, improvised sound they create – shit-kicking funk, as he sometimes calls it – and they are not without their loyal followers. But there aren't enough of them, not nearly enough, and so he spends his mornings and afternoons in the Hospital for Broken Things, putting frames around movie posters and mending relics that were built when his grandparents were children.

When Ellen Brice told him about the abandoned house in Sunset Park this past summer, he saw it as an opportunity to put his ideas to the test, to move beyond his invisible, solitary attacks on the system and participate in a communal action. It is the boldest step he has yet taken, and he has no trouble reconciling the illegality of what they are doing with their right to do it. These are desperate times for everyone, and a crumbling wooden house standing empty in a neighborhood as ragged as this one is nothing if not an open invitation to vandals and arsonists, an eyesore begging to be broken into and pillaged, a menace to the well-being of the community. By occupying that house, he and his friends are protecting the safety of the street, making life more livable for everyone around them. It is early December now, and they have been squatting there for close to four months. Because it was his idea to move there in the first place, and because he was the one who picked the soldiers of their little army, and because he is the only one who knows anything about carpentry, plumbing, and electric wiring, he is the unofficial leader of the group. Not a beloved leader, perhaps, but a tolerated leader, for they all know the experiment would fall apart without him.

Ellen was the first person he asked. Without her, he never would have set foot in Sunset Park and discovered the house, and therefore it seemed only fitting to give her the right of first refusal. He has known her since they were small children, when they went to elementary school together on the Upper West Side, but then they lost contact for many years, only to find out seven months ago that they were both living in Brooklyn and

were in fact not terribly distant Park Slope neighbors. She walked into the Hospital one afternoon to have something framed, and although he didn't recognize her at first (could anyone recognize a twenty-nine-year-old woman last seen as a girl of twelve?), when he wrote down her name on the order form he instantly understood that this was the Ellen Brice he had known as a boy. Strange little Ellen Brice, all grown up now and working as a real estate agent for a firm on Seventh Avenue and Ninth Street, an artist in her spare time in the same way he is a musician in his spare time, although he has the semblance of a career and she does not. That first afternoon in the shop, he blundered in with his usual friendly, tactless questions and soon learned that she was still unmarried, that her parents had retired to a coastal town in North Carolina, and that her sister was pregnant with twin boys. His first meeting with Millie Grant was still six weeks in the future (the same Millie who is about to be replaced by Miles Heller), and because he and Ellen were both officially available, he asked her out for a drink.

Nothing came of that drink, nor of the dinner he invited her to three nights later, but there had been nothing between them as children and that continued to be the case in adulthood as well. They were both at loose ends, however, and even if romance was not in the picture, they went on seeing each other from time to time and began to build a modest friendship. It didn't matter to him that she hadn't liked the Mob Rule concert she attended (the clanging chaos of their work was not for everyone), nor was he unduly concerned that he found her drawings and paintings dull (meticulous, well-executed still lifes and cityscapes that lacked all flair and originality, he felt). What counted was that she seemed to enjoy listening to him talk and that she never turned him down when he called. Something in him responded to the sense of loneliness that enveloped her, he was touched by her quiet goodness and the vulnerability he saw in her eyes, and yet the more their friendship advanced, the less he knew what to make of her. Ellen was not an unattractive woman. Her body was trim, her face was pleasant to look at, but she projected an aura of anxiety and defeat, and with her too pale skin and flat, lusterless hair, he wondered if she wasn't mired in some sort of depression, living out her days in an underground room at the Hotel Melancholia. Whenever he saw her, he did everything in his power to make her laugh – with mixed results.

Early in the summer, on the same scorching day that Pilar Sanchez moved in with Miles Heller down in southern Florida, a crisis broke out up north. The lease on the storefront that housed the Hospital for Broken

Things was about to expire, and his landlord was demanding a twenty percent rent increase. He explained that he couldn't afford it, that the extra monthly charges would drive him out of business, but the prick refused to budge. The only solution was to leave his apartment and find a cheaper place somewhere else. Ellen, who worked in the rental division of her real estate company on Seventh Avenue, told him about Sunset Park. It was a rougher neighborhood, she said, but it wasn't far from where he was living now, and rents were a half or a third of the rents in Park Slope. That Sunday, the two of them went out to explore the territory between Fifteenth and Sixty-fifth streets in western Brooklyn, an extensive hodgepodge of an area that runs from Upper New York Bay to Ninth Avenue, home to more than a hundred thousand people, including Mexicans, Dominicans, Poles, Chinese, Jordanians, Vietnamese, American whites, American blacks, and a settlement of Christians from Gujarat, India. Warehouses, factories, abandoned waterfront facilities, a view of the Statue of Liberty, the shut-down Army Terminal where ten thousand people once worked, a basilica named Our Lady of Perpetual Help, biker bars, check-cashing places, Hispanic restaurants, the third-largest Chinatown in New York, and the four hundred and seventy-eight acres of Green-Wood Cemetery, where six hundred thousand bodies are buried, including those of Boss Tweed, Lola Montez, Currier and Ives, Henry Ward Beecher, F.A.O. Schwarz, Lorenzo Da Ponte, Horace Greeley, Louis Comfort Tiffany, Samuel F. B. Morse, Albert Anastasia, Joey Gallo, and Frank Morgan – the wizard in *The Wizard of Oz*.

Ellen showed him six or seven listings that day, none of which appealed to him, and then, as they were walking along the edge of the cemetery, they turned at random down a deserted block between Fourth and Fifth avenues and saw the house, a dopey little two-story wooden house with a roofed-over front porch, looking for all the world like something that had been stolen from a farm on the Minnesota prairie and plunked down by accident in the middle of New York. It stood between a trash-filled vacant lot with a stripped-down car in it and the metal bones of a half-built mini-apartment building on which construction had stopped more than a year ago. The cemetery was directly across the way, which meant there were no houses lining the other side of the street, which further meant that the abandoned house was all but invisible, since it was a house on a block where almost no one lived. He asked Ellen if she knew anything about it. The owners had died, she said, and because their children had been delinquent in paying the property taxes

for several years running, the house now belonged to the city.

A month later, when he made up his mind to do the impossible, to risk everything on the chance to live in a rent-free house for as long as it took the city to notice him and give him the boot, he was stunned when Ellen accepted his offer. He tried to talk her out of it, explaining how difficult it would be and how much trouble they might be getting themselves into, but she held her ground, saying yes meant yes, and why bother to ask if he wanted her to say no?

They broke in one night and discovered that there were four bedrooms, three small ones on the top floor and a larger one below, which was part of an extension built onto the back of the house. The place was in lamentable condition, every surface coated with dust and soot, water stains streaking the wall behind the kitchen sink, cracked linoleum, splintered floorboards, a team of mice or squirrels running relay races under the roof, a collapsed table, legless chairs, spiderwebs dangling from ceiling corners, but remarkably enough not one broken window, and even if the water from the taps spurted out brown, looking more like English Breakfast tea than water, the plumbing was intact. Elbow grease, Ellen said. That's all it was going to take. A week or two of scrubbing and painting, and they would be in business.

He spent the next several days looking for people to fill the last two bedrooms, but no one from the band was interested, and as he went down the list of his other friends and acquaintances, he discovered that the idea of living as a squatter in an abandoned house did not have the broad appeal he had supposed it would. Then Ellen happened to talk to Alice Bergstrom, her old college roommate, and learned that she was about to be kicked out of her rent-controlled sublet in Morningside Heights. Alice was a graduate student at Columbia, already well into her dissertation, which she hoped to finish within a year, and moving in with her boyfriend was out of the question. Even if they had wanted to live together, it wouldn't have been possible. His apartment was the smallest of small, postage-stamp studios, and there simply wasn't enough space for two people to work in there at the same time. And they both needed to work at home. Jake Baum was a fiction writer, until now exclusively a writer of short stories (some of them published, most of them not), and he barely managed to scrape by on the salary he earned from his part-time teaching job at a community college in Queens. He had no money to lend Alice, could offer no help in her search for a new apartment, and since Alice herself was nearly broke, she didn't know where to turn. Her

fellowship came with a small stipend, but it wasn't enough to live on, and even with her part-time job at the PEN American Center, where she worked for the Freedom to Write Program, she was subsisting on a diet of buttered noodles, rice and beans, and an occasional egg sandwich. After hearing out the story of her friend's predicament, Ellen suggested that she have a talk with Bing.

The three of them met at a bar in Brooklyn the following night, and after ten minutes of conversation he was convinced that Alice would make a worthy addition to the group. She was a tall, big-boned Scandinavian girl from Wisconsin with a round face and meaty arms, a person of heft and seriousness who also happened to have a quick mouth and a sharp sense of humor – a rare combination, he felt, which made her a shoo-in from the word go. Just as important, he liked the fact that she was Ellen's friend. Ellen had proven herself to be an admirable sidekick, for reasons he would never understand she had taken on his mad, quixotic venture as her own, but he still worried about her, was still troubled by the closed-in, unabated sadness that seemed to accompany her wherever she went, and he was heartened to see how she loosened up in Alice's presence, how much happier and more animated she looked as the three of them sat there talking in the bar, and he hoped that sharing the house with her old friend would be good medicine for her.

Before he met Alice Bergstrom, he had already met Millie Grant, but it took him several weeks after that night in the bar to screw up his courage and ask her if she had any interest in taking over the fourth and last bedroom. He was in love with her by then, in love with her in a way he had never loved anyone in his life, and he was too frightened to ask her because the thought that she might turn him down was more than he could bear. He was twenty-nine years old, and until he ran into Millie after a Mob Rule gig at Barbès on the last day of spring, his history with women had been one of absolute, unending failure. He was the fat boy who never had a girlfriend in school, the bumbling naïf who didn't lose his virginity until he was twenty, the jazz drummer who had never picked up a stranger in a club, the dumbbell who bought blow jobs from hookers when he was feeling desperate, the sex-starved moron who jerked off to pornography in the darkness of his bedroom. He knew nothing about women. He had less experience with women than most adolescent boys. He had dreamed of women, he had chased after women, he had declared his love to women, but again and again he had been rebuffed. Now, as he was about to take the biggest gamble of his life, as he stood on the brink

of illegally occupying a house in Sunset Park and perhaps landing in jail, he was going into it with a team composed entirely of women. His hour of triumph had come at last.

Why did Millie fall for him? He doesn't quite know, cannot be sure of anything when it comes to the murky realms of attraction and desire, but he suspects it might be connected to the house in Sunset Park. Not the house itself, but the plan to move in there, which was already turning around in his head by the time he met her, already mutating from whim and vague speculation into a concrete decision to act, and he must have been burning with his idea that night, emitting a shower of mental sparks that surrounded him like a magnetic field and charged the atmosphere with a new and vital energy, an irresistible force, as it were, making him more attractive and desirable than usual perhaps, which could have been the reason why she was drawn to him. Not a pretty girl, no, not by the conventional standards that define prettiness (nose too sharp, left eye veering off slightly, too thin lips), but she had a terrific head of wiry red hair and a lithe, fetching body. They wound up in bed together that night, and when he understood that she wasn't put off by his shaggy, overly round *corpus horrendous*, he asked her out to dinner the following night, and they wound up in bed again. Millie Grant, a twenty-seven-year-old part-time dancer, part-time restaurant hostess, born and raised in Wheaton, Illinois, a girl with four small tattoos and a navel ring, an advocate of numerous conspiracy theories (from the Kennedy assassination to the 9/11 attacks to the dangers of the public drinking-water system), a lover of loud music, a nonstop talker, a vegetarian, an animal rights activist, a vivacious, tightly sprung piece of work with a quick temper and a machine-gun laugh – someone to hold on to for the long haul. But he couldn't hold on to her. He doesn't understand what went wrong, but after two and a half months of communal living in the house, she woke up one morning and declared that she was going to San Francisco to join a new dance company. She had auditioned for them in the spring, she said, had been the last person cut, and now that one of the dancers was pregnant and had been forced to drop out, she had been hired. Sorry, Bing. It was nice while it lasted and all that, but this was the chance she'd been waiting for, and she'd be a fool not to jump at it. He didn't know whether to believe her or not, whether *San Francisco* was simply a term that meant *good-bye* or if she was really going there. Now that she is gone, he wonders if he performed well enough in bed with her, if he

was able to satisfy her sexually. Or, just the opposite, if she felt he was too interested in sex, if all his dirty talk about the bizarre couplings he had witnessed in porno films had finally driven her away. He will never know. She has not been in touch since the morning she left the house, and he is not expecting to hear from her again.

Two days after Millie's departure, he wrote to Miles Heller. He got a little carried away, perhaps, claiming there were four people in the house rather than three, but four was a better number than three somehow, and he didn't want Miles to think that his great anarchist insurrection had been whittled down to his own paltry self and a pair of women. In his mind, the fourth person was Jake Baum, the writer, and while it's true that Jake comes around to visit Alice once or twice a week, he is not a permanent member of the household. He doubts that Miles will care one way or the other, but if he does care, it will be easy enough to invent some fib to account for the discrepancy.

He loves Miles Heller, but he also thinks that Miles is insane, and he is glad his friend's lonesome cowboy act is finally coming to an end. Seven years ago, when he received the first of the fifty-two letters Miles has written to him, he didn't hesitate to call Morris Heller and tell him that his son wasn't dead as everyone had feared but working as a short-order cook in a diner on the South Side of Chicago. Miles had been missing for over six months by then. Just after his disappearance, Morris and Willa had asked Bing over to their apartment to question him about Miles and what he thought could have happened to him. He will never forget how Willa broke down in tears, never forget the anguished look on Morris's face. He had no suggestions to offer that afternoon, but he promised that if he ever heard from Miles or heard anything about him, he would contact them at once. He has been calling them for seven years now – fifty-two times, once after every letter. It grieves him that Morris and Willa have not jumped on a plane and flown off to any of the several spots where Miles has parked his bones – not to drag him back, necessarily, but just to see him and force him to explain himself. But Morris says there is nothing to be done. As long as the boy refuses to come home, they have no option but to wait it out and hope he will eventually change his mind. Bing is glad that Morris Heller and Willa Parks are not his parents. No doubt they are both good people, but they are just as stubborn and crazy as Miles.

# ALICE BERGSTROM

No one is watching them. No one cares that the empty house is now occupied. They have settled in.

When she took the plunge and decided to join forces with Bing and Ellen last summer, she imagined they would be forced to live in the shadows, slinking in and out the back door whenever the coast was clear, hiding behind blackout shades to prevent any light from seeping through the windows, always afraid, always looking over their shoulders, always expecting the boom to fall on them at any moment. She was willing to accept those conditions because she was desperate and felt she had no choice. She had lost her apartment, and how can a person rent a new apartment when the person in question doesn't have the money to pay for it? Things would be easier if her parents were in a position to help, but they are barely getting by themselves, living on their Social Security checks and clipping coupons out of the newspaper in a perpetual hunt for bargains, sales, gimmicks, any chance to shave a few pennies from their monthly costs. She was anticipating a grim go of it, a scared and mean little life in a broken-down shithole of a house, but she was wrong about that, wrong about many things, and even if Bing can be intolerable at times, pounding his fist on the table as he subjects them to another one of his dreary exhortations, slurping his soup and smacking his lips and letting crumbs fall into his beard, she misjudged his intelligence, failed to realize that he had worked out a thoroughly sensible plan. No skulking around, he said. Acting as if they didn't belong there would only alert the neighborhood to the fact that they were trespassers. They had to operate in broad daylight, hold their heads high, and pretend they were the legitimate owners of the house, which they had bought from the city for next to nothing, yes, yes, at a shockingly low price, because they had spared them the expense of having to demolish the place. Bing was right. It was a plausible story, and people accepted it. After they moved in last August, there was a brief fluster of curiosity about their comings and goings, but that passed soon enough, and by now the short, sparsely populated block has adjusted to their presence. No one is watching them, and no one cares. The old Donohue place has

finally been sold, the sun continues to rise and set, and life goes on as if nothing ever happened.

For the first few weeks, they did what they could to make the rooms habitable, diligently attacking all manner of blight and decay, treating each small task as if it were a momentous human endeavor, and bit by bit they turned their wretchedly inadequate pigsty into something that might, with some generosity, be classified as a hovel. It is far from comfortable there, countless inconveniences impinge on them every day, and now that the weather has turned cold, bitter air rushes in on them through a thousand cracks in the walls and embrasures, forcing them to bundle up in heavy sweaters and put on three pairs of socks in the morning. But she doesn't complain. Not having to pay rent or utility bills for the past four months has saved her close to thirty-five hundred dollars, and for the first time in a long while she can breathe without feeling her chest tighten up on her, without feeling that her lungs are about to explode. Her work is moving forward, she can see the end looming on the far horizon, and she knows that she has the stamina to finish. The window in her room faces the cemetery, and as she writes her dissertation at the small desk positioned directly below that window, she often stares into the quiet of Green-Wood's vast, rolling ground, where more than half a million bodies are buried, which is roughly the same number as the population of Milwaukee, the city where she was born, the city where most of her family still lives, and she finds it strange, strange and even haunting, that there are as many dead lying under that ground across from her window as the number of people living in the place where her life began.

She isn't sorry that Millie is gone. Bing is in shock, of course, still staggered by his girlfriend's abrupt exit from the house, but she feels the group will be better off without that fractious, redheaded storm of gripes and thoughtless digs, she of the unwashed dinner plates and the blaring radio, who nearly pulverized poor, fragile Ellen with her comments about her drawings and paintings. A man named Miles Heller will be joining them tomorrow or the day after. Bing says he is hands down the smartest, most interesting person he has ever known. They met when they were teenagers apparently, all the way back in the early years of high school, so their friendship has gone on long enough for Bing to have some perspective on what he is saying – which is rather extreme in her opinion, but Bing is often given to hyperbole, and only time will tell if Señor Heller measures up to this powerful endorsement.

It is a Saturday, a gray Saturday in early December, and she is the only person in the house. Bing left an hour ago to rehearse with his band, Ellen is spending the day with her sister and the little twins on the Upper West Side, and Jake is in Montclair, New Jersey, visiting his brother and sister-in-law, who have just had a child as well. Babies are popping out all over, in every part of the globe women are huffing and heaving and disgorging fresh battalions of newborns, doing their bit to prolong the human race, and at some point in the not-too-distant future she hopes to put her womb to the test and see if she can't contribute as well. All that remains is choosing the right father. For close to two years, she felt that person was Jake Baum, but now she is beginning to have doubts about Jake, something seems to be crumbling between them, small daily erosions have slowly begun to mar their patch of ground, and if things continue to deteriorate, it won't be long before entire shorelines are washed away, before whole villages are submerged under water. Six months ago, she never would have asked the question, but now she wonders if she has it in her to carry on with him. Jake was never an expansive person, but there was a gentleness in him that she admired, a charming, ironical approach to the world that comforted her and made her feel they were well matched, comrades under the skin. Now he is pulling away from her. He seems angry and dejected, his once lighthearted quips have taken on a new edge of cynicism, and he never seems to tire of denigrating his students and fellow teachers. LaGuardia Community College has turned into Pifflebum Tech, Asswipe U, and the Institute for Advanced Retardation. She doesn't like to hear him talk that way. His students are mostly poor, working-class immigrants, attending school while holding down jobs, never an easy proposition as she damned well knows, and who is he to make fun of them for wanting an education? With his writing, it's more or less the same story. A flood of caustic remarks every time another piece is rejected, an acid contempt for the literary world, an abiding grudge against every editor who has failed to recognize his gifts. She is convinced that he has talent, that his work has been progressing, but it is a small talent in her eyes, and her expectations for his future are equally small. Perhaps that is part of the problem. Perhaps he senses that she doesn't believe in him enough, and in spite of all the pep talks she has given him, all the long conversations in which she has cited the early struggles of one important writer after another, he never seems to take her words to heart. She doesn't blame him for feeling frustrated – but does she want to spend the rest of her life with a frustrated man, a man

who is rapidly becoming a failure in his own eyes?

She mustn't exaggerate, however. More often than not, he is kind to her, and he has never once hinted that he is weary of their affair, has never once suggested that they break it off. He is still young, after all, not yet thirty-one, which is extremely young for a fiction writer, and if his stories keep improving, chances are that something good will happen, a success of one kind or another, and with that turn his spirits would undoubtedly improve as well. No, she can weather his disappointments if she has to, that isn't the problem, she can put up with anything as long as she feels he is solidly with her, but that is precisely what she doesn't feel anymore, and even if he seems content to glide along with her out of old habits, the reflex of old affections, she is becoming ever more certain, no, *certain* is probably too strong a word for it, she is becoming ever more willing to entertain the idea that he has stopped loving her. It isn't anything he ever says. It's the way he looks at her now, the way he has been looking at her for the past few months, without any noticeable interest, his eyes blank, unfocused, as if looking at her were no different from looking at a spoon or a washcloth, a speck of dust. He rarely touches her anymore when they are alone, and even before she moved to the house in Sunset Park, their sex life was in precipitous decline. That is the crux of it, without question the problem begins and ends there, and she blames herself for what has happened, she can't help believing that the fault rests entirely on her shoulders. She was always a big person, always bigger than the other girls at school – taller, broader, more robust, more athletic, never chubby, never overweight for her size, just big. When she met Jake two and a half years ago, she was five feet ten inches tall and weighed one hundred and fifty-seven pounds. She is still five-ten, but now she weighs one-seventy. Those thirteen pounds are the difference between a strong, imposing woman and a mountain of a woman. She has been dieting ever since she landed in Sunset Park, but no matter how severely she limits her intake of calories, she has not managed to lose more than three or four pounds, which she always seems to gain back within a day or two. Her body repulses her now, and she no longer has the courage to look at herself in the mirror. I'm fat, she says to Jake. Again and again she says it, I'm fat, I'm fat, unable to stop herself from repeating the words, and if she is repulsed by the sight of her own body, imagine what he must feel when she takes off her clothes and climbs into bed with him.

The light is fading now, and as she stands up from her bed to switch on a lamp, she tells herself that she must not cry, that only weaklings and

imbeciles feel sorry for themselves, and therefore she must not feel sorry for herself, for she is neither a weakling nor an imbecile, and she knows better than to think that love is simply a question of bodies, the size and shape and heft of bodies, and if Jake can't cope with his somewhat overweight, furiously dieting girlfriend, then Jake can go to hell. A moment later, she is sitting at her desk. She turns on the laptop, and for the next half hour she vanishes into her work, reading over and correcting the newest passages from her dissertation, which were written this morning.

Her subject is America in the years just after World War II, an examination of the relations and conflicts between men and women as shown in books and films from 1945 to 1947, mostly popular crime novels and commercial Hollywood movies. It is a broad terrain for an academic study, perhaps, but she couldn't picture herself spending years of her life comparing rhyme schemes in Pope and Byron (one of her friends is doing that) or analyzing the metaphors in Melville's Civil War poetry (another friend is doing that). She wanted to take on something larger, something of human importance that would engage her personally, and she knows she is working on this subject because of her grandparents and her great-uncles and great-aunts, all of whom participated in the war, lived through the war, were changed forever by the war. Her argument is that the traditional rules of conduct between men and women were destroyed on the battlefields and the home front, and once the war was over, American life had to be reinvented. She has limited herself to several texts and films, the ones that feel most emblematic to her, that expose the spirit of the time in the clearest, most forceful terms, and she has already written chapters on *The Air-Conditioned Nightmare* by Henry Miller, the brutal misogynism of Mickey Spillane's *I, the Jury,* the virgin-whore female split presented in Jacques Tourneur's film noir *Out of the Past,* and has carefully dissected a bestselling anti-feminist tract called *Modern Woman: The Lost Sex*. Now she is about to begin writing on William Wyler's 1946 film, *The Best Years of Our Lives,* a work that is central to her thesis and which she considers to be the national epic of that particular moment in American history – the story of three men broken by war and the difficulties they confront when they return to their families, which is the same story that was being lived out by millions of others at the time.

The entire country saw the film, which won the Academy Award for best picture, best director, best leading actor, best supporting actor, best editor, best original score, and best adapted screenplay, but while most critics

responded with enthusiasm (*some of the most beautiful and inspiring demonstrations of human fortitude that we have had in films,* wrote Bosley Crowther of the *New York Times*), others were less impressed. Manny Farber trashed it as *a horse-drawn truckload of liberal schmaltz,* and in his long, two-part review published in the *Nation,* James Agee both condemned and praised *The Best Years of Our Lives,* calling it *very annoying in its patness, its timidity,* and then concluded by saying: *Yet I feel a hundred times more liking and admiration for the film than distaste or disappointment.* She agrees that the movie has its faults, that it is often too tame and sentimental, but in the end she feels its virtues outweigh its deficits. The acting is strong throughout, the script is filled with memorable lines (*Last year it was kill Japs, this year it's make money; I think they ought to put you in mass production; I'm in the junk business, an occupation for which many people feel I'm well qualified by training and temperament*), and the cinematography by Gregg Toland is exceptional. She pulls out her copy of Ephraim Katz's *Film Encyclopedia* and reads this sentence from the William Wyler entry: *The revolutionary deep-focus shot perfected by Toland enabled Wyler to develop his favorite technique of filming long takes in which characters appear in the same frame for the duration of entire scenes, rather than cutting from one to another and thus disrupting intercharacter relationships.* Two paragraphs down, at the end of a brief description of *The Best Years of Our Lives,* the author remarks that the film contains *some of the most intricate compositions ever seen on celluloid.* Even more important, at least for the purposes of the dissertation she is writing, the story concentrates on precisely those elements of male–female conflict that most interest her. The men no longer know how to act with their wives and girlfriends. They have lost their appetite for domesticity, their feel for home. After years of living apart from women, years of combat and slaughter, years of grappling to survive the horrors and dangers of war, they have been cut off from their civilian pasts, crippled, trapped in nightmare repetitions of their experiences, and the women they left behind have become strangers to them. So the film begins. Peace has broken out, but what in God's name happens now?

She owns a small television set and a DVD player. Because there is no cable hookup in the house, the television doesn't receive normal broadcasts, but she can watch films on it, and now that she is about to begin her chapter on *The Best Years of Our Lives,* she feels she should take another look at it, have one last run-through before getting down to work. Night has fallen now, but as she settles onto her bed to begin watching, she turns off the lamp in order to study the film in total darkness.

It is deeply familiar to her, of course. After four or five viewings, she practically knows the film by heart, but she is determined to look for small things that might have escaped her notice earlier, the quickly passing details that ultimately give a film its texture. Already in the first scene, when Dana Andrews is at the airport, unsuccessfully trying to book a ticket back to Boone City, she is struck by the businessman with the golf clubs, Mr. Gibbons, who calmly pays his excess-baggage charge while ignoring air force captain Andrews, who has just helped win the war for Mr. Gibbons and his fellow countrymen, and from now on, she decides, she will take note of each act of civilian indifference toward the returning soldiers. She is gratified to see how rapidly they mount up as the film progresses: the desk clerk at the apartment building where Fredric March lives, for example, who is reluctant to let the uniformed sergeant into his own house, or the manager of Midway Drugs, Mr. Thorpe, who snidely dismisses Andrews's war record as he offers him a low-paying job, or even Andrews's wife, Virginia Mayo, who tells him to *snap out of it*, that he won't get anywhere until he stops thinking about the war, as if going to war ranked as a minor inconvenience, equivalent to a painful session at the dentist.

More details, more small things: Virginia Mayo removing her false eyelashes; the rheumy Mr. Thorpe squirting nasal spray into his left nostril; Myrna Loy trying to kiss the sleeping Fredric March, who nearly slugs her in response; the choked sob from Harold Russell's mother when she sees her son's prosthetic hooks for the first time; Dana Andrews reaching into his pocket to look for his bank roll after Teresa Wright wakes him up, suggesting in one quick, instinctive move how many nights he must have spent with low-life women overseas; Myrna Loy putting flowers on her husband's breakfast tray, then deciding to take them off; Dana Andrews picking up the photo from the country club dinner, tearing it in half to preserve the shot of Teresa Wright sitting next to him, and then, after a brief hesitation, tearing up that half as well; Harold Russell stumbling over his marriage vows in the wedding scene at the end; Dana Andrews's father awkwardly trying to conceal his gin bottle on his son's first day home from the war; a sign seen through the window of a passing cab: *Settle for a Hot Dog?*

She is especially interested in Teresa Wright's performance in the role of Peggy, the young woman who falls in love with unhappily married Dana Andrews. She wants to know why she is drawn to this character when everything tells her that Peggy is too perfect to be credible as a human

being – too poised, too good, too pretty, too smart, one of the purest incarnations of the ideal American girl she can think of – and yet each time she watches the film, she finds herself more involved with this character than any of the others. The moment Wright makes her first appearance on-screen, then – early in the film, when her father, Fredric March, returns home to Myrna Loy and his two children – she makes up her mind to track every nuance of Wright's behavior, to scrutinize the finest points of her performance in order to understand why this character, who is potentially the weakest link in the film, ends up holding the story together. She is not alone in thinking this. Even Agee, so harsh in his judgment of other aspects of the movie, is effusive in his admiration of Wright's accomplishment. *This new performance of hers, entirely lacking in big scenes, tricks or obstreperousness – one can hardly think of it as acting – seems to be one of the wisest and most beautiful pieces of work I have seen in years.*

Just after the long two-shot of March and Loy embracing at the end of the hall (one of the signature moments in the film), the camera cuts to a close-up of Wright – and just then, during those few seconds when Peggy occupies the screen alone, Alice knows what she has to look for. Wright's performance is concentrated entirely in her eyes and face. Follow the eyes and face, and the riddle of her mastery is solved, for the eyes are unusually expressive eyes, subtly but vividly expressive, and the face registers her emotions with such a highly sensitive, understated authenticity that you can't help but believe in her as a fully embodied character. Because of her eyes and face, Wright as Peggy is able to bring the inside to the outside, and even when she is silent, we know what she is thinking and feeling. Yes, she is without question the healthiest, most earnest character in the film, but how not to respond to her angry declaration to her parents about Andrews and his wife, *I'm going to break that marriage up,* or the irritated brush-off she gives her rich, handsome dinner date when he tries to kiss her, saying *Don't be a bore, Woody,* or the short, complicitous laugh she shares with her mother when they say good night to each other after the two drunken men have been put to bed? That explains why Andrews thinks she should be put in mass production. Because there is only one of her, and how much better off the world would be (how much better off men would be!) if there were more Peggys to go around.

She is doing her best to concentrate, to keep her eyes fixed on the screen, but midway into the film her thoughts begin to wander. Watching Harold Russell, the third male protagonist along with March and

Andrews, the nonprofessional actor who lost his hands during the war, she begins to think about her great-uncle Stan, the husband of her grandmother's sister Caroline, the one-armed D-day veteran with the bushy eyebrows, Stan Fitzpatrick, belting back drinks at family parties, telling dirty jokes to her brothers on their grandparents' back porch, one of the many who never managed to pull themselves together after the war, the man with thirty-seven different jobs, old Uncle Stan, dead for a good ten years now, and the stories her grandmother has told her lately about how he used to *knock Caroline around a bit,* the now departed Caroline, knocked around so much she lost a couple of teeth one day, and then there are her two grandfathers, both of them still alive, one fading and the other lucid, who fought in the Pacific and Europe as young men, such young men they were scarcely older than boys, and even though she has tried to get the lucid grandfather to talk to her, Bill Bergstrom, the husband of her one surviving grandmother, he never says much, speaks only in the foggiest generalities, it simply isn't possible for him to talk about those years, they all came home insane, damaged for life, and even the years after the war were still part of the war, the years of bad dreams and night sweats, the years of wanting to punch your fist through walls, so her grandfather humors her by talking about going to college on the G.I. Bill, about meeting her grandmother on a bus one day and falling in love with her at first sight, bullshit, bullshit from start to finish, but he is one of those men who can't talk, a card-carrying member from the generation of men who can't talk, and therefore she has to rely on her grandmother for the stories, but she wasn't a soldier during the war, she doesn't know what happened over there, and all she can talk about are her three sisters and their husbands, the dead Caroline and Stan Fitzpatrick and Annabelle, the one whose husband was killed at Anzio and who later married again, to a man named Jim Farnsworth, another vet from the Pacific, but that marriage didn't last long either, he was unfaithful to her, he forged checks or was involved in a stock swindle, the details are unclear, but Farnsworth vanished long before she was born, and the only husband she ever knew was Mike Meggert, the traveling salesman, who never talked about the war either, and finally there is Gloria, Gloria and Frank Krushniak, the couple with the six children, but Frank's war was different from the others' war, he faked a disability and never had to serve, which means that he has nothing to say either, and when she thinks of that generation of silent men, the boys who lived through the Depression and grew up to become soldiers or

not-soldiers in the war, she doesn't blame them for refusing to talk, for not wanting to go back into the past, but how curious it is, she thinks, how sublimely incoherent that her generation, which doesn't have much of anything to talk about yet, has produced men who never stop talking, men like Bing, for example, or men like Jake, who talks about himself at the slightest prompting, who has an opinion on every subject, who spews forth words from morning to night, but just because he talks, that doesn't mean she wants to listen to him, whereas with the silent men, the old men, the ones who are nearly gone now, she would give anything to hear what they have to say.

She is standing on the front porch of the house, looking into the fog. It is Sunday morning, and the air outside is almost warm, too warm for the beginning of December, making it feel like a day from another season or another latitude, a damp, balmy sort of weather that reminds her of the tropics. When she looks across the street, the fog is so dense that the cemetery is invisible. A strange morning, she says to herself. The clouds have descended all the way to the ground, and the world has become invisible – which is neither a good thing nor a bad thing, she decides, merely strange.

It is early, early for a Sunday in any case, a few minutes past seven o'clock, and Alice and Bing are still asleep in their beds on the second floor, but she is up at first light again as usual, even if there is little light to speak of on this dull, fog-saturated morning. She can't remember the last time she managed to sleep for six full hours, six uninterrupted hours without waking from a rough dream or discovering her eyes had opened at dawn, and she knows these sleep difficulties are a bad sign, an unmistakable warning of trouble ahead, but in spite of what her mother keeps telling her, she doesn't want to go back on the medication. Taking one of those pills is like swallowing a small dose of death. Once you start with those things, your days are turned into a numbing regimen of forgetfulness and confusion, and there isn't a moment when you don't feel your head is stuffed with cotton balls and wadded-up shreds of paper. She doesn't want to shut down her life in order to survive her life. She wants her senses to be awake, to think thoughts that don't vanish the moment they occur to her, to feel alive in all the ways she once felt alive. Crack-ups are off the agenda now. She can't allow herself to surrender anymore, but in spite of her efforts to hold her ground in the here and now, the pressure has been building up inside her again, and she is beginning to feel twinges of the old panic, the knot in her throat, the blood rushing too quickly through her veins, the clenched heart and frantic rhythms of her pulse. Fear without an object, as Dr. Burnham once described it to her. No, she says to herself now: fear of dying without having lived.

There is no question that coming here was the right move, and she

has never regretted leaving behind that small apartment on President Street in Park Slope. She feels emboldened by the risk they have taken together, and Bing and Alice have been so good to her, so generous and protective, so constant in their friendship, but in spite of the fact that she is less lonely now, there have been times, many times in fact, when being with them has only made things worse. When she lived on her own, she never had to compare herself with anyone. Her struggles were her struggles, her failures were her failures, and she could suffer through them within the confines of her small, solitary space. Now she is surrounded by impassioned, energetic people, and next to them she feels like a dim sluggard, a hopeless nonentity. Alice will soon have her Ph.D. and an academic post somewhere, Jake is publishing story after story in little magazines, Bing has his band and his goofy underground business, and even Millie, the sharp-tongued, never-to-be-missed Millie, is thriving as a dancer. As for her, she is getting nowhere fast, faster than it takes for a young dog to become an old dog, faster than it takes for a flower to bloom and wilt. Her work as an artist has crashed into a wall, and the bulk of her time is spent showing empty apartments to prospective tenants – a job for which she is thoroughly ill-suited and which she fears she could be fired from any day. All that has been hard enough, but then there is the business of sex, the fucking she has had to listen to through the thin walls upstairs, the fact of being the only single person in a house of two couples. It has been a long time since anyone made love to her, eighteen months by her latest reckoning, and she is so starved for physical contact that she can barely think about anything else now. She masturbates in her bed every night, but masturbation isn't a solution, it offers only temporary relief, it's like an aspirin you take to kill the pain of a throbbing tooth, and she doesn't know how much longer she can go on without being kissed, without being loved. Bing is available now, it's true, and she can feel that he is interested in her, but somehow she can't imagine herself with Bing, can't see herself putting her arms around his broad, hairy back or trying to find his lips through the bramble of that thick beard. Again and again since Millie's departure, she has thought about making an advance on him, but then she sees Bing at breakfast in the morning and knows it isn't possible.

Her thoughts have begun to disturb her, the little games she plays in her mind without wanting to, the sudden, uncontrollable fugues into the dark. Sometimes they come to her in brief flashes – an impulse to burn down the house, to seduce Alice, to steal money from the safe at her real

estate firm – and then, just as quickly as they arrive, they dwindle off into nothing. Others are more constant, more enduring in their impact. Even going out is fraught with hazards now, for there are days when she can no longer look at the people she passes on the street without undressing them in her imagination, stripping off their clothes with a quick, violent tug and then examining their naked bodies as they walk by. These strangers aren't people to her anymore, they are simply the bodies that belong to them, structures of flesh wrapped around bones and tissue and inner organs, and with the heavy pedestrian traffic that moves along Seventh Avenue, the street where her office is located, hundreds if not thousands of specimens are thrust before her eyes every day. She sees the enormous, unwieldy breasts of fat women, the tiny penises of young boys, the budding pubic hair of thirteen-year-old children, the pink vaginas of mothers pushing their babies in strollers, the assholes of old men, the hairless pudenda of little girls, luxuriant thighs, skinny thighs, vast, quivering buttocks, chest hair, recessed navels, inverted nipples, bellies scarred by appendix operations and cesarean births, turds sliding out of open anuses, piss flowing from long, partly erect penises. She is revolted by these images, appalled that her mind is capable of manufacturing such filth, but once they start coming to her, she is powerless to make them go away. Sometimes she even goes so far as to imagine herself pausing to slip her tongue into the mouth of each passerby, each and every person who falls within her sight, whether old or young, whether beautiful or deformed, pausing to lick the entire length of each naked body, pushing her tongue into moistened vaginas, putting her mouth around thick, hardened penises, giving herself with equal fervor to every man, woman, and child in an orgy of indiscriminate, democratic love. She doesn't know how to stop these visions. They leave her feeling wretched and exhausted, but the wild thoughts enter her head as if they were planted there by someone else, and even though she battles to suppress them, it is a battle she never wins.

Transient detours, mental conniptions, ordure rising from the inner depths, but out in the external world of solid things she has allowed her desires to run away from her only once, only once with any lasting consequences. The ballad of Benjamin Samuels dates back to the summer of 2000, eight years ago, eight and a half years ago to be exact, which means that close to one-third of her life has been lived since then, and still it remains with her, she has never stopped listening to the song in her mind, and as she stands on the porch this foggy Sunday morning,

she wonders if anything as momentous will ever happen to her again. She was twenty years old and had just finished her sophomore year at Smith. Alice was going back to Wisconsin to work as head counselor at a summer camp near Lake Oconomowoc, and she asked her if she wanted a job there as well, which was something she could easily arrange. No, she wasn't interested in summer camps, she said, she'd had an unhappy experience at camp when she was eleven, and so she wound up taking another job closer to home, for Professor Samuels and his wife, who had rented a place in southern Vermont for two and a half months and needed someone to look after their kids – Bea, Cora, and Ben, girls of five and seven and a boy of sixteen. The boy was too old to require looking after, but he had messed up in school that year, barely passing several of his courses, and she was supposed to tutor him in English, American history, and algebra. He was in a foul temper when the summer began – barred from attending his beloved soccer camp in Northampton and faced with the prospect of eleven weeks of excruciating exile with his parents and sisters in the middle of nowhere. But she was beautiful then, never more beautiful than she was that summer, so much rounder and softer than the scrawny creature she has turned into now, and why would a sixteen-year-old boy complain about having to take lessons from an enticing young woman in sleeveless tank tops and black spandex shorts? By the beginning of the second week they were friends, and by the beginning of the third week they were spending most of their evenings together in the pavilion, a small outbuilding about fifty yards from the main house, where they watched the films she would pick up from Al's Video Store on her shopping excursions to Brattleboro. The girls and their parents were always asleep by then. Professor Samuels and his wife were both writing books that summer, and they kept to a rigid schedule, up at five-thirty every morning and lights out by nine-thirty or ten. They weren't the least bit concerned that she and their son were spending so much time together in the pavilion. She was Ellen Brice, after all, the soft-spoken, dependable girl who had done so well in Professor Samuels's art history class, and they could count on her to behave responsibly in all situations.

Having sex with Ben wasn't her idea – at least not at first. She loved looking at him, the strength and leanness of his soccer player's body often aroused her, but he was still just a boy, less than six months ago he had been fifteen, and however attractive she might have found him, she had no intention of doing anything about it. But one month into the two

and a half months she stayed there, on a warm July night filled with the sounds of tree frogs and a million cicadas, the boy made the first move. They were sitting in their usual positions at opposite ends of the small sofa, the moths were banging against the screen windows as usual, the night air smelled of pines and damp earth as usual, a dumb comedy or Western was playing as usual (the selection at Al's was limited), and she was beginning to feel drowsy, drowsy enough to lean back her head and close her eyes for a few seconds, perhaps ten seconds, perhaps twenty seconds, and before she was able to open them again, young Mr. Samuels had moved over to her side of the sofa and was kissing her on the mouth. She should have pushed him away, or turned her head away, or stood up and walked away, but she couldn't think fast enough to do any of those things, and so she remained where she was, sitting on the sofa with her eyes closed, and allowed him to go on kissing her.

They were never caught. For a month and a half they carried on with their little sex affair (she could never bring herself to think of it as a love affair), and then the summer came to an end. She might not have fallen in love with Ben, but she was in love with his body, and even now, eight and a half years later, she still thinks about the uncanny smoothness of his skin, the feel of his long arms wrapped around her, the sweetness of his mouth, the taste of him. She would have continued seeing Ben in Northampton after the summer, but his miserable academic performance the previous year had alarmed his parents so much that they shipped him off to a boarding school in New Hampshire, and suddenly he was gone from her life. She missed him a good deal more than she was expecting to, but before she understood how long it would take to get over him, how many weeks or months or years, she found herself in a new kind of fix. Her period was late. She told Alice about it, and her friend promptly dragged her off to the nearest pharmacy to buy a home-pregnancy-test kit. The results were positive, which is to say, negative, disastrously and irrevocably negative. She thought they had been so prudent, so careful to avoid just this thing from happening, but clearly they had slipped up somewhere along the way, and now what was she going to do? She couldn't tell anyone who the father was. Not even Alice, who pressed her about it again and again, and not even the father himself, who was just a sixteen-year-old boy, and why punish him with this news when there was nothing he could do to help her, when she was the one to blame for the whole sordid business? She couldn't talk to Alice, she couldn't talk to Ben, and she couldn't talk to her parents – not just about

who the father was, but about who she was as well. A pregnant girl, an idiot college girl with a baby growing inside her. Her mother and father could never know what had happened. The mere thought of trying to tell them about it was enough to make her want to die.

If she had been a braver person, she would have had the child. In spite of the upheavals a full-term pregnancy would have caused, she wanted to go ahead with it and let the baby be born, but she was too scared of the questions she would be asked, too ashamed to confront her family, too weak to assert herself and drop out of school to join the ranks of *unwed mothers*. Alice drove her to the clinic. It was supposed to be a quick, uncomplicated procedure, and in medical terms everything came off as advertised, but she found it gruesome and humiliating, and she hated herself for having gone against her deepest impulses, her deepest convictions. Four days later, she downed half a bottle of vodka and twenty sleeping pills. Alice was supposed to be gone for the weekend, and if she hadn't changed her plans at the last minute and returned to their dormitory suite at four o'clock that afternoon, her sleeping roommate would still be sleeping now. They took her to Cooley Dickinson Hospital and pumped her stomach, and that was the end of Smith, the end of Ellen Brice as a so-called normal person. She was transferred to the psych ward of the hospital and kept there for twenty days, and then she returned to New York, where she spent a long, infinitely depressing period living with her parents, sleeping in her old childhood bedroom, seeing Dr. Burnham three times a week, attending group therapy sessions, and ingesting her daily quantum of the pills that were supposed to make her feel better but didn't. Eventually, she took it upon herself to enroll in some drawing classes at the School of Visual Arts, which turned into painting classes the following year, and little by little she began to feel that she was almost living in the world again, that there might be something that resembled a future for her, after all. When her sister's husband's brother-in-law offered her a job with his real estate firm in Brooklyn, she finally moved out of her parents' apartment and started living on her own. She knew that it was the wrong job for her, that having to talk to so many people every day could become an unrelenting trial on her nerves, but she accepted the job anyway. She needed to get out, needed to be free of the ever-worried eyes of her mother and father, and this was her only chance.

That was five years ago. Now, as she stands on the front porch of the house wrapped in her overcoat and drinking her morning coffee, she realizes that she must begin again. Painful as it was to listen to Millie's

words two months ago, the brutal and dismissive condemnation of her drawings and canvases was fully deserved. Her work doesn't speak to anyone. She knows she is not without skill, not without talent even, but she has boxed herself into a corner by pursuing a single idea, and that idea isn't strong enough to bear the weight of what she has been trying to accomplish. She thought the delicacy of her touch could lead her to the sublime and austere realm that Morandi had once inhabited. She wanted to make pictures that would evoke the mute wonder of pure thingness, the holy ether breathing in the spaces between things, a translation of human existence into a minute rendering of all that is *out there* beyond us, around us, in the same way she knows the invisible graveyard is standing there in front of her, even if she cannot see it. But she was wrong to put her trust in things, to trust in things only, to have squandered her time on the innumerable buildings she has drawn and painted, the empty streets devoid of people, the garages and gas stations and factories, the bridges and elevated highways, the red bricks of old warehouses glinting in the dusky New York light. It comes across as timid evasion, an empty exercise in style, whereas all she has ever wanted is to draw and paint representations of her own feelings. There will be no hope for her unless she starts again from the beginning. No more inanimate objects, she tells herself, no more still lifes. She will return to the human figure and force her strokes to become bolder and more expressive, more gestural, more wild if need be, as wild as the wildest thought within her.

She will ask Alice to pose for her. It is Sunday, a quiet Sunday without much of anything going on, and even if Alice will be working on her dissertation today, she might be able to spare her a couple of hours between now and bed. She goes back into the house and walks up the stairs to her room. Bing and Alice are still asleep, and she moves cautiously so as not to wake them, pulling off her overcoat and the flannel nightgown under it and then climbing into a pair of old jeans and a thick cotton sweater, not bothering with panties or a bra, just her bare skin under the soft fabrics, wanting to feel as loose and mobile as she can this morning, unencumbered for the day ahead. She takes her drawing pad and a Faber-Castell pencil off the top of the bureau, then sits down on the bed and opens the pad to the first empty page. Holding the pencil in her right hand, she raises her left hand in the air, tilts it at a forty-five-degree angle, and keeps it suspended about twelve inches from her face, studying it until it no longer seems attached to her body. It is an alien hand now, a hand that belongs to someone else, to no one, a woman's

hand with its slender fingers and rounded nails, the half-moons above the cuticles, the narrow wrist with its small bump of bone sticking out on the left side, the ivory-shaded knuckles and joints, the nearly translucent white skin sheathed over rivulets of veins, blue veins bearing the red blood that meanders through her system as her heart beats and the air moves in and out of her lungs. Digits, carpus, metacarpus, phalanges, dermis. She presses the point of the pencil against the blank page and begins to draw the hand.

At nine-thirty, she knocks on Alice's door. Diligent Bergstrom is already at work, a swarm of fingers darting across the keyboard of her laptop, eyes fixed on the screen in front of her, and Ellen apologizes for interrupting her. No, no, Alice says, it's perfectly all right, and then she stops typing and turns to her friend with one of those warm Alice smiles on her face, no, more than just a warm smile, a maternal smile somehow, not the way Ellen's mother smiles at her, perhaps, but the kind of smile all mothers should give their children, a smile that is not a greeting so much as an offering, a benediction. She thinks: Alice will make a terrific mother when the time comes . . . a superior mother, she says to herself, and then, because of the juxtaposition of those two words, she transforms Alice into a Mother Superior, suddenly seeing her in a nun's habit, and because of this momentary digression she loses her train of thought and doesn't have time to ask Alice if she would be willing to pose for her before Alice is asking a question of her own:

Have you ever seen *The Best Years of Our Lives*?

Of course, Ellen says. Everyone knows that film.

Do you like it?

Very much. It's one of my favorite Hollywood movies.

Why do you like it?

I don't know. It touches me. I always cry when I see it.

You don't find it a little too pat?

Of course it's pat. It's a Hollywood movie, isn't it? All Hollywood movies are a bit contrived, don't you think?

Good point. But this one is a little less contrived than most – is that what you're saying?

Think of the scene when the father helps prepare his son for bed.

Harold Russell, the soldier who lost his hands in the war.

The boy can't take off the hooks by himself, he can't button up his own pajamas, he can't put out his cigarette. His father has to do everything for him. As I remember it, there's no music in that scene, hardly a word

of dialogue, but it's a great moment in the film. Completely honest. Incredibly moving.

Does everyone live happily ever after?

Maybe yes, maybe no. Dana Andrews tells the girl –

Teresa Wright –

He tells Teresa Wright that they're going to get kicked around a lot. Maybe they will, maybe they won't. And the Fredric March character is a drunk, a serious, nonstop, raving alcoholic, so his life isn't going to be much fun a few years down the road.

What about Harold Russell?

He marries his sweetheart at the end, but what kind of marriage is it going to be? He's a simple, good-hearted boy, but so damned inarticulate, so bottled up emotionally, I don't see how he's going to make his wife very happy.

I hadn't realized you knew the film so well.

My grandmother was crazy about it. She was about sixteen when the war broke out, and she always said *The Best Years of Our Lives* was *her* movie. We must have watched it together five or six times.

They go on talking about the film for a few more minutes, and then she finally remembers to ask Alice the question that prompted her to knock on the door in the first place. Alice is busy now, but she will be glad to break for an hour after lunch and pose for her then. What Alice doesn't understand is that Ellen isn't interested in doing a portrait of her face, she wants to make a drawing of her whole body, and not that body hidden by clothes but a full nude sketch, perhaps several sketches, similar to the ones she did in her life classes at art school. It is therefore an awkward moment for both of them when they go upstairs to Ellen's room after lunch and Ellen asks Alice to take off her clothes. Alice has never worked as a model, she is not accustomed to having her naked body scrutinized by anyone, and although she and Ellen occasionally catch glimpses of each other going in and out of the bathroom, that has nothing to do with the torture of having to sit stock-still for an hour as your closest friend looks you over from top to bottom, especially now, when she is feeling so miserable about her weight, and even though Ellen tells Alice that she is beautiful, that she has nothing to worry about, it is merely an art exercise, artists are used to looking at other people's bodies, Alice is too embarrassed to give in to her friend's request, she is sorry, terribly sorry, but she can't go through with it and must say no. Ellen is stung by Alice's refusal to do this simple thing

for her, which is in fact the first step in reinventing herself as an artist, which is no less than reinventing herself as a woman, a human being, and while she understands that Alice has no intention of hurting her, she can't help feeling hurt, and when she asks Alice to leave the room, she closes the door, sits down on the bed, and starts to cry.

He thinks of it as a six-month prison sentence with no time off for good behavior. The Christmas and Easter holidays will give Pilar temporary visiting rights, but he will be confined to his cell for the full six months. He mustn't dream of escape. No digging of tunnels in the middle of the night, no confrontations with the guards, no hacking through barbed wire, no mad dashes into the woods pursued by dogs. If he can last through his term without running into trouble or going to pieces, he will be on a bus heading back to Florida on May twenty-second, and on the twenty-third he will be with Pilar to celebrate her birthday. Until then, he will go on holding his breath.

*Going to pieces.* That was the phrase he kept using during the course of his trip, during the seven conversations he had with her over the thirty-four hours he spent on the road. *You mustn't go to pieces.* When she wasn't sobbing into the phone or ranting against her maniac bitch of a sister, she seemed to understand what he was trying to tell her. He heard himself uttering platitudes that just two days earlier he couldn't have imagined would ever cross his lips, and yet a part of him believed in what he was saying. They had to be strong. This was a test, and their love would only deepen because of it. And then there was the practical advice, the injunctions to go on doing well at school, to remember to eat enough, to go to bed early every night, to change the oil in the car at regular intervals, to read the books he left for her. Was it a man talking to his future wife or a father talking to his child? A little of both, perhaps. It was Miles talking to Pilar. Miles doing his best to hold the girl together, to hold himself together.

He walks into the Hospital for Broken Things at three o'clock on Monday afternoon. That was the arrangement. If he came in after six o'clock, he was to head straight for the house in Sunset Park. If he arrived during the day, he was to meet Bing at his store on Fifth Avenue in Brooklyn. A bell tinkles as he opens and shuts the door, and when he steps inside he is struck by how small the place is, surely it is the smallest hospital in the world, he thinks, a dingy, cluttered shrine with ancient typewriters on display, a cigar-store Indian standing in the far corner to his left, model

biplanes and Piper Cubs hanging from the ceiling, and the walls covered with signs and posters advertising products that left the American scene decades ago: Black Jack gum, O'Dell's Hair Trainer, Geritol, Carter's Little Liver Pills, Old Gold cigarettes. At the sound of the bell, Bing emerges from a back room behind the counter, looking larger and bushier than he remembers, a great big grinning oaf rushing toward him with open arms. Bing is all smiles and laughs, all bear hugs and kisses on the cheek, and Miles, caught off guard by this slobbering welcome, bursts out laughing himself as he wriggles free of his friend's crushing embrace.

Bing closes up the Hospital early, and because he suspects Miles is hungry after the long trip, he leads him a few blocks down Fifth Avenue to what he calls his favorite lunch place, a scruffy beanery that serves fish and chips, shepherd's pies, bangers and mash, a full menu of authentic Limey grub. No wonder Bing has broadened so much, Miles thinks, lunching on this greasy slop several times a week, but the truth is that he is famished just now, and what could be better than a hot shepherd's pie to fill you up on a cold day? Meanwhile, Bing is talking to him about the house, about his band, about his failed love affair with Millie, punctuating his remarks every so often with a brief word about how well he thinks Miles is looking and how glad he is to see him again. Miles doesn't say much in response, he is busy with his food, but he is impressed by Bing's high spirits and lunging goodwill, and the more Bing talks, the more he feels that his pen pal of the past seven years is the same person he was when they last saw each other, a little older, of course, a little more in possession of himself, perhaps, but essentially the same person, whereas he, Miles, is altogether different now, a black sheep who bears no resemblance to the lamb he was seven years ago.

Toward the end of the meal, a look of discomfort comes over Bing's face. He pauses for a few moments, fidgeting with his fork, casting his eyes down at the table, apparently at a loss for words, and when he finally speaks again, his voice is far more subdued than it was earlier, almost hushed.

I don't mean to pry, he says, but I was wondering if you have any plans.

Plans to do what? Miles asks.

To see your parents, for one thing.

Is that any of your business?

Yes, unfortunately it is. I've been your source for a long time now, and I think I want to retire.

You already have. The moment I stepped off the bus today, you were given your gold watch. For years of devoted service. You know how grateful I am to you, don't you?

I don't want your gratitude, Miles. I just don't want to see you fuck up your life anymore. It hasn't been easy on them, you know.

I know. Don't think I don't know.

Well? Are you going to see them or not?

I want to, I'm hoping to . . .

That's no kind of answer. Yes or no?

Yes. Of course I will, he says, not knowing if he will or not, not knowing that Bing has talked to his parents fifty-two times in the past seven years, not knowing that his father and mother and Willa have all been told he will be landing in New York today. Of course I will, he says again. Just give me a chance to settle in first.

The house is like no house he has ever seen in New York. He is aware that the city is filled with anomalous structures that have no apparent connection to urban life – the brick houses and garden apartments in certain sections of Queens, for example, with their timid, suburban aspirations, or the few remaining wooden houses in the northernmost parts of Brooklyn Heights, historical remnants from the 1840s – but this house in Sunset Park is neither suburban nor historic, it is merely a shack, a forlorn piece of architectural stupidity that would not fit in anywhere, neither in New York nor out of it. Bing didn't send any photographs with his letter, didn't describe what it looked like in any detail, and therefore he had no idea what to expect, but if he did expect anything, it certainly wasn't this.

Cracked gray shingles, red trim around the three sash windows on the second floor, a flimsy balustrade on the porch with diamond-shaped openings painted white, the four posts propping up the roof on the porch painted red, the same brick red as the trim around the windows, but no paint on the front steps or handrails, which are too splintered for a paint job and have been left as bare, weathered wood. Alice and Ellen are both still at work when he and Bing walk up the six steps to the front porch and go inside. Bing gives him the grand tour, clearly proud of all they have accomplished, and while the house seems cramped to him (not just because of the size of the rooms or the number of rooms but because of the many things that have been jammed into them – Bing's drums, Ellen's canvases, Alice's books), the interior is remarkably clean, with a patched-up, freshly painted brightness, and therefore perhaps even

livable. The kitchen, the bathroom, and the back bedroom downstairs; the three bedrooms upstairs. But no living room or parlor, which means that the kitchen is the only communal space – along with the porch in times of good weather. He will be inheriting Millie's old bedroom on the ground floor, which is something of a relief, since that room affords the most privacy, if living in a room off the kitchen can be considered privacy. He puts his bag down on the bed, and as he looks out the windows on either side of him, the one with a view of the vacant lot with the junked car in it, the other with a view of the abandoned construction site, Bing is telling him about the various routines and protocols that have been established since they moved in. Each person has a job to perform, but beyond the responsibilities of that job, everyone is free to come and go at will. He is the handyman-janitor, Ellen is the cleaning woman, and Alice does the shopping and most of the cooking. Perhaps Miles would like to share Alice's job with her, taking turns with the shopping and cooking. Miles has no objection. He enjoys cooking, he says, he's developed a knack for it over the years, and that won't be a problem. Bing goes on to say they generally eat breakfast and dinner together because they are all low on money and are trying to spend as little as they can. Pooling their resources has helped them get by, and now that Miles has joined the household, everyone's expenses will go down accordingly. They will all benefit because he is here, and by that he isn't talking only about money, it's about everything Miles will add to the spirit of the house, and Bing wants him to understand how happy it makes him to know that he is finally back where he belongs. Miles shrugs, saying he hopes he can manage to fit in, but secretly he is wondering if he is cut out for this sort of group living, if he wouldn't be better off looking for a place of his own. The only problem is cash, the same problem all the others are facing. He no longer has a job, and the three thousand dollars he brought with him amount to little more than pennies. Like it or not, then, for the time being he is stuck, and unless something comes along that dramatically alters his circumstances, he will just have to make the best of it. So his prison sentence begins. Pilar's sister has turned him into the newest member of the Sunset Park Four.

That night, they throw a dinner in his honor. It is a gesture of welcome, and although he would prefer not to have been made the center of attention, he tries to get through it without showing how uncomfortable he feels. What are his first impressions of them? He finds Alice to be the most likable, the most grounded, and he is rather taken by her blunt,

boyish, Midwestern approach to things. A well-read person with a good mind, he discovers, but unaffected, self-deprecating, with a talent for tossing off subtle wisecracks at unexpected moments. Ellen is more of a puzzle to him. She is both attractive and not attractive, both open and closed off, and from one minute to the next her personality seems to change. Long, awkward silences, and then, when she finally speaks, she rarely fails to deliver some astute remark. He senses inner turbulence, disarray, and yet deep kindness as well. If only she wouldn't stare at him so much, he might be able to warm up to her a little, but her eyes have been on him ever since they sat down at the table, and he feels discomfited by her blatant, overly intrusive interest in him. Then there is Jake, the sometime visitor to Sunset Park, a thin, balding person with a sharp nose and big ears, Jake Baum the writer, Alice's boyfriend. For the first few minutes he seems pleasant enough, but then Miles begins to change his opinion of him, noticing that he barely takes the trouble to listen to anyone but himself, especially Alice, whom he interrupts again and again, often cutting her off in midsentence to pursue some thought of his own, and before long Miles concludes that Jake Baum is a bore, even if he can recite Pound from memory and reel off the opponents from every World Series since 1932. Thankfully, Bing seems to be in top fettle, exuberantly playing his role as master of ceremonies, and in spite of the invisible tensions in the air, he has deftly maintained the frivolous tone of the evening. Each time another bottle of wine is opened, he stands up to pronounce a toast, celebrating Miles's homecoming, celebrating the imminent four-month anniversary of their little revolution, celebrating the rights of squatters all over the world. The only negative in all this conviviality is the fact that Miles doesn't drink, and he knows that when people meet someone who abstains from alcohol, they automatically assume he is a recovering drunk. Miles was never an alcoholic, but there was a time when he felt he was drinking too much, and when he cut himself off three years ago, it was as much about saving money as it was about his health. They can think whatever they like, he tells himself, it's of no importance to him, but each time Bing lifts his glass for another toast, Jake turns to Miles and urges him to join in. An honest mistake the first time, perhaps, but there have been two more toasts since then, and Jake has kept on doing it. If he knew what Miles was capable of when he is angry, the needling would stop at once, but Jake doesn't know, and if he does it again the next time, he could end up with a bloody nose or a broken jaw. All the years of battling to keep his temper under control,

and now, on his first day back in New York, Miles is seething again, ready to tear someone apart.

It gets worse. Before the dinner, he asked Bing not to let anyone know who his parents were, to keep the names Morris Heller and Mary-Lee Swann out of the discussion, and Bing said of course, that went without saying, but now, just when the dinner is finally coming to an end, Jake starts talking about Renzo Michaelson's most recent novel, *The Mountain Dialogues*, which was published by his father's company in September. Perhaps there is nothing unusual about that, the book is doing extremely well, no doubt many people are talking about it, and Baum is a writer himself, which means that he is bound to be acquainted with Renzo's work, but Miles doesn't want to listen to him blather on about it, not about this book in any case, which he read down in Florida when it was first published, read only when Pilar wasn't around the apartment because it was too much for him, he understood on the first page that the two sixty-year-old men sitting and talking on that mountaintop in the Berkshires were in fact based on Renzo and his father, and it was impossible for him to read that book without breaking down in tears, knowing that he himself was implicated in the sorrows of that story, the two men talking back and forth about the things they had lived through, old friends, the best of old friends, his father and his godfather, and here is pompous Jake Baum making his declarations about that book, and with all his heart Miles wishes he would stop. Baum says he would love to interview Michaelson. He knows he rarely talks to journalists, but there are so many questions he would like to ask him, and wouldn't it be *a feather in his cap* if he could persuade Michaelson to give him a couple of hours? Baum is thinking only about his own petty ambitions, trying to aggrandize himself by feeding off someone who is ten thousand times greater than he will ever be, and then stupid Bing pipes in with the news that he is the person who cleans and repairs Renzo's typewriter, good old Michaelson, one of the last of a dying breed, a novelist who still hasn't switched over to a computer, and yes, he knows him a little bit, and maybe he could put in a word for Jake the next time Renzo comes into the shop. By now, Miles is ready to jump on Bing and strangle him, but just then, fortunately, the conversation is deflected onto another subject when Alice lets out a loud, booming sneeze, and suddenly Bing is talking about flus and winter colds, and no more mention is made of interviewing Renzo Michaelson.

After that dinner, he resolves to make himself scarce whenever Jake is

around, to avoid having any more meals with him. He doesn't want to do anything he will later regret, and Jake is the kind of man who inevitably brings out the worst in him. As it happens, the problem is not as grave as he supposes it will be. Baum comes by only once in the next two weeks, and although Alice spends a couple of nights with him in Manhattan, Miles senses there is trouble between them, that they are facing a rugged patch or perhaps even the end. It shouldn't concern him, but now that he has come to know Alice, he hopes it is the end, for Baum doesn't deserve a woman like Alice, and she herself deserves far better.

Three days after his arrival, he calls his father's office. The receptionist tells him that Mr. Heller is out of the country and won't be returning to work until January fifth. Would he like to leave a message? No, he says, he'll call back next month, thank you.

He reads in the paper that previews of his mother's play will begin on January thirteenth.

He doesn't know what to do with himself. Besides his daily conversations with Pilar, which tend to last between one and two hours, there is no structure to his life anymore. He wanders around the streets, trying to familiarize himself with the neighborhood, but he quickly loses interest in Sunset Park. There is something dead about the place, he finds, the mournful emptiness of poverty and immigrant struggle, an area without banks or bookstores, only check-cashing operations and a decrepit public library, a small world apart from the world where time moves so slowly that few people bother to wear a watch.

He spends an afternoon taking photographs of some of the factories near the waterfront, the old buildings that house the last surviving companies in the neighborhood, manufacturers of windows and doors, swimming pools, ladies' clothes and nurses' uniforms, but the pictures are nondescript somehow, lacking in urgency, uninspired. The next day, he ventures up to the Chinatown on Eighth Avenue, with its dense grouping of shops and businesses, its crowded sidewalks, the ducks hanging in the butchers' windows, a hundred potential scenes to capture, vivid colors all around him, but still he feels flattened out, unengaged, and he leaves without taking a single picture. He will need time to adjust, he tells himself. His body might be here now, but his mind is still with Pilar in Florida, and even if he is home again, this New York is not his New York, not the New York of his memory. For all the distance he has traveled, he might just as well have come to a foreign city, a city anywhere else in America.

Little by little, he has been acclimating himself to Ellen's eyes. He no longer feels threatened by her curiosity in him, and if she talks less than anyone else at their shared breakfasts and dinners around the kitchen table, she can be quite voluble when he is alone with her. She communicates largely by asking questions, not personal questions about his life or past history, but questions about his opinions on topics ranging from the weather to the state of the world. Does he like winter? Who does he think is a better artist, Picasso or Matisse? Is he worried about global warming? Was he happy when Obama was elected last month? Why do men like sports so much? Who is his favorite photographer? No doubt there is something infantile about her directness, but at the same time her questions often provoke spirited exchanges, and following the path of Alice and Bing before him, he feels an ever-growing responsibility to protect her. He understands that Ellen is lonely and would like nothing better than to spend every night in his bed, but he has already told her enough about Pilar for her to know that this won't be possible. On one of her days off, she invites him to go walking with her in Green-Wood Cemetery, a visit to the City of the Dead, as she calls it, and for the first time since coming to Sunset Park, he feels something stir inside him. There were the abandoned things down in Florida, and now he has stumbled upon the abandoned people of Brooklyn. He suspects it is a terrain well worth exploring.

With Alice, he has been given the chance to talk to someone about books, a thing that has happened to him only rarely in the years between college and Pilar. Early on, he discovers that she is mostly ignorant of European and South American literature, which comes as a small disappointment, but she is one of those specialized academics steeped in her narrow Anglo-American world, far more familiar with *Beowulf* and Dreiser than with Dante and Borges, but that hardly qualifies as a problem, there is still much they can talk about, and before many days have passed they have already developed a private shorthand to express their likes and dislikes, a language consisting of grunts, frowns, raised eyebrows, nods of the head, and sudden slaps to the knee. She doesn't talk to him about Jake, and therefore he doesn't ask her any questions. He has told her about Pilar, however, but not much, not much of anything beyond her name and the fact that she will be coming up from Florida to visit over Christmas break. He uses the word *break* instead of *vacation,* since *break* suggests college and *vacation* always means school, and he doesn't want anyone in the house to know how young Pilar is until she

is already here – at which point, he hopes, no one will bother to ask her age. But even if it happens, he isn't worried. The only person to worry about is Angela, and Angela won't know that Pilar is gone. He has discussed this detail with Pilar again and again. She mustn't let any of her sisters know that she is leaving, not just Angela, but Teresa and Maria as well, for the minute one of them knows, they will all know, and even if the odds are against it, Angela might just be crazy enough to follow Pilar to New York.

He has bought a small illustrated book about Green-Wood Cemetery, and he goes in there every day with his camera now, roaming among the graves and monuments and mausoleums, nearly always alone in the frigid December air, carefully studying the lavish, often bombastic architecture of certain plots, the marble pillars and obelisks, the Greek temples and Egyptian pyramids, the enormous statues of supine, weeping women. The cemetery is more than half the size of Central Park, ample enough space for a person to get lost in there, to forget that he is a prisoner serving out his time in a dreary part of Brooklyn, and to walk among the thousands of trees and plantings, to climb the hillocks and traverse the sweeping paths of this vast necropolis is to leave the city behind you and enclose yourself in the absolute quiet of the dead. He takes pictures of the tombs of gangsters and poets, generals and industrialists, murder victims and newspaper publishers, children dead before their time, a woman who lived seventeen years beyond her hundredth birthday, and Theodore Roosevelt's wife and mother, who were buried next to each other on the same day. There is Elias Howe, inventor of the sewing machine, the Kampfe brothers, inventors of the safety razor, Henry Steinway, founder of the Steinway Piano Company, John Underwood, founder of the Underwood Typewriter Company, Henry Chadwick, inventor of the baseball scoring system, Elmer Sperry, inventor of the gyroscope. The crematory built in the mid-twentieth century has incinerated the bodies of John Steinbeck, Woody Guthrie, Edward R. Murrow, Eubie Blake, and how many more, both known and unknown, how many more souls have been transformed into smoke in this eerie, beautiful place? He has embarked on another useless project, employing his camera as an instrument to record his stray, useless thoughts, but at least it is something to do, a way to pass the time until his life starts again, and where else but in Green-Wood Cemetery could he have learned that the real name of Frank Morgan, the actor who played the Wizard of Oz, was Wuppermann?

*Morris Heller*

# I

It is the last day of the year, and he has come home from England a week early to attend the funeral of Martin Rothstein's twenty-three-year-old daughter, who committed suicide in Venice the night before Christmas Eve. He has been publishing Rothstein's work since the founding of Heller Books. Marty and Renzo were the only Americans on the first list, two Americans along with Per Carlsen from Denmark and Annette Louverain from France, and thirty-five years later he is still publishing them all, they are the core writers of the house, and he knows he would be nothing without them. The news came on the evening of the twenty-fourth, a mass e-mail sent to hundreds of friends and acquaintances, which he read on Willa's computer in their room at the Charlotte Street Hotel in London, the grim, naked message from Marty and Nina that Suki had taken her own life, with further information to follow about the date of the funeral. Willa didn't want him to go. She thought the funeral would be too hard on him, there had been too many funerals in the past year, too many of their friends were dying now, and she knew how ravaged he was by the losses, that was the word she used, *ravaged*, but he said he had to be there for them, it wouldn't be possible not to go, the duties of friendship demanded it, and four days later he was on a plane back to New York.

Now it is December thirty-first, late morning on the final day of 2008, and as he steps off the No. 1 train and climbs the stairs to Broadway and Seventy-ninth Street, the air is clogged with snow, a wet, heavy snow is falling from the white-gray sky, thick flakes tumbling through the blustery dimness, muting the colors of the traffic lights, whitening the hoods of passing cars, and by the time he reaches the community center on Amsterdam Avenue, he looks as if he is wearing a hat of snow. Suki Rothstein, birth name Susanna, the baby girl he first glimpsed sleeping in the crook of her father's right arm twenty-three years ago, the young woman who graduated summa cum laude from the University of Chicago, the budding artist, the precociously gifted thinker, writer, photographer who went to Venice this past fall to work as an intern at the Peggy Guggenheim Collection, and it was there, in the women's room of

that museum, just days after conducting a seminar about her own work, that she hanged herself. Willa was right, he knows that, but how not to feel ravaged by Suki's death, how not to put himself inside her father's skin and suffer the ravages of this pointless death?

He remembers running into her some years back on Houston Street in the brightness of a late afternoon at the end of spring, the beginning of summer. She was on her way to her high school prom, decked out in a flamboyant red dress, as red as the reddest Jersey tomato, and Suki was all lit up with smiles when he chanced upon her that afternoon, surrounded by her friends, happy, affectionately kissing him hello and good-bye, and from that day forward he held that picture of her in his mind as the quintessential embodiment of youthful exuberance and promise, a singular example of *youth on fire.* Now he thinks about the dank chill of Venice in the dead of winter, the canals overflowing onto streets knee-deep in water, the shivering loneliness of unheated rooms, a head splitting open from the sheer force of the darkness within it, a life broken apart by the too-much and too-little of this world.

He shuffles into the building with the other people, a slowly gathering crowd that builds to two or three hundred, and he sees any number of familiar faces in the throng, Renzo's among them, but also Sally Fuchs, Don Willingham, Gordon Field, any number of old friends, writers, poets, artists, editors, and many young people as well, dozens and dozens of young men and women, Suki's friends from childhood, from high school, from college, and everyone is speaking in low voices, as if speaking above a whisper would be an offense, an insult against the silence of the dead, and as he looks at the faces around him, everyone seems numb and depleted, not quite fully there, *ravaged.* He makes his way to a small room at the end of the corridor where Marty and Nina are welcoming the visitors, the guests, the mourners, whatever word is used to describe people who come to a funeral, and as he steps forward to put his arms around his old friend, tears are pouring down Marty's face, and then Marty throws his arms around him and presses his head against his shoulder, saying Morris, Morris, Morris as his body convulses against him in a spasm of breathless sobs.

Martin Rothstein is not a man built for tragedies of this magnitude. He is a person of wit and effervescent charm, a comic writer of baroque, hilariously constructed sentences and spot-on satirical flair, an intellectual agitator with grand appetites and countless friends and a sense of humor equal to the best of the Borscht Belt wise guys. Now he is weeping

his heart out, overcome by grief, by the cruelest, most lacerating form of grief, and Morris wonders how anyone can expect a man in this condition to stand up and talk in front of all these people when the service begins. And yet, sometime later, when the mourners have taken their seats in the auditorium and Marty climbs onto the stage to deliver his eulogy, he is calm, dry-eyed, completely recovered from his breakdown in the reception room. He reads from a text he has written, a text no doubt made possible by the length of time it took for Suki's body to be shipped from Venice to New York, making the gap between death and burial longer than usual, and in those empty, unsettled days of waiting for his daughter's corpse to arrive, Marty sat down and wrote this text. With Bobby, there had been no words. Willa hadn't been capable of writing or saying anything, he hadn't been capable of writing or saying anything, the accident had crushed them into a state of mute incomprehension, a dumb, bleeding sorrow that had lasted for months, but Marty is a writer, his whole life has been spent putting words and sentences together, paragraphs together, books together, and the only way he could respond to Suki's death was to write about her.

The coffin is on the stage, a white coffin surrounded by red flowers, but it is not a religious service. No rabbi has come to officiate, no prayers are recited, and no one who appears onstage tries to draw any meaning or consolation from Suki's death – there is nothing more than the fact of it, the horror of it. Someone plays a solo piece for saxophone, someone else plays a Bach chorale on the piano, and at one point Suki's younger brother, Anton, wearing red nail polish in honor of his sister, performs an unaccompanied, dirgelike rendition of a Cole Porter song (Ev'ry time we say good-bye / I die a little) that is so drastically slowed down, so drenched in melancholy, so painful to listen to that most of the gathering is in tears by the time he comes to the end. Writers walk up to the lectern and read poems by Shakespeare and Yeats. Friends and classmates tell stories about Suki, reminisce, evoke the *burning intensity of her spirit.* The director of the gallery where she had her one and only exhibition talks about her work. Morris follows every word spoken, listens to every note played and sung, on the verge of disintegration throughout the entire one-and-a-half-hour service, but it is Marty's speech that comes closest to destroying him, a brave and stunning piece of eloquence that shocks him with its candor, the brutal precision of its thinking, the rage and sorrow and guilt and love that permeate each of its articulations. All during Marty's twenty-minute talk, Morris imagines himself trying to talk

about Bobby, about Miles, about the long-dead Bobby and the absent Miles, but he knows he would never have the courage to stand up in public and express his feelings with such naked honesty.

Afterward, there is a pause. Only the Rothsteins and their closest relatives will be going to the cemetery in Queens. Everyone is invited to Marty and Nina's apartment at four o'clock, but for now the mourners must disperse. He is glad to have been spared the ordeal of watching the coffin being lowered into the ground, the bulldozer pushing the dirt back into the hole, the sight of Marty and Nina collapsing into tears again. Renzo tracks him down in the entrance hall, and the two of them go back out into the snow together to look for a place to have lunch. Renzo is intelligent enough to have brought along an umbrella, and as Morris squeezes in beside him, Renzo puts his arm around his shoulder. Neither one of them says a word. They have been friends for fifty years, and each knows what the other is thinking.

They wind up in a Jewish delicatessen on Broadway in the low Eighties, a throwback to their New York childhoods, the all but vanished cuisine of chopped liver, matzo-ball soup, corned beef and pastrami sandwiches, pot roasts, cheese blintzes, sour pickles. Renzo has been traveling, they haven't seen each other since the publication of *The Mountain Dialogues* in September, and Morris feels that Renzo is looking tired, more haggard than usual. How did they get to be so old? he wonders. They are both sixty-two now, and while neither of them is in bad health, neither one of them fat or bald or ready for the glue factory, their heads have turned gray, their hairlines are receding, and they have reached that point in their lives when women under thirty, perhaps even forty, look right through them. He remembers Renzo as a young, young writer just out of college, living in a forty-nine-dollar-a-month apartment on the Lower East Side, one of those tenement railroad flats with a tub in the kitchen and six thousand cockroaches holding political conventions in every cupboard, so poor that he had to limit himself to one meal a day, working for three years on his first novel, which he destroyed because he felt it wasn't good enough, destroyed in the face of Morris's protests, his girlfriend's protests, who both felt it was very good indeed, and now look at him, Morris thinks, after how many books since that burned manuscript (seventeen? twenty?), published in every country of the world, even Iran, for God's sake, with how many literary prizes, how many medals, keys to cities, honorary doctorates, how many books and dissertations written about his work, and none of it matters to him, he is glad to have

some money now, glad to be free of the suffocating hardships of the early years, but his fame leaves him cold, he has lost all interest in himself as a so-called public figure. I just want to disappear, he once told Morris, muttering in the lowest of low voices, staring off with a pained look in his eyes, as if he were talking to himself. I just want to disappear.

They order their soups and sandwiches, and when the Latino waiter walks off with their menus (a Latino waiter in a Jewish restaurant, they both like that), Morris and Renzo start talking about the funeral, sharing their impressions of what they have just witnessed in the community center auditorium. Renzo didn't know Suki, he met her only once when she was a small child, but he agrees with Morris that Rothstein's talk was a powerful piece of work, almost unimaginable when you consider that it was written under the most appalling duress, at a time when few people would have the strength to pull themselves together and write a single word, let alone the passionate, complex, and clear-sighted eulogy they heard this morning. Renzo has no children, two ex-wives but no children, and given what Marty and Nina are going through now, given what he and Willa have already gone through, first with Bobby and then with Miles, Morris feels something close to envy, thinking that Renzo made the right decision all those years ago to steer clear of the kid business, to avoid the unavoidable mess and potential devastation of fatherhood. He is half-expecting Renzo to start talking about Bobby now, the parallel is so evident, and surely he understands how difficult this funeral has been for him, but precisely because Renzo does understand, he does not talk about it. He is too discreet for that, too aware of what Morris is thinking to barge in on his pain, and just seconds afterward Morris himself understands his friend's reluctance to intrude on him when Renzo changes the subject, skirting past Bobby and the gloomy realm of dead children, and asks him how he is weathering the crisis, meaning the economic crisis, and whither Heller Books in this storm of trouble?

Morris tells him that the ship is still afloat, but listing somewhat to the starboard side now, and for the past few months they have been throwing excess equipment overboard. His primary concern is to keep the staff intact, and so far he hasn't had to let anyone go, but the list has been reduced, cut down by twenty or twenty-five percent. Last year, they published forty-seven books, this year thirty-eight, but their profits have gone down by only eleven percent, in large part thanks to *The Mountain Dialogues,* which is in its third printing, with forty-five thousand hardcovers sold. The Christmas sales figures won't be in for a while, but even if

they turn out to be lower than expected, he isn't predicting out-and-out disaster. Louverain, Wyatt, and Tomesetti all published strong books this fall, and the paperback crime series seems to be off to a good start, but it's a rough time for first novels, very rough, and he's been forced to reject some good young writers, books he would have taken a chance on a year or two ago, and he finds that troubling, since the whole point of Heller Books is to encourage new talent. They're planning only thirty-three books for 2009, but Carlsen is on the list, Davenport is on the list, and then, needless to say, there is Renzo's novella, the little book he wrote just after *The Mountain Dialogues,* the unanticipated bonus book he has such high hopes for, and who knows, if every independent bookstore in America doesn't go bankrupt in the next twelve months, they might be in for a decent year. Listening to himself talk, he almost begins to feel optimistic, but he is telling Renzo only part of the story, leaving out the fact that when the returns start coming in on *The Mountain Dialogues* sales will fall by seven to ten thousand, leaving out the fact that 2008 will be the worst year for the house in three decades, leaving out the fact that he needs a new investor to put additional capital into the company or the ship will go down within two years. But there is no need for Renzo to know any of this. Renzo writes books, and he publishes them, and Renzo will go on writing and publishing books even if he is no longer in business.

After the soup comes, Renzo asks: What's the latest on the boy?

He's here, Morris says. As of two or three weeks ago.

Here in New York?

In Brooklyn. Living in an abandoned house in Sunset Park with some other people.

Our drummer friend told you this?

Our drummer friend is one of the people living there. He invited Miles to come up from Florida, and the boy accepted. Don't ask me why.

It sounds like good news to me.

Maybe. Time will tell. Bing says he's planning to call me, but no messages yet.

And what if he doesn't call?

Then nothing changes.

Think about it, Morris. All you have to do is jump in a cab, drive out to Brooklyn, and knock on the door. Aren't you tempted?

Of course I'm tempted. But I can't do it. He's the one who left, and he's the one who has to come back.

Renzo doesn't insist, and Morris is thankful to him for letting the

matter drop there. As godfather to the boy and longtime friend of the father, Renzo has been participating in this grim saga for seven years, and by now there is little of anything left to say. Morris asks him about his recent travels, the trips to Prague, Copenhagen, and Paris, his reading at the Max Reinhardt Theater in Berlin, the prize he was given in Spain, and Renzo says it was a welcome diversion, he has been in a slump lately, and it felt good to be somewhere else for a few weeks, someplace other than inside his own head. Morris has been listening to this kind of talk from Renzo for as long as he can remember. Renzo is always in a slump, each book he finishes is always the last book he will ever write, and then, somehow, the slump mysteriously ends, and he is back in his room writing another book. Yes, Renzo says, he knows he's talked this way in the past, but this time it feels different, he doesn't know why, this time the paralysis is beginning to feel permanent. *Night Walk* was finished at the end of June, he says, more than six months ago, and since then he's done nothing of any account. It was such a short book, just a hundred and fifty-something pages, but it seemed to take everything out of him, he wrote it in a kind of frenzy, less than three months from beginning to end, working harder and with more concentration than at any time in all the years he has been writing, pushing, pushing, like a runner sprinting at full tilt for seven miles, and exhilarating as it was to work at that pace, something in him collapsed when he crossed the finish line. For six months he has had no plans, no ideas, no project to occupy his days. When he hasn't been traveling, he has felt listless and without motivation, with no desire to return to his desk and start writing again. He has experienced similar lulls in the past, yes, but never anything as stubborn and protracted as this one, and although he hasn't reached a state of alarm yet, he is beginning to wonder if this isn't the end, if the old fire hasn't been extinguished at last. Meanwhile, he spends his days doing next to nothing – reading books, thinking, going out for walks, watching films, following the news of the world. In other words, he is resting, but for all that it is a strange kind of rest, he says, *an anxious repose.*

The waiter brings them their sandwiches, and before Morris can say anything about this half-serious, half-mocking account of mental exhaustion, Renzo, in an abrupt about-face, contradicting everything he has just said, tells Morris that a small notion occurred to him while he was flying home from Europe the other day, the tiniest germ of an idea – for an essay, a piece of nonfiction, something. Morris smiles. I

thought you had run out of ideas, he says. Well, Renzo answers, shrugging defensively, but with a glint of humor in his eye, one does have an occasional *flicker.*

He was on the plane, he says, a first-class ticket paid for by the people who gave him the prize, the dread of flying dulled somewhat by soft leather seats, caviar and champagne, imbecilic luxe among the clouds, with an abundant choice of films at his disposal, not just new films from Europe and America but old ones as well, venerated classics, ancient fluff from the dream factories on both sides of the Atlantic. He wound up watching *The Best Years of Our Lives,* something he had seen once a long time ago and therefore had utterly forgotten, a nice movie, he felt, well played by the actors, a charming piece of propaganda designed to persuade Americans that the soldiers returning from World War II will eventually adjust to civilian life, not without a few bumps along the way, of course, but in the end everything will work out, because this is America, and in America everything always works out. Be that as it may, he enjoyed the film, it helped pass the time, but what interested him most about the film was not the film itself but a minor role played by one of the actors in it, Steve Cochran. He has only one bit of any importance, a short, smirking confrontation with the hero, whose wife has been running around with Cochran on the sly, but that finally isn't what interested him either, Cochran's performance is a matter of complete indifference to him, what counts is the story his mother once told him about having known Cochran during the war, yes, his mother, Anita Michaelson, née Cannobio, who died four years ago at the age of eighty. His mother was an elusive woman, not given to opening up about the past, but when Cochran died at forty-eight in 1965, just after Renzo had turned nineteen, she must have been thrown sufficiently off guard to feel a need to unburden herself, and so she told him about her brief infatuation with the theater in the early forties, a girl of fifteen, sixteen, seventeen, and how she crossed paths with Cochran in some New York theater group and *fell for him.* He was such a handsome man, she said, one of those rugged black-Irish heartthrobs, but what *falling* meant was never quite clear to Renzo. Did his mother lose her virginity to Steve Cochran in 1942 when she was seventeen years old? Did they have an actual fling – or was it only a thing, an adolescent crush on an up-and-coming twenty-five-year-old actor? Impossible to say, but what his mother did report was that Cochran wanted her to go to California with him, and she was prepared to go, but when her parents got wind

of what was brewing, they put an immediate stop to it. No daughter of theirs, no scandals in this family, forget it, Anita. So Cochran left, his mother stayed and married his father, and that was how he came to be born – because his mother hadn't run off with Steve Cochran. That is the idea he is toying with, Renzo says, to write an essay about the things that don't happen, the lives not lived, the wars not fought, the shadow worlds that run parallel to the world we take to be the real world, the not-said and the not-done, the not-remembered. Chancy territory, perhaps, but it could be worth exploring.

After he came home, Renzo says, he felt curious enough to do a little digging into Cochran's life and career. Gangster roles for the most part, a couple of plays on Broadway with Mae West, of all people, *White Heat* with James Cagney, the lead in Antonioni's *Il Grido,* and appearances on various television shows in the fifties: *Bonanza, The Untouchables, Route 66, The Twilight Zone.* He formed his own production company, which produced little or nothing (information is scant, and although Renzo is curious, he is not curious enough to explore this point further), but Cochran seems to have acquired a reputation as one of the most active skirt chasers of his time. This probably explains why his mother fell for him, Renzo continues, sadly contemplating how easy it must have been for a practiced seducer to soften the heart of an inexperienced seventeen-year-old girl. How could she have resisted the man who later went on to have affairs with Joan Crawford, Merle Oberon, Kay Kendall, Ida Lupino, and Jayne Mansfield? There was also Mamie Van Doren, who apparently wrote at great length about her sex life with Cochran in an autobiography published twenty years ago, but Renzo has no plans to read the book. In the end, what fascinates him most is how thoroughly he suppressed the facts about Cochran's death, which he must have heard about when he was nineteen, but even after the conversation with his mother (which theoretically should have made the story impossible to forget), he forgot everything. In 1965, hoping to rejuvenate his moribund production company, Cochran developed a project for a film to be set in Central or South America. With three young women between the ages of fourteen and twenty-five, supposedly hired as assistants, he set out for Costa Rica on his forty-foot yacht to begin scouting locations. Some weeks later, the boat washed ashore along the coast of Guatemala. Cochran had died on board from a severe lung infection, and the three panic-stricken young women, who knew nothing about sailing, nothing about navigating forty-foot yachts,

had been drifting through the ocean for the past ten days, alone with Cochran's putrefying corpse. Renzo says he cannot efface the image from his mind. The three frightened women lost at sea with the decomposing body of the dead movie star below deck, convinced they will never touch land again.

So much, he says, for the best years of our lives.

# II

He has been invited to four New Year's Eve parties in four different parts of Manhattan, East Side and West Side, uptown and downtown, but after the funeral, after the lunch with Renzo, after the two hours spent at Marty and Nina's place, he has no desire to see anyone. He goes home to the apartment on Downing Street, unable to stop thinking about Suki, unable to free himself of the story Renzo told about the dead actor on the drifting boat. How many corpses has he seen in his life? he wonders. Not the embalmed dead lying in their open coffins, the wax-museum figures drained of blood who no longer appear to have been human, but actual dead bodies, the vivid dead, as it were, before they could be touched by the mortician's scalpel? His father, thirty years ago. Bobby, twelve years ago. His mother, five years ago. Three. Just three in more than sixty years.

He goes into the kitchen and pours himself a scotch. He already knocked off two of them at Marty and Nina's place, but he doesn't feel the least bit wobbly or disabled, his head is clear, and after the enormous lunch he consumed at the delicatessen, which is still sitting in his stomach like a stone, he has no appetite for dinner. He tells himself that he will end the year by catching up on the manuscripts he should have read in England, but he understands that this is merely a ruse, a trick to propel him into the comfortable armchair in the living room, and once he sits down in that chair, he will not return to Samantha Jewett's novel, which he has already decided not to publish.

It is seven-thirty, four and a half hours before another year begins, the tired ritual of noisemakers and fireworks, the blast of drunken voices that will echo across the neighborhood at midnight, always the same eruption on this particular midnight, but he is far from that now, alone with his scotch and his thoughts, and if he can go deeply enough into those thoughts, he won't even hear the voices and the clamor when the time comes. Five years ago this past May, the call from his mother's cleaning woman, who had just let herself into the apartment with her duplicate key. He was at the office, he remembers, a Tuesday morning around ten o'clock, talking with Jill Hertzberg about Renzo's latest manuscript and whether to use an illustration on the cover or go with pure

graphics. Why remember a detail like that? No reason, no reason that he can think of, except that reason and memory are nearly always at odds, and then he was in a cab heading up Broadway to West Eighty-fourth Street, trying to get his mind around the fact that his mother, who had been wisecracking with him over the phone on Saturday, was now dead.

The body. That is what he is thinking about now, the corpse of his mother lying on the bed five years ago, and the terror he felt when he looked down at her face, the blue-gray skin, the half-open-half-closed eyes, the terrifying *immobility* of what had once been a living person. She had been lying there for roughly forty-eight hours before she was discovered by the cleaning woman. Still dressed in her nightgown, his mother had been reading the Sunday edition of the *New York Times* when she died – no doubt of a sudden, cataclysmic heart attack. One bare leg was hanging over the edge of the bed, and he wondered if she had tried to get up when the attack began (to search for a pill? to call for help?), and if so, given that she had moved only a few inches, it struck him that she must have died within seconds.

He looked at her for a brief moment, for several moments, and then he turned away and walked into the living room. It was too much for him; to see her in that state of frozen vulnerability was more than he could bear. He can't remember if he looked at her again when the police arrived, if it was necessary for him to make a formal identification of the body or not, but he is certain that when the paramedics came to pack up the corpse in a black rubber body bag, he couldn't look. He remained in the living room staring down at the rug, studying the clouds through the window, listening to himself breathe. It was simply too much for him, and he couldn't bring himself to look anymore.

The revelation of that morning, the blunt, incontestable minim of knowledge he finally grasped when the paramedics were wheeling her out of the apartment, the idea that has continued to haunt him ever since: there can be no memories of the womb, not for him or anyone else, but he accepts it as an article of faith, or else wills himself to understand it through a leap of the imagination, that his own life as a sentient being began as part of the now dead body they were pushing through the opened door, that his life began *within her.*

She was a child of the war, just as Renzo's mother was, just as all their parents were, whether their fathers had fought in the war or not, whether their mothers had been fifteen or seventeen or twenty-two when the war began. A strangely optimistic generation, he thinks now,

tough, dependable, hardworking, and a little stupid as well, perhaps, but they all bought into the myth of American greatness, and they lived with fewer doubts than their children did, the boys and girls of Vietnam, the angry postwar children who saw their country turn into a sick, destructive monster. Spunky. That is the word that comes to him whenever he thinks about his mother. Spunky and outspoken, strong-willed and loving, impossible. She remarried twice after his father's death in seventy-eight, lost both of the new husbands to cancer, one in ninety-two, the other in oh-three, and even then, in the last year of her life, at age seventy-nine, eighty, she was still hoping to catch another man. I was born married, she said to him once. She had turned into the Wife of Bath, and fitting as that role might have been for her, playing the son of the Wife of Bath had not been entirely pleasant. His sisters had shared the burden with him, of course, but Cathy lives in Millburn, New Jersey, and Ann is in Scarsdale, just out of reach, on the fringes of the combat zone, and because he was the oldest, and because his mother trusted men more than women, he was the one she came to with her troubles, which were never classified as troubles (all negative words had been expunged from her vocabulary) but as *little somethings*, as in, I have a little something to discuss with you. Willful blindness is what he called it, an obdurate insistence on looking for silver linings, moral victories, a darkest-before-the-dawn attitude in the face of the most wrenching facts – burying three husbands, the disappearance of her grandson, the accidental death of her stepgrandson – but that was the world she came from, an ethical universe patched together from the righteous platitudes of Hollywood films – pluck, spunk, and never say die. Admirable in its way, yes, but also maddening, and as the years moved forward he understood that much of it was a sham, that inside her supposedly indomitable spirit there was also fear and panic and crushing sadness. Who could blame her? Having lived through the various maladies of her three husbands, how could she not have turned into a world-class hypochondriac? If your experience has taught you that all bodies must and will betray the person they belong to, why wouldn't you think that a small pain in the stomach is a prelude to stomach cancer, that a headache signifies brain tumor, that a forgotten word or name is an augury of dementia? Her last years were spent visiting doctors, dozens of specialists for this condition or that syndrome, and it's true that she was having problems with her heart (two angioplasties), but no one thought she was in any real danger. He figured she would go on complaining about her imaginary illnesses

until she was ninety, that she would outlive him, that she would outlive them all, and then, without warning, less than twenty-four hours after cracking jokes to him on the phone, she was dead. And once he had come to terms with it, the frightening thing about her death was that he felt relieved, or at least some part of him felt relieved, and he hates himself for being callous enough to admit it, but he knows he is lucky to have been spared the rigors of seeing her through a long old age. She left the world at the right time. No prolonged suffering, no descent into decrepitude or senility, no broken hips or adult diapers, no blank stares into empty space. A light goes on, a light goes off. He misses her, but he can live with the fact that she is gone.

He misses his father more. He is callous enough to admit that, too, but his father has been dead for thirty years now, and he has spent half his life walking beside that ghost. Sixty-three, just one year older than he is now, in good condition, still playing tennis four times a week, still strong enough to trounce his thirty-two-year-old son in three sets of singles, probably still strong enough to beat him at arm wrestling, a strict nonsmoker, alcohol consumption close to zero, never ill with anything, not even colds or flus, a broad-shouldered six-one, without flab or gut or stoop, a man who looked ten years younger than his age, and then a minor problem, an attack of bursitis in his left elbow, the proverbial tennis elbow, extremely painful, yes, but hardly life-threatening, and so he went to a doctor for the first time in how many years, a quack who prescribed cortisone pills instead of some mild painkiller, and his father, unaccustomed to taking pills, carried around the cortisone in his pocket as if it were a bottle of aspirin, tossing another pill down his throat every time the elbow acted up, thus tampering with the functioning of his heart, putting undue strain on his cardiovascular system without even knowing it, and one night, as he was making love to his wife (a consoling thought: to know that his parents were still active in the sex department at that point in their marriage), the night of November 26, 1978, as Alvin Heller was approaching an orgasm in the arms of his wife, Constance, better known as Connie, his heart gave out on him, rupturing inside his chest, exploding inside his chest, and that was the end.

There were never any of the conflicts he witnessed so often with his friends and their fathers, the boys with the slapping fathers, the shouting fathers, the aggressive fathers who pushed their frightened six-year-old sons into swimming pools, the contemptuous fathers who sneered at their adolescent sons for liking the wrong music, wearing the wrong

clothes, looking at them in the wrong way, the war-veteran fathers who punched out their twenty-year-old sons for resisting the draft, the weak fathers who were afraid of their grown-up sons, the shut-down fathers who couldn't remember the names of their sons' children. From beginning to end, there had been none of those antagonisms or dramas between them, no more than some sharp differences of opinion, small punishments doled out mechanically for small infractions of the rules, a harsh word or two when he was unkind to his sisters or forgot his mother's birthday, but nothing of any significance, no slaps or shouts or angry insults, and unlike most of his friends, he never felt embarrassed by his father or turned against him. At the same time, it would be wrong to presume that they were especially close. His father wasn't one of those warmhearted buddy fathers who thought his son should be his best pal, he was simply a man who felt responsible for his wife and children, a quiet, even-tempered man with a talent for making money, a skill his son failed to appreciate until the last years of his father's life, when his father became the principal backer and founding partner of Heller Books, but even if they weren't close in the way some fathers and sons are, even if the one thing they ever talked about with any passion together was sports, he knew that his father respected him, and to have that unflagging respect from beginning to end was more important than any open declaration of love.

When he was very young, five years old, six years old, he felt disappointed that his father had not fought in the war, unlike the fathers of most of his friends, and that while they had been off in far-flung parts of the world killing Japs and Nazis and turning themselves into heroes, his father had been in New York, immersed in the petty details of his real estate business, buying buildings, managing buildings, endlessly repairing buildings, and it puzzled him that his father, who seemed so strong and fit, had been rejected by the army when he tried to join up. But he was still too young at that point to understand how badly his father's eye was injured, to have been told that his father had been legally blind in his left eye since the age of seventeen, and because his father had so thoroughly mastered the art of living with and compensating for his handicap, he failed to understand that his powerhouse of a father was impaired. Later on, when he was eight or nine and his mother finally told him the story of the injury (his father never talked about it), he realized that his father's wound was no different from a war wound, that a part of his life had been shot down on that Bronx ball field in 1932 in the

same way a soldier's arm can be shot off on a battlefield in Europe. He was the top pitcher for his high school baseball team, a hard-throwing left-hander who was already beginning to attract attention from major league scouts, and when he took the mound for Monroe that day in early June, he had an undefeated record and what appeared to be an unhittable arm. On the first pitch of the game, just as the fielders were settling into their positions behind him, he threw a low fastball to the Clinton shortstop, Tommy DeLucca, and the line drive that came flying back at him was struck so hard, with such ferocious power and speed, that he had no time to lift his glove and protect his face. It was the same injury that destroyed Herb Score's career in 1957, the same bone-breaking shot that changes the course of a life. And if that ball hadn't slammed his father in the eye, who is to say he wouldn't have been killed in the war – before his marriage, before the birth of his children? Now Herb Score is dead, too, Morris thinks, dead as of six or seven weeks ago, Herb Score, with the prophetic middle name of Jude, and he remembers how badly shaken his father was when he read about Score's injury in the morning paper, and how, for years after, right up to the end of his life, he would periodically refer to Score, saying that injury was one of the saddest things that ever happened in the history of the game. Never a word about himself, never the slightest hint of any personal connection. Only Score, poor Herb Score.

Without his father's help, the publishing house never would have been born. He knew he didn't have the stuff to become a writer, not when he had the example of young Renzo to compare himself to, his dormitory roommate for four years at Amherst, the immense, grinding struggle of it, the long solitary hours, the everlasting uncertainty and compulsive need, and so he opted for the next best thing, teaching literature instead of making it, but after one year of graduate school at Columbia, he withdrew from the Ph.D. program, understanding that he wasn't cut out for an academic life either. He wandered into publishing instead, spent four years rising through the ranks of two different companies, at last finding a place for himself, a mission, a calling, whatever word best applies to a sense of commitment and purpose, but there were too many frustrations and compromises at the top levels of commercial publishing, and when, in the space of two short months, his senior editor quashed his recommendation that they publish Renzo's first novel (the one following the burned manuscript) and similarly rejected his proposal to publish Marty's first novel, he went to his father and told him he wanted to quit

the august company he was working for and start a little house of his own. His father knew nothing about books or publishing, but he must have seen something in his son's eyes that persuaded him to throw a losable fraction of his money into a venture that was all but certain to fail. Or perhaps he felt this certain failure would teach the boy a lesson, help him work the bug out of his system, and before long he would return to the security of a normal job. But they didn't fail, or at least the losses were not egregious enough to make them want to stop, and after that inaugural list of just four books, his father opened his pockets again, staking him to a new investment worth ten times the amount of his initial outlay, and suddenly Heller Books was off the ground, a small but viable entity, a real publishing house with an office on lower West Broadway (dirt-cheap rents back then in a Tribeca that was not yet Tribeca), a staff of four, a distributor, well-designed catalogues, and a growing stable of authors. His father never interfered. He called himself *the silent partner,* and for the last four years of his life he used those words to announce himself whenever they talked on the phone. No more *This is your father* or *This is your old man* but, without fail, one hundred percent of the time, *Hello there, Morris, this is your silent partner.* How not to miss him? How not to feel that every book he has published in the past thirty-five years is a product of his father's invisible hand?

It is nine-thirty. He meant to call Willa to say happy new year, but it is two-thirty in England now, and no doubt she has been asleep for hours. He returns to the kitchen to pour himself another scotch, his third since coming back to the apartment, and it is only now, for the first time all evening, that he remembers to check the answering machine, suddenly thinking that Willa might have called while he was at Marty and Nina's or on his way home from the Upper West Side. There are twelve new messages. One by one, he listens to them all – but no word from Willa.

He is being punished. That is why she accepted the job at Exeter for the year, and that is why she never calls – because she is punishing him for the meaningless indiscretion he committed eighteen months ago, a stupid act of sexual weakness that he regretted even as he was crawling into bed with his partner in crime. Under normal circumstances (but when is anything ever normal?) Willa never would have found out, but not long after he did what he did, she went to her gynecologist for her semi-annual checkup and was told she had something called chlamydia, a mild but unpleasant condition that can be contracted only through sexual intercourse. The doctor asked her if she had slept with anyone

besides her husband lately, and because the answer was no, the culprit could have been none other than said husband, and when Willa confronted him with the news that evening, he had no choice but to confess. He didn't provide any names or details, but he admitted that when she was in Chicago delivering her paper on George Eliot, he had gone to bed with someone. No, he wasn't having an affair, it had happened only that one time, and he had no intention of ever doing it again. He was sorry, he said, deeply and truly sorry, he had been drinking too much, it was a terrible mistake, but even though she believed him, how could he blame her for feeling angry, not just because he had been unfaithful to her for the first time in their marriage, no, that was bad enough, but because he had infected her as well. A venereal disease! she shouted. It's disgusting! You stick your dumb-ass penis into another woman's vagina, and you wind up infecting me! Aren't you ashamed of yourself, Morris? Yes, he said, he was horribly ashamed, more ashamed than he had ever been in his life.

It torments him to think about that evening now, the idiocy of it all, the frantic little coupling that led to such enduring havoc. A dinner invitation from Nancy Greenwald, a literary agent in her early forties, someone he had been doing business with for six or seven years, divorced, not unattractive, but until that night he had never given her much thought. A dinner for six at Nancy's apartment in Chelsea, and the only reason he accepted was because Willa was out of town, a fairly tedious dinner as it turned out, and when the four other guests gathered up their things and left, he agreed to stay on for a last drink before walking home to the Village. That was when it happened, about twenty minutes after the others disappeared, a quick crazy fuck of no earthly importance to anyone. After Willa's announcement about chlamydia, he wondered how many other dumb-ass penises had found comfort in Nancy's vagina, although the truth was that there hadn't been much comfort for him, and even as they went at it together, he had felt too wretched about betraying Willa to lose himself in the supposed pleasure of the moment.

After his confession, after the round of antibiotics that purged the venereal microbes from Willa's system, he thought that would be the end of it. He knew she believed him when he told her it had happened only once, but this tiny lapse of attention, this breach of solidarity after close to twenty-four years of marriage, had shaken Willa's confidence in him. She doesn't trust him anymore. She believes he is on the prowl, searching for younger and more beautiful women, and even if he isn't

up to anything at this particular moment, she has convinced herself that sooner or later it is bound to happen again. He has done everything he can to reassure her, but his arguments seem to have no effect. He is too old for adventures now, he says, he wants to live out the rest of his days with her and die in her arms. And she says: A sixty-two-year-old man is still young, a sixty-year-old woman is old. He says: After all they've been through together, all the nightmares and sorrows, all the poundings they've taken, all the miseries they've survived, how can a little thing like this make any difference? And she answers: Maybe it's been too much for you, Morris. Maybe you want a fresh start with someone else.

The trip to England didn't help. They had been apart for three and a half months when he finally went over there for the Christmas break, and he understood that she was using this enforced separation as a test, to see whether it would be possible for her to live without him over the long haul. So far, the experiment seems to be working rather well. Her anger toward him has changed into a kind of willed detachment, an aloofness that made him feel awkward around her for much of the visit, never quite sure what he should say or how he should act. The first night, she was reluctant to have sex with him, but then, just as he was drifting off, she reached out for him in bed and started kissing him in the old way, giving herself up to the old intimacies as if there were no trouble between them. That was the thing that so confounded him – their silent companionship in bed at night followed by moody, disjointed days, tenderness and irritability alternating in wholly unpredictable patterns, a feeling that she was both pushing him away from her and trying to hold on to him at the same time. There was only one vicious outburst, one full-blown argument. It occurred on the third or fourth day, when they were still in her Exeter flat, taking out their bags to prepare for their trip to London, and the quarrel began as many others had in the past few years, with Willa attacking him for not wanting to have children of their own, for being content with her son and his son as their only family, but no family of their own, just the two of them and their own boy or girl, without the specters of Karl and Mary-Lee hovering in the background, and now that Bobby was dead and Miles had gone missing, just look at them, she said, they were nothing, they had nothing, and it was his fault for talking her out of another child all those years ago, and she was a goddamned fool for listening to him. In principle, he didn't disagree with her, had never disagreed with her, but how could they have known what would happen, and by the time Miles took off, they were too old

to think about having babies. He didn't resent her for bringing up the subject again, it was altogether natural for her to feel this grief, this loss, the history of the past twelve years could have produced no other outcome, but then she said something that shocked him, that hurt him so badly he still hasn't recovered from it. But Miles is back in New York, he said. He'll be contacting them any day now, any week, and before long the whole miserable chapter will come to an end. Instead of answering him, Willa picked up her suitcase and threw it angrily on the floor – a furious gesture, more violent than any response he had ever seen from her. It's too late, she shouted. Miles is sick. Miles is no good. Miles has wrecked them, and from this day forward she cuts him out of her heart. She doesn't want to see him. Even if he calls, she doesn't want to see him. Never again. It's finished, she said, it's finished, and every night she will get down on her knees and pray he doesn't call.

It was somewhat better in London. The hotel was neutral ground, a no-man's-land devoid of any associations with the past, and there were some good days of walking through museums and sitting in pubs, seeing old friends for dinner, browsing in bookstores, not to mention the sublime indulgence of doing nothing at all, which seemed to have a restorative effect on Willa. One afternoon, she read aloud to him from the most recent chapter of the book she is writing on the late novels of Dickens. The next morning, over breakfast, she asked him about his search for a new investor, and he told her about his meeting with the German at the Frankfurt Book Fair in October, his conversation with the Israeli in New York last month, the steps he has taken to find the needed cash. Several good days, or at least not bad days, and then came the e-mail from Marty and the news of Suki's death. Willa didn't want him to go back to New York, she argued fiercely and persuasively why she thought the funeral would be too much for him, but when he asked her to make the trip with him, her face tensed up, she seemed thrown by the suggestion, which was an entirely reasonable suggestion to his mind, and then she said no, she couldn't. He asked her why. Because she couldn't, she said, repeating her answer as she searched for the right words, clearly at war with herself, unprepared to make any crucial decisions at that moment, because she wasn't ready to go back, she said, because she needed more time. Again, she asked him to stay, to remain in London until January third as originally planned, and he understood that she was testing him, forcing him to make a choice between her and his friends, and if he didn't choose her, she would feel betrayed. But he

had to go back, he said, it was out of the question not to go back.

One week later, as he sits in his New York apartment on New Year's Eve, sipping scotch in the darkened living room and thinking about his wife, he tells himself that a marriage can't stand or fall on a simple matter of leaving London a few days early to attend a funeral. And if it does stand or fall on that matter, perhaps it was destined to fall in the first place.

He is in danger of losing his wife. He is in danger of losing his business. As long as there is breath in him, he says to himself, remembering that homely, worn-out phrase, which he has always been fond of, as long as there is breath in him he will not allow either one of those things to happen.

Where is he now? Straddling the border between inevitable extinction and the possibility of continued life. Overall, the situation is bleak, but there are some encouraging signs that have given him cause for hope – or, if not quite hope, a sense that it is still too early to succumb to resignation and despair. How much he reminds himself of his mother whenever he starts thinking like this, how obstinately she goes on living inside him. Let the house come crashing down around him, let his marriage burst into flames, and Connie Heller's son will find a way to rebuild the house and put out the fire. Lucky Lohrke walking calmly through a barrage of bullets. Or else the ghost dance of the Oglala Sioux – and the conviction that the white man's bullets would evaporate into thin air before they ever touched them.

He drinks another scotch and then staggers off to bed. Exhausted, so exhausted that he is already asleep before the shouting and the fireworks begin.

# III

He knows why Miles left. Even before the letter came, he was all but certain the boy had spent the night in the apartment, the night preceding the morning when he and Willa had talked so brutally about him in the kitchen. After breakfast, he had cracked open the door of Miles's room to find out if the boy had come home for the weekend, and when he saw that the bed was empty, he went in to discover an ashtray filled with cigarette butts, a forgotten paperback anthology of Jacobean drama lying on the floor, and a flattened, unplumped pillow on the hastily made bed – sure signs that the boy had spent the night there, and if he had stolen off early that morning without bothering to greet them, without a hello or a good-bye, it could only mean that he had overheard the cruel things that had been said about him and was too upset to face his parents. Morris didn't mention his discovery to Willa, but at that point there was no reason to suspect the conversation would lead to such a drastic response from Miles. He felt terrible about having said those things, angry with himself for not having defended the boy more vociferously against Willa's harsh attacks, but he figured he would have a chance to apologize the next time they saw each other, to clear the air somehow and put the matter behind them. Then came the letter, the mad, falsely cheerful letter with the disturbing news that Miles had quit college. *Burned out on school*. The boy wasn't burned out. He loved being in school, he was sailing through with top honors, and just two weeks before, when they met for Sunday breakfast at Joe Junior's, Miles had been talking about the courses he was planning to take in his senior year. No, quitting had been a hostile act of revenge and self-sabotage, a symbolic suicide, and there was no doubt in Morris's mind that it was a direct result of that conversation overheard in the apartment a few days earlier.

Still, there was no reason to panic. Miles was going to L.A. to spend a couple of weeks with his mother, and all Morris had to do was pick up the telephone and call him. He would do what he could to talk some sense into the boy, and if that didn't work, he would fly to California and have it out with him face to face. But not only was Miles not at Mary-Lee's, Mary-Lee was not at home either. She was in San Francisco,

filming the pilot of a new television series, and the person he spoke to was Korngold, who told him that Miles hadn't been heard from in more than a month and that as far as he knew there were no plans for him to visit California anytime that summer.

From that moment on, they were in it together, all four of them, the two parents and the two stepparents, and when they hired a private detective to look for the missing boy, each couple bore half the cost, living through eight dismal months of progress reports that reported no progress, no leads, no signs of hope, not a single microdot of information. Morris held fast to the theory that Miles had vanished on purpose, but after three or four months both Willa and Korngold began to waver, gradually coming to the conclusion that Miles was dead. An accident of some kind, they thought, perhaps murdered, perhaps killed by his own hand, it was impossible to say. Mary-Lee took an agnostic position on the matter – she simply didn't know. He could have been dead, yes, but on the other hand, the kid had *issues,* the thing with Bobby had been an absolute devastation, Miles had closed in on himself since then, and it was clear that he had *a lot of stuff to work out.* Running away was a stupid thing to do, of course, but maybe some good would come of it in the end, maybe being on his own for a while would give him a chance to straighten himself out. Morris didn't disagree with this analysis. In fact, he found Mary-Lee's attitude rather impressive – calm, compassionate, and thoughtful, not judging Miles so much as trying to understand him – and now that they were locked in this crisis together, he realized that the indifferent, irresponsible mother was far more attached to her son than he had imagined. If anything positive emerged from Miles's disappearance, it was this shift in his perception of Mary-Lee. They were no longer enemies. They had become allies now, perhaps even friends.

Then Bing Nathan called, and everything turned upside down again. Miles was working as a short-order cook in Chicago, and Morris's first impulse was to go out there and talk to him – not to make any demands, merely to find out what was going on – but Willa was against it, and after he called California to share the good news with Mary-Lee and Korngold, they took Willa's side. Their argument was this: the boy was twenty-one now and capable of making his own decisions; as long as his health was sound, as long as he wasn't in trouble with the law, as long as he wasn't in a mental hospital, as long as he wasn't asking them for money, they had no right to force him to do anything against his will – not even to make him talk to them, which he obviously had no wish to

do. Give him time, they said. He'll figure it out.

But Morris didn't listen to them. He took a plane to Chicago the next morning, and by three o'clock he had parked his rented car across the street from Duke's, a shabby, heavily frequented diner in a rough neighborhood on the South Side. Two hours later, Miles walked out of the restaurant wearing his leather jacket (the one Morris had bought for him on his nineteenth birthday) and looking well, very well in fact, a bit taller and more filled out than he'd been at that Sunday breakfast eight and a half months ago, and at his side there was a tall, attractive black woman who appeared to be in her mid-twenties, and the moment the two of them walked out the door, Miles put his arm around the woman's shoulder, drew her toward him, and planted a kiss on her mouth. It was a joyful kiss, somehow, the kiss of a man who has just put in eight hours of work and is back with the woman he loves, and the woman laughed at this sudden outburst of affection, threw her arms around him, and returned his kiss with one of her own. A moment after that, they were walking down the street together, holding hands and talking in that intense, intimate way that is possible only in the closest friendships, the closest loves, and Morris just sat there, frozen in the seat of his rented car, not daring to roll down the window and call out to Miles, not daring to jump out and run after him, and ten seconds later Miles and the woman turned left at the first corner they came to and vanished from sight.

He has done it three more times since then, once in Arizona, once in New Hampshire, and once in Florida, always watching from a place where he couldn't be seen, the warehouse parking lot where Miles was loading crates onto the back of a truck, the hotel lobby where the boy rushed past him in a bellhop's uniform, the little park he sat in one day as his son read *The Great Gatsby* and then talked to the cute high school girl who happened to be reading the same book, always tempted to step forward and say something, always tempted to pick a fight with him, to punch him, to take him in his arms, to take the boy in his arms and kiss him, but never doing anything, never saying anything, keeping himself hidden, watching Miles grow older, watching his son turn into a man as his own life dwindles into something small, too small to care about anymore, listening to Willa's tirade in Exeter, all the damage that has been done to her, his brave, battered Willa, Bobby on the road, Miles gone, and yet he grimly perseveres, never quite able to let go of it, still thinking the story hasn't come to an end, and when thinking about the story becomes unbearable, he sometimes diverts himself with childish reveries about

dressing up in costumes, disguising himself so thoroughly that not even his own son would recognize him, a demon of disguise in the spirit of Sherlock Holmes, not just the clothes and the shoes but an entirely different face, entirely different hair, an entirely different voice, an utter transformation from one being into another, and how many different old men has he invented since the idea occurred to him, wrinkled pensioners hobbling along with their canes and aluminum walkers, old men with flowing white hair, flowing white beards, Walt Whitman in his dotage, a friendly old fellow who has lost his way and stops the young man to ask for directions, and then they would begin to talk, the old man would invite the young man for a drink, and little by little the two of them would become friends, and now that Miles is living in Brooklyn, out there in Sunset Park next to Green-Wood Cemetery, he has come up with another character, a New York character he calls the Can Man, one of those old, broken-down men who forage among dumpsters and recycling bins for bottles and cans, five cents a bottle, five cents a can, a tough way to make a living, but times are tough and one mustn't complain, and in his mind the Can Man is a Mohawk Indian, a descendent of the Mohawks who settled in Brooklyn in the early part of the last century, the community of Mohawks who came here to become construction workers on the tall buildings going up in Manhattan, Mohawks because for some reason Mohawks have no fear of heights, they feel at home in the air and were able to dance along the beams and girders without the slightest dread or vertiginous wobble, and the Can Man is a descendent of those fearless people who built the towers of Manhattan, a crazy customer, alas, not quite right in the head, a daft old loon who spends his days pushing his shopping cart through the neighborhood, collecting the bottles and cans that will fetch him five cents apiece, and when the Can Man speaks, more often than not he will punctuate his remarks with absurd, outlandishly inappropriate advertising slogans, such as, *I'd walk a mile for a Camel*, or: *Don't leave home without it*, or: *Reach out and touch someone*, and perhaps Miles will be amused by a man who would walk a mile for a Camel, and when the Can Man wearies of his advertising slogans, he will start quoting from the Bible, saying things like: *The wind goeth toward the south, and turneth about unto the north, it whirleth about continually* or *And that which is done is that which shall be done*, and just when Miles is about to turn around and walk away, the Can Man will push his face up against his and shout: *Remember, boy! Bankruptcy is not the end! It's just a new beginning!*

It is ten o'clock in the morning, the first morning of the new year, and he is sitting in a booth at Joe Junior's, the diner on the corner of Sixth Avenue and Twelfth Street where he last spoke to Miles more than two thousand seven hundred days ago, sitting, as it happens, in the same booth the two of them sat in that morning, eating his scrambled eggs and buttered toast as he toys with the notion of turning himself into the Can Man. Joe Junior's is a small place, a simple, down-at-the-heels neighborhood joint featuring a curved Formica counter with chrome trim, eight swivel stools, three tables by the window in front, and four booths along the northern wall. The food is ordinary at best, the standard greasy-spoon fare of two dozen breakfast combinations, grilled ham-and-cheese sandwiches, tuna fish salads, hamburgers, hot open turkey sandwiches, and fried onion rings. He has never sampled the onion rings, but legend has it that one of the old regulars, Carlton Rabb, now deceased, was so enamored of them that he added a clause to his will stipulating that an order of Joe Junior's fried onion rings be smuggled into his coffin before his body was laid to rest. Morris is fully aware of Joe Junior's shortcomings as a dining establishment, but among its advantages are the total absence of music, the chance to eavesdrop on stimulating, often hilarious conversations, the broad spectrum of its clientele (from homeless beggars to wealthy home owners), and, most important, the role it plays in his memory. Joe Junior's was the site of the ritual Saturday breakfast, the place where he brought the boys every week throughout their childhoods, the quiet Saturday mornings when the three of them would tiptoe out of the apartment as Willa caught an extra hour or two of sleep, and to sit in this place now, this drab little restaurant on the corner of Sixth Avenue and Twelfth Street, is to return to those countless Saturdays of long ago and remember the Eden he once lived in.

Bobby lost interest in coming here when he was thirteen (the boy liked his sleep), but Miles carried on the tradition all the way to the end of high school. Not every Saturday morning, of course, at least not after he turned seven and started playing in the local kids' baseball league, but often enough to feel that the room is still saturated with his presence. Such a bright young thing, such an earnest young thing, so little laughter in that somber face of his, but just below the surface a frolicking sort of inner mirth, and the pleasure he took in the various teams they made up together with the names of real players, the all-body-parts team, for example, with a lineup of Bill Hands, Barry Foote, Rollie Fingers, Elroy Face, Ed Head, and Walt "No-Neck" Williams, along with substitutes such as Tony

Armas (Arm) and Jerry Hairston (Hair), or the all-finance team, consisting of Dave Cash, Don Money, Bobby Bonds, Barry Bonds, Ernie Banks, Elmer Pence, Bill Pounds, and Wes Stock. Yes, Miles loved that nonsense when he was a boy, and when laughter did come out of him, it was propulsive and unstoppable, red-faced, breathless, as if an unseen phantom were tickling him all over his body. But most often the breakfasts were subdued affairs, quiet conversations about his classmates, his aversion to his piano lessons (he eventually quit), his disagreements with Bobby, his homework, the books he was reading, the fortunes of the Mets and football Giants, the finer points of pitching. Of all the regrets Morris has accumulated over the course of his life, there is the lingering sadness that his father did not live long enough to know his grandson, but if he had, and if by some miracle he had lasted into the boy's teens, there would have been the happiness of seeing Miles pitch, the right-handed version of his young self, living proof that all the hours he had spent teaching his son how to throw properly had not been wasted, that even if Morris never developed much of an arm himself, he had passed on his father's lessons to his own son, and until Miles quit in his junior year, the results had been promising – no, more than promising – excellent. Pitching was the ideal position for him. Solitude and strength, concentration and will, the lone wolf standing in the middle of the infield, carrying the entire game on his back. It was all fastballs and changeups back then, two pitches and endless work on his delivery, the fluid motion, the arm whipping forward at the same angle every time, the coiled right leg pushing off the rubber until the moment of release, but no curveballs or sliders, at sixteen he was still growing, and young arms can be ruined by the unnatural torque required to snap off a good breaking ball. He was disappointed, yes, but he never blamed Miles for quitting when he did. The self-flagellating grief of surviving Bobby had demanded a sacrifice of some kind, and so he gave up the thing he loved doing most at that point in his life. But willing yourself out of something is not the same as renouncing it in your heart. Four years ago, when Bing called to report the arrival of another letter – from Albany, California, just outside Berkeley – he mentioned that Miles was pitching for a team in a Bay Area amateur league, competing against ex-college players who hadn't been good enough or interested enough to turn pro, but serious competition for all that, and he was holding his own, Miles said, winning twice as many games as he lost, and he had finally taught himself how to throw a curveball. He went on to say that the San Francisco Giants were sponsoring an open tryout later that

month, and his teammates were urging him to go, recommending that he lie about his age and tell them he was nineteen, not twenty-four, but he wasn't going to do it. Imagine him signing a contract to play in the low minor leagues, he said. Preposterous.

The Can Man is thinking, remembering, sifting through the countless Saturday mornings he ate breakfast here with the boy, and now, as he lifts his arm and asks for the check, just a minute or two before he will be stepping out into the cold air again, he stumbles across something that hasn't occurred to him in years, an unearthed shard, a shining piece of glass to put in his pocket and take home with him. Miles was ten or eleven. It was one of the first times they came here without Bobby, just the two of them sitting across from each other in one of the booths, perhaps this booth, perhaps another, he can't recall which one now, and the boy had brought along a book report he had written for his fifth- or sixth-grade class, no, not a report exactly, a short paper of six or seven hundred words, an analysis of the book the teacher had assigned to the pupils, the book they had been reading and discussing for the past several weeks, and now each child had to produce a paper, an interpretation of the novel they had all finished, *To Kill a Mockingbird,* a sweet book, Morris felt, a good book for children of that age, and the boy wanted his father to read over what he had done. The Can Man remembers how tense the boy looked as he removed the three sheets of paper, the four sheets of paper from his backpack, awaiting his father's judgment on what he had written, his first attempt at literary criticism, his first grown-up assignment, and from the look in the boy's eyes, his father understood how much work and thought had gone into this little piece of writing. The paper was about wounds. The father of the two children, the lawyer, is blind in one eye, the boy wrote, and the black man he defends against the false charge of rape has a withered arm, and late in the book, when the lawyer's son falls out of the tree, he breaks his arm, the same arm as the withered arm of the innocent black man, left or right, the Can Man no longer remembers, and the point of all this, the young Miles wrote, is that wounds are an essential part of life, and until you are wounded in some way, you cannot become a man. His father wondered how it was possible for a ten- or eleven-year-old child to read a book so carefully, to pull together such disparate, unemphasized elements of a story and see a pattern develop over the course of hundreds of pages, to hear the repeated notes, notes so easily lost in the whirl of fugues and cadenzas that form the totality of a book, and not only was he impressed

by the mind that had paid such close attention to the smallest details of the novel, he was impressed by the heart that had come up with such a profound conclusion. Until you are wounded, you cannot become a man. He told the boy he had done a superior job, that most readers twice or three times his age could never have written anything half as good as this, and only a person with a great soul could have thought about the book in this way. He was very moved, he said to his son that morning seventeen or eighteen years ago, and the fact is that he is still moved by the thoughts expressed in that short paper, and as he collects his change from the cashier and walks out into the cold, he goes on thinking about these thoughts, and just before he reaches his house, the Can Man stops and says to himself: When?

# IV

She has come to New York to act in Samuel Beckett's *Happy Days*. She will be Winnie, the woman buried up to her waist in Act I and then buried up to her neck in Act II, and the challenge in front of her, the formidable challenge will be to hold forth within these constricted emplacements for an hour and a half, delivering what amounts to a sixty-page monologue, with occasional interruptions from the hapless, mostly invisible Willie, and she can think of no theatrical role she has played in the past, neither Nora nor Miss Julie, neither Blanche nor Desdemona, that is more demanding than this one. But she loves Winnie, she responds deeply to the combination of pathos, comedy, and terror in the play, and even if Beckett is inordinately difficult, cerebral, at times obscure, the language is so clean and precise, so gorgeous in its simplicity, that it gives her physical pleasure to feel the words coming out of her mouth. Tongue, palate, lips, and throat are all in harmony as she pronounces Winnie's long, halting rambles, and now that she has finally mastered and memorized the text, the rehearsals have been steadily improving, and when the previews begin ten days from now, she hopes she will be ready to give the performance she hopes to give. Tony Gilbert has been hard on her, and every time the young director cuts her off for making the wrong gesture or not pausing long enough between phrases, she consoles herself with the thought that he begged her to come to New York to play Winnie, that again and again he has told her that no actress alive could do a better job in this role. He has been hard on her, yes, but the play is hard, and she has worked hard because of it, even letting her body go to hell in order to put on the twenty extra pounds she felt she needed to become Winnie, to inhabit Winnie (*About fifty, well preserved, blond for preference, plump, arms and shoulders bare, low bodice, big bosom* . . . ), and she has done much homework in preparation, reading up on Beckett, studying his correspondence with Alan Schneider, the original director of the play, and she now knows that a *bumper* is a brimming glass, that *bast* is a fibrous twine used by gardeners, that the words Winnie speaks at the beginning of Act II, *Hail, holy light,* are a quotation from Book III of *Paradise Lost,* that *beechen green* comes from *Ode to a Nightingale,* and

that *bird of dawning* comes from *Hamlet.* What world the play is set in has never been clear to her, a world without darkness, a world of hot, unending light, a sort of purgatory, perhaps, a post-human wilderness of ever-diminishing possibilities, ever-diminishing movement, but she also suspects that this world might be none other than the stage she will be performing on, and even if Winnie is essentially alone, talking to herself and Willie, she is also aware that she is in the presence of others, that the audience is out there in the dark. *Someone is looking at me still. Caring for me still. That is what I find so wonderful. Eyes on my eyes.* She can understand this. Her entire life has been about this, only this.

It is the third day of the year, the evening of Saturday, January third, and Morris is having dinner with Mary-Lee and Korngold at the Odeon, not far from the Tribeca loft they have rented for their four-month stay in New York. They arrived in the city just as he was preparing to leave for England, and although they have talked on the telephone several times in the past few months, they have not seen each other in a long while, not since 2007, he thinks, perhaps even 2006. Mary-Lee has just turned fifty-four, and their brief, disputatious marriage is no more than a dim memory now. He bears her no grudge or ill will, is in fact quite fond of her, but she is still a conundrum to him, a puzzling mixture of warmth and distance, keen intelligence hidden behind brash, rough-and-tumble manners, by turns good-hearted and selfish, droll and boring (she tends to go on at times), vain and utterly indifferent to herself. Witness the increased poundage for her new role. She has always taken pride in her slim, well-maintained figure, has fretted over the fat content of every morsel of food that enters her mouth, has made a religion of eating *properly,* but now, for the sake of her work, she has calmly tossed her diet to the four winds. Morris is intrigued by this fuller, more ample version of his ex-wife, and he tells her that she is looking beautiful, to which she responds, laughing and then puffing out her cheeks: A big, beautiful hippo. But she *is* beautiful, he thinks, still beautiful even now, and unlike most actresses of her generation, she has not marred her face with cosmetic surgery or wrinkle-removing injections, for the simple reason that she intends to go on working as long as she can, deep into her old age if possible, and, as she once jokingly put it to him, If all the sixty-year-old broads come across as bizarre-looking thirty-year-olds, who's going to be left to play the mothers and grandmothers?

She has been acting steadily for a long time now, ever since she was in her early twenties, and there is not a person in the crowded restaurant

who does not know who she is, glance after glance is directed toward their table, *eyes are on her eyes,* but she pretends to pay no attention, she is used to this kind of thing, but Morris senses that she is secretly enjoying it, that silent adulation of this sort is a boon that never grows old. Not many actors manage to keep it going for thirty years, especially women, especially women who act in films, but Mary-Lee has been smart and flexible, willing to reinvent herself at each step along the way. Even during the early run of successful films that got her started, she would take time off to work in plays, always good plays, the best plays, the Bard and his modern heirs, Ibsen, Chekhov, Williams, Albee, and then, when she was in her mid-thirties and the big studios stopped making films for grown-ups, she didn't hesitate to accept parts in small, low-budget independent films (many of them produced by Korngold), and then, more years down the road, when she reached the point at which she was beginning to play mothers, she jumped into television, starring in a weekly series called *Martha Kane, Attorney-at-Law,* something Morris and Willa actually watched from time to time, and during the five-year span of that show she attracted an audience in the millions and grew ever more popular, which is very popular indeed. Drama and comedy, good girls and bad girls, feisty secretaries and drug-addicted hookers, wives, lovers, and mistresses, a singer and a painter, an undercover cop and the mayor of a large city, she has played all kinds of roles in all kinds of films, many of them quite decent, a few clumsy stinkers, but no mediocre performances that Morris can recall, with a number of memorable turns that have touched him in the same way he was touched when he first saw her as Cordelia in 1978. He is glad she is doing the Beckett, he thinks she is wise to have accepted such a daunting role, and as he looks at her across the table now, he wonders how this attractive but wholly ordinary woman, this woman with her fluctuating moods and vulgar passion for dirty jokes, has it in her to transform herself into so many distinct and totally different characters, to make one feel she carries all humanity inside her. Does it require an act of courage to stand up and turn your guts inside out before an audience of strangers, or is it a compulsion, a need to be looked at, a reckless lack of inhibition that drives a person to do what she does? He has never been able to put his finger on the line that separates life from art. Renzo is the same as Mary-Lee, they are both prisoners of what they do, for years both have been plunging forward from one project to the next, both have produced lasting works of art, and yet their lives have been a bollix, both divorced twice, both

with a tremendous talent for self-pity, both ultimately inaccessible to others – not failed human beings, exactly, but not successful ones either. Damaged souls. The walking wounded, opening their veins and bleeding in public.

He finds it odd to be with her now, sitting across from his ex-wife and her husband, sitting in yet another booth in yet another New York restaurant, odd because the love he once felt for her is entirely gone, and he knows that Korngold is a far better husband for her than he ever could have been, and she is lucky to have a man like this to take care of her, to prop her up whenever she begins to stagger, to give her the advice she has been listening to and following for years, to love her in a way that has tamped down her anxieties and frantic distempers, whereas he, Morris, was never up to the task of loving her in the way she needed to be loved, could never give her advice about her career, could never prop her up or understand what was whirling about in that beautiful head of hers. She is so much better than she was thirty years ago, and he gives Korngold all the credit, he admires him for having rescued her after two bad marriages, for throwing out the vodka bottles and the pill bottles she began collecting after the second divorce, for sticking by her through what must have been some harrowing moments, and beyond what Korngold has done for Mary-Lee, Morris admires him pure and simple, in and of himself, not just because he was good to his son during the years when the boy was still visible, not just because he has anguished over Miles's disappearance as a true member of the family, but because he discovered many years ago that Simon Korngold is a thoroughly likable person, and what Morris likes most about him is the fact that he never complains. Everyone is suffering because of the crash, the slump, whatever word people are using to talk about the new depression, book publishers not excepted, of course, but Simon is in much worse shape than he is, the independent film business has been destroyed, production companies and distributors are folding up like collapsible chairs every day of the week, and it has been two years now since he last put a movie together, which means that he unofficially retired this fall, accepting a job to teach film courses at UCLA instead of making films, but he isn't bitter about it, or at least he shows no bitterness, and the only thing he says to account for what has happened to him is to mention that he is fifty-eight years old and that independent film producing is a young person's job. The grinding search for money can crush the spirit out of you unless you're made of steel, he says, and the tall and short of it is that he isn't made of steel anymore.

But that comes later. The talk about Winnie and *Hail, holy light* and men of steel does not begin until after they have talked about why Mary-Lee called Morris three hours ago and asked him to dinner on such short notice. There is news. That is the first article on the agenda, and moments after they enter the restaurant and take their seats at the table, Mary-Lee tells him about the message she found on her answering machine at four o'clock this afternoon.

It was Miles, she says. I recognized his voice.

His voice, Morris says. You mean he didn't give his name?

No. Only the message – a short, confusing message. As follows, in its entirety. *Um.* Long pause. *Sorry.* Long pause. *I'll call back.*

Are you sure it was Miles?

Positive.

Korngold says: I'm still trying to figure out what *sorry* means. Sorry for calling? Sorry because he was too flustered to leave a proper message? Sorry for everything he's done?

Impossible to say, Morris replies, but I would tend to go with flustered.

Something's going to happen, Mary-Lee says. Very soon. Any day now.

I talked to Bing this morning, Morris says, just to check in and see if everything is all right. He told me Miles has a girlfriend, a young Cuban girl from Florida, and that she's been in New York for the past week or so visiting him. I think she went back today. According to Bing, Miles was planning to get in touch with us as soon as she left. That would explain the message.

But why call me and not you? Mary-Lee asks.

Because Miles thinks I'm still in England and won't be reachable until Monday.

And how does he know that? Korngold says.

Apparently, he called my office two or three weeks ago and was told I'd be back at work on the fifth. That's what Bing reported, in any case, and I don't see why the boy would lie to him.

We owe Bing Nathan a lot, Korngold says.

We owe him everything, Morris says. Try to imagine these past seven years without him.

We should do something for him, Mary-Lee says. Write him a check, send him on a world cruise, something.

I've tried, Morris says, but he won't take any money from me. He was very insulted the first time I offered, and even more insulted the second

time. He says: You don't accept money for acting like a human being. A young man with principles. I can respect that.

What else? Mary-Lee asks. Any word on how Miles is doing?

Not much, Morris answers. Bing says he mostly keeps to himself, but the other people in the house like him and he gets on well with them. Quiet, as usual. A bit low, as usual, but then he perked up when the girl came.

And now she's gone, Mary-Lee says, and he's left a message on my machine saying he'll call me back. I don't know what I'm going to do when I see him. Slap him across the face – or throw my arms around him and kiss him?

Do both, Morris says. The slap first, and then the kiss.

They stop talking about Miles after that and move on to *Happy Days,* the future of independent films, the strange death of Steve Cochran, the advantages and disadvantages of living in New York, Mary-Lee's new rotundity (which inspires the puffed-out cheeks and the beautiful-hippo comment), the forthcoming novels from Heller Books, and Willa, needless to say Willa, it is the polite question that must be asked, but Morris has no desire to tell them the truth, no desire to unburden himself and talk about his fear that he might be losing her, that he has already lost her, and so he says that Willa is flourishing, in top form, that his trip to England was like a second honeymoon, and he is hard-pressed to recall a time when he ever felt happier. His answer comes and goes in just a few seconds, and then they move on to other things, other digressions, other chatter about any number of relevant and irrelevant subjects, but Willa is on his mind now, he can't shake free of her, and watching Korngold and his ex-wife across the table, the comfort and amiability of their interactions, the furtive, unspoken complicity that exists between them, he understands how lonely he is, how lonely he has become, and now that the dinner is nearing its conclusion, he dreads returning to the empty apartment on Downing Street. Mary-Lee has drunk enough wine to be in one of those expansive, bountiful moods of hers, and when the three of them go outside to part company, she opens her arms and says to him, Give us a hug, Morris. A nice long squeeze for the fat old woman. He embraces the bulky winter overcoat hard enough to feel the flesh inside it, the body of the mother of his son, and as he does so, she holds on to him just as tightly, and then, with her left hand, she begins patting the back of his head, as if to tell him not to worry anymore, the dark time will soon be over, and all will be forgiven.

He walks back to Downing Street in the cold, his red scarf wrapped around his neck, hands thrust deep into the pockets of his coat, and the wind shooting off the Hudson is especially strong tonight as he heads up Varick toward the West Village, but he doesn't stop to flag down a taxi, he wants to walk this evening, the rhythm of his steps calms him in the way that music sometimes calms him, in the way children can be calmed when their parents rock them to sleep. It is ten o'clock, not late, several hours to go before he will be ready for sleep himself, and as he unlocks the door of the apartment, he imagines he will settle into the comfortable chair in the living room and spend the last hours of the day reading a book, but which book, he asks himself, which book from all the thousands crammed onto the shelves of the two floors of the duplex, perhaps the Beckett play if he can find it, he thinks, the one Mary-Lee is doing now, the one they talked about tonight, or if not that play perhaps another play by Shakespeare, the little project he has taken on in Willa's absence, rereading all of Shakespeare, the words that have filled the hours between work and sleep these past months, and he is up to *The Tempest* now, he believes, or perhaps *The Winter's Tale,* and if reading is too much for him tonight, if his thoughts are too jumbled with Miles and Mary-Lee and Willa for him to concentrate on the words, he will watch a film on television, the one sedative that can always be counted on, the tranquilizing flicker of images, voices, music, the pull of the stories, always the stories, the thousands of stories, the millions of stories, and yet one never tires of them, there is always room in the brain for another story, another book, another film, and after pouring himself a scotch in the kitchen, he walks into the living room thinking film, he will opt for a film if anything watchable is playing tonight.

Before he can sit down in the comfortable chair and switch on the TV, however, the telephone starts ringing in the kitchen, and so he turns around and walks back into the kitchen to answer it, puzzled by the lateness of the call, wondering who could possibly want to talk to him at ten-thirty on a Saturday night. His first thought is Miles, Miles following up his call to his mother with a call to his father, but no, that couldn't be it, Miles won't be calling him until Monday at the earliest, unless he supposes, perhaps, that his father has already returned from England and is spending the weekend at home, or, if not that, perhaps he simply wants to leave a message on the machine, in the same way he left a message on his mother's machine this afternoon.

It is Willa, calling from Exeter at three-thirty in the morning, Willa

sobbing and in distress, saying that she is cracking apart, that her world is in ruins, that she no longer wants to be alive. Her tears are relentless, and the voice talking through those tears is barely audible, high-pitched, the voice of a child, and it is a true collapse, he tells himself, a person beyond anger, beyond hope, a person entirely spent, miserable, miserable, pulverized by the weight of the world, a sadness as heavy as the weight of the world. He doesn't know what to do except talk to her in the most comforting voice he can manage, to tell her he loves her, that he will be on the early plane to London tomorrow morning, that she must hold on until he gets there, less than twenty-four hours, just one more day, and he reminds her of the breakdown about a year after Bobby's death, the same tears, the same weakened voice, the same words, and she pulled through that crisis then and will pull through this crisis now, trust him, he knows what he is talking about, he will take care of her, he will always take care of her, and she mustn't blame herself for things that aren't her fault. They talk for an hour, for two hours, and eventually the tears subside, eventually she begins to calm down, but just when he is beginning to feel it will be safe to hang up the phone, the tears begin again. She needs him so much, she says, she can't survive without him, she has been so horrible to him, so mean and vindictive and cruel, she has become a horrible person, a monster, and she hates herself now, she can never forgive herself, and again he tries to soothe her, telling her that she must go to sleep now, that she is exhausted and must go to sleep, that he will be there with her tomorrow, and finally, finally, she promises that she will go to bed, and even if she can't sleep, she promises not to do anything stupid, she will behave herself, she promises. They hang up at last, and before another night falls in New York City, Morris Heller is back in England, traveling between London and Exeter to see his wife.

*All*

# MILES HELLER

It was the best thing that could have happened to him, it was the worst thing that could have happened to him. Eleven days with Pilar in New York, and then the agony of putting her on the bus and sending her back to Florida.

One thing is certain, however. He loves her more than any other person on this earth, and he will go on loving her until the day he stops breathing.

The joy of looking at her face again, the joy of holding her again, the joy of listening to her laugh again, the joy of hearing her voice again, the joy of watching her eat again, the joy of looking at her hands again, the joy of looking at her naked body again, the joy of touching her naked body again, the joy of kissing her naked body again, the joy of watching her frown again, the joy of watching her brush her hair again, the joy of watching her paint her nails again, the joy of standing in the shower with her again, the joy of talking to her about books again, the joy of watching her eyes fill up with tears again, the joy of watching her walk again, the joy of listening to her insult Angela again, the joy of reading out loud to her again, the joy of listening to her burp again, the joy of watching her brush her teeth again, the joy of undressing her again, the joy of putting his mouth against her mouth again, the joy of looking at her neck again, the joy of walking down the street with her again, the joy of putting his arm around her shoulders again, the joy of licking her breasts again, the joy of entering her body again, the joy of waking up beside her again, the joy of discussing math with her again, the joy of buying clothes for her again, the joy of giving and receiving back rubs again, the joy of talking about the future again, the joy of living in the present with her again, the joy of being told she loves him again, the joy of telling her he loves her again, the joy of living under the gaze of her fierce dark eyes again, and then the agony of watching her board the bus at the Port Authority terminal on the afternoon of January third with the certain knowledge that it will not be until April, more than three months from now, that he will have a chance to be with her again.

It was her first trip to New York, the only time she has ever set foot

outside the state of Florida, her maiden voyage to the land of winter. Miami is the one large city she is familiar with, but Miami is not large when compared to New York, and he hoped she wouldn't feel intimidated by the jangle and immensity of the place, that she wouldn't be put off by the noise and the dirt, the crowded subway cars, the bad weather. He imagined he would have to lead her into it cautiously, like someone walking into a cold lake with a young swimmer, giving her time to adjust to the frigid water, letting her tell him when she was ready to go in up to her waist, up to her neck, and if and when she wanted to put her head under. Now that she is gone, he cannot fathom why he felt so timid on her behalf, why or how he could have underestimated her resolve. Pilar ran into the lake with flapping arms, whooping excitedly as the cold water hit her bare skin, and seconds after that she was taking the plunge, dunking her head below the surface and gliding along as smoothly as a practiced veteran. The little one had done her homework. During the long trek up the Atlantic coast, she digested the contents of three guidebooks and a history of New York, and by the time the bus pulled into the terminal, she had already drawn up a list of the places she wanted to see, the things she wanted to do. Nor had she neglected his advice to prepare herself for the low temperatures and possible storms. She had gone out and bought a pair of snow boots, a couple of warm sweaters, a scarf, woolen gloves, and a snappy green down parka with a fur-fringed hood. She was Nanook of the North, he said, his intrepid Eskimo girl armed to beat back the assaults of the harshest climes, and yes, she looked adorable in that thing, and again and again he told her the Cuban-American-Eskimo look was destined to stay in fashion for years to come.

They went to the top of the Empire State Building, they walked through the marble halls of the Public Library at Fifth Avenue and Forty-second Street, they visited Ground Zero, they spent one day going from the Metropolitan Museum to the Frick Collection to MoMA, he bought her a dress and a pair of shoes at Macy's, they walked across the Brooklyn Bridge, they ate oysters at the Oyster Bar in Grand Central Station, they watched the ice skaters at Rockefeller Center, and then, on the seventh day of her visit, they rode the subway uptown to 116th Street and Broadway and checked out the Barnard College campus, the Columbia campus across the street, the various seminaries and music academies spread across Morningside Heights, and he said to her, Look, all this is possible for you now, you're as good as any of the people studying here,

and when they send you your letter of acceptance this spring, which I'm sure they will, there's a better than eighty percent chance they're going to want you, think long and hard before you decide to stay in Florida, all right? He wasn't telling her what to do, he was merely asking her to consider the matter carefully, to weigh the consequences of accepting or turning down what in all likelihood would be offered to her, and for once Pilar was silent, not willing to share her thoughts with him, and he didn't press her to say anything, for it was clear from the look in her eyes that she was already pondering this very question, trying to project herself into the future, trying to imagine what going to college in New York would mean to her or not mean to her, and as they walked among the deserted grounds and studied the façades of the buildings, he felt as if she were changing in front of him, growing older in front of him, and he suddenly understood what she would be like ten years from now, twenty years from now, Pilar in the full vigor of her evolving womanhood, Pilar all grown into herself and yet still walking with the shadow of the pensive girl walking beside him now, the young woman walking beside him now.

He wishes they could have been alone for the full eleven days, living and sleeping in a room or an apartment not shared with anyone else, but the only option available to them was the house in Sunset Park. A hotel would have been perfect, but he didn't have the money for a hotel, and besides, there was the question of Pilar's age, and even if he could have afforded to put them up in style, there was the same risk in New York as there was in Florida, and he wasn't willing to take it. About a week before Christmas, he and Ellen discussed the possibility of borrowing the keys to one of the empty apartments on her firm's rental list, but little by little they talked themselves out of that absurd idea. Not only could Ellen have found herself in serious trouble, with instant dismissal from her job just one of the many gruesome things that could happen to her, but when they pictured what it would be like to hole up in a place without furniture, without blinds or curtains, without electricity, without a bed to sleep in, they both realized that staying in the shabby little house across from Green-Wood Cemetery would be far better.

Pilar knows they are squatting there illegally, and she doesn't approve. Not only is it wrong to break the law, she says, but she is frightened that something will happen to him, something bad, something irreversible, and how ironic it would be, she says (they have had this conversation on the phone more than once), if he left Florida to avoid going to jail only to

land in another jail up north. But he won't go to jail for squatting, he tells her, the worst that can happen is an untimely eviction, and she mustn't forget that living there is only a stopgap arrangement for him, and once he heads back to Florida on May twenty-second, his little adventure in trespassing will be over. At this point in the conversation, Pilar invariably starts talking about Angela, cursing her greedy, no-good sister for having done this to them, the injustice of it all, the sickness of it all, and now she lives in constant fear that something will happen to him, and Angela is entirely to blame for it.

Because the house frightened her, she wanted to spend as little time there as possible. For very different reasons, he felt the same way, which meant they were out and about for the better part of her visit, mostly in Manhattan, mostly eating dinner in restaurants, cheap restaurants so as not to waste their money, diners and pizzerias and Chinese dumpling houses, and ninety percent of the time they spent in the house they were in his room, either making love or sleeping. Still, there were the unavoidable encounters with the others, the breakfasts in the morning, the accidental meetings in front of the bathroom door, the night when they returned to the house around ten o'clock and Alice asked them up to her room to watch a movie, which she described as her *obsession of the moment*, a film called *The Best Years of Our Lives*, since she wanted to know what they thought of it (he gave it a B-plus overall and an A for photography, Pilar gave it an A for everything), but his objective was to keep her contacts with the rest of the household to a minimum. It wasn't that they weren't friendly to her, but he had watched their faces when he introduced her to them on the first evening, and one by one he had noted the brief instant of shock when they understood how young she was, and he felt reluctant to expose her to situations in which she could be patronized by them, talked down to, hurt. It might have been different if she were taller than five feet four, if her breasts were larger, if her hips were wider, but Pilar must have struck them as a tiny, childlike thing, just as she had struck him the first time he saw her, and there was no point in trying to undo their initial impressions of her. The visit was going to be too short for that, and he wanted her to himself anyway. To be fair to them, however, nothing unpleasant happened. Alice had agreed to cook all the dinners while Pilar was in town, and therefore it was up to him to do the grocery shopping, which he took care of first thing every morning, and while he was out at the store, Alice and Pilar had a number of one-on-one talks at the kitchen table. It didn't take Alice long to

figure out how intelligent Pilar was, and later on, after they had left the house, Pilar would tell him how impressed she was by Alice, how she admired the work she was doing, how much she liked her. But Alice was the only one who actively reached out to Pilar. Bing seemed nonplussed, a bit bowled over, befuddled by her presence, and by the second day he had adopted a jocular persona to communicate with her (Bing trying to be funny), talking in the voice of a movie cowboy, addressing her as Miss Pilar and coming out with such original remarks as Howdy there, Miss Pilar, and how's the purdy lady this mornin'? Ellen was polite but distant, and the one time Jake was there, he ignored her.

She is coping with her altered circumstances in Florida, but this is the first time she has lived alone, and there have been some difficult days, dark days when she has had to struggle against the urge to let go and cry for hours on end. She is still on good terms with Teresa and Maria, but the rift with Angela is absolute and forever, and she avoids going to the house when her oldest sister will be there. Maria continues to date Eddie Martinez, and Teresa's husband, Carlos, is coming to the end of his tour of duty and is scheduled to be rotated out of Iraq in March. She is bored with school, she hates going there every morning, and it requires an enormous effort of will not to cut classes, not to skip whole days, but she forges on because she doesn't want to disappoint him. She finds the other students to be idiots, especially the boys, and she has only two or three friends, just two or three girls in her A.P. English class who seem worth talking to. She has been careful with the money, spending as little as she can, and the only unforeseen expense came just before her trip to New York, when she had to replace the carburetor and spark plugs in the Toyota. She is still a pathetic cook, but a little less pathetic than before, and she hasn't lost or gained any weight, which must mean she is on top of things in spite of her shortcomings. Lots of fruits and vegetables, rice and beans, an occasional chicken cutlet or hamburger (both are easy to cook), and a real breakfast every morning – melon, plain yogurt and berries, Special K. It's been a strange time, she said to him on her last morning in New York, the strangest time she has ever known, and she wishes the days would pass more quickly down there, that they wouldn't drag so much, but each turn of the clock creeps along like a tired fat man walking up a hundred flights of stairs, and now that she has to go back, it's bound to be even worse, because at least there was New York to look forward to after he left, for three weeks that was the thing that kept her going, but now they are looking at three months, she can barely wrap

her mind around that thought, three months before she gets to see him again, and it will be like living in limbo, like going on a vacation in hell, and all because of a stupid date on her birth certificate, an arbitrary number, an irrational number that means nothing to anyone.

All during her visit, he was tempted to tell her the truth about himself, to open up to her and give the full story about everything – his parents and Bobby, his childhood in New York, the three years at Brown, the seven and a half years of crazed, self-inflicted exile, everything. On the morning they walked around the Village, they went past Saint Vincent's, the hospital where he was born, went past P.S. 41, the school he attended as a boy, went past the house on Downing Street, the place where his father and stepmother still live, and then they ate lunch at Joe Junior's, the family canteen for the first twenty years of his life, a whole morning and part of an afternoon in the very heart of his old stomping grounds, and that was the day when he came closest to doing it, but desperate as he was to tell her these things about himself, he held back and told her nothing. It wasn't a question of fear. He could have told her then, but he didn't want to spoil the good time they were having together. Pilar was struggling down in Florida, the trip to New York had reanimated her and brought her back to her hopeful, spirited self, and it simply wasn't the moment to confess his lies to her, to pull her down into the bleakness of the Heller family chronicle. He will do it when the time is right, and that time will come only after he has talked to his father and mother, only after he has seen his father and mother, only after he has asked them to take him back into their lives. He is ready to face them now, ready to confront the terrible thing he did to them, and Pilar is solely responsible for giving him the courage to do this – because in order to be worthy of Pilar, he must have this courage.

She left for Florida on the third, two days ago. Wretched farewells, the agony of looking at her face through the window, and then the bus drove down the ramp and disappeared. He took the subway back to Sunset Park, and the moment he walked into his room, he sat down on the bed, took out his cell phone, and called his mother. He wouldn't be able to talk to his father until Monday, but he had to do something now, watching the bus drive down the ramp had made it impossible not to do something, and if his father wasn't available, then he would begin with his mother. He was about to call the theater first, thinking that would be the best way to get hold of her, but then it occurred to him that perhaps her cell phone number was the same one she had seven years ago. He

called to find out, and there was her voice telling the world that she would be in New York for the next four months, and if you wanted to get in touch with her there, this was the number. It was a Saturday afternoon, a cold Saturday afternoon in early January, and he assumed she would be at home on a crummy day like this, keeping her toes warm and doing crossword puzzles on the sofa, and when he called the New York number, he was fully confident she would pick up on the second or third ring. But she didn't. The telephone rang four times, and then a message came on, another message with her voice, telling the caller that she was out and please wait for the beep. He was so flummoxed by this unexpected turn that he suddenly went blank, and all he could think to say was: *Um.* Long pause. *Sorry.* Long pause. *I'll call back.*

He decided to reverse course, return to his original plan, and talk to his father first.

It is Monday morning now, January fifth, and he has just called his father's office, only to be told that his father flew back to England yesterday on urgent business. He asks when Mr. Heller will be coming back to New York. It isn't clear, the voice tells him. Call at the end of the week. There might be some news then.

Nine hours later, he calls his mother's New York number again. This time she is in. This time she picks up the phone and answers it.

Two trumps one. One is better than four. Three can be too many or just enough. Five is taking it too far. Six is delirium.

She is advancing now, traveling deeper and deeper into the netherworld of her own nothingness, the place in her that coincides with everything she is not. The sky above her is gray or blue or white, sometimes yellow or red, at times purple. The earth below her is green or brown. Her body stands at the juncture of earth and sky, and it belongs to her and no one else. Her thoughts belong to her. Her desires belong to her. Stranded in the realm of the one, she conjures up the two and three and four and five. Sometimes the six. Sometimes even the sixty.

After the unfortunate scene with Alice last month, she understood that she would have to carry on alone. Because of her job, she is too busy to enroll in a class, to waste precious hours riding on subways to and from Pratt or Cooper Union or SVA. The work is what counts, and if she intends to make any progress, she must work continually, with or without a teacher, with or without live models, for the essence of the work resides in her hand, and whenever she manages to lift herself out of herself and put her mind in abeyance, she can will that hand to see. Experiment has taught her that wine helps. A couple of glasses of wine to make her forget who she is, and then she can keep on going for hours, often far into the night.

The human body is strange and flawed and unpredictable. The human body has many secrets, and it does not divulge them to anyone, except those who have learned to wait. The human body has ears. The human body has hands. The human body is created inside another human body, and the human being who emerges from that other human body is necessarily small and weak and helpless. The human body is created in the image of God. The human body has feet. The human body has eyes. The human body is multitudinous in its forms, its manifestations, its degrees of size and shape and color, and to look at one human body is to apprehend only that human body and no other. The human body can be apprehended, but it cannot be comprehended. The human body has shoulders. The human body has knees. The human body is an object and

a subject, the outside of an inside that cannot be seen. The human body grows from the small of infancy to the large of adulthood, and then it begins to die. The human body has hips. The human body has elbows. The human body lives in the mind of one who possesses a human body, and to live inside the human body possessed of the mind that perceives another human body is to live in a world of others. The human body has hair. The human body has a mouth. The human body has genitals. The human body is created out of dust, and when that human body is no more, it returns to the dust from whence it came.

She works from several different sources now: reproductions of paintings and drawings by other artists, black-and-white photographs of male and female nudes, medical photographs of babies, children, and old people, the body-length mirror she attached to the wall opposite her bed in order to have a full view of herself, porn magazines aimed at various appetites and proclivities (from cheesecake shots of women to two-sex copulations to male–male copulations to female–female copulations to threesome, foursome, and fivesome copulations in all their mathematical permutations), and the small hand mirror she uses to study her own vagina. A door has opened inside her, and she has crossed the threshold into a new way of thinking. The human body is an instrument of knowledge.

There is no time for painting now. Drawing is faster and more tactile, better suited to the urgency of her project, and she has filled sketchbook after sketchbook this past month with her attempts to break free of her old methods. For the first hour after setting to work, she warms up by concentrating on details, isolated areas of a body culled from her collection of images or found in one of the two mirrors. A page of hands. A page of eyes. A page of buttocks. A page of arms. Then she moves on to whole bodies, portraits of single figures in various poses: a naked woman standing with her back to the viewer, a naked man sitting on the floor, a naked man stretched out on a bed, a naked girl squatting on the ground and urinating, a naked woman sitting in a chair with her head thrown back as she cups her right breast in her right hand and squeezes the nipple of her left breast with her left hand. These are intimate portraits, she tells herself, not erotic drawings, human bodies doing what human bodies do when no one is watching them, and if many of the men in these single portraits have erections, that is because the average man has fifty erections and semi-erections per day – or so she has been told. Then, in the last part of the exercise, she brings these figures together. A

naked woman holding a naked infant in her arms. A naked man kissing the neck of a naked woman. An old naked man and an old naked woman sitting on a bed with their arms around each other. A naked woman kissing a naked man's penis. Two trumps one, followed by the mystery of three: three naked women; two naked women and one naked man; one naked woman and two naked men; three naked men. The porn magazines are quite explicit about what goes on in these situations, and their frankness inspires her to work without fear or inhibition. Fingers have entered vaginas. Mouths have encircled erect penises. Penises have entered vaginas. Anuses have been breached. It is important to note the difference between photography and drawing, however. If one leaves nothing to the imagination, the other dwells exclusively in the realm of the imagination, and therefore her entire being is ablaze when she works on these drawings, since she never simply copies the photograph she is looking at but uses it to imagine a new scene of her own invention. She is sometimes aroused by what her pencil does to the page in front of her, aroused because of the pictures bubbling in her head as she draws, which are similar to the pictures that bubble in her head when she masturbates at night, but arousal is only a minor by-product of the effort, and mostly what she feels are the demands of the work itself, the constant, ever-pressing desire to get it right. The drawings are rough and usually left unfinished. She wants her human bodies to convey the miraculous strangeness of being alive – no more than that, as much as all that. She doesn't concern herself with the idea of beauty. Beauty can take care of itself.

Two weeks ago, there was a heartening development, something unexpected that is still in the process of playing itself out. Several days before the girl from Florida came to Brooklyn and destroyed her hopes of ever conquering Miles, Bing asked to see her new work. She took him upstairs to her bedroom after dinner, trepidation mounting in her with each step they climbed, certain he would laugh at her as he casually flipped through the sketchbooks and then dismiss her with a polite smile and a pat on the shoulder, but she felt she had to risk this potential humiliation, she was burning up inside, the drawings were consuming her now, and someone had to look at them besides herself. Normally, she would have asked Alice, but Alice had let her down that day in December when the fog had blanked out the cemetery, and even though they had long since forgiven each other for that ludicrous misunderstanding, she was afraid to ask Alice because she thought Alice

would be embarrassed by the pictures, shocked by them, repulsed by them even, because good and loyal a friend as Alice has been to her, she has always been something of a stodge. Bing is more open-minded, more direct (if often crude) in discussing sexual matters, and as she walked up the stairs with him and opened the door, she realized there was a lot of sexy stuff in those drawings, pretty dirty stuff if you wanted to look at it that way, and maybe this obsession with human bodies was getting a little out of hand, maybe it showed that she was beginning to fall apart again – the first sign of another crack-up. But Bing loved the pictures, he thought they were *stupendous*, a bold, extraordinary breakthrough, and because he spontaneously jumped off the bed and kissed her after he had looked at the last drawing, she knew he wasn't lying to her.

Bing's opinion means nothing, of course. He has no understanding of visual art, no knowledge of the history of art, no ability to judge what he is seeing. When she showed him a reproduction of Courbet's *The Origin of the World*, his eyes opened wide, but when she showed him a similar image of a woman's private parts in one of her skin magazines, his eyes opened wide then too, and she felt saddened to be with someone who was so handicapped aesthetically, a man unable to tell the difference between a brave and revolutionary work of art and a piece of impoverished, run-of-the-mill smut. Nevertheless, she was encouraged by his enthusiasm, stunned by how happy she felt as she listened to him praise her. Untutored or not, Bing's response to the drawings was visceral and genuine, he was moved by what she had done, he couldn't stop talking about how honest and powerful the work was, and in all the years she had been painting and drawing, no one had ever spoken like that to her, not once.

The goodwill emanating from Bing that night made her feel confident enough to ask a question, *the* question, the one question she had not dared ask anyone since Alice turned her down last month. Would he be willing to pose for her? Working from mirrors and two-dimensional images could take her only so far, she said, but if she meant to accomplish anything with this investigation of the human figure, she would have to begin working with live models at some point, three-dimensional people, living and breathing people. Bing seemed flattered by her request, but also a little pained. We're not talking about the body beautiful here, he said. Nonsense, she replied. You embody you, and because you don't want to be anyone but you, you mustn't be afraid.

They each drank two glasses of wine, which is to say, they finished

off a bottle between them, and then Bing removed his clothes and sat down in the chair by the desk as she settled onto the bed, sitting Indian-style with the sketchbook in her lap. Remarkably enough, he didn't seem afraid. Lumpy body and all, with his bulging stomach and thick thighs and hirsute chest and broad, flaccid buttocks, he sat there calmly as she drew him, showing no signs of discomfort or timidity, and ten minutes into the first sketch, when she asked him how he was doing, he said fine, he trusted her, he hadn't known how much he would enjoy being looked at in this way. The room was small, they were no more than four feet apart, and when she began drawing his penis for the first time, it occurred to her that she wasn't looking at a penis anymore but a cock, that penis was the word for the thing in the drawing, but cock was the word for the thing just four feet in front of her, and, objectively speaking, she had to admit that Bing had a handsome cock, no longer or shorter than the majority of those she had seen in her life, but thicker than most, well formed and without peculiarities or blemishes, a first-rate example of male equipment, not what they call a pencil dick (where had she heard that phrase?) but a bulky fountain pen, a substantial plug for any orifice. By the third drawing, she asked him if he would mind playing with himself for a little while so she could see what happened to him when he was hard, and he said no problem, posing for her was actually making him rather hot, and he wouldn't mind at all. By the fourth drawing, she asked him to masturbate for her, and again he willingly obliged, but just to make sure, he asked her if she wouldn't prefer taking her clothes off and letting him join her on the bed, but she said no, she would rather keep her clothes on and continue drawing, but if, at the last moment, he would like to get out of the chair, walk over to the bed, and finish off what he was doing in her mouth, she would have no objection.

There have been five more sessions since then. The same thing has happened all five times, but they are no more than brief interruptions, small gifts they bestow on each other for the space of a few minutes, and then the work goes on as before. It is a perfectly fair arrangement, she feels. Her drawings have already improved because of Bing, and she is certain that the prospect of coming in her mouth will keep him interested in posing for her, at least for now, at least for the foreseeable future, and even if she has no desire to shed her clothes for him, the contact is comforting to her, and she takes pleasure in it as well. She would rather be drawing Miles, of course, and if Miles were the one who posed for her and not Bing, she wouldn't hesitate to shed her clothes for him

and let him do whatever he wanted to her, but that will never happen, she knows that now, and she mustn't let her disappointment throw her off course. Miles scares her. The power he has over her scares her as much as anything has scared her in years, and yet she can't stop herself from wanting him. But Miles wants the girl from Florida, he adores the girl from Florida, and when the girl came to Brooklyn and she saw how Miles looked at her, she knew that was the end of it. Poor Ellen, she mutters, speaking to no one in the empty room, poor Ellen Brice who always loses out to someone else, don't feel sorry for yourself, go on with your drawings, go on letting Bing come in your mouth, and sooner or later all of you will be gone from Sunset Park, this ratty little house will be torn down and forgotten, and the life you are living now will fade into oblivion, not one person will remember you were ever here, not even you, Ellen Brice, and Miles Heller will vanish from your heart, in the same way you have already vanished from his heart, have never been in his heart, have never been in anyone's heart, not even your own.

Two is the only number that counts. One defines the real, perhaps, but all the others are pure fantasy, pencil lines on a blank white page.

On Sunday, January fourth, she goes to visit her sister on the Upper West Side, and one by one she holds the naked bodies of her twin nephews, Nicholas and Bruno. Such masculine names for such tiny fellows, she thinks, just two months old and everything still before them in a world coming apart at the seams, and as she holds first the one and then the other in her arms, she is awed by the softness of their skin, the smoothness of their bodies as she presses them against her neck and cheeks, feels the young flesh in the palms of her hands and along her bare forearms, and again she remembers the phrase that has been repeating itself to her ever since it came into her head last month: the strangeness of being alive. Just think, she says to her sister, Larry puts his cock in you one night, and nine months later out come these two little men. It doesn't make any sense, does it? Her sister laughs. That's the deal, honey, she says. A few minutes of pleasure, followed by a lifetime of hard work. Then, after a short pause, she looks at Ellen and says: But no, it doesn't make any sense – no sense at all.

Riding home on the subway that evening, she thinks about her own child, the child who was never born, and wonders if that was her only chance or if a time will come when a child starts growing inside her again. She takes out her notebook and writes:

The human body cannot exist without other human bodies.

The human body needs to be touched – not just small human bodies, but large human bodies as well.

The human body has skin.

# ALICE BERGSTROM

Every Monday, Wednesday, and Thursday she takes the subway into Manhattan and goes to her part-time job at the PEN American Center at 588 Broadway, just south of Houston Street. She started working there last summer, abandoning her post as an adjunct at Queens College because that job ate up too many hours and left her with no time for her dissertation. Remedial English and freshman English, just two classes, but fifty students writing one paper a week, and then the obligatory three private conferences with each student every semester, one hundred and fifty conferences in all, seven hundred papers to read and correct and grade, preparation for class, drawing up reading lists, inventing good assignments, the challenge of holding the students' attention, the need to dress well, the long commute out to Flushing and back, and all for an insultingly low salary with no benefits, a salary that came out to less than the minimum wage (she did the math once and calculated how much she earned by the hour), which meant that the pay she received for doing work that prevented her from doing her own work was less than she would have made as a car-wash attendant or a flipper of hamburgers. PEN doesn't pay much either, but she gives them only fifteen hours a week, her dissertation is advancing again, and she believes in the purpose of the organization, the only human rights group in the world devoted exclusively to defending writers – writers imprisoned by unjust governments, writers living under the threat of death, writers banned from publishing their work, writers in exile. P-E-N. Poets and publishers, essayists and editors, novelists. They can pay her only twelve thousand seven hundred dollars for her part-time position, but whenever she walks into the building at 588 Broadway and takes the elevator to the third floor, at least she knows she isn't wasting her time.

She was ten years old when the fatwa was declared against Salman Rushdie. She was already a committed reader then, a girl who lived in the land of books, at that point immersed in the eight novels of the Anne of Green Gables series, dreaming of becoming a writer herself one day, and then came the news about a man living in England who had published a book that angered so many people in distant parts of the world that

the bearded leader of one country actually stood up and declared that the man in England should be killed for what he had written. This was incomprehensible to her. Books weren't dangerous, she said to herself, they brought only pleasure and happiness to the people who read them, they made people feel more alive and more connected to one another, and if the bearded leader of that country on the other side of the world was against the Englishman's book, all he had to do was stop reading it, put it away somewhere, and forget about it. Threatening to kill someone for writing a novel, a make-believe story set in a make-believe world, was the stupidest thing she had ever heard of. Words were harmless, with no power to hurt anyone, and even if some words were offensive to some people, words weren't knives or bullets, they were simply black marks on pieces of paper, and they couldn't kill or wound or cause any real damage. That was her response to the fatwa at ten, her naïve but earnest reaction to the absurd injustice that had been committed, and her outrage was all the more intense because it was tinged with fear, for this was the first time she had been exposed to the ugliness of brute, irrational hatred, the first time her young eyes had looked into the darkness of the world. The affair continued, of course, it went on for many years after that denunciation on Valentine's Day 1989, and she grew up with the story of Salman Rushdie – the bookstore bombings, the knife in the heart of his Japanese translator, the bullets in the back of his Norwegian publisher – the story was embedded inside her as she moved from childhood into adolescence, and the older she grew the more she understood about the danger of words, the threat to power words can represent, and in states ruled by tyrants and policemen, every writer who dares to express himself freely is at risk.

PEN's Freedom to Write Program is run by a man named Paul Fowler, a poet in his spare time, a human rights activist by profession, and when he gave Alice her job last summer, he told her that the underlying philosophy of their work was quite simple: to make a lot of noise, as much noise as possible. Paul has a full-time deputy, Linda Nicholson, a woman born on the same day as Alice, and the three of them make up the staff of the small department dedicated to the production of noise. About half of what they do is focused on international issues, the campaign to reform Article 301 of the Turkish penal code, for example, the insult law that has threatened the lives and safety of scores of writers and journalists for making critical remarks about their country, as well as the attempts to win the release of writers imprisoned in various places around the

world, the Burmese writers, the Chinese writers, the Cuban writers, many of them suffering from grave medical problems because of harsh treatment and/or neglect, and by putting pressure on the various governments responsible for these violations of international law, exposing these stories to the world press, circulating petitions signed by hundreds of celebrated writers, PEN has often succeeded in embarrassing these governments into letting prisoners go, not as often as they would like, but often enough to know that these methods can work, often enough to keep on trying, and in many cases to keep on trying for years. The other half of what they do is concerned with domestic issues: the banning of books by schools and libraries, for example, or the ongoing Campaign for Core Freedoms, initiated by PEN in 2004 in response to the Patriot Act passed by the Bush administration, which has given the U.S. government unprecedented authority to monitor the activities of American citizens and collect information about their personal associations, reading habits, and opinions. In the report Alice helped Paul compose not long after starting her job, PEN is now calling for the following actions: expanding safeguards for bookstore and library records weakened by the Patriot Act; reining in the use of the National Security Letters; limiting the scope of secret surveillance programs; closing Guantánamo and all remaining secret prisons; ending torture, arbitrary detentions, and extraordinary rendition; expanding refugee resettlement programs for endangered Iraqi writers. On the day she was hired, Paul and Linda told her not to be alarmed by the clicking sounds she would hear when she used the phone. The lines at PEN were tapped, and both the U.S. and Chinese governments had hacked into their computers.

It is the first Monday of the new year, January fifth, and she has just traveled into Manhattan to begin another five-hour stint at PEN headquarters. She will be working from nine in the morning until two o'clock today, at which point she will return to Sunset Park and put in another few hours on her dissertation, forcing herself to sit at her desk until six-thirty, trying to eke out another paragraph or two on *The Best Years of Our Lives*. Six-thirty is when she and Miles arranged to meet in the kitchen to start preparing dinner. They will be cooking together for the first time since Pilar went back to Florida, and she is looking forward to it, looking forward to being alone with Señor Heller again for a little while, for Señor Heller has proved to be every bit as interesting as Bing advertised, and she takes pleasure in being near him, in talking to him, in watching him move. She has not fallen for him in the way poor Ellen has, has not

lost her head or cursed the innocent Pilar Sanchez for robbing his heart, but the soft-spoken, brooding, impenetrable Miles Heller has touched a nerve in her, and she finds it difficult to remember what things were like in the house before he moved in. For the fourth night in a row, Jake will not be coming, and it pains her to realize that she is glad.

She is still thinking about Jake as she steps out of the elevator on the third floor, wondering if the moment has finally come for a showdown with him or if she should put it off a little longer, wait until the four pounds she lost in December have become eight pounds, twelve pounds, however many pounds it will take before she stops counting. Paul is already sitting at his desk, talking to someone on the telephone, and he waves to her from the other side of the glass window that separates his office from the outer room, where her desk is located, her small, cluttered desk, where she now sits down and switches on her computer. Linda comes in a couple of minutes later, cheeks flushed from the cold morning air, and before she removes her coat and gets to work, she walks over to Alice, plants a big kiss on her left cheek, and wishes her a happy new year.

Paul makes a grunting sound from within his office, a sound that could signify surprise or disappointment or dismay, nothing is clear, Paul often emits confusing sounds after he hangs up the phone, and as Alice and Linda turn to look through the glass window, Paul is already on his feet and walking toward them. There has been a new development. On December thirty-first, the Chinese authorities allowed Liu Xiaobo to be visited by his wife.

This is their new case, the most pressing case on the current agenda, and ever since Liu Xiaobo was detained in early December, they have worked on little else. Paul and Linda are both pessimistic about the immediate future, both are certain that the Beijing Public Security Bureau will hold Liu until enough evidence has been gathered against him to make a formal arrest on the charge of *inciting subversion of state power,* which could land him in prison for fifteen years. His offense: cowriting a document called Charter 08, a declaration calling for political reform, greater human rights, and an end to one-party rule in China.

Liu Xiaobo began as a literary critic and professor at Beijing Normal University, an important enough figure to have worked as a visiting scholar at a number of foreign institutions, notably the University of Oslo and Columbia University in New York, Alice's Columbia University, the place where she is pushing toward her doctorate, and

Liu's activism dates all the way back to 1989, the year of years, the year the Berlin Wall came down, the year of the fatwa, the year of Tiananmen Square, and it was precisely then, in the spring of 1989, that Liu quit his post at Columbia and went back to Beijing, where he staged a hunger strike in Tiananmen Square in support of the students and advocated nonviolent methods of protest in order to prevent further bloodshed. He spent two years in prison for this, and then, in 1996, was sentenced to three years of *reeducation through labor* for suggesting that the Chinese government open discussions with the Dalai Lama of Tibet. More harassments have followed, and he has been living under police surveillance ever since. His latest arrest occurred on December 8, 2008, coincidentally or not coincidentally just one day before the sixtieth anniversary of the Universal Declaration of Human Rights. He is being held in an undisclosed location, with no access to a lawyer, no writing materials, no way to communicate with anyone. Does his wife's visit on New Year's Eve signify an important turn, or was it simply a small act of mercy that will have no bearing on the outcome of the case?

Alice spends the morning and early afternoon writing e-mails to PEN centers all around the world, enlisting support for the massive protest Paul wants to mount in Liu's defense. She works with a kind of righteous fervor, knowing that men like Liu Xiaobo are the bedrock of humanity, that few men or women are brave enough to stand up and risk their lives for others, and beside him the rest of us are nothing, walking around in the chains of our weakness and indifference and dull conformity, and when a man like this is about to be sacrificed for his belief in others, the others must do everything they can to save him, and yet even if Alice is filled with anger as she works, she works in a kind of despair as well, feeling the hopelessness of the effort they are about to launch, sensing that no amount of indignation will alter the plans of the Chinese authorities, and even if PEN can roust a million people to pound on drums across the entire globe, there is little chance those drums will be heard.

She skips lunch and works straight through until it is time for her to leave, and when she walks out of the building and heads for the subway, she is still under the spell of the Liu Xiaobo case, still trying to figure out how to interpret the visit from his wife on New Year's Eve, the same New Year's Eve she spent with Jake and a group of their friends on the Upper West Side, everyone kissing everyone else at midnight, a silly custom, but she enjoyed it anyway, she liked being kissed by everyone, and she wonders now, as she descends the stairs into the subway,

if the Chinese police allowed Liu's wife to stay with him until midnight, and if they did, whether she and her husband kissed at the stroke of twelve, assuming they were allowed to kiss at all, and if they were, what it would be like to kiss your husband under those circumstances, with policemen watching you and no guarantee that you will ever see your husband again.

Normally, she carries along a book to read on the subway, but she overslept by half an hour this morning, and in the scramble to get out of the house in time for work, she forgot to take one with her, and because the train is nearly empty at two-fifteen in the afternoon, there aren't enough people on board for her to use the forty-minute ride to study her fellow passengers, a cherished New York pastime, especially for a New York transplant who grew up in the Midwest, and with nothing to read and not enough faces to look at, she digs into her purse, pulls out a small notebook, and jots down some remarks about the passage she is planning to write when she gets home. Not only are the returning soldiers estranged from their wives, she will argue, but they no longer know how to talk to their sons. There is a scene early in the movie that sets the tone for this generational split, and that is what she will be tackling today, that one scene, in which Fredric March presents his high-school-age boy with his war trophies, a samurai sword and a Japanese flag, and she finds it unexpected but entirely appropriate that the boy shows no interest in these things, that he would rather talk about Hiroshima and the prospect of nuclear annihilation than the presents his father has given him. His mind is already fixed on the future, the *next* war, as if the war that has just been fought is already in the distant past, and consequently he asks his father no questions, is not curious enough to learn how these souvenirs were obtained, and a scene in which one would have imagined the boy wanting to hear his father talk about his adventures on the battlefield ends with the boy forgetting to take the sword and the flag with him when he walks out of the room. The father is not a hero in the eyes of his son – he is a superannuated figure from a bygone age. A bit later, when March and Myrna Loy are alone in the room, he turns to her and says: It's terrifying. Loy: What is? March: Youth! Loy: Didn't you run across any young people in the army? March: No. They were all old men – like me.

Miles Heller is old. The thought comes to her out of nowhere, but once it settles in her mind, she knows that she has discovered an essential truth, the thing that sets him apart from Jake Baum and Bing Nathan

and all the other young men she knows, the generation of talking boys, the logorrhea class of 2009, whereas Señor Heller says next to nothing, is incapable of making small talk, and refuses to share his secrets with anyone. Miles has been in a war, and all soldiers are old men by the time they come home, shut-down men who never talk about the battles they have fought. What war did Miles Heller march off to, she wonders, what action has he seen, how long has he been away? It is impossible to know, but there is no question that he has been wounded, that he walks around with an inner wound that will never heal, and perhaps that is why she respects him so much – because he is in pain, and he never says anything about it. Bing rants and Jake whines, but Miles holds his tongue. It is not even clear to her what he is doing in Sunset Park. One day early last month, just after he moved in, she asked him why he had left Florida, but his answer was so vague – *I have some unfinished business to take care of* – it could have meant anything. What unfinished business? And why move away from Pilar? He is so obviously in love with the girl, why on earth would he have come to Brooklyn?

If not for Pilar, she would actively worry about Miles. Yes, it was a little disconcerting to be introduced to someone so young, a *high school girl* in her funny green parka and red woolen gloves, but that sensation quickly wore off when one understood how bright and pulled together she was, and the best thing about this girl is the simple fact that Miles is devoted to her, and from Alice's observations during Pilar's visit, she believes she was looking at what is probably an exceptional love, and if Miles can love someone in the way he loves this girl, it must mean the damage inside him is not systemic, that his wounds are specific wounds in specific areas of his soul and are not bleeding into other parts of him, and therefore the darkness in Miles does not prey on her mind as it did before Pilar lived among them for those ten or eleven days. It was difficult not to feel some envy, of course, watching Miles as he looked at his beloved, talked to his beloved, touched his beloved, not because she wants him to look at her in that way but because Jake doesn't do it anymore, and foolish as it is to measure Jake against Señor Heller, there are times when she can't stop herself. Jake has brains, talent, and ambition, whereas Miles, for all his mental and physical virtues, is completely lacking in ambition, seems content to drift through his days without passion or purpose, and yet Miles is a man and Jake is still a boy, because Miles has been to war and has grown old. Perhaps that explains why the two of them seem to dislike each other so much. Even at the first dinner, when

Jake began talking about interviewing Renzo Michaelson, she felt that Miles was ready to punch him or pour a drink over his head. Who knows why Michaelson provoked that response, but the animosity has continued – to such a degree that Miles is rarely at home when Jake comes for dinner. Jake is continuing to pester Bing about helping him set up a meeting with Michaelson, but Bing keeps putting him off, saying that Michaelson is an ornery, reclusive sort of person, and the best way to handle it is to wait until he comes into the store again to have his typewriter cleaned. Alice could probably arrange it herself if she wanted to. Michaelson is a longtime member of PEN, a past vice president with a special attachment to the Freedom to Write Program, and she talked to him on the phone only last week about the Liu Xiaobo case. She could easily call him tomorrow and ask if he has any time to talk to her boyfriend, but she doesn't want to do it. Jake has stuck a knife in her, and she isn't in the mood to do him any favors.

She returns to the empty house just after three o'clock. By three-thirty, she is sitting at her desk, typing up her notes about the father–son conversation in *The Best Years of Our Lives*. At three-fifty, someone starts knocking on the front door. Alice stands up and goes downstairs to see who it is. When she opens the door, a tall, blubbery man in a strange khaki uniform grins at her and tips his hat. He has a splayed, multifaceted nose, pockmarked cheeks, and a large, full-lipped mouth, a curious assortment of facial characteristics that somehow reminds her of a platter of mashed potatoes. She also notes, with a certain sadness, that he is wearing a gun. When she asks him who he is, he says that he is Nestor Gonzalez, New York City marshal, and then he hands her a folded-up piece of paper, a document of some kind. What is this? Alice asks. A court order, Gonzalez says. For what? Alice asks, pretending that she doesn't know. You're breaking the law, ma'am, the marshal replies. You and your friends have to get out.

Miles is worried about money. He didn't have enough to begin with, and now that he has spent the better part of two weeks running around the city with Pilar, eating twice a day in restaurants, buying her clothes and perfume, springing for expensive theater tickets, his reserve has been melting even more quickly than he imagined it would. They talk about it on January third, a few hours after Pilar climbs onto the bus and heads back to Florida, a few minutes after Miles leaves the garbled message on his mother's answering machine, and Bing says there is a simple solution to the problem if Miles is willing to accept his offer. He needs help at the Hospital for Broken Things. Mob Rule has finally found a booking agent, and they will be out of town for two weeks at the end of January and two more weeks in February, playing at colleges in New York State and Pennsylvania, and he can't afford to shut down the business while he is away. He can teach Miles how to frame pictures, clean and repair typewriters, fix anything the customers want fixed, and if Miles agrees to work full-time for so many dollars an hour, they can catch up on the unfinished jobs that have been mounting over the past few months, Bing can cut out early to practice with his band whenever the mood strikes him, and whenever the band is traveling, Miles will be in charge. Bing can cover an extra salary now because of the money he has saved by living rent-free in Sunset Park for the past five months – and then, on top of that, it looks as if Mob Rule will be bringing in more cash than at any time in its history. What does Miles think? Miles looks down at his shoes, turns the proposition around for several moments, and then lifts his head and says he is for it. He thinks it will be better to work at the Hospital than to spend his days walking around the cemetery taking photographs, and before he goes out to shop for dinner, he thanks Bing for having rescued him again.

What Miles doesn't understand is that Charles Bingham Nathan would do anything for him, and even if Miles had turned down the offer to work for so many dollars an hour at the Hospital for Broken Things, his friend would have been happy to advance him as much money as he needed, with no obligation to pay back the loan anytime before the end

of the twenty-second century. He knows that Miles is only half a person, that his life has been sundered and will never be fully repaired, but the half of Miles that remains is more compelling to him than two of anyone else. It began when they met twelve years ago, in the fall immediately after the death of Miles's brother, Miles just sixteen and Bing a year older, the one following the smart-kid road at Stuyvesant and the other in the music program at LaGuardia, two angry boys who found common cause in their contempt for the hypocrisies of American life, and it was the younger one who taught the older one the value of resistance, how it was possible to refuse to participate in the meaningless games society was asking them to play, and Bing knows that much of what he has become in the years since then is a direct result of Miles's influence on him. It was more than what Miles said, however, more than any one of the hundreds of cutting observations he made about politics and economics, the clarity with which he broke down *the system,* it was what Miles said in combination with who Miles was, and how he seemed to embody the ideas he believed in, the gravity of his bearing, the grief-stricken boy with no illusions, no false hopes, and even if they never became intimate friends, he doubts there is anyone from his generation he admires more.

He was not the only one who felt that way. As far back as he can remember, Miles seemed different from everyone else, to possess some magnetic, animal force that changed the atmosphere whenever he walked into a room. Was it the power of his silences that made him attract so much attention, the mysterious, closed-in nature of his personality that turned him into a kind of mirror for others to project themselves onto, the eerie sense that he was both there and not there at the same time? He was intelligent and good-looking, yes, but not all intelligent and good-looking people exude that magic, and when you added in the fact that everyone knew he was the son of Mary-Lee Swann, the only child of Mary-Lee Swann, perhaps the aura of her fame helped to enhance the feeling that Miles was one of the anointed. Some people resented him, of course, boys in particular, boys but never girls, but why wouldn't boys resent him for his luck with girls, for being the one the girls wanted? Even now, so many years later, the Heller touch seems to have survived the long odyssey to nowhere and back. Look at Alice and Ellen. Alice finds him *wholly admirable* (a direct quote), and Ellen, dear little Ellen, is besotted with him.

Miles has been living in Sunset Park for a month now, and Bing is glad he is here, glad the Paltry Three has been turned back into the Solid Four,

although he is still baffled by Miles's sudden change of heart about coming to Brooklyn. First it was no, and the long letter explaining why he wanted to stay in Florida, and then the urgent phone call to the Hospital late one Friday, just as Bing was about to close up and return to the house in Sunset Park, and Miles telling him that *something had come up* and if a place was still open for him, he would be on a bus to New York that weekend. Miles will never explain himself, of course, and it would be pointless to ask, but now that he is here, Bing is heartened that old Mr. Sullen is finally prepared to make peace with his parents and put a stop to the idiocy that has been going on for so long, much too long, and that his own role as double agent and liar will soon be coming to an end. He feels no guilt about having deceived Miles. If anything, he is proud of what he has done, and when Morris Heller called the Hospital this morning to ask for the latest news, he felt a sense of victory when he was able to report that Miles had called his office while he was in England and would be calling back on Monday, and now that Miles has just told him he has called his mother as well, the victory is almost complete. Miles has come round at last, and it is probably a good thing that he is in love with Pilar, even if that love feels a bit strange, more than a little disturbing in fact, such a young girl, the last person one would expect Miles to get himself entangled with, but without question charming and pretty, old beyond her years perhaps, and therefore let Miles have his Pilar and think no more about it. Good news all around, positive things happening on so many fronts, and yet it has been a difficult month for him, one of the most anguishing months of his life, and when he hasn't been wallowing in mud baths of confusion and disarray, he has been close to despair. It started when Miles returned to New York, the moment when he saw Miles standing in the store and he threw his arms around him and kissed him, and ever since that day he has found it nearly impossible not to touch Miles, not to want to touch Miles. He knows that Miles doesn't like it, that he is put off by his spontaneous hugs, his pats on the back, his neck squeezes and shoulder squeezes, but Bing can't stop himself, he knows he should stop but he can't, and because he is afraid he has fallen in love with Miles, because he is afraid he has always been in love with Miles, he is living in a state of despair.

He remembers a summer outing eleven years ago, the summer after he graduated from high school, three boys and two girls packed into a little car driving north to the Catskills. Someone's parents owned a cottage up there, an isolated spot in the woods with a pond and a tennis court, and

Miles was in the car with his love of the moment, a girl named Annie, and there was Geoff Taylor with his newest conquest, someone whose name has been forgotten, and last but not least himself, the one with no girlfriend, the odd man out as usual. They arrived late, sometime between midnight and one o'clock in the morning, and because they were hot and stiff after the long drive, someone suggested they cool off in the pond, and suddenly they were running toward the water, stripping off their clothes, and wading in. He remembers how pleasant it was, splashing around in that remote place with the moon and the stars overhead, the crickets singing in the woods, the warm breeze blowing against his back, along with the pleasure of seeing the bodies of the girls, the long-legged Annie with her flat stomach and delightfully curved rear end, and Geoff's girlfriend, short and round, with large breasts and frizzy strands of dark hair twining over her shoulders. But it wasn't sexual pleasure, there was nothing erotic about what they were doing, it was simple corporeal ease, the pleasure of feeling the water and the air against your skin, of lolling around in the open on a hot summer night, of being with your friends. He was the first one to come out, and as he stood at the edge of the pond, he saw that the others had paired off, that the two couples were standing chest-deep in the water, and each couple was embracing, and as he watched Miles and Annie with their arms around each other and their mouths locked in a prolonged kiss, the strangest thought occurred to him, something that took him completely by surprise. Annie was incontestably a beautiful girl, one of the loveliest girls he had ever met, and the logic of the situation demanded that he feel envious of Miles for having such a beautiful girl in his arms, for being attractive enough to have won the affections of such a desirable creature, but as he watched the two of them kissing in the water, he understood that the envy he felt was directed toward Annie, not Miles, that he wanted to be in Annie's place and to be kissing Miles himself. A moment later, they began walking toward the edge of the pond, walking straight toward him, and as Miles's body emerged from the water, Bing saw that he had an erection, a large, fully formed erection, and the sight of that stiffened penis aroused him, excited him in a way he never would have thought possible, and before Miles had touched dry ground, Bing had an erection of his own, a turn of events that so bewildered him that he ran back into the pond and dove under the water to conceal his embarrassment.

He suppressed the memory of that night for years, never returned to it even in the darkest, most private realms of his imagination, but then

Miles came back, and with Miles the memory came back, and for the past month Bing has been replaying that scene in his head five times a day, ten times a day, and by now he no longer knows who or what he is. Does his response to that erect phallus glimpsed in the moonlight eleven years ago mean that he prefers men to women, that he is more attracted to male bodies than female bodies, and if that is the case, could that account for his singular run of failure with the women he has courted over the years? He doesn't know. The only thing he can say with any certainty is that he is drawn to Miles, that he thinks about Miles's body and that erect phallus whenever he is with him, which is often, and that he thinks about touching Miles's body and that erect phallus whenever he is not with him, which is more often, and yet to act on these desires would be a grave error, an error that would lead to the most horrendous consequences, for Miles has no interest in coupling with other men, and if Bing even suggested such a possibility, even whispered a single word about what is on his mind, he would lose Miles's friendship forever, which is something he devoutly does not wish to do.

Miles is off-limits, on permanent loan to the world of women. But the tormenting power of that erect phallus has driven Bing to consider other options, to think about looking elsewhere to satisfy his curiosity, for in spite of the fact that Miles is the only man he craves, he wonders if the time hasn't come to experiment with another man, which is the only way he will ever find out who and what he is – a man made for men, a man made for women, a man made for both men and women, or a man made for no one but himself. The problem is where to look. All the members of his band are married or living with their girlfriends, he has no gay friends he can think of, and the idea of cruising for some pickup in a gay bar leaves him cold. He has thought about Jake Baum a few times, plotting various strategies about how and when he could approach him without tipping his hand and humiliating himself in the event of a rebuff, but he suspects there is something ambiguous about Alice's boyfriend, and even if he is with a woman now, it is possible that he has been with men in the past and is not immune to the charms of phallic love. Bing regrets that he is not more attracted to Jake, but in the interests of scientific self-discovery he would be willing to bed down with him to see if he himself has any taste for phallic love. He has yet to do anything about it, however, for just when he was gearing up to cajole Baum into having sex with him by promising to arrange the interview with Renzo Michaelson (not the strongest idea, perhaps, but ideas have

been hard to come by), Ellen asked him to pose for her, and his quest for knowledge was temporarily derailed.

He has no idea what they are up to. Something perverse, he feels, but at the same time altogether innocent and without danger. A silent pact of some sort, a mutual understanding that allows them to share their loneliness and frustrations, but even as they draw closer to each other in that silence, he is still lonely and frustrated, and he senses that Ellen is no better off than he is. She draws and he drums. Drumming has always been a way for him to scream, and Ellen's new drawings have turned into screams as well. He takes off his clothes for her and does everything she asks him to do. He doesn't know why he feels so comfortable with her, so unthreatened by her eyes, but donating his body to the cause of her art is a small thing, finally, and he intends to go on doing it until she asks him to stop.

On Sunday, January fourth, he spends eight hours with Miles at the Hospital for Broken Things, giving him his first lessons in the delicate, exacting work of picture framing, introducing him to the sturdy mechanisms of manual typewriters, familiarizing him with the tools and materials in the back room of the tiny shop. The next morning, Monday, January fifth, they go back for more of the same, but this time Miles seems worried, and when Bing asks him what is wrong, Miles explains that he has just called his father's office and was told his father returned to England yesterday *on urgent business,* and he is concerned that it might have something to do with his stepmother. Bing, too, is both worried and perplexed by this news, but he cannot reveal the full scope of his anxiety to Morris Heller's son, nor can he tell him that he spoke to Morris Heller just forty-eight hours ago and that nothing seemed amiss at the time. They work steadily until five-thirty, at which point Miles informs Bing that he wants to take another stab at calling his mother, and Bing deferentially withdraws to a bar down the street, understanding that such a call demands total privacy. Fifteen minutes later, Miles walks into the bar and tells Bing that he and his mother have arranged to meet for dinner tomorrow night. There are a hundred questions Bing would like to ask, but he confines himself to just one: How did she sound? Very well, Miles says. She called him a no-good shithead, an imbecile, and a rotten coward, but then she cried, then they both cried, and afterward her voice became warm and affectionate, she talked to him with far more kindness than he deserved, and hearing her again after all these years was almost too much for him. He regrets everything, he says. He thinks he is the

stupidest person who ever lived. If there were any justice in the world, he should be taken outside and shot.

Bing has never seen Miles look more distressed than he is now. For a few moments, he thinks Miles might actually break down in tears. Forgetting his vow not to touch him anymore, he puts his arms around his friend and holds on to him tightly. Cheer up, asshole, he says. At least you know you're the stupidest person who ever lived. How many people are smart enough to admit that?

They take a bus back to Sunset Park and walk into the house a couple of minutes before six-thirty, a couple of minutes before Miles's scheduled rendezvous with Alice in the kitchen. As expected, Alice is already there, as is Ellen, and both of them are sitting at the table, not preparing food, not doing anything but sitting at the table and looking into each other's eyes. Alice is stroking the back of Ellen's right hand, Ellen's left hand is stroking Alice's face, and both of them look miserable. What is it? Bing asks. This, Alice says, and then she picks up a piece of paper and hands it to him.

Bing has been expecting this piece of paper since the day they moved into the house last August. He knew it would come, and he knew what he was going to do when it came, which is precisely what he does now. Without even bothering to read the full text of the court order to vacate the premises, he tears the sheet once, twice, and then a third time, and then he tosses the eight scraps of paper onto the floor.

Don't worry, he says. This doesn't mean a thing. They've found out we're here, but getting us to move will take more than a dumb piece of paper. I know how this stuff works. They've given us notice, and now they'll forget about us for a while. In a month or so, they'll be back with another piece of paper, which we'll tear up and throw on the floor again. And another time, and another time after that, and maybe even another time after that. The city marshals won't do anything to us. They don't want trouble. Their job is to deliver pieces of paper, and that's it. We don't have to worry until they come with the cops. Then it gets serious, but we won't be seeing any cops around here for a long time – if ever. We're small potatoes, and the cops have better things to think about than four quiet people living in a quiet little house in a quiet little nothing neighborhood. Don't panic. We might have to leave someday, but that day isn't today, and until the cops show up, I'm not giving an inch. And even when they do come, they'll have to beat me over the head and drag me out in handcuffs. This is our house. It belongs to us now, and I'd

rather go to jail than give up my right to live here.

That's the spirit, Miles says.

So you're with me? Bing asks.

Of course I am, Miles says, lifting his right hand into the air, as if taking an oath. Chief Miles no budge from tepee.

And what about you, Ellen? Do you want to leave or stay?

Stay, Ellen says.

And you, Alice?

Stay.

Simon left last night, back to L.A. to teach his film history class, and so begins the grind of comings and goings, the poor man traveling back and forth across the country every week for the next three months, the diabolical red-eye, jet lag, sticky clothes and swollen feet, the awful air in the cabin, the pumped-in artificial air, three days in L.A., four days in New York, and all for the pittance they are paying him, but he says he enjoys the teaching, and surely it is better for him to stay busy, to be doing something rather than nothing, but the timing couldn't have been worse, how much she needs him to be with her now, how much she hates to sleep alone, and this part, Winnie, so grueling and difficult, she fears she will not be up to it, dreads she will fall on her face and become a laughingstock, jitters, jitters, the old knot in the belly before the curtain rises, and how was she to know an emmet is an ant, an archaic word for ant, she had to look it up in the dictionary, and why would Winnie say emmet instead of ant, is it funnier to say emmet instead of ant, yes, no doubt it is funnier, or at least unexpected and therefore strange, *An emmet!*, which leads to Willie's one-word utterance, *Formication*, very droll that, you think he is mispronouncing fornication, but she had to look that one up in the dictionary too before she got the joke, *a sensation of the body resembling that made by the creeping of ants on the skin*, and Fred delivers the word wonderfully well, he is a fine Willie, a good soul to work with, and how nicely he reads the paper early in the first act, *Opening for smart youth, Wanted bright boy*, she burst out laughing at the first read-through when he spoke those lines, Fred Derry, the same name as a character in that movie she watched with Simon the other night, the one he will be showing to his class today, *The Best Years of Our Lives*, an excellent old film, she choked up at the end and cried, and when she went to rehearsal the next day and asked Fred if his parents had named him after the character in that movie, her stage husband grinned at her and said, Alas, dear woman, no, I am an aged fart who crept into this world five years before that film was made.

*Alas, dear woman.* She doubts she has ever been dear. Many other things on the long journey from the first day to this day, but not dear,

no, never that. Intermittently kind, intermittently lovable, intermittently loving, intermittently unselfish, but not often enough to qualify as dear.

She misses Simon, the place feels sickeningly empty without him, but perhaps it is just as well that he isn't here tonight, this one night, a Tuesday night in early January, the sixth night of the year, because in one hour Miles will be ringing the bell downstairs, in one hour he will be walking into this third-floor loft on Franklin Street, and after seven and a half years of no contact with her son (*seven and a half years*), it is probably best that she see him alone, talk to him alone. She has no idea what will happen, is entirely in the dark about what to expect from the evening, and because she is too afraid to dwell on these imponderables, she has concentrated her attention on the dinner, the meal itself, what to serve and what not to serve, and because rehearsal was going to run too late for her to cook the meal herself, she has called two different restaurants to deliver food to the loft at eight-thirty sharp, two restaurants because after ordering steak dinners from the first, thinking steak was a good bet, everyone likes steak, especially men with healthy appetites, she began to fret that she had made the wrong choice, that maybe her son has become a vegetarian or has an aversion to steak, and she didn't want things to get off to an awkward start by putting Miles in a position that would force him to eat something he doesn't like or, even worse, to serve him a meal that he couldn't or wouldn't eat, and therefore, just to play it safe, she called a second restaurant and ordered a second pair of dinners – meatless lasagna, salads, and grilled winter vegetables. As with food, so with drink. She remembers that he used to like scotch and red wine, but his preferences might have changed since the last time she saw him, and consequently she has bought one case each of red wine and white wine and filled the liquor cabinet with an abundant range of possibilities: scotch, bourbon, vodka, gin, tequila, rye, and three different brands of cognac.

She assumes that Miles has already seen his father, that he made the call to the office first thing yesterday morning as Bing Nathan said he would, and that the two of them had dinner together last night. She was expecting Morris to call her today and give a full account of what happened, but no word yet, no message on the machine or her cell phone, even though Miles must have told him he would be coming here tonight, since she and Miles spoke before dinner hour yesterday, in other words before Miles saw his father, and it is hard to imagine that the subject would not have come up somewhere in their conversation. Who knows

why she hasn't heard from Morris? It could be that things went badly last night and he is still too upset to talk about it. Or else he was simply too busy today, his second day back at work after the trip to England, and maybe he got caught up in problems at the office, the publishing house is going through hard times just now, and it's even possible that he's still at the office at seven o'clock, eating Chinese takeout for dinner and settling in for a long night of work. Then, too, it could be that Miles lost his nerve and didn't make the call. Not likely, since he wasn't too afraid to call her, and if this is the week for burying hatchets, his father is the logical place to begin, the one he would go to first, since Morris had a hell of a lot more to do with raising him than she did, but still, it could be true, and while she mustn't let Miles know what Bing Nathan has been up to all these years, she can ask the question tonight and find out if he has been in touch with his father or not.

That was why she shouted at Miles on the phone yesterday – out of solidarity with Morris. He and Willa have borne the brunt of this long, wretched affair, and when she saw him at dinner on Saturday night, he looked so much older to her, the hair so gray now, the cheeks so thin, the eyes so dull with sadness, and she understood what a toll this story has taken on him, and now that she is older and presumably wiser (although that is a matter of some dispute, she believes), she was moved by the surge of affection she felt for him in the restaurant that night, the aging shadow of the man she married so long ago, the father of her only child, and it was for Morris's sake that she shouted at Miles, pretending to share Morris's anger at him for what he has done, trying to act like a proper parent, the hurt, scolding mother, but most of it was performance, nearly every word was a pretend word, the insults, the name-calling, for the fact is that she resents Miles far less than Morris does, and she has not walked around all these years feeling bitter about what happened – disappointed, yes, confused, yes, but not bitter.

She has no right to blame Miles for anything he has done, she has let him down by being such a fitful, incompetent mother, and she knows she has failed at this more dreadfully than anything else in her life, the two failed marriages included, every one of her lapses and bad deeds included, but she wasn't up to motherhood when Miles was born, twenty-six years old but still not ready, too distracted to concentrate, preoccupied by the jump from theater to film, indignant with Morris for having talked her into it, and struggle as she did to fulfill her duties for those first six months, she found herself bored with the baby, there

was so little pleasure in taking care of him, and not even the pleasure of breast-feeding was enough, not even the pleasure of looking into his eyes and watching him smile back at her could compensate for the smothering tedium of it all, the incessant wailing, the wet, yellow shit in the diapers, the puked-up milk, the howls in the middle of the night, the lack of sleep, the mindless repetitions, and then *Innocent Dreamer* came along, and she bolted. Looking back on her actions now, she finds them unpardonable, and even if she did fall for the boy later, after the divorce, after he started growing up, she was no good at it, she kept letting him down, couldn't even remember to go to his bloody high school graduation for God's sake, but that was the turning point, the unpardonable sin of not being there when she should have been there, and from then on she became more conscientious, tried to make amends for all the sins she had committed over the years (the beautiful weekend in Providence with Simon, the three of them together as if they were a family, she was so happy there, so proud of the boy), and then, six months after that, he bolted. Mother bolts, boy bolts. Hence her tears on the phone yesterday. She shouted at him for Morris's sake, but the tears were for herself, and the tears spoke the truth. Miles is twenty-eight now, older than she was when she gave birth to him, but he is still her son, and she wants him back, she wants the story to begin again.

Pity the poor hippo, she thinks. Too fat, dear woman, too many extra pounds on the old bones. Why did it have to be Winnie now and not someone a little more graceful, a little more *svelte*? Svelte Salome, for instance. Because she is too old to play Salome, and Tony Gilbert has asked her to play Winnie. *That is what I find so wonderful. (Pause.) Eyes on my eyes.* She has changed three times since returning to the loft, but she still isn't satisfied with the results. The hour is fast approaching, however, and it is too late to consider a fourth option. Pale blue silk pants, white silk blouse, and a gauzy, loose-flowing, semi-transparent, knee-length jacket to mask the flab. Bracelets on each wrist, but no earrings. Chinese slippers. Winnie's short hair, nothing to be done about that. Too much makeup or too little makeup? The red lipstick a bit harsh, perhaps, remove some of it now. Perfume or no perfume? No perfume. And the hands, the telltale hands with their too plump fingers, nothing to be done about them either. A necklace would probably be too much, and besides, no one could see it under the gauzy wrap. What else? The nail polish. Winnie's nail polish, nothing to be done about that either. Jitters, jitters, the old lump in the gut before the emmet crawls out and formicates. *Your*

*eyes on my eyes*. She goes into the bathroom for a last look in the mirror. Old Mother Hubbard or Alice in Motherland? Somewhere in between, perhaps. *Wanted bright boy*. She goes into the kitchen and pours herself a glass of wine. Time for one sip, time for a second sip, and then the doorbell rings.

So much to absorb all at once, so many particulars bombarding her the instant the door opens, the tall young man with his father's dark hair and eyebrows, his mother's gray-blue eyes and mouth, so complete now, the work of growing finally finished, a sterner face than before, she thinks, but softer, more giving eyes, eyes looking into her eyes, and the fierce hug he gives her before either of them can say a word, feeling the great strength of his arms and shoulders through his leather jacket, and again she goes stupid on him without wanting to, breaking down and crying as she holds on to him for dear life, blubbering how sorry she is for all the misunderstandings and grievances that drove him away, but he says none of it has anything to do with her, she is entirely blameless, everything is his fault, and he is the one who is sorry.

He doesn't drink anymore. That is the first new fact she learns about him after she dries her eyes and leads him into the living room. He doesn't drink, but he isn't particular about food, he will be happy to have the steak or the meatless lasagna, whichever she prefers. Why does she feel so nervous around him, so apologetic? She has already apologized, he has already apologized, it is time to move on to more substantial matters, time to begin talking, but then she does the one thing she promised herself she wouldn't do, she mentions the play, she says that is why she is so large now, he is looking at Winnie, not Mary-Lee, an illusion, an imaginary character, and the boy who is no longer a boy smiles at her and says he thinks she is looking grand, *grand* she says to herself, what a curious word, such an old-fashioned way of putting it, no one says *grand* anymore, unless he is referring to her size, of course, her newly begotten rotundity, but no, he seems to be paying her a compliment, and yes, he adds, he has read about the play and is looking forward to seeing it. She notices that she is fidgeting with her bracelet, her lungs feel tight, she can't sit still. I'll go get the wine, she says, but what will it be for you, Miles? Water, juice, ginger ale? As she walks across the large open space of the loft, Miles stands up and follows her, saying he's changed his mind, he'll have some wine after all, he wants to celebrate, and who knows if he means it or is simply dying for a drink because he is just as nervous as she is?

They clink glasses, and as they do so she tells herself to be careful, to remember that Bing Nathan must be kept out of it, that Miles must not discover how closely they have kept track of him, the different jobs in all the different places for all these years, Chicago, New Hampshire, Arizona, California, Florida, the restaurants, the hotels, the warehouses, pitching for the baseball team, the women who have come and gone, the Cuban girl who was with him in New York just now, all the things they know about him must be suppressed, and she must feign ignorance whenever he divulges something, but she can do that, it is her business to do that, she can do that even when she has drunk too much, and from the way Miles has gulped down the first sip of his Pouilly-Fumé, it looks as if much wine will be consumed tonight.

And what about your father? she asks. Have you been in touch with him?

I've called twice, he says. He was in England the first time. They told me to call back on the fifth, but when I tried to reach him yesterday, they said he'd flown off to England again. Something urgent.

Strange, she says. I had dinner with Morris Saturday night, and he didn't say anything about going back. He must have left on Sunday. Very strange.

I hope everything is okay with Willa.

Willa. What makes you think she's in England?

I know she's in England. People tell me things, I have my sources.

I thought you turned your back on us. Not a peep in all this time, and now you tell me you know what we've been up to?

More or less.

If you still cared, why run away in the first place?

That's the big question, isn't it? (*Pause. Another sip of wine.*) Because I thought you'd be better off without me – all of you.

Or you'd be better off without us.

Maybe.

Then why come back now?

Because circumstances brought me up to New York, and once I was here, I understood that the game was over. I'd had enough.

But why so long? When you first went missing, I thought it would be for a few weeks, a few months. You know: confused young man lights out for the territories, grapples with his demons in the wilderness, and comes back a stronger, better person. But seven years, Miles, one-quarter of your life. You see how crazy that is, don't you?

I did want to become a better person. That was the whole point. Become better, become stronger – all very worthy, I suppose, but also a little vague. How do you know when you've become better? It's not like going to college for four years and being handed a diploma to prove you've passed all your courses. There's no way to measure your progress. So I kept at it, not knowing if I was better or not, not knowing if I was stronger or not, and after a while I stopped thinking about the goal and concentrated on the effort. (*Pause. Another sip of wine.*) Does any of this make sense to you? I became addicted to the struggle. I lost track of myself. I kept on doing it, but I didn't know why I was doing it anymore.

Your father thinks you ran away because of a conversation you overheard.

He figured that out? I'm impressed. But that conversation was only the start, the first push. I'm not going to deny how terrible it felt to hear them talking about me like that, but after I took off, I understood they were right, right to be so worried about me, right in their analysis of my fucked-up psyche, and that's why I stayed away – because I didn't want to be that person anymore, and I knew it would take me a long time to get well.

Are you well now?

(*Laughs.*) I doubt it. (*Pause.*) But not as bad off as I was then. Lots of things have changed, especially in the past six months.

Another glass, Miles?

Yes, please. (*Pause.*) I shouldn't be doing this. Out of practice, you know. But it's awfully good wine, and I'm awfully, awfully nervous.

(*Refilling both their glasses.*) Me too, baby.

It was never about you, I hope you understand that. But once I made the break with my father and Willa, I had to break with you and Simon as well.

It's all about Bobby, isn't it?

(*Nods.*)

You have to let it go.

I can't.

You have to.

(*Shakes his head.*) Too many bad memories.

You didn't run him over. It was an accident.

We were arguing. I pushed him into the road, and then the car came – going too fast, coming out of nowhere.

Let it go, Miles. It was an accident.

(*Eyes welling up with tears. Silence, four seconds. Then the downstairs buzzer rings.*)

It must be the food. (*Stands up, walks over to Miles, kisses him on the forehead, and then goes off to let in the deliveryman from the restaurant. Over her shoulder, addressing Miles.*) Which one do you think it is? The vegetarians or the carnivores?

(*Long pause. Forcing a smile.*) Both!

## MORRIS HELLER

The Can Man has been to England and back, and his experiences there have changed the color of the world. Since returning to New York on January twenty-fifth, he has given up his cans and bottles in order to devote himself to a life of pure contemplation. The Can Man nearly died in England. The Can Man contracted pneumonia and spent two weeks in a hospital, and the woman he went there to rescue from mental collapse and potential suicide wound up rescuing him from almost certain death and in so doing rescued herself from mental collapse and possibly saved a marriage as well. The Can Man is glad to be alive. The Can Man knows his days are numbered, and therefore he has put aside his quest for cans and bottles in order to study the days as they slip past him, one after the other, each one more quickly than the day before it. Among the numerous observations he has noted down in his book of observations are the following:

January 25. We do not grow stronger as the years advance. The accumulation of sufferings and sorrows weakens our capacity to endure more sufferings and sorrows, and since sufferings and sorrows are inevitable, even a small setback late in life can resound with the same force as a major tragedy when we are young. *The straw that broke the camel's back*. Your dumb-ass penis in another woman's vagina, for example. Willa was on the verge of collapse before that ignominious adventure ever occurred. She has been through too much in her life, has borne more than her fair share of pains, and tough as she has had to be, she is not half as tough as she thinks she is. A dead husband, a dead son, a runaway stepson, and an unfaithful second husband – a nearly dead second husband. What if you had taken the initiative years ago, when you first saw her in that seminar in Philosophy Hall at Columbia, the bright Barnard girl let into a class for graduate students, the one with the delicate, pretty face and slender hands? There was a strong attraction then, all those years ago, long before Karl and Mary-Lee, and young as you both were at the time, twenty-two and twenty, what if you had pursued her a bit harder, what if your little dalliance had led to marriage? Result: no dead husband, no dead son, no runaway stepson. Other sufferings and

sorrows, of course, but not those. Now she has brought you back from the dead, averting the final eclipse of all hope, and your still-breathing body must be counted as her greatest triumph. Hope endures, then, but not certainty. There has been a truce, a declaration of a desire for peace, but whether this has been a genuine meeting of minds is not clear. The boy remains an obstacle. She cannot forgive and forget. Not even after he and his mother called from New York to find out how you were, not even after the boy went on calling every day for two weeks to ask for the latest news on your condition. She will remain in England for the Easter break, and you will not be going there again. Too much time has been lost already, and you are needed at the office, the captain of a sinking ship must not abandon his crew. Perhaps she will change her mind as the months roll on. Perhaps she will bend. But you cannot renounce the boy for her sake. Nor can you renounce her for the boy's sake. You want them both, you must have them both, and one way or another, you will, even if they do not have each other.

January 26. Now that you and the boy have spent an evening together, you find yourself curiously let down. Too many years of anticipation, perhaps, too many years of imagining how the reunion would unfold, and therefore a feeling of anticlimax when it finally happened, for the imagination is a powerful weapon, and the imagined reunions that played out in your head so many times over the years were bound to be richer, fuller, and more emotionally satisfying than the real thing. You are also disturbed by the fact that you can't help resenting him. If there is to be any hope for the future, then you too must learn to forgive and forget. But the boy is already standing between you and your wife, and unless your wife undergoes a change of heart and allows him into her world again, the boy will continue to represent the distance that has grown between you. Still and all, it was a miraculous occasion, and the boy is so earnestly repentant, one would have to be made of stone not to want a new chapter to begin. But it will take some time before the two of you feel comfortable together, before you can trust each other again. Physically, he looks well. Strong and fit, with an encouraging brightness in his eyes. Mary-Lee's eyes, the indelible imprint of his mother. He says he has been to two performances of *Happy Days* and thinks she is a splendid Winnie, and when you suggested that the two of you go to see her together – if he could stand to watch the play a third time – he eagerly accepted. He talked at length about the young woman he has fallen in love with, Pilar, Pilar Hernandez, Sanchez, Gomez, her last name escapes

you now, and he is looking forward to introducing her to you when she comes back to New York in April. He has no definite plans for the future. For the time being, he is working in Bing Nathan's store, but if he can put together enough money, he is toying with the idea of returning to college next year and getting his degree. Perhaps, maybe, it all depends. You didn't have the courage to confront him with difficult questions about the past. Why he ran away, for example, or why he kept himself hidden for so long. Not to speak of why he left his girlfriend in Florida and came to New York alone. There will be time for questions later. Last night was simply the first round, two boxers feeling each other out before getting down to business. You love him, of course, you love him with all your heart, but you no longer know what to think of him. Let him prove himself to be a worthy son.

January 27. If the company goes down, you will write a book called *Forty Years in the Desert: Publishing Literature in a Country Where People Hate Books*. The Christmas sales figures were even worse than you feared they would be, the worst showing ever. In the office, everyone looks worried – the old hands, the young kids, everyone from senior editors to baby-faced interns. Nor can the sight of your weakened, emaciated body inspire much confidence about the future. Nevertheless, you are glad to be back, glad to be in the place where you feel you belong, and even though the German and the Israeli have both turned you down, you feel less desperate about the situation than you did before you became ill. Nothing like a brief chat with Death to put things in perspective, and you figure that if you managed to avoid an untimely exit in that British hospital, you will find a way to steer the company through this nasty typhoon. No storm lasts forever, and now that you are back at the helm, you realize how much you savor your position as boss, how nourishing this little enterprise has been for you all these years. And you must be a good boss, or at least an appreciated boss, for when you returned to work yesterday, Jill Hertzberg threw her arms around you and said, Good God, Morris, don't ever do that again, please, I beg of you, and then, one by one, each member of the staff, all nine of them, men and women alike, came into your office and hugged you, welcoming you back after your long, tumultuous absence. Your own family might be in ruins, but this is your family as well, and your job is to protect them and make them understand that in spite of the idiot culture that surrounds them, books still count, and the work they are doing is important work, essential work. No doubt you are a sentimental old fool, a man out of

step with the times, but you enjoy swimming against the current, that was the founding principle of the company thirty-five years ago, and you have no intention of changing your ways now. They are all worried about losing their jobs. That is what you see in their faces when you watch them talking to one another, and so you called a general meeting this afternoon and told them to forget 2008, 2008 is history now, and even if 2009 is no better, there will be no layoffs at Heller Books. Consider the publishers' softball league, you said. Any reductions of staff and it will be impossible to field a team in the spring, and Heller Books' proud record of twenty-seven consecutive losing seasons would come to an end. No softball team this year? Unthinkable.

February 6. Writers should never talk to journalists. The interview is a debased literary form that serves no purpose except to simplify that which should never be simplified. Renzo knows this, and because he is a man who acts on what he knows, he has kept his mouth shut for years, but tonight at dinner, concluded just one hour ago, he informed you that he spent part of the afternoon talking into a tape recorder, answering questions posed to him by a young writer of short stories, who intends to publish the results once the text has been edited and Renzo has given his approval. Special circumstances, he said, when you asked him why he had done it. The request came from Bing Nathan, who happens to be a friend of the young writer of short stories, and because Renzo is aware of the great debt you owe Bing Nathan, he felt it would have been rude to turn him down, unforgivable. In other words, Renzo has broken his silence out of friendship for you, and you told him how touched you were by this, grateful, glad he understood how much it meant to you that he could do something for Bing. An interview for Bing's sake, then, for your sake, but with certain restrictions the young writer had to accept before Renzo would agree to talk to him. No questions about his life or work, no questions about politics, no questions about anything except the work of other writers, dead writers, recently dead writers whom Renzo had known, some well, some casually, and whom he wanted to praise. No attacks, he said, only praise. He provided the interviewer with a list of names in advance and instructed him to choose some of them, just five or six, because the list was far too long to talk about them all. William Gaddis, Joseph Heller, George Plimpton, Leonard Michaels, John Gregory Dunne, Alain Robbe-Grillet, Susan Sontag, Arthur Miller, Robert Creeley, Kenneth Koch, William Styron, Ryszard Kapuściński, Kurt Vonnegut, Grace Paley, Norman Mailer, Harold Pinter, and John

Updike, who died just last week, an entire generation gone in the space of a few years. You knew many of those writers as well, talked to them, rubbed shoulders with them, admired them, and as Renzo reeled off their names, you were astonished by how many there were, and a terrible sadness descended on both of you as you raised a glass to their memory. To brighten the mood, Renzo launched into a story about William Styron, an amusing little anecdote from many years ago concerning a French magazine, *Le Nouvel Observateur,* which was planning an entire issue on the subject of America, and among the features they were hoping to include was a long conversation between an older American novelist and a younger American novelist. The magazine had already contacted Styron, and he proposed Renzo as the younger writer he would like to talk to. An editor called Renzo, who was deep into a novel at the time (as usual), and when he told her he was too busy to accept – tremendously flattered by Styron's offer, but too busy – the woman was so shocked by his refusal that she threatened to kill herself, *Je me suicide!,* but Renzo merely laughed, telling her that no one commits suicide over such a trivial matter and she would feel better in the morning. He didn't know Styron well, had met him only once or twice, but he had his number, and after the conversation with the suicidal editor, he called Styron to thank him for suggesting his name, but he wanted him to know that he was hard at work on a novel and had turned down the invitation. He hoped Styron would understand. Completely, Styron said. In fact, that's why he'd suggested Renzo in the first place. He didn't want to do the conversation either, and he was fairly certain, more or less convinced, that Renzo would say no to them and get him off the hook. Thanks, Renzo, he said, you've done me a great favor. Laughter. You and Renzo both cracked up over Styron's remark, and then Renzo said: "Such a polite man, so well mannered. He simply didn't have the heart to turn the editor down, so he used me to do it for him. On the other hand, what would have happened if I had said yes? I suspect he would have pretended to be thrilled, delighted that the two of us would be given a chance to sit down together and shoot our mouths off about the state of the world. That's the way he was. A good person. The last thing he wanted was to hurt anyone's feelings." From Styron's goodness, the two of you went on to talk about the PEN campaign in support of Liu Xiaobo. A large petition signed by writers from all over the world was published on January 20, and PEN is planning to honor him in absentia at its annual fundraising dinner in April. You will be there, of course, since you never fail

to attend that dinner, but the situation looks bleak, and you have little hope that giving Liu Xiaobo a prize in New York will have any effect on his status in Beijing – detained man, no doubt soon-to-be arrested man. According to Renzo, a young woman who works at PEN lives in the same house where the boy is camped out in Brooklyn. A small world, no? Yes, Renzo, a small world indeed.

February 7. You have met with the boy twice more since your reunion on January twenty-sixth. The first time, you went to *Happy Days* together (courtesy of Mary-Lee, who had two tickets waiting for you at the box office), watched the play in a kind of stunned rapture (Mary-Lee was brilliant), and then went to her dressing room after the performance, where she assaulted you both with wild, ebullient kisses. The ecstasy of acting before a live audience, a superabundance of adrenaline coursing through her body, her eyes on fire. The boy looked inordinately pleased, especially at the moment when you and his mother embraced. Later on, you realized that this was probably the first time in his life he had seen this happen. He understands that the war is over now, that the combatants have long since put down their arms and beaten their swords into plowshares. Afterward, dinner with Korngold and Lady Swann in a small restaurant off Union Square. The boy said little but was extremely attentive. Some astute remarks about the play, parsing the opening line of the second act, *Hail, holy light,* and why Beckett chose to refer to Milton at that point, the irony of those words in the context of a world of everlasting day, since light cannot be holy except as an antidote to darkness. His mother's eyes looking at him while he spoke, glistening with adoration. Mary-Lee, the queen of excess, the Madonna of naked feelings, and yet you sat there watching her with a twinge of envy – somewhat amused, yes, but also asking yourself why you continue to hold back. You felt more at ease in the boy's presence that second time. Getting used to him again, perhaps, but still not ready to warm up to him. The next encounter was more intimate. Dinner at Joe Junior's tonight for old times' sake, just the two of you, chomping on greasy hamburgers and soggy fries, and mostly you talked about baseball, reminding you of numerous conversations you had with your own father, that passionate but wholly neutral subject, safe ground as it were, but then he brought up Herb Score's death and told you how badly he'd wanted to call you that day and talk about it, the pitcher whose career was ruined by the same kind of injury that knocked down your father, the grandfather he never met, but then he decided that a long-distance call was inappropriate, and how

odd that his first contact with you ended up being by telephone anyway, the calls between Brooklyn and Exeter when you were in the hospital, and how afraid he was that he would never see you again. You took him back to Downing Street after dinner, and it was there, in the living room of the old apartment, that he suddenly broke down and wept. He and Bobby were fighting that day, he said, out on the hot road all those years ago, and just before the car came, he pushed Bobby, pushed the smaller Bobby hard enough to make him fall down, and that was why he was run over and killed. You listened in silence. No words were available to you anymore. All the years of not knowing, and now this, the sheer banality of it, an adolescent spat between stepbrothers, and all the damage that ensued from that push. So many things became clearer to you after the boy's confession. His savage withdrawal into himself, the escape from his own life, the punishing blue-collar jobs as a form of penance, more than a decade in hell because of one moment of anger. Can he be forgiven? You couldn't get the words out of your mouth tonight, but at least you had the sense to take him in your arms and hold him. More to the point: is there anything that needs to be forgiven? Probably not. But still, he must be forgiven.

February 8. The Sunday phone conversation with Willa. She is worried about your health, wonders how you are holding up, asks if it wouldn't be better if she quit her job and came home to take care of you. You laugh at the thought of your diligent, hardworking wife telling the university administrators: "So long, fellas, my man's got a tummy ache, gotta be going, and fuck the students I'm teaching, by the way, they can bloody well teach themselves." Willa giggles as you present that scene to her, and it is the first good laugh you have heard from her in some time, the best laugh in many months. You tell her about seeing the boy for dinner last night, but she is unresponsive, asks no questions, a small grunt to let you know she is listening but nothing more than that, and yet you forge on anyway, remarking that the boy finally seems to be coming into his own. Another grunt. Needless to say, you do not bring up the confession. A little pause, and then she tells you that at last she is feeling strong enough to return to her book, which is another good sign in your opinion, and then you tell her that Renzo sends his love, that you send your love, and you are covering her body with a thousand kisses. The conversation ends. Not a bad conversation, all in all, but after you hang up, you wander around the apartment feeling you have been stranded in the middle of nowhere. The boy has asked many questions about Willa,

but you still haven't found the courage to tell him that she has *cut him out of her heart*. The Can Man dresses in a suit and tie now. The Can Man goes to work, pays his bills, and has become a model citizen. But the Can Man is still touched in the head, and on nights when the world closes in on him, he still gets down on his hands and knees and howls at the moon.

March 15. You have seen the boy six more times since the last entry about him on February seventh. A visit to the Hospital for Broken Things one Saturday afternoon, where you watched him framing pictures and asked yourself if this is all he aspires to, if he will be content to knock around from one odd job to another until he becomes an old man. You don't push him into making decisions, however. You leave him alone and wait to see what will happen next, although you are privately hoping he will return to college next fall and finish up his degree, which is something he still mentions from time to time. Another dinner foursome with Korngold and La Swann on a Monday night, when the theater was dark. A night out at the movies together to see Bresson's old masterpiece *A Man Escaped*. A midweek lunch, preceded by a visit to the office, where you showed him around and introduced him to your little band of stalwarts, and the mad thought that rushed through your head that afternoon, wondering if a boy with his intelligence and interest in books might not find a place for himself in publishing, as an employee of Heller Books, for example, where he could be groomed as his father's successor, but one mustn't dream too much, thoughts of that kind can plant poisonous seeds in one's head, and it is best to refrain from writing another person's future, especially if that person is your son. A dinner with Renzo near his house in Park Slope, the godfather in good spirits that night, embarked on yet another novel, and no more talk of slumps and doldrums and extinguished flames. And then the visit out to the house where he is living, a chance to see the Sunset Park Four in action. A sad little run-down place, but you enjoyed seeing his friends, Bing most of all, of course, who appears to be flourishing, as well as the two girls, Alice, the one who works at PEN, who talked with great intensity about the Liu Xiaobo case and then asked you a number of probing questions about your parents' generation, the young men and women of World War II, and Ellen, so meek and pretty, who late in the evening showed you a sketchbook filled with some of the raunchiest erotic drawings you have ever seen, which made you stop and wonder – just for an instant – if you couldn't rescue your company by introducing a new line of pornographic art books. They have already been served with two

eviction notices, and you expressed your concern that they were pushing their luck and could wind up in a dangerous spot, but Bing slammed his fist down on the table and said they were holding out to the bitter end, and you didn't press your argument any further, since it is not your business to tell them what to do, they are all grown people (more or less) and are perfectly capable of making their own decisions, even if they are the wrong ones. Six more times, and little by little you and the boy have grown closer. He has been opening up to you now, and on one of the nights when you were alone with him, after the Bresson film most likely, he told you the full story about the girl, Pilar Sanchez, and why he had to run away from Florida. To be perfectly honest, you were appalled when he told you how young she is, but after you had thought about it for a moment, you realized that it made sense for him to be in love with someone that age, for the boy's life has been stunted, cut off from its proper and natural development, and although he looks like a full-grown man, his inner self is stuck somewhere around eighteen or nineteen. There was a moment back in January when he was afraid he was going to lose her, he said, there was a terrible flare-up, their first serious argument, and he claimed it was largely his fault, entirely his fault, since when they first met and he still had no idea how important she would become to him, he had lied to her about his family, telling her that his parents were dead, that he had no brother, had never had a brother, and now that he had come back to his parents, he wanted her to know the truth, and when he did tell her the truth, she was so angry at him for having lied to her, she hung up the phone. A week of battles followed, and she was right to feel burned, he said, he had let her down, she had lost faith in him, and it was only when he asked her to marry him that she began to soften, to understand that he would never let her down again. Marriage! Engaged to a girl not yet out of high school! Wait until you meet her next month, the boy said. And you replied, as calmly as you could, that you were looking forward to it very much.

March 29. The Sunday phone conversation with Willa. You finally tell her about the boy's confession, not knowing if this will help matters or make them worse. It is too much for her to take in all at once, and therefore her reaction evolves through several distinct stages over the minutes that follow. First: total silence, a silence that lasts long enough for you to feel compelled to repeat what you have just told her. Second: a soft voice saying "This is horrible, this is too much to bear, how can it be true?" Third: sobbing, as her mind travels back to the road and she fills

in the missing parts of the picture, imagines the fight between the boys, sees Bobby being crushed all over again. Fourth: growing anger. "He lied to us," she says, "he betrayed us with his lies," and you answer her by saying that he didn't lie, he simply didn't speak, he was too traumatized by his guilt to speak, and living with that guilt has nearly destroyed him. "He killed my son," she says, and you answer her by saying that he pushed her son into the road and that her son's death was an accident. The two of you go on talking for more than an hour, and again and again you tell her you love her, that no matter what she decides or how she chooses to deal with the boy, you will always love her. She breaks down again, finally putting herself in the boy's shoes, finally telling you that she understands how much he has suffered, but she doesn't know if understanding is enough, it isn't clear to her what she wants to do, she isn't certain if she will have the strength to face him again. She needs time, she says, more time to think it over, and you tell her there is no rush, you will never force her to do anything she doesn't want to do. The conversation ends, and once again you feel you have been stranded in the middle of nowhere. By late afternoon, you have begun to resign yourself to the fact that nowhere is your home now and that is where you will be spending the last years of your life.

April 12. She reminds you of someone you know, but you can't put your finger on who that person is, and then, five or six minutes after you are introduced to her, she laughs for the first time, and you know beyond a shadow of a doubt that the person is Suki Rothstein. Suki Rothstein in the incandescent sunlight of that late afternoon on Houston Street nearly seven years ago, laughing with her friends, decked out in her bright red dress, the promise of youth in its fullest, most glorious incarnation. Pilar Sanchez is the twin of Suki Rothstein, a small luminescent being who carries the flame of life within her, and may the gods be more gentle with her than they were with the doomed child of your friends. She arrived from Florida early Saturday evening, and the next day, Easter Sunday, she and the boy came to the apartment on Downing Street. The boy had trouble keeping his hands off her, and even as they sat side by side on the sofa talking to you in your comfortable chair, he was kissing her neck, stroking her bare knee, putting his arm around her shoulder. You had already seen her, of course, almost a year ago in that little park in southern Florida, you were a clandestine witness to their first encounter, their first conversation, but you were too far away from her to look into her eyes and see the power that is in them, the dark steady eyes that absorb

everything around her, that emit the light that has made the boy fall in love with her. They came with good news, the boy said, the best news, and a moment later you were told that Pilar had been accepted at Barnard with a full scholarship and will be coming to live in New York immediately after her high school graduation in June. You told her that your wife went to Barnard as well, that you saw her for the first time when she was a Barnard student, and the torch has now been passed from the boy's stepmother to her. And then (you almost fell out of your chair when you heard this) the boy announced that he has enrolled in the School of General Studies at Columbia and will start the final leg toward his B.A. in the fall. You asked him how he was going to pay for it, and he said he has some money in the bank and will cover the rest by applying for a student loan. You were impressed that he didn't ask for your help, even though you would be willing to give it, but you know it is better for his morale to take on this burden himself. As the talk continued, you realized that you were becoming more and more happy, that you were happier today than you have been at any time in the past thirteen years, and you wanted to drink in this happiness, to become drunk on this happiness, and it occurred to you that no matter what Willa decides concerning the boy, you will be able to tolerate a split life with the two people you care about most in the world, that you will take your pleasures wherever and whenever you can find them. You booked a table for dinner at the Waverly Inn, that venerable establishment from the old New York, the New York that no longer exists, thinking Pilar would enjoy going to such a place, and she did enjoy it, she actually said she felt she was in heaven, and as the three of you packed away your Easter dinner, the girl was full of questions, she wanted to know everything about running a publishing house, how you met Renzo Michaelson, how you decide whether to accept a book or not, and as you answered her questions, you understood that she was listening to you with intense concentration, that she would not forget a word you had said. At one point, the talk drifted onto math and science, and you found yourself listening to a discussion about quantum physics, a subject that you freely admitted escapes you entirely, and then Pilar turned to you and said: "Think of it this way, Mr. Heller. In the old physics, three times two equals six and two times three equals six are reversible propositions. Not in quantum physics. Three times two and two times three are two different matters, distinct and separate propositions." There are many things in this world for you to worry about, but the boy's love for this girl is not one of them.

April 13. You wake up this morning to the news that Mark Fidrych is dead. Just fifty-four years old, killed on his farm in Northborough, Massachusetts, when the dump truck he was repairing collapsed on top of him. First Herb Score, and now Mark Fidrych, the two cursed geniuses who dazzled the country for a few days, a few months, and then vanished from sight. You remember your father's old refrain: Poor Herb Score. Now you add another casualty to the roster of the fallen: Mark Fidrych. May the Bird rest in peace.

## ALICE BERGSTROM AND ELLEN BRICE

It is Thursday, April thirtieth, and Alice has just completed another five-hour stint at the PEN American Center. Breaking from her established routine of the past several months, she will not be rushing home to Sunset Park to work on her dissertation. Instead, she is on her way to meet Ellen, who has Thursdays off, and the two of them will be splurging on a late lunch at Balthazar, the French brasserie on Spring Street in SoHo, less than a two-minute walk from the PEN offices at 588 Broadway. Yesterday, another court order was delivered to the house by yet another New York City marshal, bringing the total number of eviction notices they have received to four, and earlier in the month, when the third notice arrived, she and Ellen agreed that the next warning would be the last one, that they would turn in their squatters' badges at that point and move on, reluctantly move on. That is why they have arranged to meet in Manhattan this afternoon – to talk things over and figure out what to do next, calmly and thoughtfully, in an environment far from Bing and his aggressive, hotheaded pronouncements, and what better place for a calm and thoughtful discussion than this pricey, elegant restaurant during the quiet interlude between lunch and dinner?

Jake is out of the picture now. The showdown she was preparing herself for when last seen on January fifth finally took place in mid-February, and the hurtful thing about that last conversation was how quickly he assented to her reading of their present circumstances, how little resistance he mounted to the idea of going their separate ways, calling it quits. Something was wrong with him, he said, but it was true that he no longer felt excited when he was with her, that he no longer looked forward to seeing her, and he blamed himself for this shift in his feelings and frankly could not understand what had happened to him. He told her that she was a remarkable person, with numerous outstanding qualities – intelligence, compassion, wisdom – and that he was a damaged soul incapable of loving her in the way she deserved to be loved. He did not explore the problem more deeply than that, did not, for example, delve into the reasons why he had lost interest in her sexually, but that would have been too much to hope for, she realized, since he openly

admitted that these changes confused him just as much as they confused her. She asked him if he had ever thought about psychotherapy, and he said yes, he was considering it, his life was in a shambles and there was no question that he needed help. Alice sensed that he was telling her the truth, but she wasn't entirely certain of it, and whenever she replays that conversation in her mind now, she wonders if his passive, self-accusatory position was not simply the easiest way out for him, a lie to mask the fact that he had fallen for someone else. But which someone else? She doesn't know, and in the two and a half months since she last saw him, none of their mutual friends has talked to her about a new person in connection with Jake. It could be that there is no one – or else his love life has become a well-guarded secret. One way or the other, she misses him. Now that he is gone, she tends to recall the good moments they had together and ignore the difficult ones, and oddly enough, what she finds herself missing most about him are the occasional jags of humor that would pour out of him at unpredictable moments, the moments when the distinctly unhumorous Jake Baum would drop his defenses and begin impersonating various comical figures, mostly ones who spoke with heavy foreign accents, Russians, Indians, Koreans, and he was surprisingly good at this, he always got the voices just right, but that was the old Jake, of course, the Jake of a year ago, and the truth is that it had been a long time since he had made her laugh by turning himself into one of those funny characters. *Meese Aleece. Keese mee, Meese Aleece.* She doubts that another man will come along anytime soon, and this worries her, since she is thirty years old now, and the prospect of a childless future fills her with dread.

Her weight is down, however, more from lack of appetite than from scrupulous dieting, but one fifty-four is a decent number for her, and she has stopped thinking of herself as a repulsive cow – that is, whenever she thinks about her body, which seems to happen less often now that Jake is gone and there is no one to touch her anymore. Her dissertation stalled for about two weeks after his departure, but then she pulled herself together and has been working hard ever since, so hard, in fact, that she is well into the concluding chapter now and feels she can finish off the first draft in approximately ten days. For the past three years, the dissertation has been an end in itself, the mountain she set out to climb, but she has rarely thought about what would happen to her after she reached the top. If and when she did think about it, she complacently assumed the next step would be to apply for a teaching position somewhere. That's

why you spend all those years struggling to get your Ph.D., isn't it? They give you your doctorate, and then you go out and teach. But now that the end is in sight, she has been reexamining the question, and it is by no means certain anymore that teaching is the answer. She is still inclined to give it a shot, but after her less than happy experience as an adjunct last year, she wonders if toiling in some English department for the next four decades will be fulfilling enough to sustain her. Other possibilities have occurred to her in the past month or so. A bigger, more demanding job at PEN, for example. That work has engaged her far more than she thought it would, and she doesn't want to give it up, which she would be forced to do if she landed a post in an English department – which, by the by, would most likely be at a college eight hundred miles to the south or west of New York. That's the problem, she says to herself, as she pulls open the door of the restaurant and walks in, not the job but the place. She doesn't want to leave New York. She wants to go on living in this immense, unlivable city for as long as she can, and after all these years, the thought of living anywhere else strikes her as insane.

Ellen is already there, sitting at one of the tables along the eastern wall of the restaurant, nursing a glass of white wine as she waits for her friend to show up. Ellen knows more about what Alice's ex-lover has been up to for the past few months than Alice does, but Ellen hasn't said anything to Alice about these goings-on because she promised Bing to keep them a secret, and Ellen is not someone who breaks her word. Bing has continued posing for her once or twice a week throughout the first four months of the year, and many walls have come down between them in that time, all walls in fact, and they have shared confidences with each other that neither one of them would have been willing to share with anyone else. Ellen knows about Bing's infatuation with Miles, for example, and she knows about his anxieties concerning the man–woman problem, the man–man problem, and his doubts about who and what he is. She knows that sometime in late January Bing ventured up to Jake's small apartment in Manhattan and, with the aid of abundant quantities of alcohol and a guarantee to contact Renzo Michaelson about the interview Jake so earnestly wished to conduct with him, managed to seduce Alice's ex-amour into a sexual encounter. That was Bing's first and last experiment in self-discovery, since he found little or no pleasure in Jake Baum's arms, mouth, or private parts, and grudgingly had to admit that while he was still deeply attracted to Miles, he had no interest in making love to men, not even

to Miles. Jake, on the other hand, much as Bing had suspected, had been through a number of male–male experiences as an adolescent, and on the strength of his encounter with Bing, which brought him much pleasure, he realized that his interest in men had not waned with the years as he supposed it had. Two weeks later, when Alice forced him into the showdown, he quietly bowed out of their affair to pursue that other interest. Ellen knows about this because Jake and Bing are still in touch. Jake has told Bing about what he has been doing, Bing has passed along this information to Ellen, and Ellen has kept silent. Alice doesn't know it, but she is much better off without Jake, and if Ellen has any knowledge or understanding of the world, it won't be long before Alice finds herself another man.

This is the new Ellen, the Ellen Brice who last month overhauled the outward trappings of her person in order to express the new relation she has developed with her body, which is a product of the new relation she has developed with her heart, which in turn is a product of the new relation she has developed with her innermost self. In one bold, decisive week in the middle of March, she had her long, stringy hair cut into a short 1920s bob, threw out every article of clothing in her bureau and closet, and began adorning her face with lipstick, rouge, eyeliner, eye shadow, and mascara every time she left the house, so that the woman described in Morris Heller's journal as *meek,* the woman who for years inspired feelings of compassion and protectiveness in those who knew her, no longer projects an aura of victimhood and skittish uncertainty, and as she sits on the banquette along the eastern wall of Balthazar dressed in a black leather miniskirt and a tight cashmere sweater, sipping her white wine and watching Alice come through the door, heads turn when people walk past her, and she exults in the attention she receives, exults in the knowledge that she is the most desirable woman in the room. This revolution in her appearance was inspired by an unlikely event that occurred in February, just one week after Alice and Jake put an end to their tottering romance, when none other than Benjamin Samuels, the high school boy who impregnated Ellen nearly nine years ago in the pavilion of his parents' summer house in southern Vermont, walked into the real estate office where Ellen works, looking for an apartment to rent in Park Slope or one of its adjacent neighborhoods, a twenty-five-year-old Benjamin Samuels, fully grown now and employed as a cell phone salesman in a T-Mobile store on Seventh Avenue, a college dropout, a young man devoid of the intellectual

skills required to pursue one of the professions, law or medicine, say, which his parents once hoped would be his destiny, but just as handsome as ever, more handsome than ever, the beautiful boy with the beautiful soccer player's body now ripened into a large beautiful man. He didn't recognize Ellen at first, and although she suspected that the broad-shouldered fellow sitting across from her was the matured incarnation of the boy she had given herself to so many years earlier, she waited until he had filled in the blanks on the rental application form before she announced who she was. She spoke quietly and tentatively, not knowing if he would be pleased or displeased, not knowing if he would even remember her, but Ben Samuels did remember her, and Ben Samuels was pleased to have found her again, so pleased that he stood up from his chair, walked around to the other side of Ellen's desk, and put his arms around her in a great welcoming hug. They spent the afternoon walking in and out of empty apartments together, kissing in the first apartment, making love in the second apartment, and now that Ben Samuels has moved into the neighborhood, he and Ellen have continued making love nearly every day. That is why Ellen cut her hair – because Ben is aroused by the back of her neck – and once she cut her hair, she understood that he would be even more aroused by her if she started wearing different, more alluring clothes. Until now, she has kept Ben a secret from Alice, Bing, and Miles, but with so many changes suddenly afoot, the fourth court order, the imminent dispersal of their little gang, she has decided that this is the day she will tell Alice about the extraordinary thing that has happened to her.

Alice is kissing her on the cheek now and smiling her Alice smile, and as Ellen watches her friend sit down in the chair facing the banquette, she wonders if she will ever be good enough to do a drawing that would fully capture that smile, which is the warmest, most luminous smile on earth, a smile that sets Alice apart from every other person she knows, has known, or will ever know until the end of her life.

Well, kid, Alice says, I guess the grand experiment is over.

For us, maybe, Ellen says, but not for Bing and Miles.

Miles is going back to Florida in three weeks.

I forgot. Bing alone, then. How sad.

I'm thinking ten more days. If I work hard, I should be able to finish the last chapter by then. Is that okay with you, or would you rather pull out now?

I don't ever want to pull out. It's just that I'm getting scared. If the

cops show up, they'll toss our stuff out onto the street, things could get broken, Bing could go crazy, all sorts of unpleasant possibilities come to mind. Ten days is too long, Alice. I think you should start looking for a new place tomorrow.

How many rentals do you have?

Plenty in the Slope, not so many in Sunset Park.

But Sunset Park is cheaper, which means that Sunset Park is better.

How much can you afford to pay?

As little as the market will bear.

I'll check the listings after lunch and let you know what we have.

But maybe you've had enough of Sunset Park. If you want to go somewhere else, I have no problem with that. As long as I can pay my half of the rent, anywhere is fine.

Dear Alice . . .

What?

I hadn't realized you wanted to share.

Don't you?

In principle, yes, but something has come up, and I'm considering other options.

Options?

One option.

Oh?

He's called Benjamin Samuels, and he's asked me to move in with him.

You little devil. How long as this been going on?

A couple of months.

A couple of months? What's gotten into you? A couple of months, and you never even told me.

I wasn't sure enough to tell anyone. I thought it might be just a sex thing that would flame out before it was worth mentioning. But it seems to be getting bigger. Big enough for me to want to give it a try, I think.

Are you in love with him?

I don't know. But I'm crazy about him, that much I do know. And the sex is pretty sensational.

Who is he?

The one.

What one?

The one from the summer of two thousand.

The man who got you pregnant?

The boy who got me pregnant.

So, the story finally comes out . . .

He was sixteen, and I was twenty. Now he's twenty-five, and I'm twenty-nine. Those four years are a lot less important today than they were back then.

Christ. I thought it might have been the father, but never the son.

That's why I couldn't talk about it. He was too young, and I didn't want to get him into trouble.

Did he ever know what happened?

Not then, no, and not now either. There's no point in telling him, is there?

Twenty-five years old. And what does he do with himself?

Nothing much. He has a dreary little job, and he isn't terribly bright. But he adores me, Alice, and no one has ever treated me better. We fuck during our lunch break every afternoon in his apartment on Fifth Street. He turns me inside out. I swoon when he touches me. I can't get enough of his body. I feel I might be going mad, and then I wake up in the morning and realize that I'm happy, happier than I've been in a long, long time.

Good for you, El.

Yes, good for me. Who ever would have thought?

On Saturday, May second, he reads in the morning paper that Jack Lohrke is dead at the age of eighty-five. The short obituary recounts the three miraculous escapes from certain death – the felled comrades in the Battle of the Bulge, the crashed airplane after the war, the bus that toppled into the ravine – but it is a skimpy article, a perfunctory article, which glides over Lucky's undistinguished major league career with the Giants and Phillies and mentions only one detail Miles was not aware of: in the most celebrated game of the twentieth century, the final round of the National League championship play-off between the Giants and the Dodgers in 1951, Don Mueller, the Giants' right fielder, broke his ankle sliding into third base in the last inning, and if the Giants had tied the score rather than win the game with a walk-off home run, Lohrke would have taken over for Mueller in the next inning, but Branca threw the pitch, Thomson hit the pitch, and the game ended before Lucky could get his name in the box score. The young Willie Mays on deck, Lucky Lohrke warming up to replace Mueller in right field, and then Thomson clobbered the final pitch of the season over the left-field wall, and the Giants won the pennant, the Giants won the pennant. The obituary says nothing about Jack "Lucky" Lohrke's private life, not a single word about marriage or children or grandchildren, no information about the people he might have loved or the people who might have loved him, simply the dull and insignificant fact that the patron saint of good fortune worked in security at Lockheed after he retired from baseball.

The instant he finishes reading the obituary, he calls the apartment on Downing Street to commiserate with his father over the death of the man they discussed so often during the years of their own good fortune, the years before anyone knew about roads in the Berkshires, the years before anyone was buried or anyone else ran away, and his father has of course read the paper over his morning coffee and knows about Lucky's departure from this world. A bad stretch, his father says. First Herb Score in November, then Mark Fidrych in April, and now this. Miles says he regrets they never wrote a letter to Jack Lohrke to tell him what an important figure he was in their family, and his father

says, yes, that was a stupid oversight, why didn't they think of that years ago? Miles answers that maybe it was because they assumed their man would live forever, and his father laughs, saying that Jack Lohrke wasn't immortal, just lucky, and even if they considered him their patron saint, he mustn't forget that saints die too.

The worst of it is behind him now. Just twenty days before he is released from prison, then back to Florida until Pilar finishes school, and after that New York again, where they will spend the early part of the summer looking for a place to live uptown. In an astounding act of generosity, his father has offered to let them stay with him on Downing Street until they find their own apartment, which means that Pilar will never have to spend another night in the house in Sunset Park, which scared her even before the eviction notices started coming and now puts her in a full-blown panic. How much longer before the cops come to throw them out? Alice and Ellen have already made up their minds to decamp, and even though Bing went into a rage when they announced their decision at dinner two nights ago, they both held their ground, and Miles believes their position is the only sensible one to take anymore. They will be moving out the minute Ellen manages to find Alice an affordable replacement, which is likely to happen by the middle of next week, and if his circumstances were similar to theirs, he would be on his way out as well. Just twenty days, however, and in the meantime he must not abandon Bing, not when the venture is falling apart, not when Bing so desperately needs him to be here, and therefore he intends to stay put until the twenty-second and prays that no cops show up before then.

He wants those twenty days, but he does not get them. He gets the day and the night of the second, the day and the night of the third, and early in the morning on the fourth, there is a loud knock on the front door. Miles is fast asleep in his downstairs bedroom behind the kitchen, and by the time he wakes up and slips into his clothes, the house has already been invaded. He hears the tread of heavy footsteps clomping up the stairs, he hears Bing shouting angrily at the top of his voice (*Get your fucking hands off me!*), he hears Alice shrieking at someone to back off and leave her computer alone, and he hears the cops yelling (*Clear out! Clear out!*), how many cops he doesn't know, he thinks two, but there could be three, and by the time he opens the door of his room, walks across the kitchen, and reaches the entrance hall, the commotion upstairs has turned into a clamorous roar. He glances to his right, sees that the front door is open, and there is Ellen, standing on the porch with her hand

over her mouth, her eyes wide with fear, with horror, and then he looks to his left, fixing his eyes on the staircase, at the top of which he sees Alice, large Alice trying to wrestle herself out of the arms of an enormous cop, and just then, as he continues looking up, he sees Bing on the top landing as well, his wrists shackled in handcuffs as a second enormous cop holds him by the hair with one hand and jabs a nightstick into his back with the other, and just when he is about to turn around and run out of the house, he sees the first enormous cop push Alice down the stairs, and as Alice tumbles toward him, cracking the side of her head against a wooden step, the enormous cop who pushed her races down the stairs, and before Miles can pause to think about what he is doing, he is punching that enormous cop in the jaw with his clenched fist, and as the cop falls down from the blow, Miles turns around, rushes out of the house, finds Ellen standing on the porch, takes hold of her right hand with his left hand, drags her down the front steps with him, and the two of them begin to run.

An entrance to Green-Wood Cemetery is just around the corner, and that is where they go, not certain if they are being chased or not, but Miles thinks that if there were two cops in the house and not three, then the uninjured cop would be tending to the cop he punched in the jaw, which would mean that no one is pursuing them. Still, they run for as long as they can, and when Ellen is out of breath and can go no farther, they flop down on the grass for a spell, leaning their backs against the headstone of a man named Charles Everett Brown, 1858–1927. Miles's hand is in terrific pain, and he fears it might be broken. Ellen wants to take him to the emergency room for X-rays, but Miles says no, that would be too dangerous, he must keep himself hidden. He has assaulted a police officer and that is a crime, a serious offense, and even if he hopes the bastard's jaw is broken, even if he feels no regret about smashing in the face of someone who threw a woman down a flight of stairs, Alice Bergstrom no less, the best woman in the world, there is no question that he is in bad trouble, the worst trouble he has ever known.

He doesn't have his cell phone, she doesn't have her cell phone. They are sitting on the grass in the cemetery with no way to reach anyone, no way to know if Bing has been arrested or not, no way to know if Alice has been hurt or not, and for the time being Miles is still too stunned to have formulated a plan about what to do next. Ellen tells him that she woke early as usual, six-fifteen or six-thirty, and that she was standing on the porch with her coffee when the cops arrived. She was the one

who opened the door and let them in. What choice did she have but to open the door and let them in? They went upstairs, there were two of them, and she remained on the porch as the two cops went upstairs, and then all hell broke loose, she saw nothing, she was still standing on the porch, but Bing and Alice were both shouting, the two cops were shouting, everyone was shouting, Bing must have resisted, he must have started fighting, and no doubt Alice was afraid they would push her out before she could gather up her papers and books and films and computer, the computer in which her entire dissertation is stored, three years of work in one small machine, and no doubt that was why she snapped and started struggling with the cop, Alice's dissertation, Bing's drums, and all her drawings of the past five months, hundreds and hundreds of drawings, and all of it still in the house, in the house that is no doubt sealed up now, off-limits, and everything gone forever now. She wants to cry, she says, but she is unable to cry, she is too angry to cry, there was no need for all that pushing and shoving, why couldn't the cops have behaved like men instead of animals, and no, she can't cry even if she wants to, but please, Miles, she says, put your arms around me, hold me, Miles, I need someone to hold me, and Miles puts his arms around Ellen and strokes her head.

They have to do something about his hand. It is swelling now, the area around the knuckles looks bloated and blue, and even if no bones are broken (he has discovered that he can wiggle his fingers a bit without increasing the pain), the hand must be iced to bring down the swelling. Hematoma. He thinks that is the word he is looking for – localized swelling filled with blood, a small lake of blood sloshing around just under the skin. They must ice the hand, and they also must eat something. They have been sitting on the grass in the cemetery for close to two hours now, and they are both hungry, although it is far from certain that either one of them would be able to eat if food were set before them. They stand up and begin walking, moving quickly past the tombs and mausoleums in the direction of Windsor Terrace and Park Slope, the Twenty-fifth Street entrance to the cemetery, the exit from the cemetery, and once they reach Seventh Avenue, they go on walking all the way to Sixth Street. Ellen tells Miles to wait outside for her, and then she goes into a T-Mobile cell phone store to talk to her new boyfriend, her old boyfriend, it's a complicated story, and a few moments later, she is unlocking the door to Ben Samuels's apartment on Fifth Street between Sixth and Seventh Avenues.

They can't stay here for long, she says, just a few hours, she doesn't want Ben to get involved in this, but at least it's something, a chance for a breather until they can figure out what to do next. They wash up, Ellen makes them cheese sandwiches, and then she fills a plastic bag with ice cubes and hands it to Miles. He wants to call Pilar, but it is too early, she is at school now, and she doesn't switch on her phone until she returns to the apartment at four o'clock. Where do we go from here? Ellen asks. Miles thinks for a moment, and then he remembers that his godfather lives nearby, just a few blocks from where they are sitting, but when he calls Renzo's number, no one picks up, it is the answering machine that talks to him, and he knows that Renzo is either working or out of town and therefore does not bother to leave a message. There is no one left except his father, but just as Ellen is reluctant to involve her friend, he balks at the idea of dragging his father into this mess, his father is the last person in the world he wants to turn to for help now.

As if she is able to read his thoughts, Ellen says: You have to call your father, Miles.

He shakes his head. Impossible, he says. I've already put that man through enough.

If you won't do it, Ellen says, then I will.

Please, Ellen. Leave him alone.

But Ellen insists, and a moment later she is dialing the number of Heller Books in Manhattan. Miles is so upset by what she is doing that he walks out of the kitchen and locks himself in the bathroom. He can't bear to listen, he refuses to listen. He would rather stab himself in the heart than listen to Ellen talk to his father.

Time passes, how much time he doesn't know, three minutes, eight minutes, two hours, and then Ellen is knocking on the door, telling him to come out, telling him that his father knows everything about what happened in Sunset Park this morning, that his father is waiting for him on the other end of the line. He unlocks the door, sees that Ellen's eyes are rimmed with tears, gently touches her face with his left hand, and walks into the kitchen.

His father's voice says: Two detectives came to the office about an hour ago. They say you broke a policeman's jaw. Is that true?

He pushed Alice down the stairs, Miles says. I lost my temper.

Bing is in jail for resisting arrest. Alice is in the hospital with a concussion.

How bad is it?

She's awake, her head hurts, but no permanent damage. They'll probably let her out tomorrow morning.

To go where? She doesn't have a place to live anymore. She's homeless. We're all homeless now.

I want you to turn yourself in, Miles.

No chance. They'd lock me up for years.

Extenuating circumstances. Police brutality. First offense. I doubt you'd serve any time.

It's their word against ours. The cop will say Alice tripped and fell, and the jury will believe him. We're just a bunch of illegal trespassers, squatters, freeloading bums.

You don't want to spend the rest of your life running from the police, do you? You've already done enough running. Time to stand up and face the music, Miles. And I'll stand up there with you.

You can't. You have a good heart, Dad, but I'm in this thing alone.

No, you're not. You'll have a lawyer. And I know some damned good ones. Everything is going to be all right, believe me.

I'm so sorry. So fucking, terribly sorry.

Listen to me, Miles. Talking on the phone is no good. We have to hash it out in person, face to face. The minute I hang up, I'll go straight home. Get yourself into a taxi and meet me there as soon as you can. All right?

All right.

You promise?

Yes, I promise.

Half an hour later, he is sitting in the backseat of a car-service Dodge, on his way to Downing Street in Manhattan. Ellen has gone to the bank for him with his ATM card and returned with a thousand dollars in cash, they have kissed and said good-bye, and as the car moves through the heavy traffic toward the Brooklyn Bridge, he wonders how long it will be before he sees Ellen Brice again. He wishes he could go to the hospital to see Alice, but he knows he can't. He wishes he could go to the jail where Bing is locked up, but he knows he can't. He presses the ice against his swollen hand, and as he looks at the hand, he thinks about the soldier with the missing hands in the movie he saw with Alice and Pilar last winter, the young soldier home from the war, unable to undress himself and go to bed without his father's help, and he feels he has become that boy now, who can do nothing without his father's help, a boy without hands, a boy who should be without hands, a boy whose hands have brought him nothing but trouble in his life, his angry punching hands,

his angry pushing hands, and then the name of the soldier in the movie comes back to him, Homer, Homer Something, Homer as in the poet Homer, who wrote the scene about Odysseus and Telemachus, father and son reunited after so many years, in the same way he and his father have been reunited, and the name Homer makes him think of home, as in the word *homeless,* they are all homeless now, he said that to his father on the phone, Alice and Bing are homeless, he is homeless, the people in Florida who lived in the houses he trashed out are homeless, only Pilar is not homeless, he is her home now, and with one punch he has destroyed everything, they will never have their life together in New York, there is no future for them anymore, no hope for them anymore, and even if he runs away to Florida to be with her now, there will be no hope for them, and even if he stays in New York to fight it out in court, there will be no hope for them, he has let his father down, let Pilar down, let everyone down, and as the car travels across the Brooklyn Bridge and he looks at the immense buildings on the other side of the East River, he thinks about the missing buildings, the collapsed and burning buildings that no longer exist, the missing buildings and the missing hands, and he wonders if it is worth hoping for a future when there is no future, and from now on, he tells himself, he will stop hoping for anything and live only for now, this moment, this passing moment, the now that is here and then not here, the now that is gone forever.

[2009]